Digital Filter Designer's Handbook

Other Reference Books of Interest by McGraw-Hill

Handbooks

BENSON • *Television Engineering Handbook*
CHEN • *Fuzzy Logic and Neural Network Handbook*
CHRISTIANSEN • *Electronics Engineers' Handbook, 4/e*
COOMBS • *Printed Circuits Handbook, 4/e*
DI GIACOMO • *Digital Bus Handbook*
DI GIACOMO • *VLSI Handbook*
GRAEME • *Photodiode Amplifiers Op Amp Solutions*
GRAEME • *Optimizing Op Amp Performance*
HARPER • *Electronic Packaging and Interconnection Handbook, 2/e*
JURAN AND GRYNA • *Juran's Quality Control Handbook*
OSA • *Handbook of Optics, 2/e*
SERGENT AND HARPER • *Hybrid Microelectronic Handbook*
WAYNANT • *Electro-Optics Handbook*
WILLIAMS AND TAYLOR • *Electronic Filter Design Handbook*
ZOMAYA • *Parallel and Distributed Computing Handbook*

Other

ANTOGNETTI AND MASSOBRIO • *Semiconductor Device Modeling with SPICE*
BEST • *Phase-Locked Loops, 3/e*
HECHT • *The Laser Guidebook*
KIELKOWSKI • *Inside SPICE*
SMITH • *Thin-Film Deposition*
SZE • *VLSI Technology*
TSUI • *LSI/VLSI Testability Design*
WOBSCHALL • *Circuit Design for Electronic Instrumentation*
WYATT • *Electro-Optical System Design*

Digital Filter Designer's Handbook

With C++ Algorithms

C. Britton Rorabaugh

Second Edition

McGraw-Hill

New York San Francisco Washington, D.C. Auckland Bogotá
Caracas Lisbon London Madrid Mexico City Milan
Montreal New Delhi San Juan Singapore
Sydney Tokyo Toronto

Library of Congress Cataloging-in-Publication Data
Rorabaugh, C. Britton.
Digital filter designer's handbook : with C++ algorithms / C. Britton Rorabaugh.—2nd ed.
p. cm.
Includes bibliographical references and index.
ISBN 0-07-053806-9 (hc)
1. Electric filters, Digital—Design and construction—Data processing. 2. Electric circuit design—Data processing. I. Title.
TK7878.F5R68 1997
621.3815′324—dc21 97-6189
CIP

McGraw-Hill

A Division of The ***McGraw-Hill*** *Companies*

1 2 3 4 5 6 7 8 9 0 DOC/DOC 9 0 2 1 0 9 8 7

P/N 054044-6
PART OF
ISBN 0-07-053806-9

The sponsoring editor for this book was Stephen S. Chapman, the editing supervisor was M. R. Carey, and the production supervisor was Pamela A. Pelton. It was set in Century Schoolbook by North Market Street Graphics.

Printed and bound by R. R. Donnelley & Sons Company.

This book was printed on recycled, acid-free paper containing a minimum of 50% recycled de-inked fiber.

To Joyce, Geoff, and Amber

Contents

List of Programs

Preface

In the Preface to the first edition, I wrote:

> If you're going to own only one book on digital filters, this is the one to have. If you already own several, you need this book anyway—it contains quite a lot of useful information not available in any other book. I wrote this book for individuals faced with the need to design working digital filters—it is not intended as an academic text. All the necessary theoretical background is provided in the early chapters, and practical filter design techniques are provided in the later chapters. These design techniques are supported by numerous computer routines written in the C programming language. The techniques and programs presented in this book will prove to be very useful to engineers, students, and hobbyists engaged in the design of digital filters.

Most of what I wrote still applies to the second edition. The one major difference is that all of the software has been rearchitected and rewritten in (mostly) object-oriented C++. In Chaps. 15 and 16, the design methods are highly procedural so the software was intentionally left in a procedure-oriented form to enhance clarity and ease understanding. Check the `Readme.txt` files on the diskette for the latest information on the various programs that are provided.

Britt Rorabaugh

ABOUT THE AUTHOR

C. Britton Rorabaugh holds BSEE and MSEE degrees from Drexel University. His previous books include *Circuit Design and Analysis*, *Communications Formulas and Algorithms, Data Communications and LAN Handbook,* and *Signal Processing Design Techniques,* all published by McGraw-Hill.

Chapter

1

Signals and Spectra

Digital signal processing is based on the use of mathematical functions to represent or model real-world electronic signals as illustrated in Fig. 1.1. Actual signals can be complicated phenomena, and their exact behavior is impossible to describe completely. However, simple mathematical models can describe signals well enough to yield some very useful results that can be applied in a variety of practical situations. The distinction between a signal and its mathematical representation is not always rigidly observed in signal-processing literature—functions which only *model* signals are commonly referred to as signals, and properties of these models are often presented as properties of the signals themselves. Nevertheless, mathematical models of signals are crucial to digital signal processing in general and to digital filter design in particular. This chapter is devoted to a concise review of the mathematical techniques that are used to model and analyze signals throughout the rest of the book. Appendix A presents some of the purely mathematical material upon which this chapter is based.

1.1 Mathematical Modeling of Signals

Mathematical models of signals are generally categorized as either *steady-state* or *transient models.* The typical voltage output from an oscillator is sketched in Fig. 1.2. This signal exhibits three different parts—a *turn-on transient* at the beginning, an interval of *steady-state operation* in the middle, and a *turn-off transient* at the end. It is possible to formulate a single mathematical expression that describes all three parts, but for most uses, such an expression would be unnecessarily complicated. In cases where the primary concern is steady-state behavior, simplified mathematical expressions that ignore the transients will often be adequate. The steady-state portion of the oscillator output can be modeled as a sinusoid that theoretically exists for all time. This

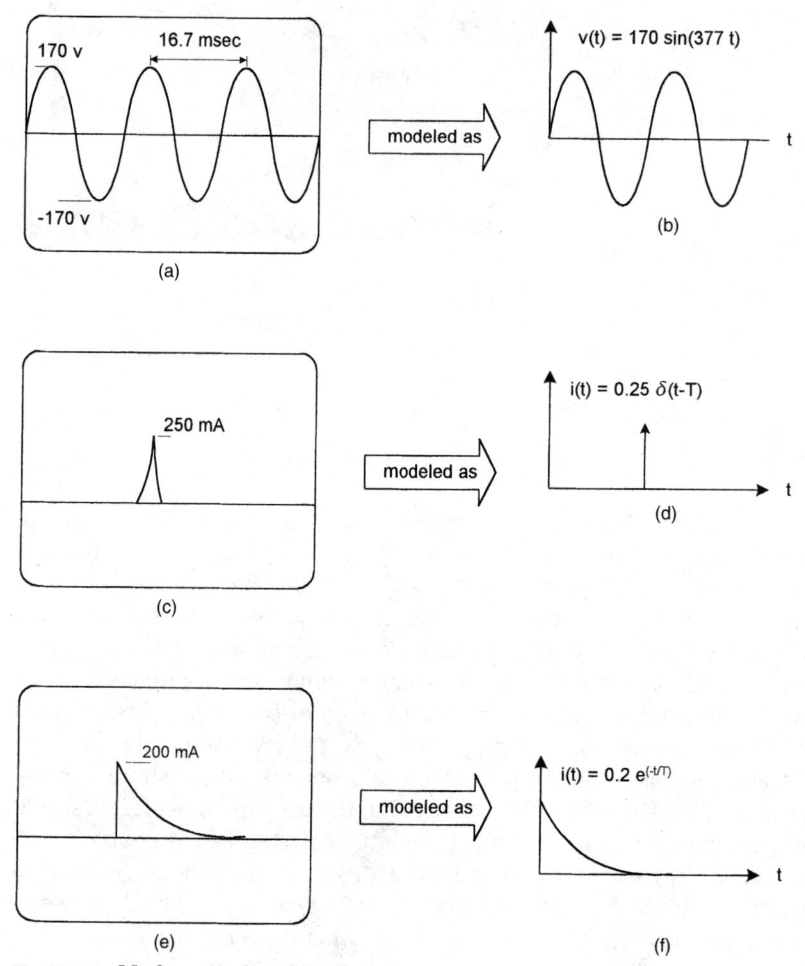

Figure 1.1 Mathematical models of some practical signals.

seems to be a contradiction to the obvious fact that the oscillator output exists for some limited time interval between turn on and turn off. However, this is not really a problem; over the interval of steady-state operation that we are interested in, the mathematical sine function accurately describes the behavior of the oscillator's output voltage. Allowing the mathematical model to assume that the steady-state signal exists over all time greatly simplifies matters since the transients' behavior can be excluded from the model. In situations where the transients are important, they can be modeled as exponentially saturating and decaying sinusoids, as shown in Figs. 1.3 and 1.4. In Fig. 1.3, the saturating exponential envelope continues to increase, but it never quite reaches the steady-state value. Likewise, the decaying exponential enve-

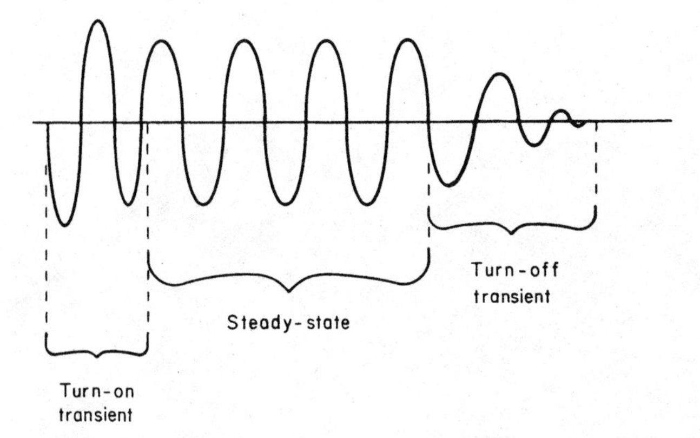

Figure 1.2 Typical output of an audio oscillator.

lope of Fig. 1.4 continues to decrease, but it never quite reaches zero. In this context, the steady-state value is sometimes called an *asymptote,* or the envelope can be said to *asymptotically* approach the steady-state value. Steady-state and transient models of signal behavior inherently contradict each other, and neither constitutes a "true" description of a particular signal. The formulation of the appropriate model requires an understanding of the signal to be modeled and of the implications that a particular choice of model will have for the intended application.

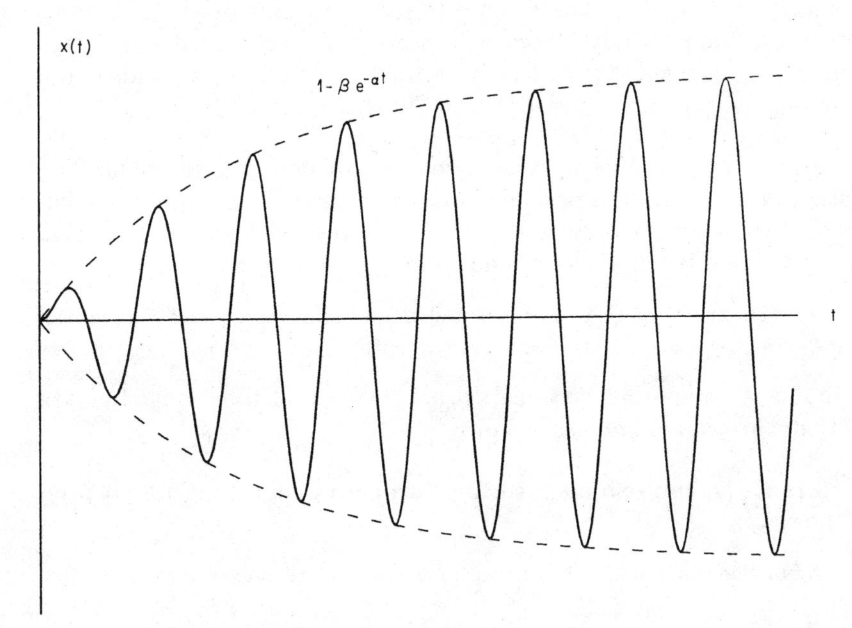

Figure 1.3 Exponentially saturating sinusoid.

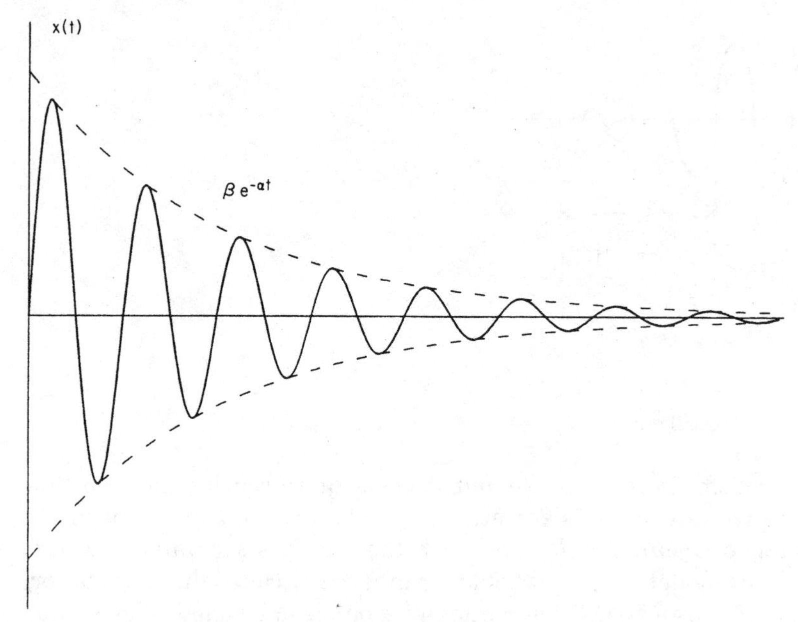

Figure 1.4 Exponentially decaying sinusoid.

Steady-state signal models

Generally, steady-state signals are limited to just sinusoids or sums of sinusoids. This will include virtually all periodic signals of practical interest, since such signals can be resolved into sums of weighted and shifted sinusoids using the Fourier analysis techniques presented in Sec. 1.2.

Periodicity. Sines, cosines, and square waves are all periodic functions. The characteristic that makes them periodic is the way in which each of the complete waveforms can be formed by repeating a particular cycle of the waveform over and over at a regular interval, as shown in Fig. 1.5.

Definition: A function $x(t)$ is periodic with a period of T if and only if $x(t + nT) = x(t)$ for all integer values of n.

Functions that are not periodic are called *aperiodic,* and functions that are "almost" periodic are called *quasi-periodic.*

Symmetry. A function can exhibit a certain symmetry regarding its position relative to the origin.

Definition: A function $x(t)$ is said to be *even,* or to exhibit *even symmetry,* if for all t, $x(t) = x(-t)$.

Definition: A function $x(t)$ is said to be *odd,* or to exhibit *odd symmetry,* if for all t, $x(t) = -x(-t)$.

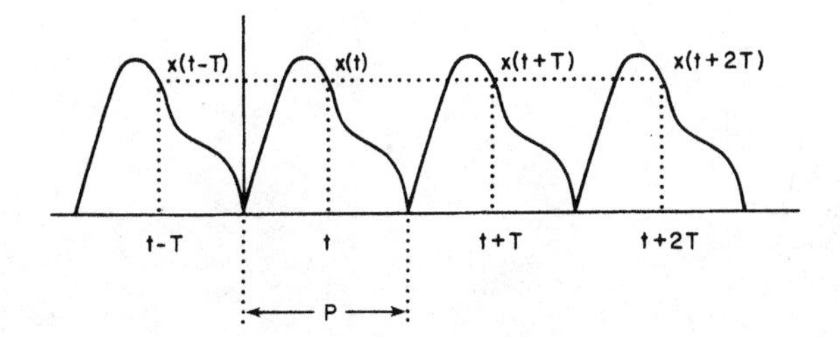

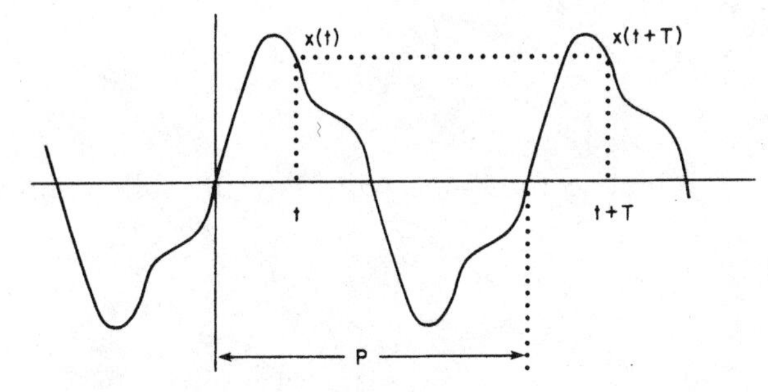

Figure 1.5 Periodic functions.

An even function is shown in Fig. 1.6, and an odd function is shown in Fig. 1.7.

Symmetry may appear at first to be something that is only "nice to know" and not particularly useful in practical applications where the definition of time zero is often somewhat arbitrary. This is far from the case, however, because symmetry considerations play an important role in Fourier analysis—especially the discrete Fourier analysis that will be discussed in Chap. 9. Some functions are neither odd nor even, but any *periodic* function can be resolved into a sum of an even function and an odd function as given by

$$x(t) = x_{\text{even}}(t) + x_{\text{odd}}(t)$$

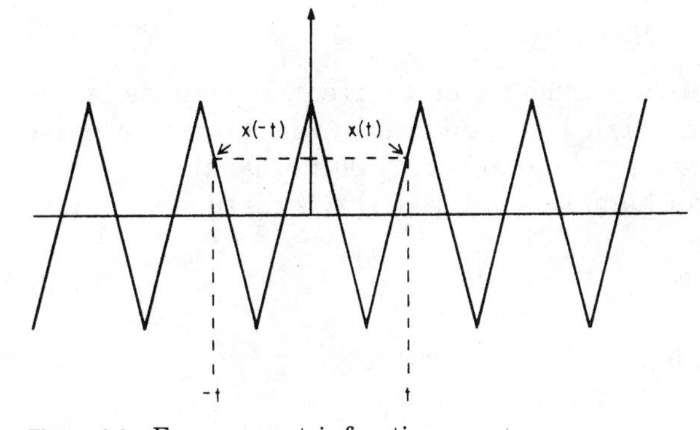

Figure 1.6 Even-symmetric function.

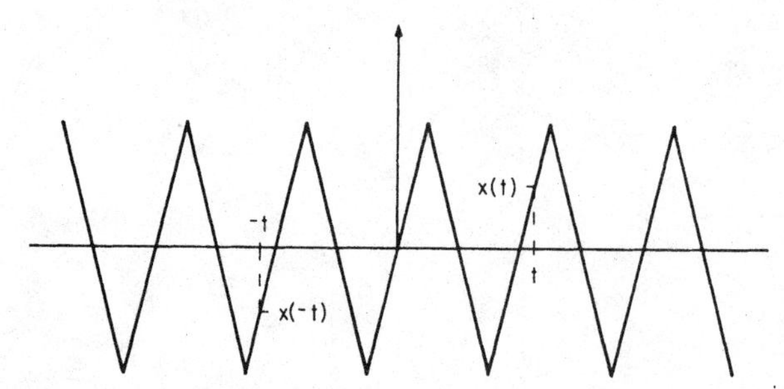

Figure 1.7 Odd-symmetric function.

where $x_{\text{even}}(t) = \frac{1}{2}[x(t) + x(-t)]$
$x_{\text{odd}}(t) = \frac{1}{2}[x(t) - x(-t)]$

Addition and multiplication of symmetric functions will obey the following rules:

Even + even = even

Odd + odd = odd

Odd × odd = even

Even × even = even

Odd × even = odd

Energy signals versus power signals

It is a common practice to deal with mathematical functions representing abstract signals as though they are either voltages across a 1-Ω resistor or currents through a 1-Ω resistor. Sincc, in cither case, the resistance has an assumed value of unity, the voltage and current for any particular signal will be numerically equal—thus obviating the need to select one viewpoint over the other. Thus, for a signal $x(t)$, the instantaneous power $p(t)$ dissipated in the 1-Ω resistor is simply the squared amplitude of the signal

$$p(t) = |x(t)|^2 \tag{1.1}$$

regardless of whether $x(t)$ represents a voltage or a current. To emphasize the fact that the power given by Eq. (1.1) is based upon unity resistance, it is often referred to as the *normalized power.* The total energy of the signal $x(t)$ is then obtained by integrating the right-hand side of Eq. (1.1) over all time:

$$E = \int_{-\infty}^{\infty} |x(t)|^2 \, dt \tag{1.2}$$

and the average power is given by

$$P = \lim_{T \to \infty} \frac{1}{T} \int_{-T/2}^{T/2} |x(t)|^2 \, dt \tag{1.3}$$

A few texts (for example, Haykin 1983) equivalently define the average power as

$$P = \lim_{T \to \infty} \frac{1}{2T} \int_{-T}^{T} |x(t)|^2 \, dt \tag{1.4}$$

If the total energy is finite and nonzero, $x(t)$ is referred to as an *energy signal.* If the average power is finite and nonzero, $x(t)$ is referred to as a *power signal.* Note that a power signal has infinite energy, and an energy signal has zero average power; thus the two categories are mutually exclusive. Periodic signals and most random signals are power signals, while most deterministic aperiodic signals are energy signals.

1.2 Frequency Spectra of Periodic Signals: Fourier Series

Periodic signals can be resolved into linear combinations of phase-shifted sinusoids using the *Fourier series,* which is given by

$$x(t) = \frac{a_0}{2} + \sum_{n=1}^{\infty} [a_n \cos(n\omega_0 t) + b_n \sin(n\omega_0 t)] \tag{1.5}$$

where $$a_0 = \frac{2}{T} \int_{-T/2}^{T/2} x(t) \, dt \tag{1.6}$$

$$a_n = \frac{2}{T} \int_{-T/2}^{T/2} x(t) \cos(n\omega_0 t) \, dt \tag{1.7}$$

$$b_n = \frac{2}{T} \int_{-T/2}^{T/2} x(t) \sin(n\omega_0 t) \, dt \tag{1.8}$$

T = period of $x(t)$

$\omega_0 = \frac{2\pi}{T} = 2\pi f_0$ = fundamental radian frequency of $x(t)$

Upon application of the appropriate trigonometric identities, Eq. (1.5) can be put into the following alternative form:

$$x(t) = c_0 + \sum_{n=1}^{\infty} c_n \cos(n\omega_0 t - \theta_n) \tag{1.9}$$

where the c_n and θ_n are obtained from a_n and b_n using

$$c_0 = \frac{a_0}{2} \tag{1.10}$$

$$c_n = \sqrt{a_n^2 + b_n^2} \tag{1.11}$$

$$\theta_n = \tan^{-1}\left(\frac{b_n}{a_n}\right) \tag{1.12}$$

Examination of Eqs. (1.5) and (1.6) reveals that a periodic signal contains only a dc component plus sinusoids whose frequencies are integer multiples of the original signal's *fundamental frequency.* (For a fundamental frequency of f_0, $2f_0$ is the *second harmonic,* $3f_0$ is the *third harmonic,* and so on.) Theoretically, periodic signals will generally contain an infinite number of harmonically related sinusoidal components. In the real world, however, periodic signals will contain only a finite number of measurable harmonics. Consequently, pure mathematical functions are only approximately equal to the practical signals which they model.

Exponential form

The trigonometric form of the Fourier series given by Eq. (1.5) makes it easy to visualize periodic signals as summations of sine and cosine waves, but mathematical manipulations are often more convenient when the series is in the exponential form given by

$$x(t) = \sum_{n=-\infty}^{\infty} c_n \, e^{j2\pi n f_0 t} \tag{1.13}$$

where $$c_n = \frac{1}{T} \int_T x(t) \, e^{-j2\pi n f_0 t} \, dt \tag{1.14}$$

The integral notation used in Eq. (1.14) indicates that the integral is to be evaluated over one period of $x(t)$. In general, the values of c_n are complex, and they are often presented in the form of a magnitude spectrum and phase spectrum, as shown in Fig. 1.8. The magnitude and phase values plotted in such spectra are obtained from c_n using

$$|c_n| = \sqrt{[\mathrm{Re}\,(c_n)]^2 + [\mathrm{Im}\,(c_n)]^2} \tag{1.15}$$

$$\theta_n = \tan^{-1}\left[\frac{\mathrm{Im}\,(c_n)}{\mathrm{Re}\,(c_n)}\right] \tag{1.16}$$

The complex c_n of Eq. (1.14) can be obtained from the a_n and b_n of Eqs. (1.7) and (1.8) using

$$c_n = \begin{cases} \dfrac{a_n + jb_n}{2} & n < 0 \\ a_0 & n = 0 \\ \dfrac{a_n - jb_n}{2} & n > 0 \end{cases} \tag{1.17}$$

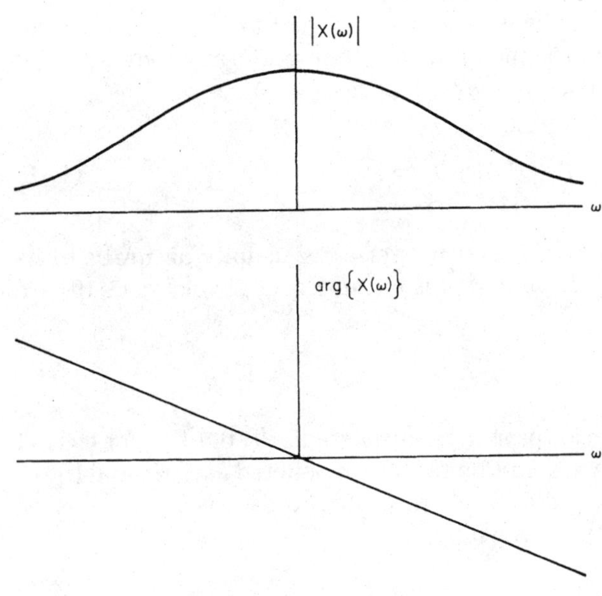

Figure 1.8 Magnitude and phase spectra.

Conditions of applicability

The Fourier series can be applied to almost all periodic signals of *practical* interest. However, there are some functions for which the series will not converge. The Fourier series coefficients are guaranteed to exist and the series will converge uniformly if $x(t)$ satisfies the following conditions:

1. The function $x(t)$ is a single-valued function.
2. The function $x(t)$ has, at most, a finite number of discontinuities within each period.
3. The function $x(t)$ has, at most, a finite number of extrema (that is, maxima and minima) within each period.
4. The function $x(t)$ is absolutely integrable over a period:

$$\int_T |x(t)|\, dt < \infty \tag{1.18}$$

These conditions are often called the *Dirichlet conditions* in honor of Peter Gustav Lejeune Dirichlet (1805–1859) who first published them in the 1828 issue of *Journal für die reine und angewandte Mathematik* (commonly known as *Crelle's Journal*). In applications where it is sufficient for the Fourier series coefficients to be convergent in the mean, rather than uniformly convergent, it suffices for $x(t)$ to be integrable square over a period:

$$\int_T |x(t)|^2 \, dt < \infty \tag{1.19}$$

For most engineering purposes, the Fourier series is usually assumed to be identical to $x(t)$ if conditions 1 through 3 plus either Eq. (1.18) or Eq. (1.19) are satisfied.

Properties of the Fourier series

A number of useful Fourier series properties are listed in Table 1.1. For ease of notation, the coefficients c_n corresponding to $x(t)$ are denoted as $X(n)$, and the c_n corresponding to $y(t)$ are denoted as $Y(n)$. In other words, the Fourier series representations of $x(t)$ and $y(t)$ are given by

$$x(t) = \sum_{n=-\infty}^{\infty} X(n) \exp\left(\frac{j2\pi nt}{T}\right) \tag{1.20}$$

$$y(t) = \sum_{n=-\infty}^{\infty} Y(n) \exp\left(\frac{j2\pi nt}{T}\right) \tag{1.21}$$

where T is the period of both $x(t)$ and $y(t)$. In addition to the properties listed in Table 1.1, the Fourier series (FS) coefficients exhibit certain symmetries. If

TABLE 1.1 Properties of the Fourier Series

Property	Time function	Transform
1. Homogeneity	$ax(t)$	$aX(n)$
2. Additivity	$x(t) + y(t)$	$X(n) + Y(n)$
3. Linearity	$ax(t) + by(t)$	$aX(n) + bY(n)$
4. Multiplication	$x(t)\,y(t)$	$\sum_{m=-\infty}^{\infty} X(n-m)\,Y(m)$
5. Convolution	$\frac{1}{T}\int_0^T x(t-\tau)\,y(\tau)\,d\tau$	$X(n)\,Y(n)$
6. Time shifting	$x(t-\tau)$	$\exp\left(\frac{-j2\pi n\tau}{T}\right) X(n)$
7. Frequency shifting	$\exp\left(\frac{j2\pi mt}{T}\right) x(t)$	$X(n-m)$

NOTE: $x(t)$, $y(t)$, $X(n)$, and $Y(n)$ are as given in Eqs. (1.20) and (1.21).

(and only if) $x(t)$ is real, the corresponding FS coefficients will exhibit even symmetry in their real part and odd symmetry in their imaginary part:

$$\operatorname{Im}[x(t)] = 0 \Leftrightarrow \operatorname{Re}[X(-n)] = \operatorname{Re}[X(n)]$$

$$\operatorname{Im}[X(-n)] = -\operatorname{Im}[X(n)] \tag{1.22}$$

Equation (1.22) can be rewritten in more compact form as

$$\operatorname{Im}[x(t)] = 0 \Leftrightarrow X(-n) = X^*(n) \tag{1.23}$$

where the superscript asterisk indicates complex conjugation. Likewise, for purely imaginary $x(t)$, the corresponding FS coefficients will exhibit odd symmetry in their real part and even symmetry in their imaginary part:

$$\operatorname{Re}[x(t)] = 0 \Leftrightarrow X(-n) = -[X^*(n)] \tag{1.24}$$

If and only if $x(t)$ is (in general) complex with even symmetry in the real part and odd symmetry in the imaginary part, then the corresponding FS coefficients will be purely real:

$$x(-t) = x^*(t) \Leftrightarrow \operatorname{Im}[X(n)] = 0 \tag{1.25}$$

If and only if $x(t)$ is (in general) complex with odd symmetry in the real part and even symmetry in the imaginary part, then the corresponding FS coefficients will be purely imaginary:

$$x(-t) = -[x^*(t) \Leftrightarrow \operatorname{Re}[X(n)] = 0 \tag{1.26}$$

In terms of the amplitude and phase spectra, Eq. (1.23) means that for real signals, the amplitude spectrum will have even symmetry and the phase spectrum will have odd symmetry. If $x(t)$ is both real and even, then both Eqs. (1.23) and (1.25) apply. In this special case, the FS coefficients will be both real and even symmetric. At first glance, it may appear that real even-symmetric coefficients are in contradiction to the expected odd-symmetric phase spectrum; but, in fact, there is no contradiction. For all the positive real coefficients, the corresponding phase is, of course, zero. For each of the negative real coefficients, we can choose a phase value of either plus or minus 180°. By appropriate selection of positive and negative values, odd symmetry in the phase spectrum can be maintained.

Fourier series of a square pulse train

Consider the square pulse train shown in Fig. 1.9. The Fourier series representation of this signal is given by

$$x(t) = \sum_{n=-\infty}^{\infty} c_n \exp\left(\frac{j2\pi nt}{T}\right) \tag{1.27}$$

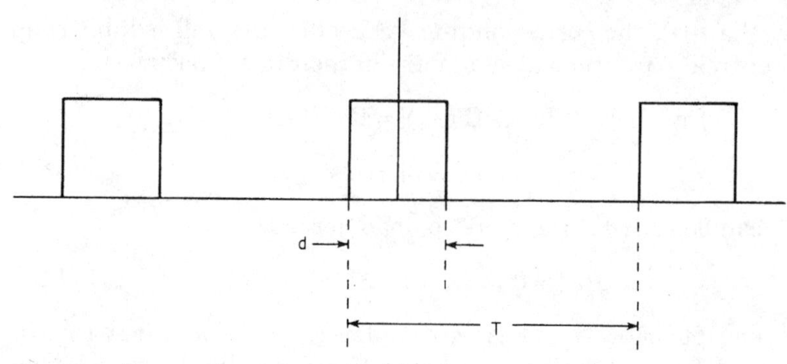

Figure 1.9 Square pulse train.

$$\text{where} \quad c_n = \frac{\tau A}{T} \operatorname{sinc}\left(\frac{n\tau}{T}\right)$$

Since the signal is both real and even-symmetric, the FS coefficients are real and even-symmetric, as shown in Fig. 1.10. The corresponding magnitude spectrum will be even, as shown in Fig. 1.11*a*. Appropriate selection of $\pm 180°$ values for the phase of negative coefficients will allow an odd-symmetric phase spectrum to be plotted as in Fig. 1.11*b*.

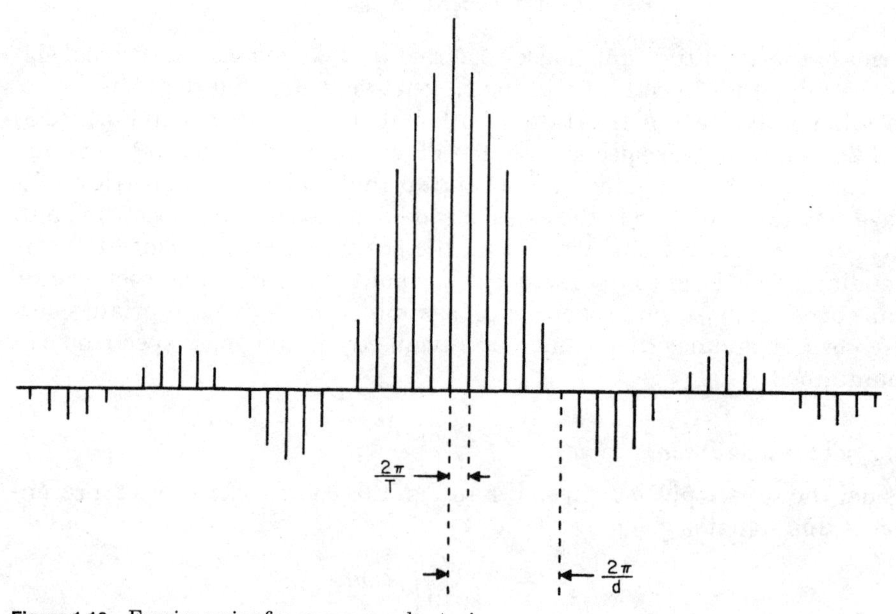

Figure 1.10 Fourier series for a square pulse train.

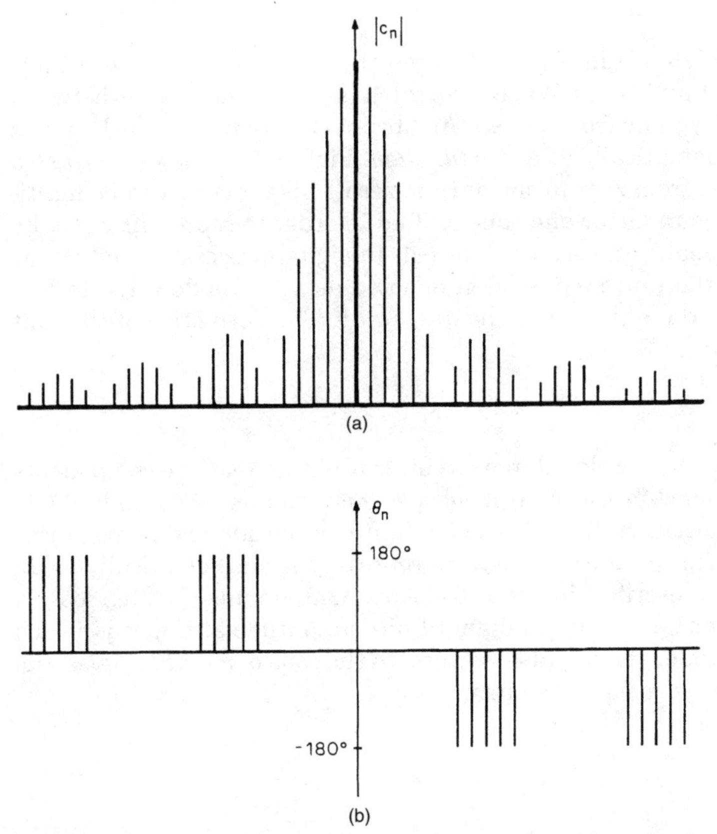

Figure 1.11 Fourier series spectra for a square pulse train: (*a*) amplitude spectrum; (*b*) phase spectrum.

Parseval's theorem

The average power (normalized for 1 Ω) of a real-valued periodic function of time can be obtained directly from the Fourier series coefficients by using Parseval's theorem:

$$P = \frac{1}{T} \int_T |x(t)|^2 \, dt$$

$$= \sum_{n=-\infty}^{\infty} |c_n|^2 = c_0^2 + \sum_{n=1}^{\infty} \frac{1}{2} |2c_n|^2 \tag{1.29}$$

1.3 Transient Signals

There are several transient signals, modeled by aperiodic functions, that are frequently encountered in signal-processing work. These include the *unit step, unit impulse,* and *exponentials,* which are each discussed in the following sections.

Unit step

Consider the circuit shown in Fig. 1.12. When the switch is open, the voltage between terminals A and B is 0. When the switch is closed, the voltage between A and B will abruptly jump from 0 to 9 V. An abrupt change in level such as this is represented mathematically as a *step function.* Figure 1.13 shows a *unit step* which shifts its level from zero to one at time zero. This function can be multiplied by a constant gain factor and time-shifted in order to represent virtually any abrupt dc level shift of practical interest. In signal-processing and linear systems literature the unit step is often denoted as $u_1(t)$. As depicted in Fig. 1.14, the integral of the unit step is the *unit ramp.* The derivative of the unit step is the *unit impulse.*

Unit impulse

When a switch is opened or closed in a circuit containing reactive components (i.e., capacitors or inductors), a spike of voltage or current as shown in Fig. 1.1*c* may be produced. Although this spike has a finite amplitude and nonzero rise time and fall time, it is often convenient to represent it mathematically as an *impulse function.* As described in Sec. A.6 of App. A, an impulse is often loosely described as having a zero width and an infinite amplitude at the origin such that the total area under the impulse is finite. In the case of a *unit impulse,* the area under the impulse is equal to unity.

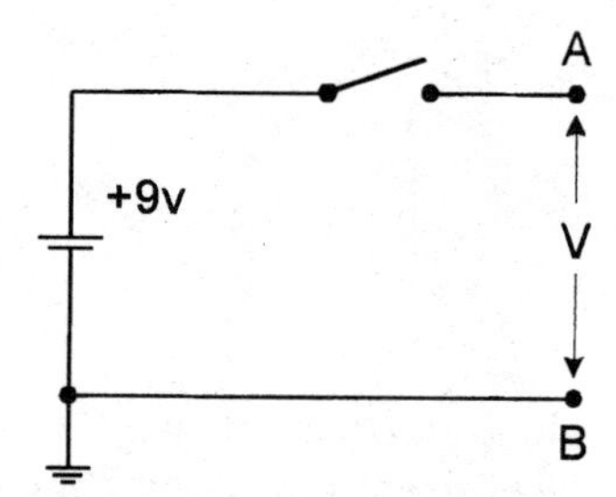

Figure 1.12 Circuit used in discussion of the unit step function.

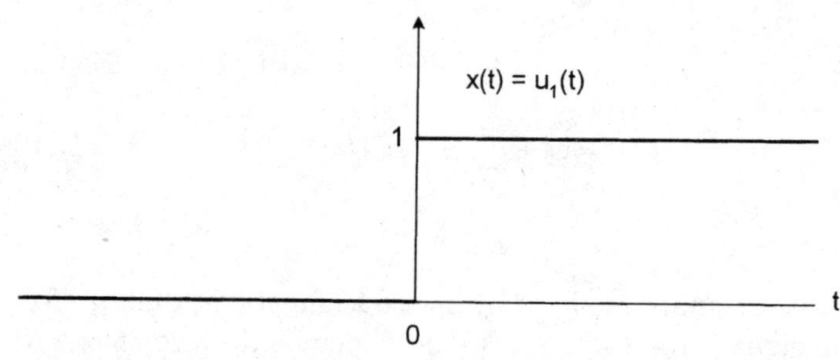

Figure 1.13 Unit step function.

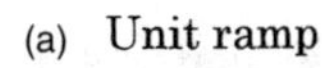

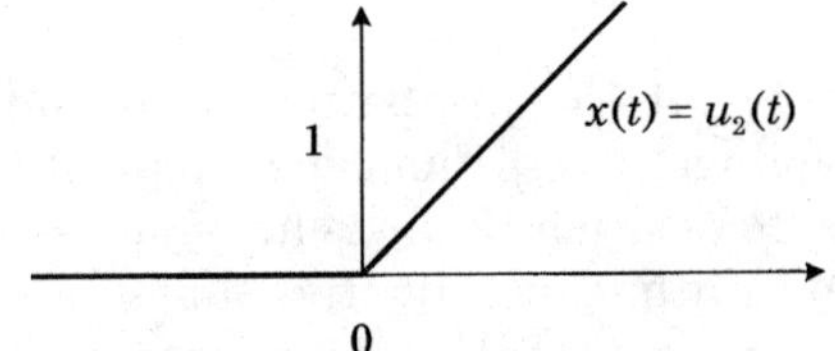

$u_2(t) = \int u_1(t)\,dt$ $\qquad$ $u_1(t) = \frac{d}{dt} u_2(t)$

(b) Unit step

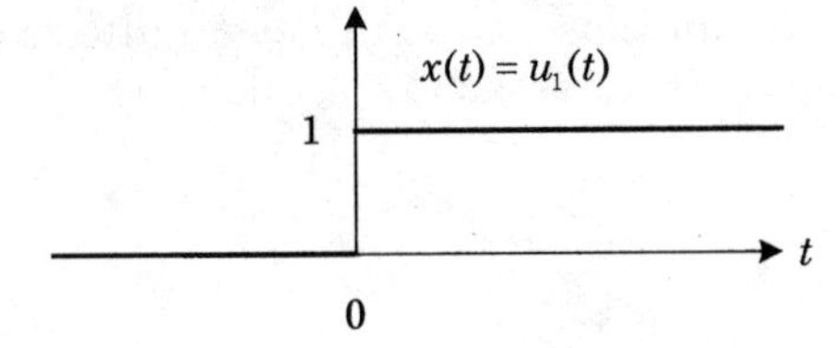

$u_1(t) = \int u_0(t)\,dt$ $\qquad$ $u_0(t) = \frac{d}{dt} u_1(t)$

(c) Unit impulse

$x(t) = u_0(t) = \delta(t)$

1

0

t

$u_0(t) = \int u_{-1}(t)\,dt$ $\qquad$ $u_{-1}(t) = \frac{d}{dt} u_0(t)$

(d) Unit doublet

$x(t) = u_{-1}(t)$

1

t

Figure 1.14 Elementary time functions: (*a*) unit ramp, (*b*) unit step, (*c*) unit impulse, and (*d*) unit doublet.

As with the unit step, the unit impulse can be time-shifted and multiplied by a constant gain in order to represent almost any spiking phenomenon of practical interest. The unit impulse is denoted as either $u_0(t)$ or $\delta(t)$. As depicted in Fig. 1.14, the integral of the unit impulse is the *unit step,* and the derivative of the unit impulse is the *unit doublet.*

Decaying exponential

Consider the circuit shown in Fig. 1.15. The battery is initially connected across the capacitor, and the voltage across the capacitor will be 9 V. If the switch is moved from position A to position B, the voltage across the capacitor terminals will decay as shown. Mathematically, the shape of this decaying waveform is described as a *decaying exponential* of the form

$$y = \beta \exp(-\alpha t) \tag{1.30}$$

A decaying exponential is shown in Fig. 1.16. As time increases, the amplitude of the function approaches closer and closer to—but never quite reaches—zero. The function is said to *asymptotically* approach zero, and the horizontal line at $y = 0$ is called an *asymptote.*

Saturating exponential

Referring again to the circuit in Fig. 1.15, let's assume that the switch is in position B and the voltage across the capacitor is zero. If the switch is moved to position A, the voltage across the capacitor will begin to increase as a saturating exponential of the form

$$y = 1 - \beta \exp(-\alpha t) \tag{1.31}$$

A saturating exponential is shown in Fig. 1.17. The function approaches an asymptote at $y = \beta$.

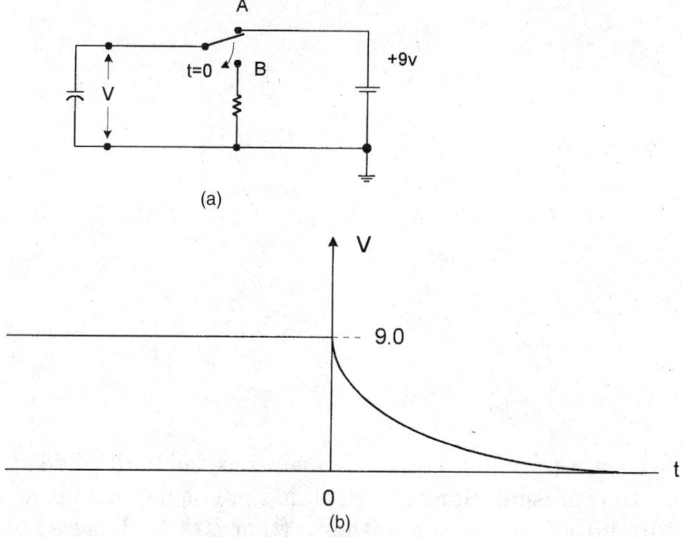

Figure 1.15 Circuit used in discussion of decaying and saturating exponentials: (*a*) diagram of the circuit, and (*b*) voltage decay across the capacitor when the switch is moved to position B.

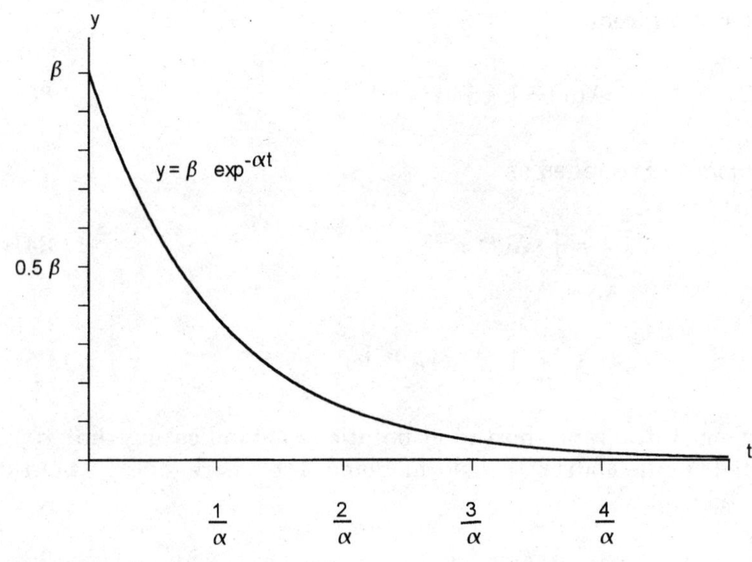

Figure 1.16 Decaying exponential.

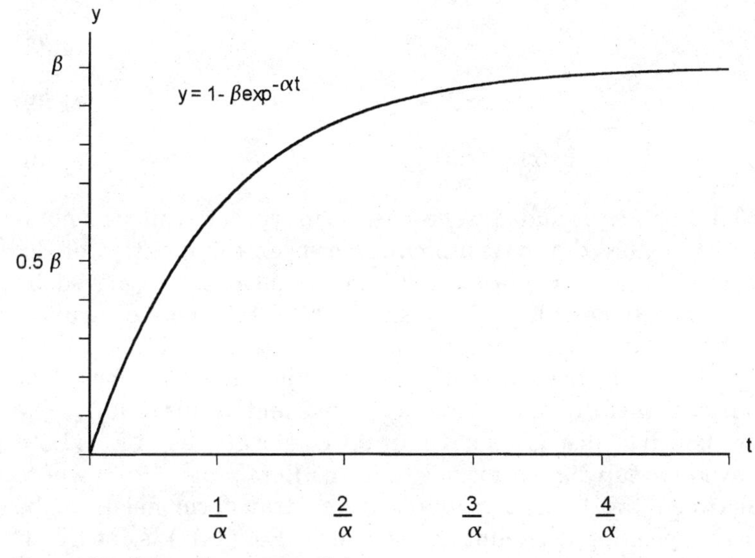

Figure 1.17 Saturating exponential.

1.4 Fourier Transform

The *Fourier transform* is defined as

$$X(f) = \int_{-\infty}^{\infty} x(t)\, e^{-j2\pi ft}\, dt \tag{1.32}$$

or, in terms of the radian frequency $\omega = 2\pi f$:

$$X(\omega) = \int_{-\infty}^{\infty} x(t)\, e^{-j\omega t}\, dt \tag{1.33}$$

The *inverse transform* is defined as

$$x(t) = \int_{-\infty}^{\infty} X(f)\, e^{j2\pi ft}\, df \tag{1.34}$$

$$= \frac{1}{2\pi} \int_{-\infty}^{\infty} X(\omega)\, e^{j\omega t}\, d\omega \tag{1.35}$$

There are a number of different shorthand notations for indicating that $x(t)$ and $X(f)$ are related via the Fourier transform. Some of the more common notations include the following:

$$X(f) = \mathcal{F}\,[x(t)] \tag{1.36}$$

$$x(t) = \mathcal{F}^{-1}[X(f)] \tag{1.37}$$

$$x(t) \overset{\text{FT}}{\longleftrightarrow} X(f) \tag{1.38}$$

$$x(t) \underset{\text{IFT}}{\overset{\text{FT}}{\rightleftarrows}} X(f) \tag{1.39}$$

$$x(t) \circledcirc X(f) \tag{1.40}$$

The notation used in Eqs. (1.36) and (1.37) is easiest to typeset, while the notation of Eq. (1.40) is probably the most difficult. However, the notation of Eq. (1.40) is used in the classic work on fast Fourier transforms described by Brigham (1974). The notations of Eqs. (1.38) and (1.39), while more difficult to typeset, offer the flexibility of changing the letters FT to FS, DFT, or DTFT to indicate, respectively, "Fourier series," "discrete Fourier transform," or "discrete-time Fourier transform" as is done in Roberts and Mullis (1987). (The latter two transforms will be discussed in Chap. 9.) The form used in Eq. (1.39) is perhaps best saved for tutorial situations (such as Rorabaugh 1986) where the distinction between the transform and inverse transform needs to be emphasized. Strictly speaking, the equality shown in Eq. (1.37) is incorrect, since the inverse transform of $X(f)$ is only guaranteed to approach $x(t)$ in the sense of convergence in the mean. Nevertheless, the notation of Eq. (1.37) appears often throughout the engineering literature. Often the frequency domain function is written as $X(j\omega)$ rather than $X(\omega)$ in order to facilitate comparison with the Laplace transform. We can write

$$X(j\omega) = \int_{-\infty}^{\infty} x(t)\, e^{-j\omega t}\, dt \tag{1.41}$$

and realize that this is identical to the two-sided Laplace transform defined by Eq. (3.21), with $j\omega$ substituted for s. A number of useful Fourier transform properties are listed in Table 1.2.

Fourier transforms of periodic signals

Often there is a requirement to analyze systems that include both periodic power signals and aperiodic energy signals. The mixing of Fourier transform results and Fourier series results implied by such an analysis may be quite cumbersome. For the sake of convenience, the spectra of most periodic signals can be obtained as Fourier transforms that involve the Dirac delta function. When the spectrum of a periodic signal is determined via the Fourier series, the spectrum will consist of lines located at the fundamental frequency and its harmonics. When the spectrum of this same signal is obtained as a Fourier transform, the spectrum will consist of Dirac delta functions located at the fundamental frequency and its harmonics. Obviously, these two different mathematical representations must be equivalent in their physical significance. Specifically, consider a periodic signal $x_p(t)$ having a period of T. The Fourier series representation of $x_p(t)$ is obtained from Eq. (1.13) as

$$x_p(t) = \sum_{n=-\infty}^{\infty} c_n \exp\left(\frac{j2\pi nt}{T}\right) \tag{1.42}$$

We can then define a *generating function* $x(t)$ that is equal to a single period of $x_p(t)$:

$$x(t) = \begin{cases} x_p(t) & |t| \leq \dfrac{T}{2} \\ 0 & \text{elsewhere} \end{cases} \tag{1.43}$$

The periodic signal $x_p(t)$ can be expressed as an infinite summation of time-shifted copies of $x(t)$:

$$x_p(t) = \sum_{n=-\infty}^{\infty} x(t - nT) \tag{1.44}$$

The Fourier series coefficients c_n appearing in Eq. (1.42) can be obtained as

$$c_n = \frac{1}{T} X\left(\frac{n}{T}\right) \tag{1.45}$$

where $X(f)$ is the Fourier transform of $x(t)$. Thus, the Fourier transform of $x_p(t)$ can be obtained as

$$\mathcal{F}[x_p(t)] = \frac{1}{T} \sum_{n=-\infty}^{\infty} X\left(\frac{n}{T}\right) \delta\left(f - \frac{n}{T}\right) \tag{1.46}$$

TABLE 1.2 Properties of the Fourier Transform

Property	Time function, $x(t)$	Transform, $X(f)$
1. Homogeneity	$ax(t)$	$aX(f)$
2. Additivity	$x(t) + y(t)$	$X(f) + Y(f)$
3. Linearity	$ax(t) + by(t)$	$aX(f) + bY(f)$
4. Differentiation	$\frac{d^n}{dt^n} x(t)$	$(j2\pi f)^n X(f)$
5. Integration	$\int_{-\infty}^{t} x(\tau)\, d\tau$	$\frac{X(f)}{j2\pi f} + \frac{1}{2} X(0)\, \delta(f)$
6. Frequency shifting	$e^{-j2\pi f_0 t} x(t)$	$X(f + f_0)$
7. Sine modulation	$x(t) \sin(2\pi f_0 t)$	$\frac{1}{2}[X(f - f_0) + X(f + f_0)]$
8. Cosine modulation	$x(t) \cos(2\pi f_0 t)$	$\frac{1}{2}[X(f - f_0) - X(f + f_0)]$
9. Time shifting	$x(t - \tau)$	$e^{-j\omega\tau} X(f)$
10. Time convolution	$\int_{-\infty}^{\infty} h(t - \tau)\, x(\tau)\, d\tau$	$H(f)\, X(f)$
11. Multiplication	$x(t)\, y(t)$	$\int_{-\infty}^{\infty} X(\lambda)\, Y(f - \lambda)\, d\lambda$
12. Time and frequency scaling	$x\left(\frac{t}{a}\right) \quad a > 0$	$aX(af)$
13. Duality	$X(t)$	$x(-f)$
14. Conjugation	$x^*(t)$	$X^*(-f)$
15. Real part	$\text{Re}\,[x(t)]$	$\frac{1}{2}[X(f) + X^*(-f)]$
16. Imaginary part	$\text{Im}\,[x(t)]$	$\frac{1}{2j}[X(f) - X^*(-f)]$

TABLE 1.3 Some Common Fourier Transform Pairs

Pair no.	$x(t)$	$X(\omega)$	$X(f)$
1	1	$2\pi\,\delta(\omega)$	$\delta(f)$
2	$u_1(t)$	$\dfrac{1}{j\omega} + \pi\delta(\omega)$	$\dfrac{1}{2\pi f} + \dfrac{1}{2}\delta(f)$
3	$\delta(t)$	1	1
4	t^n	$2\pi j^n\,\delta^{(n)}(\omega)$	$\left(\dfrac{j}{2\pi}\right)^n \delta^{(n)}(f)$
5	$\sin \omega_0 t$	$j\pi[\delta(\omega + \omega_0) - \delta(\omega - \omega_0)]$	$\dfrac{j}{2}\,[\delta(f + f_0) - \delta(f - f_0)]$
6	$\cos \omega_0 t$	$\pi[\delta(\omega + \omega_0) + \delta(\omega - \omega_0)]$	$\dfrac{1}{2}[\delta(f + f_0) + \delta(f - f_0)]$
7	$e^{-at}u_1(t)$	$\dfrac{1}{j\omega + a}$	$\dfrac{1}{j2\pi f + a}$
8	$u_1(t)\,e^{-at}\sin \omega_0 t$	$\dfrac{\omega_0}{(a + j\omega)^2 + \omega_0^2}$	$\dfrac{2\pi f_0}{(a + j2\pi f)^2 + (2\pi f_0)^2}$
9	$u_1(t)\,e^{-at}\cos \omega_0 t$	$\dfrac{a + j\omega}{(a + j\omega)^2 + \omega_0^2}$	$\dfrac{a + j2\pi f}{(a + j2\pi f)^2 + (2\pi f_0)^2}$
10	$\begin{cases} 1 & \lvert t \rvert \le \dfrac{1}{2} \\ 0 & \text{elsewhere} \end{cases}$	$\operatorname{sinc}\left(\dfrac{\omega}{2\pi}\right)$	$\operatorname{sinc} f$
11	$\operatorname{sinc} t \triangleq \dfrac{\sin \pi t}{\pi t}$	$\begin{cases} 1 & \lvert \omega \rvert \le \pi \\ 0 & \text{elsewhere} \end{cases}$	$\begin{cases} 1 & \lvert f \rvert \le \dfrac{1}{2} \\ 0 & \text{elsewhere} \end{cases}$
12	$\begin{cases} at \exp(-at) & t > 0 \\ 0 & \text{elsewhere} \end{cases}$	$\dfrac{a}{(a + j\omega)^2}$	$\dfrac{a}{(a + j2\pi f)^2}$
13	$\exp(-a\lvert t \rvert)$	$\dfrac{2a}{a^2 + \omega^2}$	$\dfrac{2a}{a^2 + 4\pi^2 f^2}$
14	$\operatorname{signum} t \triangleq \begin{cases} 1 & t > 0 \\ 0 & t = 0 \\ -1 & t < 0 \end{cases}$	$\dfrac{2}{j\omega}$	$\dfrac{1}{j\pi f}$

Common Fourier transform pairs

A number of frequently encountered Fourier transform pairs are listed in Table 1.3. Several of these pairs are actually obtained as Fourier transforms-in-the-limit.

1.5 Spectral Density

Energy spectral density

The *energy spectral density* of an energy signal is defined as the squared magnitude of the signal's Fourier transform:

$$S_e(f) = |X(f)|^2 \tag{1.47}$$

Analogous to the way in which Parseval's theorem relates the Fourier series coefficients to the average power of a power signal, *Rayleigh's energy theorem* relates the Fourier transform to the total energy of an energy signal as follows:

$$E = \int_{-\infty}^{\infty} |x(t)|^2 \, dt = \int_{-\infty}^{\infty} S_e(f) \, df = \int_{-\infty}^{\infty} |X(f)|^2 \, df \tag{1.48}$$

In many texts where $x(t)$ is assumed to be real-valued, the absolute-value signs are omitted from the first integrand in Eq. (1.48). In some texts (such as Kanefsky 1985), Eq. (1.48) is loosely referred to as "Parseval's theorem."

Power spectral density of a periodic signal

The *power spectral density* (*PSD*) of a periodic signal is defined as the squared magnitude of the signal's line spectrum obtained via either a Fourier series or a Fourier transform with impulses. Using the Dirac delta notational conventions of the latter, the PSD is defined as

$$S_p(f) = \frac{1}{T^2} \sum_{n=-\infty}^{\infty} \delta\left(f - \frac{n}{T}\right) \left|X\left(\frac{n}{T}\right)\right|^2 \tag{1.49}$$

where T is the period of the signal $x(t)$. Parseval's theorem as given by Eq. (1.29) of Sec. 1.2 can be restated in the notation of Fourier transform spectra as

$$P = \frac{1}{T^2} \sum_{n=-\infty}^{\infty} \left|X\left(\frac{n}{T}\right)\right|^2 \tag{1.50}$$

Chapter

2

Noise

Noise is present in virtually all signals. In some situations it is negligible, and in other situations it all but obliterates the signal of interest. Removing unwanted noise from signals has historically been a driving force behind the development of filter technology, and it continues to be a major application for both analog and digital filters. A complete, mathematically rigorous treatment of noise and noiselike phenomena could fill volumes and is clearly beyond the scope of this chapter. Rather, the goal of this chapter is a practical treatment of noise that provides sufficient information to support the design and use of digital filters in applications that involve significant noise processes. A review of probability and random variable theory is provided in App. B.

2.1 Noise Processes

Let's assume that we want to make a single measurement of the voltage across the output terminals of a benchtop dc power supply. The nominal output voltage of the supply is 5.000 V. If we measure to 3 digits of precision, we may read a value of 4.997 V. Or, we may read a value of 5.001 V. Or maybe 5.013 V. Mathematically, we can represent this measurement M as the sum of two parts:

$$M = V + E$$

where the *deterministic* part V is the "true" output voltage, which we might assume to be exactly 5.000 V, and the *random* or *stochastic* part E is the measurement error, which we assume to be small relative to V. Typically, E will be treated as a *random variable* whose characterization includes a *distribution,* a *mean,* and a *variance.* (Random variables and their properties are reviewed in App. B.) For the example under discussion, E might be gaussian-distributed with zero mean and some nonzero variance, say 0.02. From this information alone it would be possible to calculate the probability of reading a measurement value that falls within any particular range, say perhaps 4.995 to 5.005. Each time the measurement is repeated, it is possible to read a different value.

If we were to repeat the measurement at regular intervals we would obtain a sequence of values that vary over time. (This sequence constitutes a discrete-time noise signal which could be subjected to processing in a digital filter.) Each individual sample in this sequence can be viewed as a random variable, but the *sequence* of samples has additional properties beyond the properties of the individual samples. These additional properties are captured when the repeated measurement *process* is treated mathematically as a *random process.* These additional properties deal with the relationships between individual measurement samples. In a *wideband* noise process, the measurement values from one sample to the next exhibit little or no correlation, while in a *narrowband* noise process, the measurement values from one sample to the next can exhibit significant correlation.

Autocorrelation and autocovariance

The *autocorrelation function* (*acf*) of a random process is denoted by $R_x(t_1, t_2)$ and is obtained by forming the cross-correlation of the ensemble random variables at time t_1 and t_2.

$$R_x(t_1, t_2) = E[x_1, x_2] = \int_{-\infty}^{\infty}\int_{-\infty}^{\infty} x_1 x_2^* \, p_{x_1 x_2}(x_1, x_2)\, dx_1\, dx_2 \tag{2.1}$$

where x_1 represents $x(t_1)$ and x_2 represents $x(t_2)$. In general, $x(t)$ can be complex-valued, and the superscript asterisk denotes complex conjugation. Many texts assume that $x(t)$ is real-valued and define the autocorrelation without the conjugation operator shown here. The acf of a discrete random process is defined by

$$R_x(t_1, t_2) = \sum_{i=1}^{N}\sum_{j=1}^{N} x(t_1)x^*(t_2)\, P[x(t_1) = a_i,\, x(t_2) = a_j] \tag{2.2}$$

If $R_x(t_1, t_2)$ is a function of only the difference $t_2 - t_1$ and not of the specific values of t_1 and t_2, the autocorrelation can be written as:

$$R_x(\tau) = E[x(t)\, x(t + \tau)] \tag{2.3}$$

Properties of autocorrelation functions

1. The autocorrelation function is nonnegative.
2. The power in the process x is given by

$$\text{Power} = E\{x^2(t)\} = R_x(t, t) = \sigma_x^2$$

3. A second-order process is one for which $R_x(t, t) < \infty$ for all t.

4. $R_x(t, s) = R_x(s, t)$ for all t and s.
5. $|R_x(t, s)| \leq \sqrt{R_x(t, t)R(s, s)}$.
6. $R_x(t, s)$ is nonnegative definite. In other words, for all n and all $t_1, t_2, t_3, \ldots,$ t_n, there are complex numbers $\alpha_1, \alpha_2, \alpha_3, \ldots, \alpha_n$ such that

$$\sum_{j=1}^{n}\sum_{k=1}^{m} \alpha_j \alpha_k^* R_x(t_j, t_k) \geq 0 \qquad \text{for} \quad j, k \in \{t_1, t_2, \ldots, t_n\}$$

7. For wss processes, $R_x(\tau) = R_x(-\tau)$.
8. For wss processes, $|R_x(\tau)| \leq R_x(0)$.

2.2 Power Spectral Density of Noise Processes

The *power spectral density* $S_x(f)$ and the *autocorrelation function* $R_x(\tau)$ of a wide-sense stationary random process $X(t)$ comprise a Fourier transform pair.

$$S_x(f) = \mathscr{F}\{R_x(\tau)\} = \int_{-\infty}^{\infty} R_x \exp(-j2\pi ft)\, dt \tag{2.4}$$

$$R_x(\tau) = \mathscr{F}^{-1}\{S_x(f)\} = \int_{-\infty}^{\infty} S_x \exp(j2\pi ft)\, df \tag{2.5}$$

In some of the literature, the autocorrelation and power spectral density (PSD) are developed separately, and then the fact that they form a Fourier transform pair is demonstrated and dubbed the *Wiener-Khintchine theorem.* Some texts take the alternative approach of developing the autocorrelation function and then *defining* the PSD as the Fourier transform of the acf. In this case, Eqs. (2.4) and (2.5) are called the *Wiener-Khintchine relations* since they are defined rather than derived.

There is some disagreement concerning the proper spelling of *Khintchine.* The spelling used here agrees with Haykin (1983) and Simpson and Houts (1971). Other observed spellings include *Kinchin* (Urkowitz 1983), *Khinchin* (Blachman 1966), *Kinchine* (Whalen 1971; Carlson 1968), and *Khinchine* (Stein and Jones 1967). This is somewhat understandable due to various transliterations from Cyrillic to Latin alphabets, but there is even some disagreement over *Wiener,* which in at least two texts (Stein and Jones 1967; Simpson and Houts 1971) appears as *Weiner.* At least one text (Taub and Schilling 1986) avoids the issue completely by presenting the relationship but not giving it a name.

2.3 White Noise

White noise is an idealized noise process having a power spectral density that is constant over all frequencies, as shown in Fig. 2.1. The term *white* derives from the fact that the spectrum of white light is constant over all frequencies in the visible range. By convention, the constant value of the two-sided PSD for white noise is usually denoted as $N_0/2$. The factor of 2 in the denominator is a convenience so that the noise power passed by an ideal low-pass filter (LPF) having a bandwidth of B will be equal to N_0B. In a similar vein, the constant value of the one-sided PSD for white noise is denoted as N_0. When the noise generated within a system is modeled as white noise applied to the system's input, the value of N_0 is simply kT, where k is Boltzmann's constant and T is the equivalent noise temperature of the system.

The power spectral density and autocorrelation function for a random process form a Fourier transform pair. Using Pair 3 from Table 1.3, we conclude that the autocorrelation function of white noise is an impulse or delta function located at the origin.

$$\frac{N_0}{2}\delta(\tau) \overset{\text{FT}}{\longleftrightarrow} \frac{N_0}{2}$$

Physically, an impulse at the origin signifies that the white noise has infinite average power. Obviously, no noise process in the real world can have infinite average power, which is why the word *idealized* appears in the opening sentence of this section. Nevertheless, the concept of white noise is a mathematical convenience that finds widespread use in theoretical work. Once white noise is (conceptually) passed through a filter of finite bandwidth, the objectionable attribute of infinite average power disappears. Although it theoretically need not be so, whenever a white noise process is assumed, it is almost always assumed to be a gaussian process and is called *white gaussian noise* (*WGN*) or *additive white gaussian noise* (*AWGN*).

Example 2.1 Ideal low-pass filtering of white noise is a classic example which is presented in numerous texts (Taub and Schilling 1986; Haykin 1983; Cooper and McGillem 1986; Proakis 1983). The transfer function of the ideal LPF is given by

$$H(f) = \begin{cases} 1 & |f| \leq B \\ 0 & \text{elsewhere} \end{cases}$$

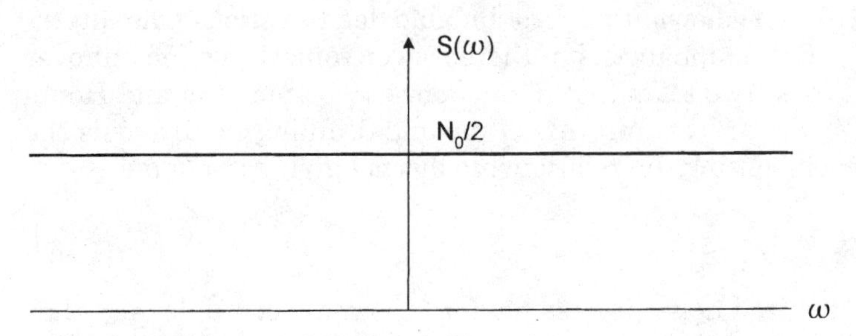

Figure 2.1 Power spectral density of white noise.

If white noise with a PSD of $N_0/2$ is applied to the input of such a filter, the PSD of the output noise process will be given by

$$S(f) = \begin{cases} \dfrac{N_0}{2} & |f| \leq B \\ 0 & \text{elsewhere} \end{cases}$$

Using Pair 11 from Table 1.3, we find that the autocorrelation of the output noise is

$$R(\tau) = N_0 B \operatorname{sinc}(2B\tau)$$

The average power is equal to $R(\tau)$ evaluated at $\tau = 0$ or simply N_0B—an intuitively pleasing result.

When white noise is subjected to filtering, the output noise process is referred to as *band-limited white noise.* In order to avoid the verbal tap dancing needed to deal with the infinite average power of ideal white noise, it may be helpful to consider band-limited white noise first and then simply think of ideal white noise as a limiting process that is approached as the bandwidth approaches infinity.

2.4 Noise Equivalent Bandwidth

The magnitude response $|H(f)|$ of an arbitrary low-pass filter is sketched (solid line) in Fig. 2.2. If zero-mean white noise having a two-sided PSD of $N_0/2$ is applied to the input of such a filter, the resulting output will have a finite average power that is given by

$$N = \frac{N_0}{2} \int_{-\infty}^{\infty} |H(f)|^2 \, df \tag{2.6}$$

Figure 2.2 also shows (dashed line) the magnitude response of an ideal low-pass filter. The *noise equivalent bandwidth* of the arbitrary filter is defined as the value of B for which the ideal filter and arbitrary filter produce the same output power from identical white noise inputs. The average output noise power from the ideal filter is

$$N = N_0 B \, H^2(0) \tag{2.7}$$

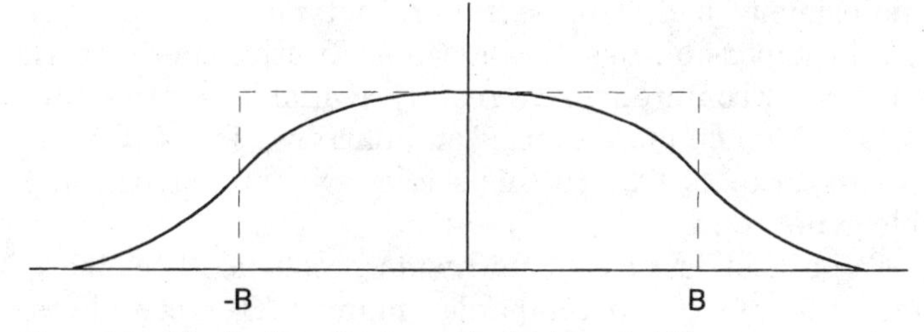

Figure 2.2 Illustration of noise equivalent bandwidth.

The value of B for which the two filters produce the same output noise power is found by equating Eqs. (2.6) and (2.7) and solving for B to yield

$$B = \frac{\int_{-\infty}^{\infty} |H(f)|^2 \, df}{2H^2(0)} = \frac{\int_{0}^{\infty} |H(f)|^2 \, df}{H^2(0)}$$

2.5 Uniform Distribution

A uniformly distributed random variable x has a probability density function (pdf) given by

$$p(x) = \begin{cases} \dfrac{1}{b - a} & a \leq x \leq b \\ 0 & \text{elsewhere} \end{cases} \tag{2.8}$$

The mean is given by

$$\mu = \frac{a + b}{2} \tag{2.9}$$

and the variance is given by

$$\sigma^2 = \frac{(b - a)^2}{12} \tag{2.10}$$

The characteristic function $\phi_x(\omega)$ of a uniform random variable x with pdf as in Eq. (2.8) is given by

$$\phi_x(\omega) = \frac{\exp(j\omega b) - \exp(j\omega a)}{j\omega(b - a)} \tag{2.11}$$

Software issues

There are many different random number generators that can be used to produce sequences of uniform deviates. Some of these generators are better than most—and some are notoriously bad. This section is not meant to provide exhaustive coverage of all the possibilities. Chapter 3 of Knuth's classic work (Knuth 1981) remains the most comprehensive readily available treatment of random number generators. A much more concise and narrowly focused treatment can be found in Press, et al. (1992). In this section we will explore only two of the many possible generators.

The first generator is one that is sure to find widespread use because it appears in the standard library that accompanies many C/C++ compilers. There is no true standard for a C/C++ random number generator, but by including source code for an easily implemented example within the standard, the standards committee has virtually guaranteed that this generator will appear in C/C++ libraries for years to come. The example code is provided in Listing 2.1. This generator is of the linear congruential type and uses the following recursion for generating the seed sequence:

$$x_{n+1} = ax_n + c(\text{mod } m) \tag{2.12}$$

where $a = 1103515245$, $c = 12345$, and $m = 2^{32}$. (NOTE: The code provided in the standard uses the name `next` for the seed value, reserving the name `seed` for the initial value of the seed that is passed into `srand`.) The generator's output value is an integer value from 0 to `RAND_MAX` inclusive, where `RAND_MAX` is defined to be 32767. This output value is obtained by shifting the new seed value 16 bits to the right and then taking the 15 rightmost bits after the shift. In the example published within the standard, the 16-place shift is accomplished via dividing the seed by $2^{16} = 65536$. Keeping only the 15 rightmost bits of the shifted value is accomplished by computing the remainder modulo $2^{15} = 32768$. An alternative approach would be to use the shift operator followed by a bit-wise `AND`ing with a 15-bit mask as in

```
return ((unsigned int) (next >> 16) & 32767);
```

There are several different schools of thought regarding how a random number generator should be packaged. The *module* approach taken in Listing 2.1 is midway between a stand-alone function and a full class implementation. This approach is *object-like* in that it has state memory and separate functions for initializing the state and for obtaining the next number in the pseudorandom sequence. However, because of the way that state memory must be implemented using a global variable, there can be only one instance of this generator in any given program. Even if random numbers are used at several different places in a program, they must all be drawn from the generator. This can sometimes be an inconvenience. For example, let's assume that in order to evaluate some filter design we need to simulate a noisy digital signal that randomly switches between 0 and 1. We will be running the simulation several times, using the same bit sequence each time. However, the sequence of added noise values will be different each time the simulation is run. In this situation, it would be very convenient to use one generator for the bit values and a second generator for the noise values. The bit generator would be given the same initial seed value each time the program is run, but the noise generator would be given a different initial seed value each time the program is run.

Listings 2.2 and 2.3 provide a full class implementation of a generator that uses the same algorithm as the generator in Listing 2.1. Using this class, several different generators can be instantiated in the same program, with each instance being given a different initial seed value. A third alternative would be to move the state memory out of the generator routine and transfer to the calling program the responsibility for maintaining this memory. This *function* approach is the approach that has been used most often for random number generators implemented in FORTRAN. However, there is no reason why this approach cannot also be used in a C/C++ implementation, as shown in Listing 2.4.

It is not possible to select one of these three different approaches as being the "best"—each approach has different strengths and weaknesses. The `class` approach allows for multiple instances within the same program, but it runs slower than the other two approaches. Furthermore, this approach is reasonable only for C++. A C implementation using the class approach is possible, but it is somewhat cumbersome. The `function` approach also allows for multiple instances within the same program, runs reasonably fast, but violates principles of good objected-oriented design by making the calling program responsible for the care and feeding of the seed which is actually an attribute of the generator. The `module` approach runs reasonably fast, keeps all generator attributes inside the module, but does not conveniently support multiple instances. This is, however, the approach chosen by the C standards committee for their example of how to implement a portable random number generator. Although this particular generator is widely available, it is not a particularly good choice for many applications. This generator, as do all linear congruential generators, has a tendency to exhibit sequential correlation on successive calls.

Minimal standard generator

Park and Miller (1988) have proposed a *Minimal Standard* uniform random number generator which uses the multiplicative congruential algorithm

$$x_{n+1} = ax_n (\text{mod } m) \tag{2.13}$$

where $a = 7^5 = 16807$ and $m = 2^{31} - 1 = 2147483647$. Equation (2.13) cannot be implemented directly in a high-level language using 32-bit integers. An implementation in C or C++ can be devised if an arithmetic trick known as *Schrage's algorithm* is employed as described in Press, et al. (1992). Briefly, Schrage's algorithm provides a means for computing ax mod m using only 32-bit integers even when the product ax is larger than 32 bits. Specifically, ax mod m can be calculated as

$$ax \text{ mod } m = a(x \text{ mod } q) - r\left\lfloor \frac{z}{q} \right\rfloor \tag{2.14}$$

when the right-hand side evaluates to a nonnegative value and where

$$q = \left\lfloor \frac{m}{a} \right\rfloor$$

$$r = m \text{ mod } a$$

and

$$m = aq + r$$

If the right-hand side of Eq. (2.14) evaluates to a negative value, simply add m to obtain the correct value for ax mod m. To apply Schrage's algorithm to the calculation of Eq. (2.13), use the values $q = 127773$ and $r = 2836$. A class implementation of the Minimal Standard generator is provided in Listings 2.5 and 2.6.

2.6 Gaussian Distribution

A zero-mean, unity variance gaussian random variable y has a probability density function given by

$$p(y) = \frac{1}{\sqrt{2\pi}} \exp \frac{-y^2}{2} \tag{2.15}$$

A sketch of Eq. (2.15) is shown in Fig. 2.3. The corresponding cumulative distribution function is obtained by integrating Eq. (2.15):

$$P(y \le Y) = \frac{1}{\sqrt{2\pi}} \int_{-\infty}^{Y} e^{-y^2/2} \, dy \tag{2.16}$$

A sketch of Eq. (2.16) is shown in Fig. 2.4. The integral in Eq. (2.16) cannot be evaluated in closed form, but it occurs so often in engineering and science that

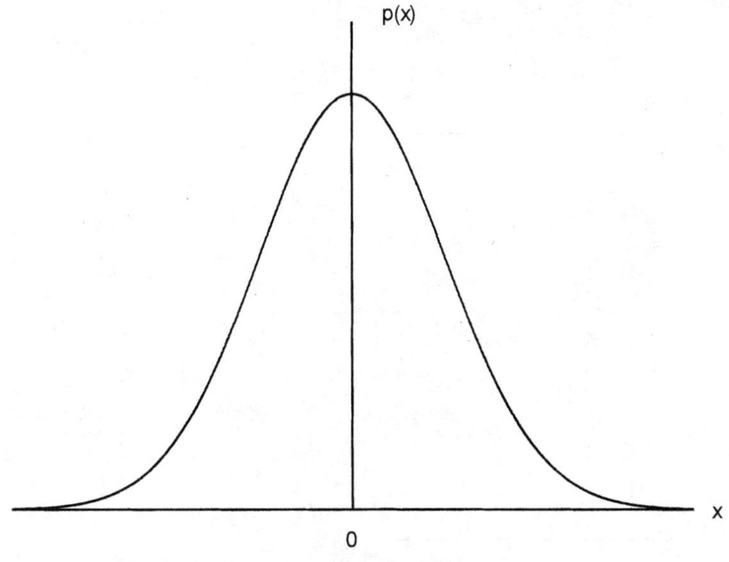

Figure 2.3 Gaussian probability density function.

a special function, called the *error function* and denoted as erf, has been defined as:

$$\text{erf}\, x = \frac{1}{\sqrt{2\pi}} \int_0^x e^{-y^2/2}\, dy \tag{2.17}$$

Closed-form approximations for the error function have been established (see following), and values for erf x, along with other closely related functions, have been extensively tabulated. Thus, $P(y \le Y)$ can be obtained as:

$$P(y \le Y) = \frac{1}{2} + \text{erf}\, y \tag{2.18}$$

For a gaussian random variable of mean μ variance σ^2, the pdf given in Eq. (2.15) can be scaled by σ and shifted by μ to yield

$$p(y) = \frac{1}{\sigma\sqrt{2\pi}} \exp\left(\frac{-(y-\mu)^2}{2\sigma^2}\right)$$

The characteristic function $\phi_y(\omega)$ of the gaussian random variable y is given by

$$\phi_y(\omega) = \exp \frac{j\mu\omega - \sigma^2\omega^2}{2}$$

The gaussian distribution is named in honor of Johann Karl Friedrich Gauss (1777–1855), a German mathematician who is widely regarded as perhaps the greatest mathematician of all time. A gaussian random variable is also called

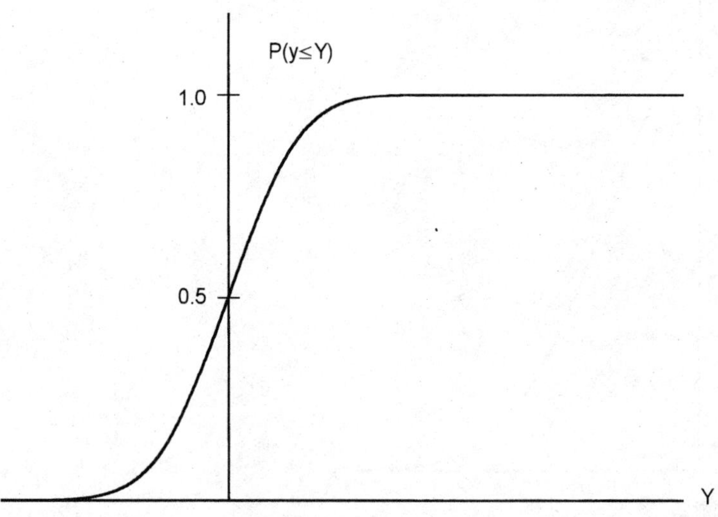

Figure 2.4 Cumulative distribution function for a gaussian random variable.

a *normal variate.* Engineering literature seems to favor the use of "gaussian," while the mathematical literature favors "normal"—perhaps this is due to the multitude of other things to which mathematicians attach the name of Gauss. A normal variate of mean μ and variance σ^2 is sometimes denoted as $N(\mu; \sigma^2)$.

Error function

The error function of x, written as erf x, is defined by

$$\operatorname{erf} x \triangleq \frac{2}{\sqrt{\pi}} \int_0^x \exp(-u^2)\, du \tag{2.19}$$

The complementary error function of x, written as erfc x, is defined by

$$\operatorname{erfc} x \triangleq \frac{2}{\sqrt{\pi}} \int_x^\infty \exp(-u^2)\, du$$

$$= 1 - \operatorname{erf} x \tag{2.20}$$

The integral in Eq. (2.19) cannot be solved in closed form, but numerically computed values have been extensively tabulated. A short table of values for erf x is presented in Table 2.1. (A more extensive table can be found in Abromowitz and Stegun 1966.) Although erfc x cannot be evaluated in closed form, analytical expressions for upper and lower bounds have been established.

TABLE 2.1 Values of the Error Function

x	erf x	x	erf x
0.00	0.0000000	1.00	0.8427008
0.05	0.0563720	1.05	0.8624361
0.10	0.1124629	1.10	0.8802051
0.15	0.1679960	1.15	0.8961238
0.20	0.2227026	1.20	0.9103140
0.25	0.2763264	1.25	0.9229001
0.30	0.3286268	1.30	0.9340079
0.35	0.3793821	1.35	0.9437622
0.40	0.4283924	1.40	0.9522851
0.45	0.4754817	1.45	0.9596950
0.50	0.5204999	1.50	0.9661051
0.55	0.5633234	1.55	0.9716227
0.60	0.0638561	1.60	0.9763484
0.65	0.6420293	1.65	0.9803756
0.70	0.6778012	1.70	0.9837904
0.75	0.7111556	1.75	0.9866717
0.80	0.7421010	1.80	0.9890905
0.85	0.7706681	1.85	0.9911110
0.90	0.7969082	1.90	0.9927904
0.95	0.8208908	1.95	0.9941793
1.00	0.8427008	2.00	0.9953223

$$\text{erfc}\, x > \left(1 - \frac{1}{2x^2}\right) \frac{\exp(-x^2)}{x\sqrt{\pi}} \tag{2.21}$$

$$\text{erfc}\, x < \frac{\exp(-x^2)}{x\sqrt{\pi}} \tag{2.22}$$

For values of $x \geq 2$, both Eqs. (2.21) and (2.22) closely approximate erfc x.

The following expansions may be useful in work involving the error function.

$$\int_0^x \text{erf}(y)\, dy = x\, \text{erf}(x) - \frac{1}{\sqrt{\pi}} [1 - \exp(-x^2)]$$

$$\text{erf}(x) = \frac{2}{\sqrt{\pi}} \exp(-x^2) \sum_{n=0}^{\infty} \frac{2^{2n+1} x^{2n+1} (n+1)!}{(2n+2)}$$

$$\text{erf}(x) = \frac{2}{\sqrt{\pi}} \sum_{n=0}^{\infty} \frac{(-1)^n x^{2n+1}}{n!\,(2n+1)}$$

Values of erf for negative x are obtained using the identity $\text{erf}(-x) = -\text{erf}(x)$.

2.7 Simulation of White Gaussian Noise

The pseudorandom number generators commonly available in most high-level programming languages provide sequences of numbers which are uniformly distributed on the interval [0, 1). The simulation of noise for evaluating digital filter performance usually requires gaussian-distributed numbers rather than uniformly distributed numbers. Using one of the two methods presented in this section, it is possible to take values from a sequence of independent, uniformly distributed numbers and from them generate a sequence of independent pseudorandom numbers which are approximately gaussian-distributed.

Method A

1. Generate a pseudorandom value U_1 uniformly distributed on [0, 1).
2. Generate a second pseudorandom value U_2 which is uniform on [0, 1) and independent of U_1.
3. Compute

$$G_1 = \cos(2\pi U_2) \sqrt{-2\sigma^2 \ln(U_1)}$$

$$G_2 = \sin(2\pi U_2) \sqrt{-2\sigma^2 \ln(U_1)}$$

The resulting G_1 and G_2 will be independent, zero-mean gaussian-distributed random variates each with variance σ^2. A histogram based on 10,000 samples of G_1 is shown in Fig. 2.5, along with a sketch of the corresponding theoretical probability density function.

Method B

1. Generate two pseudorandom values U_A and U_B which are independent and uniformly distributed on [0, 1).
2. Compute

$$U_1 = 1 - 2U_A$$

$$U_2 = 1 - 2U_B$$

3. Compute

$$S = U_1^2 + U_2^2$$

   If $S \geq 1$, then go back to step 1; otherwise continue on to step 4.
4. Compute

$$G_1 = U_1 \sqrt{\frac{-2\sigma^2 \ln (S)}{S}}$$

$$G_2 = U_2 \sqrt{\frac{-2\sigma^2 \ln (S)}{S}}$$

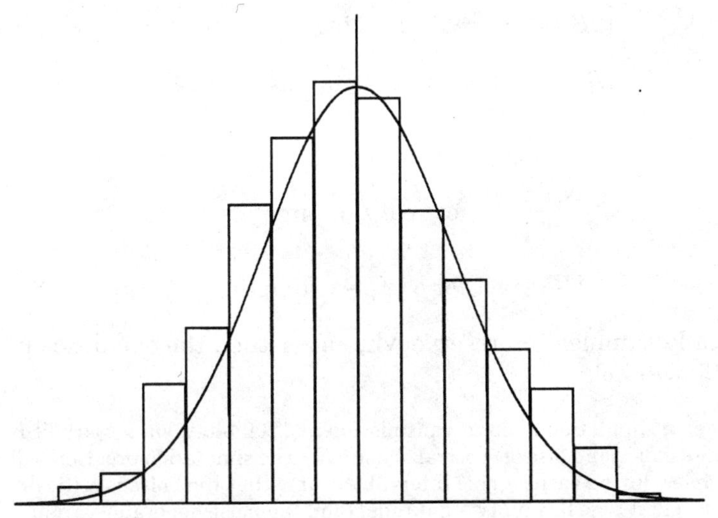

Figure 2.5 Histogram of outputs from a gaussian-distributed pseudorandom number generator.

The resulting G_1 and G_2 will be independent, zero-mean gaussian-distributed random variables each with variance σ^2.

Variance for simulation of white noise

In system performance specifications and theoretical analyses of signal-processing systems, levels of white gaussian background noise are often specified in terms of the constant spectral density N_0. However, generation of gaussian-distributed pseudorandom numbers for simulating noise requires that a noise variance σ^2 be specified. In order to compare computer simulations against specifications and theoretical results, we need to establish a relationship between N_0 and σ^2.

The variance of a random noise process equals the process autocorrelation at lag zero:

$$\sigma^2 = R(0) \tag{2.23}$$

In the case of white noise (which is, recall, just an unrealizable but convenient idealization), $R(0)$ is infinite. However, in the analysis of communication system performance, we will usually be concerned with the noise power contained within some particular bandwidth of interest. Given a white noise density of N_0, the noise power in a bandwidth B is

$$P = \sigma^2 = N_0 B \tag{2.24}$$

To satisfy the uniform sampling theorem and prevent aliasing (see Sec. 8.1), the sampling rate must be chosen such that

$$R_s \geq \begin{cases} 2B & \text{for real sampling} \\ B & \text{for complex sampling} \end{cases} \tag{2.25}$$

Thus

$$\sigma^2 = N_0 B \leq \begin{cases} \dfrac{N_0 R_S}{2} & \text{for real sampling} \\ N_0 R_S & \text{for complex sampling} \end{cases} \tag{2.26}$$

If the noise is critically sampled to preserve whiteness, then the equalities in Eqs. (2.25) and (2.26) will hold.

Example 2.2 Consider a simulation of data transmission at 1200 bits/s via a 4-ary FSK signal in additive white gaussian noise of spectral density N_0. The simulation program will generate 32 real samples during each symbol interval. Assume that the noise is critically sampled and that the signal tone has unity amplitude. Find the noise generator variance σ^2 which corresponds to $E_b/N_0 = 5$ dB, where E_b denotes energy per transmitted bit.

solution During each symbol interval, the energy in the signal tone is given by

$$E = \frac{A^2T}{2} \tag{2.27}$$

where A is the signal tone amplitude and T is the symbol duration. Since each 4-ary symbol conveys 2 bits, the stated data rate of 1200 bits/s corresponds to a symbol duration of $T = 1/600$. Thus, $E = 1/1200$. The energy per bit is one-half of the energy per symbol:

$$E_b = \frac{E}{2} = \frac{A^2T}{4} = \frac{1}{2400} \tag{2.28}$$

The sampling rate is simply the symbol rate multiplied by the number of samples per symbol:

$$R_s = (32)(600) = 19{,}200 \tag{2.29}$$

From Eq. (2.26)

$$N_0 = \frac{2\sigma^2}{R_s} = \frac{\sigma^2}{9600} \tag{2.30}$$

Thus

$$\frac{E_b}{N_0} = \frac{1/2400}{\sigma^2/9600} = \frac{4}{\sigma^2}. \tag{2.31}$$

The specified E_b/N_0 of 5 dB is easily converted into a numeric value using

$$\frac{E_b}{N_0} = 10^{[(E_b/N_0)\,\text{dB}/10]} = 10^{0.5}$$

Substituting this into Eq. (2.31), we obtain

$$\sigma^2 = 4 \times 10^{10^{-0.5}}$$
$$= 1.2649$$

Software

There are several different approaches we can take to implement the methods described in the preceding for generating normally distributed random numbers. Since both of the methods operate by transforming uniform random numbers, one of the first design choices that must be made is whether to provide the gaussian generator with a built-in means for generating uniform numbers or whether to have the gaussian generator call a separate uniform generator of the sort presented in Sec. 2.5.

Calling a separate uniform generator results in code that is easier to test and maintain, but which incurs a significant speed penalty for the overhead associated with the additional calls to the separate generator. In many simulations, a random number generator may be called millions of times and even a slight increase in per-call overhead can add up quickly. One possible way to provide both easy maintenance and higher execution speeds is to implement a uniform generator as an inline function for use by nonuniform generators that need a source of uniform random numbers. The gaussian random number generator shown in Listing 2.7 takes this approach.

Listing 2.1 Example RNG from the Standard C/C++ Library

```
static unsigned long int next=1;

int rand(void)
{
 next = next * 1103515245 + 12345;
 return (unsigned int) (next/65536) }

void srand( unsigned int seed)
{
 next = seed;
}
```

Listing 2.2 Header for Class Implementation of the Example RNG

```
#ifndef _SRAND_H_
#define _SRAND_H_

class srand
{
 public:

  srand(); // default constructor sets seed=1

  srand(int seed); // constructor for user-supplied initial seed

  unsigned int rand(void);

 private:

  long int Seed;
};

#endif
```

Listing 2.3 Class Implementation of the Example RNG

```
#include "srand.h"
#include <iostream.h>

srand::srand()
      :Seed(1)
{
};

srand::srand(int seed)
{
 Seed = seed;
}

unsigned int srand::rand(void)
{
 Seed = Seed * 1103515245 + 12345;
 return((unsigned int)((Seed >> 16) & 32767));
}
```

Listing 2.4 Function Implementation of `rand`

```
unsigned int rand(long *seed)
{
 *seed = (*seed) * 1103515245 + 12345;
 return((unsigned int) ((*seed >> 16) & 32767));
}
```

Listing 2.5 Header for the Minimal Standard Random Number Generator

```
#ifndef _UNIFORMRANDOM_H_
#define _UNIFORMRANDOM_H_

class UniformRandom
{
public:
void Initialize(long seed);
float RandomFloat(void);
double RandomDouble(void);

private:
long Ran_Seed;
};

#endif
```

Listing 2.6 Class Implementation of the Minimal Standard Random Number Generator

```
#include "min_rand.h"

#define MULTIPLIER 16807
#define MODULUS 2147483647
#define ONE_OVER_MOD (1.0/MODULUS)
#define QUOT 127773
#define REMAIN 2836

void UniformRandom::Initialize(long seed)
{
Ran_Seed = seed;
}

float UniformRandom::RandomFloat(void)
{
 long k;
 float result;
 long seed;

 seed = Ran_Seed;
 k=seed/QUOT;
 seed = MULTIPLIER * (seed-k*QUOT)-REMAIN*k;
 if(seed<0) seed += MODULUS;
 result = float(ONE_OVER_MOD*seed);
 Ran_Seed = seed;

 return(result);
 }

double UniformRandom::RandomDouble(void)
{
 long k, seed;
 double result;
 seed = Ran_Seed;
 k=(seed)/QUOT;
 seed = MULTIPLIER * (seed-k*QUOT)-REMAIN*k;
 if(seed<0) seed += MODULUS;
 result = ONE_OVER_MOD*seed;
 Ran_Seed = seed;

 return(result);
 }
```

Listing 2.7 Gaussian Random Number Generator

```
#include <math.h>
#include "uni_rand.h"
#include "gausrand.h"

double GaussRandom(long *seed)
{
 double u1, u2, g1;
 double UA, UB, S;
 double radical;

 new_start:
 UA = DoubleUniformRandom(seed);
 UB = DoubleUniformRandom(seed);
 u1 = 1.0 - 2.0 * UA;
 u2 = 1.0 - 2.0 * UB;
 S = u1*u1 + u2*u2;
 if(S >= 1.0 ) goto new_start;
 radical = sqrt(-2.0*log(S)/S);
 g1 = u1 * radical;
 return(g1);
 }
```

Chapter

3

Filter Fundamentals

Digital filters are often based upon common analog filter functions. Therefore, a certain amount of background material concerning analog filters is a necessary foundation for the study of digital filters. This chapter reviews the essentials of analog system theory and filter characterization. Some common analog filter types—Butterworth, Chebyshev, elliptical, and Bessel—are given more detailed treatment in subsequent chapters.

3.1 Systems

Within the context of signal processing, a *system* is something that accepts one or more input signals and operates upon them to produce one or more output signals. Filters, amplifiers, and digitizers are some of the systems used in various signal-processing applications. When signals are represented as mathematical functions, it is convenient to represent systems as *operators* that operate upon input functions to produce output functions. Two alternative notations for representing a system H with input x and output y are given in Eqs. (3.1) and (3.2). Note that x and y can each be scalar valued or vector valued.

$$y = H[x] \tag{3.1}$$

$$y = Hx \tag{3.2}$$

This book uses the notation of Eq. (3.1) as this is less likely to be confused with multiplication of x by a value H.

A system H can be represented pictorially in a flow diagram as shown in Fig. 3.1. For vector-valued x and y, the individual components are sometimes explicitly shown as in Fig. 3.2*a* or lumped together as shown in Fig. 3.2*b*. Sometimes, in order to emphasize their vector nature, the input and output are drawn as in Fig. 3.2*c*.

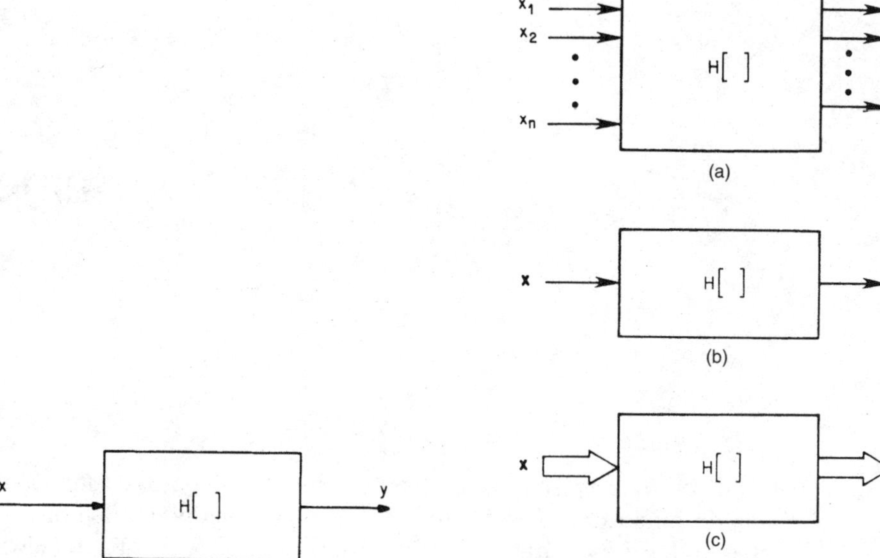

Figure 3.1 Pictorial representation of a system.

Figure 3.2 Pictorial representations of a system with multiple inputs and outputs.

In different presentations of system theory, the notational schemes used exhibit some variation. The more precise treatments (such as Chen 1984) use x or $x(\cdot)$ to denote a function of time defined over the interval $(-\infty, \infty)$. A function defined over a more restricted interval such as $[t_0, t_1)$ would be denoted as $x_{(t_0, t_1)}$. The notation $x(t)$ is reserved for denoting the value of x at time t. Less precise treatments (such as Schwartz and Friedland 1965) use $x(t)$ to denote both functions of time defined over $(-\infty, \infty)$ and the value of x at time t. When not evident from context, words of explanation must be included to indicate which particular meaning is intended. Using the less precise notational scheme, Eq. (3.1) could be rewritten as

$$y(t) = H[x(t)] \tag{3.3}$$

While it appears that the precise notation should be the more desirable, the relaxed conventions exemplified by Eq. (3.3) are widespread in the literature.

Linearity

If the relaxed system H is *homogeneous,* multiplying the input by a constant gain is equivalent to multiplying the output by the same constant gain, and the two configurations shown in Fig. 3.3 are equivalent. Mathematically stated, the relaxed system H is homogeneous if, for constant a,

$$H[ax] = aH[x] \tag{3.4}$$

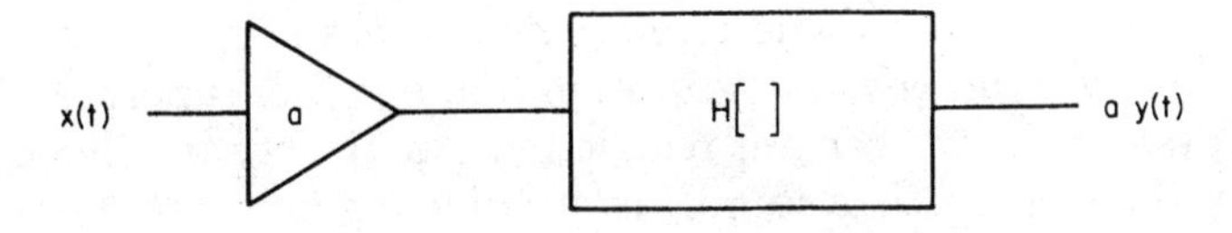

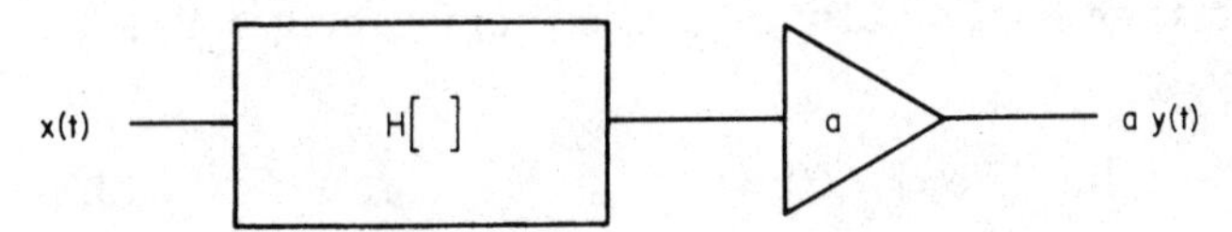

Figure 3.3 Homogeneous system.

If the relaxed system H is additive, the output produced for the sum of two input signals is equal to the sum of the outputs produced for each input individually, and the two configurations shown in Fig. 3.4 are equivalent. Mathematically stated, the relaxed system H is additive if

$$H[x_1 + x_2] = H[x_1] + H[x_2] \tag{3.5}$$

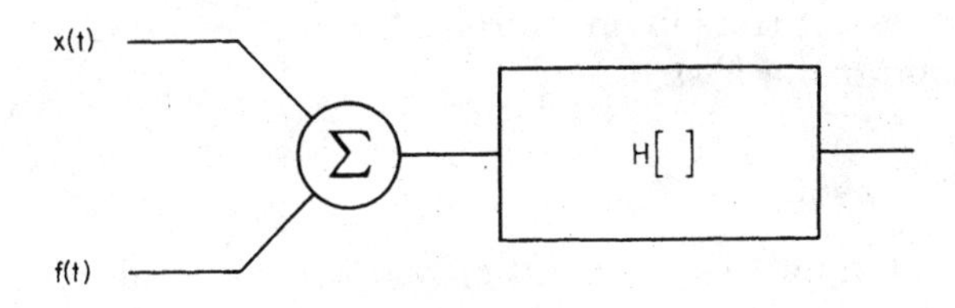

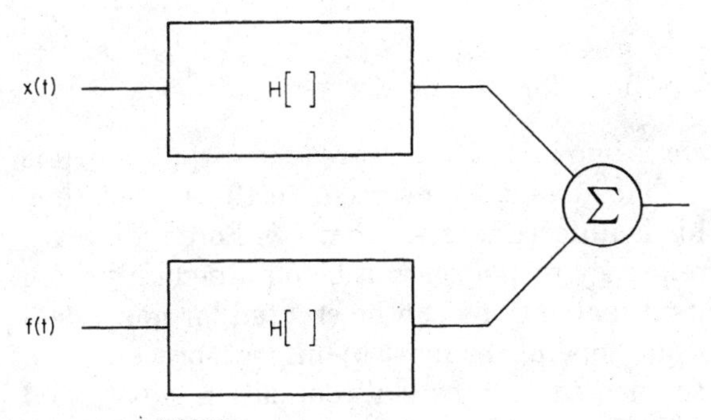

Figure 3.4 Additive system.

A system that is both homogeneous and additive is said to *exhibit superposition* or to *satisfy the principle of superposition.* A system that exhibits superposition is called a *linear system.* Under certain restrictions, additivity implies homogeneity. Specifically, the fact that a system H is additive implies that

$$H[\alpha x] = \alpha H[x] \tag{3.6}$$

for any rational α. Any real number can be approximated with arbitrary precision by a rational number; therefore, additivity implies homogeneity for real a provided that

$$\lim_{\alpha \to a} H[\alpha x] = H[ax] \tag{3.7}$$

Time invariance

The characteristics of a *time-invariant system* do not change over time. A system is said to be *relaxed* if it is not still responding to any previously applied input. Given a relaxed system H such that

$$y(t) = H[x(t)] \tag{3.8}$$

then H is time invariant if and only if

$$y(t - \tau) = H[x(t - \tau)] \tag{3.9}$$

for any τ and any $x(t)$. A time-invariant system is also called a *fixed system* or *stationary system.* A system that is not time invariant is called a *time-varying system, variable system,* or *nonstationary system.*

Causality

In a *causal system,* the output at time t can depend only upon the input at times t and prior. Mathematically stated, a system H is causal if and only if

$$H[x_1(t)] = H[x_2(t)] \qquad \text{for} \quad t \le t_0 \tag{3.10}$$

given that

$$x_1(t) = x_2(t) \qquad \text{for} \quad t \le t_0$$

A *noncausal* or *anticipatory system* is one in which the present output depends upon future values of the input. Noncausal systems occur in theory, but they cannot exist in the real world. This is unfortunate, since we will often discover that some especially desirable frequency responses can be obtained only from noncausal systems. However, causal realizations can be created for noncausal systems in which the present output depends at most upon past, present, and a finite extent of future inputs. In such cases, a causal realization is obtained by simply delaying the output of the system for a finite interval until all the required inputs have entered the system and are available for determination of the output.

3.2 Characterization of Linear Systems

A linear system can be characterized by a differential equation, step response, impulse response, complex-frequency-domain system function, or a transfer function. The relationships among these various characterizations are given in Table 3.1.

Impulse response

The *impulse response* of a system is the output response produced when a unit impulse $\delta(t)$ is applied to the input of a previously relaxed system. This is an especially convenient characterization of a linear system, since the response $y(t)$ to any continuous-time input signal $x(t)$ is given by

$$y(t) = \int_{-\infty}^{\infty} x(\tau)\, h(t, \tau)\, d\tau \tag{3.11}$$

where $h(t, \tau)$ denotes the system's response at time t to an impulse applied at time τ. The integral in Eq. (3.11) is sometimes referred to as the *superposition integral.* The particular notation used indicates that, in general, the system is time varying. For a time-invariant system, the impulse response at time t depends only upon the time delay from τ to t, and we can redefine the impulse response to be a function of a single variable and denote it as $h(t - \tau)$. Equation (3.11) then becomes

$$y(t) = \int_{-\infty}^{\infty} x(\tau)\, h(t - \tau)\, d\tau \tag{3.12}$$

TABLE 3.1 Relationships among Characterizations of Linear Systems

Starting with	Perform	To obtain
Time domain differential equation relating $x(t)$ and $y(t)$	Laplace transform	Complex-frequency-domain system function
	Compute $y(t)$ for $x(t)$ = unit impulse	Impulse response $h(t)$
	Compute $y(t)$ for $x(t)$ = unit step	Step response $a(t)$
Step response $a(t)$	Differentiate with respect to time	Impulse response $h(t)$
Impulse response $h(t)$	Integrate with respect to time	Step response $a(t)$
	Laplace transform	Transfer function $H(s)$
Complex-frequency-domain system function	Solve for $H(s) = \dfrac{Y(s)}{X(s)}$	Transfer function $H(s)$
Transfer function $H(s)$	Inverse Laplace transform	Impulse response $h(t)$

Via the simple change of variables $\lambda = t - \tau$, Eq. (3.12) can be rewritten as

$$y(t) = \int_{-\infty}^{\infty} x(t - \lambda)\, h(\lambda)\, d\lambda \tag{3.13}$$

If we assume that the input is 0 for $t < 0$, the lower limit of integration can be changed to 0; and if we further assume that the system is causal, the upper limit of integration can be changed to t, thus yielding

$$y(t) = \int_{0}^{t} x(\tau)\, h(t - \tau)\, d\tau = \int_{0}^{t} x(t - \lambda)\, h(\lambda)\, d\lambda \tag{3.14}$$

The integrals in Eq. (3.14) are known as *convolution integrals,* and the equation indicates that $y(t)$ equals the *convolution* of $x(t)$ and $h(t)$. It is often more compact and convenient to denote this relationship as

$$y(t) = x(t) \otimes h(t) = h(t) \otimes x(t) \tag{3.15}$$

Various texts use different symbols, such as stars or asterisks, in place of $\otimes$ to indicate convolution. The asterisk is probably favored by most printers, but in some contexts its usage to indicate convolution could be confused with the complex conjugation operator. A typical system's impulse response is sketched in Fig. 3.5.

Step response

The *step response* of a system is the output signal produced when a unit step $u(t)$ is applied to the input of the previously relaxed system. Since the unit step is simply the time integration of a unit impulse, it can easily be shown that the step response of a system can be obtained by integrating the impulse response. A typical system's step response is shown in Fig. 3.6.

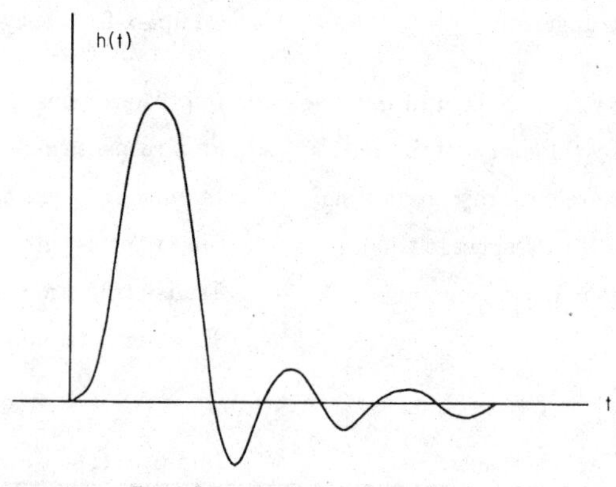

Figure 3.5 Impulse response of a typical system.

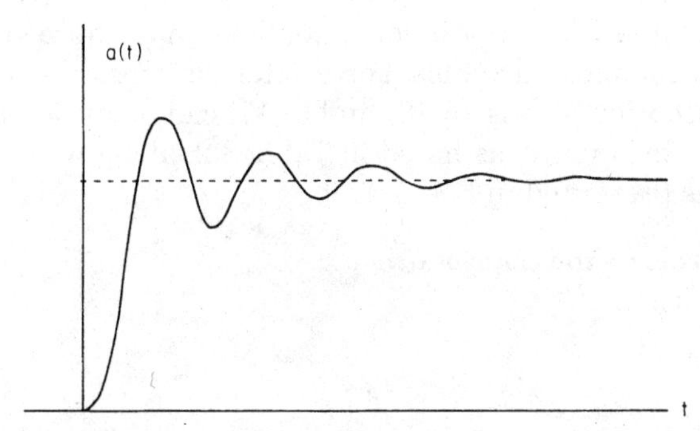

Figure 3.6 Step response of a typical system.

3.3 Laplace Transform

The *Laplace transform* is a technique that is useful for transforming differential equations into algebraic equations that can be more easily manipulated to obtain desired results.

In most communications applications, the functions of interest will usually (but not always) be functions of time. The Laplace transform of a time function $x(t)$ is usually denoted as $X(s)$ or $\mathscr{L}[x(t)]$ and is defined by

$$X(s) = \mathscr{L}[x(t)] = \int_{-\infty}^{\infty} x(t)\, e^{-st}\, dt \tag{3.16}$$

The complex variable s is usually referred to as *complex frequency* and is of the form $\sigma + j\omega$, where σ and ω are real variables sometimes referred to as *neper frequency* and *radian frequency,* respectively. The Laplace transform for a given function $x(t)$ is obtained by simply evaluating the given integral. Some mathematics texts (such as Spiegel 1965) denote the time function with an uppercase letter and the frequency function with a lowercase letter. However, the use of lowercase for time functions is almost universal within the engineering literature.

If we transform both sides of a differential equation in t using the definition Eq. (3.16), we obtain an algebraic equation in s that can be solved for the desired quantity. The solved algebraic equation can then be transformed back into the time domain by using the inverse Laplace transform.

The inverse Laplace transform is defined by

$$x(t) = \mathscr{L}^{-1}[X(s)] = \frac{1}{2\pi j} \int_{C} X(s)\, e^{st}\, ds \tag{3.17}$$

where C is a contour of integration chosen so as to include all singularities of $X(s)$. The inverse Laplace transform for a given function $X(s)$ can be obtained by evaluating the given integral. However, this integration is often a major chore—when tractable, it will usually involve application of the residue theorem from the theory of complex variables. Fortunately, in most cases of practical interest, direct evaluation of Eqs. (3.16) and (3.17) can be avoided by using some well-known transform pairs, as listed in Table 3.2, along with a number of transform properties presented in Sec. 3.4.

Example 3.1 Find the Laplace transform of $x(t) = e^{-\alpha t}$.

solution

$$X(s) = \int_0^\infty e^{-\alpha t} e^{-st}\, dt \tag{3.18}$$

$$= \int_0^\infty e^{-(\alpha + s)t}\, dt \tag{3.19}$$

$$= \frac{1}{s + \alpha} \tag{3.20}$$

Notice that this result agrees with entry 8 in Table 3.2.

TABLE 3.2 Laplace Transform Pairs

Ref. no.	$x(t)$	$X(s)$
1	1	$\frac{1}{s}$
2	$u_1(t)$	$\frac{1}{s}$
3	$\delta(t)$	1
4	t	$\frac{1}{s^2}$
5	t^n	$\frac{n!}{s^{n+1}}$
6	$\sin \omega t$	$\frac{\omega}{s^2 + \omega^2}$
7	$\cos \omega t$	$\frac{s}{s^2 + \omega^2}$
8	e^{-at}	$\frac{1}{s + a}$
9	$e^{-at} \sin \omega t$	$\frac{\omega}{(s + a)^2 + \omega^2}$
10	$e^{-at} \cos \omega t$	$\frac{s + a}{(s + a)^2 + \omega^2}$

Background

The Laplace transform defined by Eq. (3.16) is more precisely referred to as the *one-sided Laplace transform,* and it is the form generally used for the analysis of causal systems and signals. There is also a *two-sided transform* that is defined as

$$\mathscr{L}_{\mathrm{II}}[x(t)] = \int_{-\infty}^{\infty} x(t)\, e^{-st}\, dt \tag{3.21}$$

The Laplace transform is named for the French mathematician Pierre Simon de Laplace (1749–1827).

3.4 Properties of the Laplace Transform

Some properties of the Laplace transform are listed in Table 3.3. These properties can be used in conjunction with the transform pairs presented in Table 3.2 to obtain most of the Laplace transforms that will ever be needed in practical

TABLE 3.3 Properties of the Laplace Transform

Property	Time function	Transform
1. Homogeneity	$af(t)$	$aF(s)$
2. Additivity	$f(t) + g(t)$	$F(s) + G(s)$
3. Linearity	$af(t) + bg(t)$	$aF(s) + bG(s)$
4. First derivative	$\frac{d}{dt}f(t)$	$sF(s) - f(0)$
5. Second derivative	$\frac{d^2}{dt^2}f(t)$	$sF(s) - sf(0) - \frac{d}{dt}f(0)$
6. kth derivative	$\frac{d^{(k)}}{dt^k}f(t)$	$s^kF(s) = \sum_{n=0}^{k-1} s^{k-1-n} f^{(n)}(0)$
7. Integration	$\int_{-\infty}^{t} f(\tau)\, d\tau$	$\frac{F(s)}{s} + \frac{1}{s}\left(\int_{-\infty}^{t} f(\tau)\, d\tau\right)_{t=0}$
	$\int_0^t f(\tau)\, d\tau$	$\frac{F(s)}{s}$
8. Frequency shift	$e^{-at} f(t)$	$X(s+a)$
9. Time shift right	$u_1(t-\tau)\, f(t-\tau)$	$e^{-\tau s} F(s)$ $\quad a > 0$
10. Time shift left	$f(t+r), f(t) = 0 \quad$ for $\quad 0 < t < \tau$	$e^{\tau s} F(s)$
11. Convolution	$y(t) = \int_0^t h(t-\tau)\, x(\tau)\, d\tau$	$Y(s) = H(s)\, X(s)$
12. Multiplication	$f(t)\, g(t)$	$\frac{1}{2\pi j}\int_{c-j\infty}^{c+j\infty} F(s-r)\, G(r)\, dr$ $\quad \sigma_g < c < \sigma - \sigma_f$

NOTE: $f^{(k)}(t)$ denotes the kth derivative of $f(t)$; $f^{(0)}(t) = f(t)$.

engineering situations. Some of the entries in the table require further explanation, which is provided in the following.

Time shifting

Consider the function $f(t)$ shown in Fig. 3.7*a*. The function has nonzero values for $t < 0$, but since the one-sided Laplace transform integrates only over positive time, these values for $t < 0$ have no impact on the evaluation of the transform. If we now shift $f(t)$ to the right by τ units as shown in Fig. 3.7*b*, some of the nonzero values from the left of the origin will be moved to the right of the origin, where they will be included in the evaluation of the transform. The Laplace transform's properties with regard to a time-shift right must be stated in such a way that these previously unincluded values will not be included in the transform of the shifted function either. This can be easily accomplished

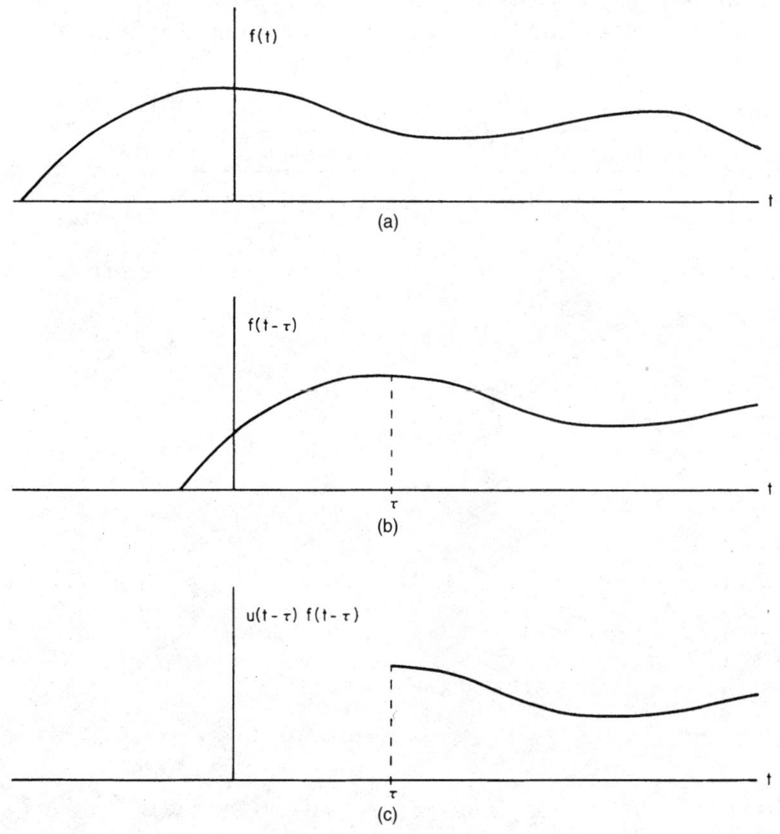

Figure 3.7 Signals for explanation of the Laplace transform's "time-shift-right" property.

through multiplying the shifted function $f(t - \tau)$ by a shifted unit step function $u_1(t - \tau)$ as shown in Fig. 3.7*c*. Thus, we have

$$\mathcal{L}[u_1(t - \tau) f(t - \tau)] = e^{-\tau s} F(s) \qquad a > 0 \tag{3.22}$$

Consider now the case when $f(t)$ is shifted to the right. Such a shift will move a portion of $f(t)$ from positive time, where it is included in the transform evaluation, into negative time, where it will not be included in the transform evaluation. The Laplace transform's properties with regard to a time-shift left must be stated in such a way that all included values from the unshifted function will likewise be included in the transform of the shifted function. This can be accomplished by requiring that the original function be equal to 0 for all values of t from 0 to τ, if a shift to the left by τ units is to be made. Thus for a shift left by τ units

$$\mathcal{L}[f(t + \tau)] = F(s)\, e^{\tau s} \qquad \text{if } f(t) = 0 \qquad \text{for } 0 < t < \tau \tag{3.23}$$

Multiplication

Consider the product of two time functions $f(t)$ and $g(t)$. The transform of the product will equal the complex convolution of $F(s)$ and $G(s)$ in the frequency domain.

$$\mathcal{L}[f(t)\, g(t)] = \frac{1}{2\pi j} \int_{c - j\infty}^{c + j\infty} F(s - r)\, G(r)\, dr \qquad \sigma_g < c < \sigma - \sigma_f \tag{3.24}$$

3.5 Transfer Functions

The *transfer function* $H(s)$ of a system is equal to the Laplace transform of the output signal divided by the Laplace transform of the input signal:

$$H(s) = \frac{Y(s)}{X(s)} = \frac{\mathcal{L}[y(t)]}{\mathcal{L}[x(t)]} \tag{3.25}$$

It can be shown that the transfer function is also equal to the Laplace transform of the system's impulse response:

$$H(s) = \mathcal{L}[h(t)] \tag{3.26}$$

Therefore,

$$y(t) = \mathcal{L}^{-1}\{H(s)\, \mathcal{L}[x(t)]\} \tag{3.27}$$

Equation (3.27) presents an alternative to the convolution defined by Eq. (3.14) for obtaining a system's response $y(t)$ to any input $x(t)$, given the impulse response $h(t)$. Simply perform the following steps:

1. Compute $H(s)$ as the Laplace transform of $h(t)$.
2. Compute $X(s)$ as the Laplace transform of $x(t)$.
3. Compute $Y(s)$ as the product of $H(s)$ and $X(s)$.
4. Compute $y(t)$ as the inverse Laplace transform of $Y(s)$. (The Heaviside expansion presented in Sec. 3.6 is a convenient technique for performing the inverse transform operation.)

A transfer function defined as in Eq. (3.25) can be put into the form

$$H(s) = \frac{P(s)}{Q(s)} \tag{3.28}$$

where $P(s)$ and $Q(s)$ are polynomials in s. For $H(s)$ to be stable and realizable in the form of a lumped-parameter network, it can be shown (Van Valkenburg 1974) that all of the coefficients in the polynomials $P(s)$ and $Q(s)$ must be real. Furthermore, all of the coefficients in $Q(s)$ must be positive. The polynomial $Q(s)$ must have a nonzero term for each degree of s from the highest to the lowest, unless all even-degree terms or all odd-degree terms are missing. If $H(s)$ is a voltage ratio or current ratio (that is, the input and output are either both voltages or both currents), the maximum degree of s in $P(s)$ cannot exceed the maximum degree of s in $Q(s)$. If $H(s)$ is a transfer impedance (that is, the input is a current and the output is a voltage) or a transfer admittance (that is, the input is a voltage and the output is a current), then the maximum degree of s in $P(s)$ can exceed the maximum degree of s in $Q(s)$ by at most 1. Note that these are only upper limits on the degree of s in $P(s)$; in either case, the maximum degree of s in $P(s)$ may be as small as 0. Also note that these are necessary but not sufficient conditions for $H(s)$ to be a valid transfer function. A candidate $H(s)$ satisfying all of these conditions may still not be realizable as a lumped-parameter network.

Example 3.2 Consider the following alleged transfer functions:

$$H_1(s) = \frac{s^2 - 2s + 1}{s^3 - 3s^2 + 3s + 1} \tag{3.29}$$

$$H_2(s) = \frac{s^4 + 2s^3 + 2s^2 - 3s + 1}{s^3 + 3s^2 + 3s + 2} \tag{3.30}$$

$$H_3(s) = \frac{s^2 - 2s + 1}{s^3 + 3s^2 + 1} \tag{3.31}$$

Equation (3.29) is not acceptable because the coefficient of s^2 in the denominator is negative. If Eq. (3.30) is intended as a voltage- or current-transfer ratio, it is not acceptable because the degree of the numerator exceeds the degree of the denominator. However, if Eq. (3.30) represents a transfer impedance or transfer admittance, it may be valid since the degree of the numerator exceeds the degree of the denominator by just 1. Equation (3.31) is not acceptable because the term for s is missing from the denominator.

A system's transfer function can be manipulated to provide a number of useful characterizations of the system's behavior. These characterizations are listed in Table 3.4 and examined in more detail in subsequent sections.

Some authors, such as Van Valkenburg (1974), use the term *network function* in place of *transfer function.*

3.6 Heaviside Expansion

The Heaviside expansion provides a straightforward computational method for obtaining the inverse Laplace transform of certain types of complex-frequency functions. The function to be inverse-transformed must be expressed as a ratio of polynomials in s, where the order of the denominator polynomial exceeds the order of the numerator polynomial. If

$$H(s) = K_0 \frac{P(s)}{Q(s)} \tag{3.32}$$

where

$$Q(s) = \prod_{k=1}^{n} (s - s_k)^{m_k} = (s - s_1)^{m_1}(s - s_2)^{m_2} \cdots (s - s_n)^{m_n} \tag{3.33}$$

then inverse transformation via the Heaviside expansion yields

$$\mathcal{L}^{-1}[H(s)] = K_0 \sum_{r=1}^{n} \sum_{k=1}^{m_r} [K_{rk} t^{m_r - k} \exp(s_r t)] \tag{3.34}$$

where

$$K_{rk} = \frac{1}{(k-1)!(m_r - k)!} \frac{d^{k-1}}{ds^{k-1}} \left[\frac{(s - s_r)m_r P(s)}{Q(s)} \right]_{s = s_r} \tag{3.35}$$

A method for computing the derivative in (3.35) can be found in Sec. A.4 of App. A.

TABLE 3.4 System Characterizations Obtained from the Transfer Function

Starting with	Perform	To obtain
Transfer function $H(s)$	Compute roots of $H(s)$ denominator	Pole locations
	Compute roots of $H(s)$ numerator	Zero locations
	Compute $\lvert H(j\omega) \rvert$ over all ω	Magnitude response $A(\omega)$
	Compute arg $[H(j\omega)]$ over all ω	Phase response $\theta(\omega)$
Phase response $\theta(\omega)$	Divide by ω	Phase delay $\tau_p(\omega)$
	Differentiate with respect to ω	Group delay $\tau_g(\omega)$

Simple pole case

The complexity of the expansion is significantly reduced for the case of $Q(s)$ having no repeated roots. The denominator of Eq. (3.32) is then given by

$$Q(s) = \prod_{k=1}^{n} (s - s_k) = (s - s_1)(s - s_2) \cdots (s - s_n) \qquad s_1 \neq s_2 \neq s_3 \neq \cdots s_n \tag{3.36}$$

Inverse transformation via the Heaviside expansion then yields

$$\mathcal{L}^{-1}[H(s)] = K_0 \sum_{r=1}^{n} K_r \, e^{s_r t} \tag{3.37}$$

where

$$K_r = \left[\frac{(s - s_r)P(s)}{Q(s)} \right]_{s = s_r} \tag{3.38}$$

The Heaviside expansion is named for Oliver Heaviside (1850–1925), an English physicist and electrical engineer who was the nephew of Charles Wheatstone (as in Wheatstone bridge).

3.7 Poles and Zeros

As pointed out previously, the transfer function for a realizable linear time-invariant system can always be expressed as a ratio of polynomials in *s:*

$$H(s) = \frac{P(s)}{Q(s)} \tag{3.39}$$

The numerator and denominator can each be factored to yield

$$H(s) = H_0 \frac{(s - z_1)(s - z_2)(s - z_3) \cdots (s - z_m)}{(s - p_1)(s - p_2)(s - p_3) \cdots (s - p_n)} \tag{3.40}$$

where the roots $z_1, z_2, \ldots, z_m$ of the numerator are called *zeros* of the transfer function, and the roots $p_1, p_2, \ldots, p_n$ of the denominator are called *poles* of the transfer function. Together, poles and zeros can be collectively referred to as *critical frequencies.* Each factor $(s - z_i)$ is called a *zero factor,* and each factor $(s - p_j)$ is called a *pole factor.* A repeated zero appearing n times is called either an *nth-order zero* or a *zero of multiplicity n.* Likewise, a repeated pole appearing n times is called either an *nth-order pole* or a *pole of multiplicity n.* Nonrepeated poles or zeros are sometimes described as *simple* or *distinct* to emphasize their nonrepeated nature.

Example 3.3 Consider the transfer function given by

$$H(s) = \frac{s^3 + 5s^2 + 8s + 4}{s^3 + 13s^2 + 59s + 87} \tag{3.41}$$

The numerator and denominator can be factored to yield

$$H(s) = \frac{(s+2)^2(s+1)}{(s+5+2j)(s+5-2j)(s+3)} \tag{3.42}$$

Examination of Eq. (3.42) reveals that

$s = -1$ is a simple zero.
$s = -2$ is a second-order zero.
$s = -5 + 2j$ is a simple pole.
$s = -5 - 2j$ is a simple pole.
$s = -3$ is a simple pole.

A system's poles and zeros can be depicted graphically as locations in a complex plane as shown in Fig. 3.8. In mathematics, the complex plane itself is called the *gaussian plane,* while a plot depicting complex values as points in the plane is called an *Argand diagram* or a *Wessel-Argand-Gaussian diagram.* In the 1798 transactions of the Danish academy, Caspar Wessel (1745–1818) published a technique for graphical representation of complex numbers, and Jean Robert Argand published a similar technique in 1806. Geometric interpretation of complex numbers played a central role in the doctoral thesis of Gauss.

Pole locations can provide convenient indications of a system's behavior as indicated in Table 3.5. Furthermore, poles and zeros possess the following properties that can sometimes be used to expedite the analysis of a system:

1. For real $H(s)$, complex or imaginary poles and zeros will each occur in complex conjugate pairs that are symmetric about the σ axis.
2. For $H(s)$ having even symmetry, the poles and zeros will exhibit symmetry about the $j\omega$ axis.
3. For nonnegative $H(s)$, any zeros on the $j\omega$ axis will occur in pairs.

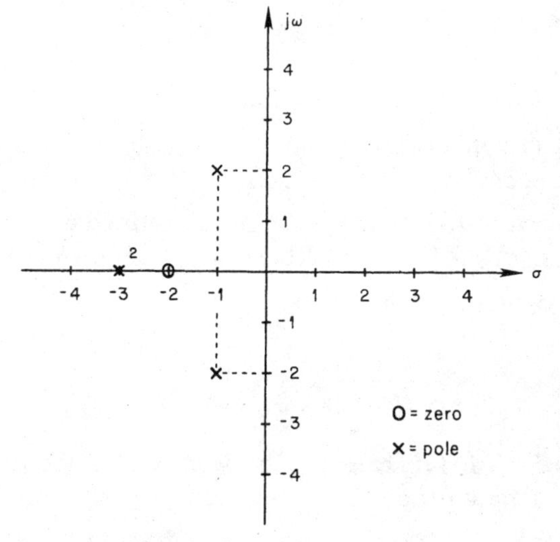

Figure 3.8 Plot of pole and zero locations.

TABLE 3.5 Impact of Pole Locations upon System Behavior

Pole type	Corresponding natural response component	Corresponding description of system behavior
Single real, negative	Decaying exponential	Stable
Single real, positive	Divergent exponential	Divergent instability
Real pair, negative, unequal	Decaying exponential	Overdamped (stable)
Real pair, negative equal	Decaying exponential	Critically damped (stable)
Complex conjugate pair with negative real parts	Exponentially decaying sinusoid	Underdamped (stable)
Complex conjugate pair with zero real parts	Sinusoid	Undamped (marginally stable)
Complex conjugate pair with positive real parts	Exponentially saturating sinusoid	Oscillatory instability

In many situations, it is necessary to determine the poles of a given transfer function. For some systems, such as Chebyshev filters or Butterworth filters, explicit expressions have been found for evaluation of pole locations. For other systems, such as Bessel filters, the poles must be found by numerically solving for the roots of the transfer function's denominator polynomial. Several root-finding algorithms appear in the literature, but I have found the *Laguerre method* to be the most useful for approximating pole locations. The approximate roots can be subjected to small-step iterative refinement or polishing as needed.

Algorithm 3.1 Laguerre method for approximating one root of a polynomial $P(z)$

Step 1. Set z equal to an initial guess for the value of a root. Typically, z is set to zero so that the smallest root will tend to be found first.

Step 2. Evaluate the polynomial $P(z)$ and its first two derivatives $P'(z)$ and $P''(z)$ at the current value of z.

Step 3. If $P(z)$ evaluates to zero or to within some predefined epsilon of zero, exit with the current value of z as the root. Otherwise, continue on to Step 4.

Step 4. Compute a correction term Δz, using

$$\Delta z = \frac{N}{F \pm \sqrt{(N-1)(NG - G^2)}}$$

where $F \triangleq P'(z)/P(z)$, $G \triangleq F^2 - P''(z)/P(z)$, and the sign in the denominator is taken so as to minimize the magnitude of the correction (or, equivalently, so as to maximize the denominator).

Step 5. If the correction term Δz has a magnitude smaller than some specified fraction of the magnitude of z, then take z as the value of the root and terminate the algorithm.

Step 6. If the algorithm has been running for a while (let's say six iterations) and the correction value has gotten bigger since the previous iteration, then take z as the value of the root and terminate the algorithm.

Step 7. If the algorithm was not terminated in Step 3, 5, or 6, then subtract Δz from z and go back to Step 2.

A function `laguerreMethod( )` that implements Algorithm 3.1 is provided in Listing 3.1.

3.8 Magnitude, Phase, and Delay Responses

A system's *steady-state response* $H(j\omega)$ can be determined by evaluating the transfer function $H(s)$ at $s = j\omega$:

$$H(j\omega) = |H(j\omega)|\, e^{j\theta(\omega)} = H(s)\big|_{s=j\omega} \tag{3.43}$$

The *magnitude response* is simply the magnitude of $H(j\omega)$:

$$|H(j\omega)| = (\{\mathrm{Re}\,[H(j\omega)]\}^2 + \{\mathrm{Im}\,[H(j\omega)]\}^2)^{1/2} \tag{3.44}$$

It can be shown that

$$|H(j\omega)|^2 = H(s)\,H(-s)\big|_{s=j\omega} \tag{3.45}$$

If $H(s)$ is available in factored form as given by

$$H(s) = H_0 \frac{(s - z_1)(s - z_2)(s - z_3) \cdots (s - z_m)}{(s - p_1)(s - p_2)(s - p_3) \cdots (s - p_n)} \tag{3.46}$$

then the magnitude response can be obtained by replacing each factor with its absolute value evaluated at $s = j\omega$:

$$|H(j\omega)| = H_0 \frac{|j\omega - z_1| \cdot |j\omega - z_2| \cdot |j\omega - z_3| \cdot \cdots \cdot |j\omega - z_m|}{|j\omega - p_1| \cdot |j\omega - p_2| \cdot |j\omega - p_3| \cdot \cdots \cdot |j\omega - p_n|} \tag{3.47}$$

The *phase response* $\theta(\omega)$ is given by

$$\theta(\omega) = \tan^{-1}\left\{\frac{\mathrm{Im}\,[H(j\omega)]}{\mathrm{Re}\,[H(j\omega)]}\right\} \tag{3.48}$$

Phase delay

The *phase delay* $\tau_p(\omega)$ of a system is defined as

$$\tau_p(\omega) = \frac{-\theta(\omega)}{\omega} \tag{3.49}$$

where $\theta(\omega)$ is the phase response defined in Eq. (3.48). When evaluated at any specific frequency ω_1, Eq. (3.49) will yield the time delay experienced by a sinusoid of frequency ω passing through the system. Some authors define $\tau_p(\omega)$ without the minus sign shown on the right-hand side of Eq. (3.49). As illustrated in Fig. 3.9, the phase delay at a frequency ω_1 is equal to the negative slope of a secant drawn from the origin to the phase response curve at ω_1.

Group delay

The *group delay* $\tau_g(\omega)$ of a system is defined as

$$\tau_g(\omega) = \frac{-d}{dt}\,\theta(\omega) \tag{3.50}$$

where $\theta(\omega)$ is the phase response defined in Eq. (3.48). In the case of a modulated carrier passing through the system, the modulation envelope will be delayed by an amount that is in general not equal to the delay $\tau_p(\omega)$ experienced by the carrier. If the system exhibits constant group delay over the entire bandwidth of the modulated signal, then the envelope will be delayed by an amount equal to τ_g. If the group delay is not constant over the entire bandwidth of the signal, the envelope will be distorted. As shown in Fig. 3.10, the group delay at a frequency ω_1 is equal to the negative slope of a tangent to the phase response at ω_1.

Assuming that the phase response of a system is sufficiently smooth, it can be approximated as

$$\theta(\omega + \omega_c) = \tau_p\omega_c + \tau_g\omega_c \tag{3.51}$$

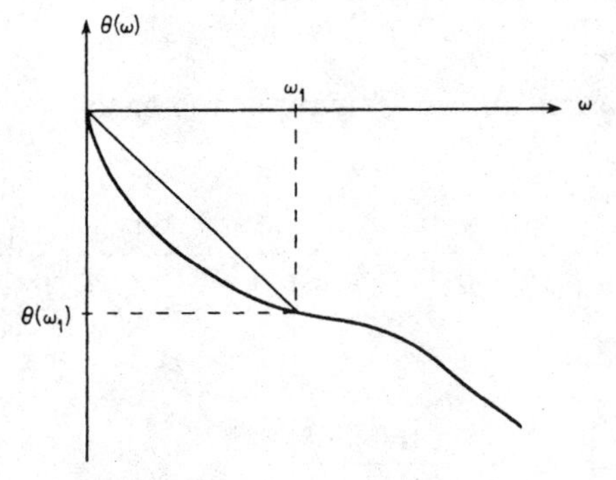

Figure 3.9 Phase delay.

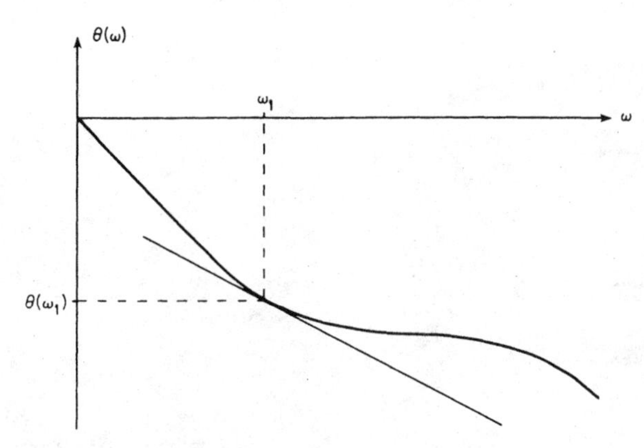

Figure 3.10 Group delay.

If an input signal $x(t) = a(t) \cos \omega_c t$ is applied to a system for which Eq. (3.51) holds, the output response will be given by

$$y(t) = Ka(t - \tau_g) \cos [\omega_c(t - \tau_p)] \tag{3.52}$$

Since the envelope $a(t)$ is delayed by τ_g, the group delay is also called the *envelope delay.* Likewise, since the carrier is delayed by τ_p, the phase delay is also called the *carrier delay.*

3.9 Filter Fundamentals

Ideal filters would have rectangular magnitude responses, as shown in Fig. 3.11. The desired frequencies are passed with no attenuation, while the undesired frequencies are completely blocked. If such filters could be implemented, they would enjoy widespread use. Unfortunately, ideal filters are noncausal and therefore not realizable. However, there are practical filter designs that approximate the ideal filter characteristics and which are realizable. Each of the major types—Butterworth, Chebyshev, and Bessel—optimizes a different aspect of the approximation.

Magnitude response features of low-pass filters

The magnitude response of a practical low-pass filter will usually have one of the four general shapes shown in Figs. 3.12 through 3.15. In all four cases the filter characteristics divide the spectrum into three general regions as shown. The *pass band* extends from direct current up to the cutoff frequency ω_c. The *transition band* extends from ω_c up to the beginning of the stop band at ω_1, and the *stop band* extends upward from ω_1 to infinity. The cutoff frequency ω_c is the frequency at which the amplitude response falls to a specified fraction (usually

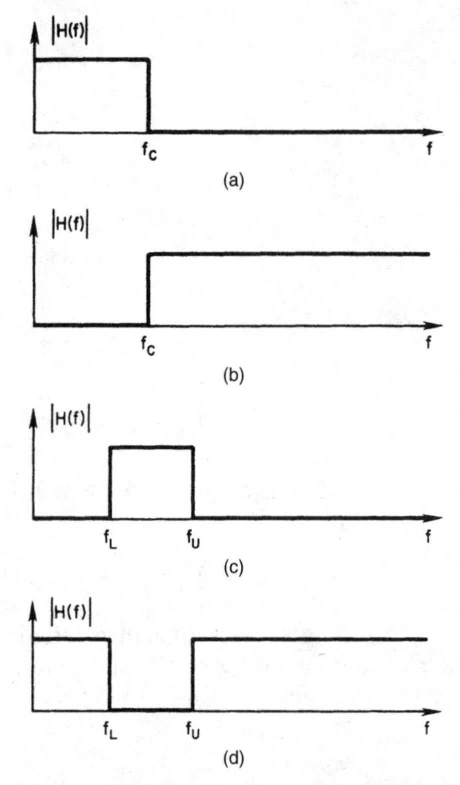

Figure 3.11 Ideal filter responses: (*a*) low-pass, (*b*) high-pass, (*c*) bandpass, and (*d*) bandstop.

–3 dB, sometimes –1 dB) of the peak pass-band values. Defining the frequency ω_1 which marks the beginning of the stop band is not quite so straightforward. In Fig. 3.12 or 3.13 there really isn't any particular feature that indicates just where ω_1 should be located. The usual approach involves specifying a *minimum stop-band loss* α_2 (or conversely a maximum stop-band amplitude A_2) and then defining ω_1 as the lowest frequency at which the loss exceeds and subsequently continues to exceed α_2. The width W_T of the transition band is equal to $\omega_c - \omega_1$. The quantity W_T/ω_c is sometimes called the *normalized transition width.* In the case of response shapes like those shown in Figs. 3.14 and 3.15, the minimum stop-band loss is clearly defined by the peaks of the stop-band ripples.

Scaling of low-pass filter responses

In plots of practical filter responses, the frequency axes are almost universally plotted on logarithmic scales. Magnitude response curves for low-pass filters are scaled so that the cutoff frequency occurs at a convenient frequency such as 1 rad/s (radian per second), 1 Hz, or 1 kHz. A single set of such normalized curves can then be denormalized to fit any particular cutoff requirement.

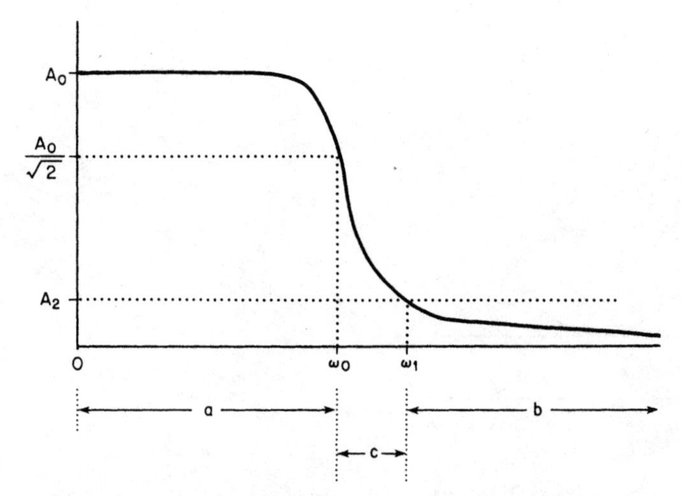

Figure 3.12 Monotonic magnitude response of a practical low-pass filter: (*a*) pass band, (*b*) stop band, and (*c*) transition band.

Transfer functions. For common filter types such as Butterworth, Chebyshev, and Bessel, transfer functions are usually presented in a scaled form such that $\omega_c = 1$. Given such a response normalized for $\omega_c = 1$, we can scale the transfer function to yield the corresponding response for $\omega_c = \alpha$. If the normalized response for $\omega_c = 1$ is given by

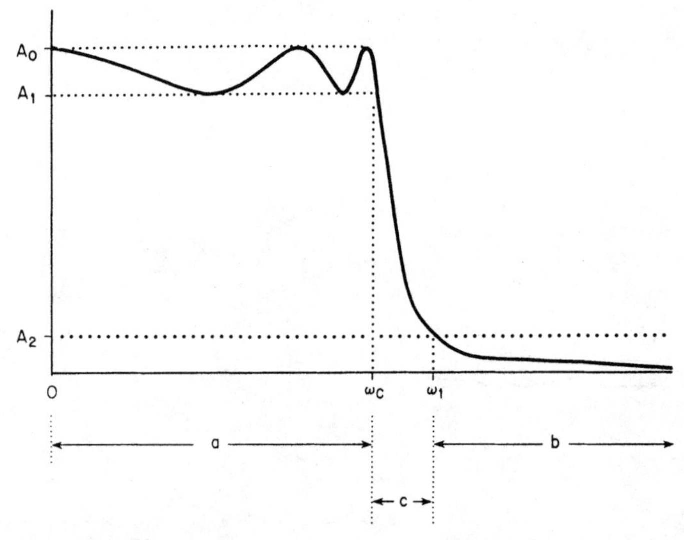

Figure 3.13 Magnitude response of a practical low-pass filter with ripples in the pass band: (*a*) pass band, (*b*) stop band, and (*c*) transition band.

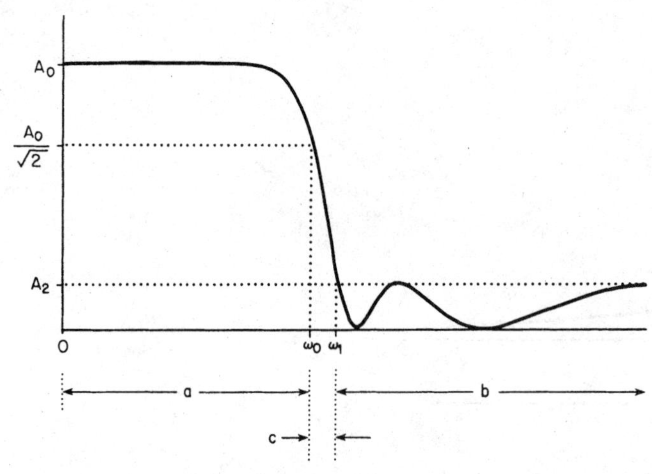

Figure 3.14 Magnitude response of a practical low-pass filter with ripples in the stop band: (*a*) pass band, (*b*) stop band, and (*c*) transition band.

$$H_N(s) = \frac{K \prod_{i=1}^{m} (s - z_i)}{\prod_{i=1}^{n} (s - p_i)} \tag{3.53}$$

then the corresponding response for $\omega_c = \alpha$ is given by

$$H_\alpha(s) = \frac{K \prod_{i=1}^{m} (s - \alpha z_i)}{\alpha^{(m-n)} \prod_{i=1}^{n} (s - \alpha p_i)} \tag{3.54}$$

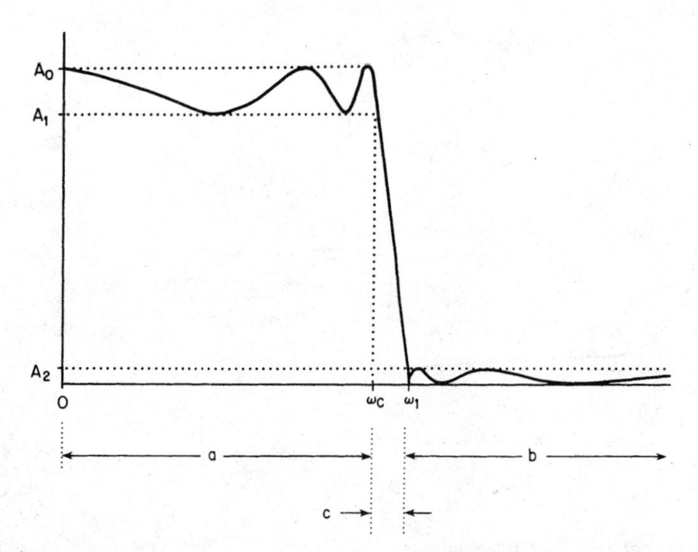

Figure 3.15 Magnitude response of a practical low-pass filter with ripples in the pass band and stop band: (*a*) pass band, (*b*) stop band, and (*c*) transition band.

Magnitude scaling. The vertical axes of a filter's magnitude response can be presented in several different forms. In theoretical presentations, the magnitude response is often plotted on a linear scale. In practical design situations it is convenient to work with plots of attenuation in decibels, using a high-resolution linear scale in the pass band and a lower-resolution linear scale in the stop band. This allows details of the pass-band response to be shown, as well as large attenuation values deep into the stop band. In nearly all cases, the data are normalized to present a 0-dB attenuation at the peak of the pass band.

Phase response. The phase response is plotted as a phase angle in degrees or radians versus frequency. By adding or subtracting the appropriate number of full-cycle offsets (that is, 2π rad or 360°), the phase response can be presented either as a single curve extending over several full cycles (Fig. 3.16) or as an equivalent set of curves, each extending over a single cycle (Fig. 3.17). Phase calculations will usually yield results confined to a single 2π cycle.

Step response. Normalized step response plots are obtained by computing the step response from the normalized transfer function. The inherent scaling of

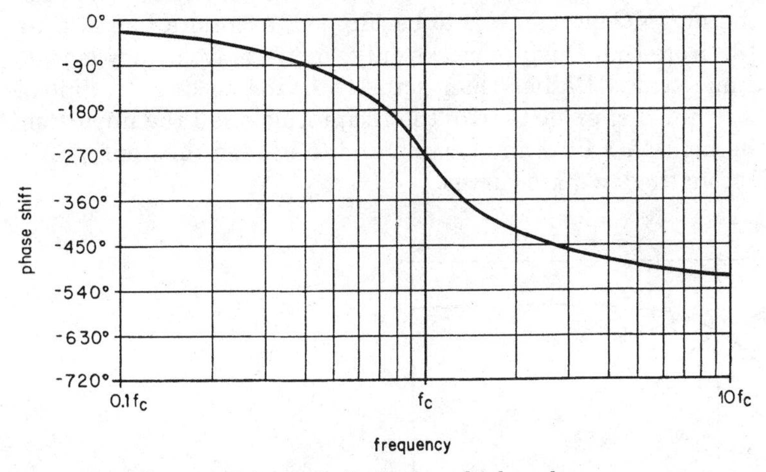

Figure 3.16 Phase response extending over multiple cycles.

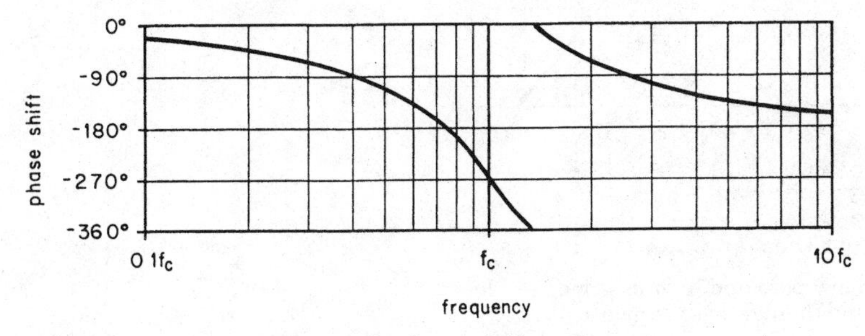

Figure 3.17 Phase response confined to a single-cycle range.

the time axis will thus depend upon the transient characteristics of the normalized filter. The amplitude axis scaling is not dependent upon normalization. The usual low-pass presentation will require that the response be denormalized by dividing the frequency axis by some form of the cutoff frequency.

Impulse response. Normalized impulse response plots are obtained by computing the impulse response from the normalized-transfer function. Since an impulse response will always have an area of unity, both the time axis and the amplitude axis will exhibit inherent scaling that depends upon the transient characteristics of the normalized filter. The usual low-pass presentation will require that the response be denormalized by multiplying the amplitude by some form of the cutoff frequency and dividing the time axis by the same factor.

High-pass filters

High-pass filters are usually designed via transformation of low-pass designs. Normalized low-pass transfer functions can be converted into corresponding high-pass transfer functions by simply replacing each occurrence of s with $1/s$. This will cause the magnitude response to be "flipped" around a line at f_c as shown in Fig. 3.18. (Note that this flip works only when the frequency is plotted on a logarithmic scale.) Rather than actually trying to draw a flipped response curve, it is much simpler to take the reciprocals of all the important frequencies for the high-pass filter in question and then read the appropriate response directly from the low-pass curves.

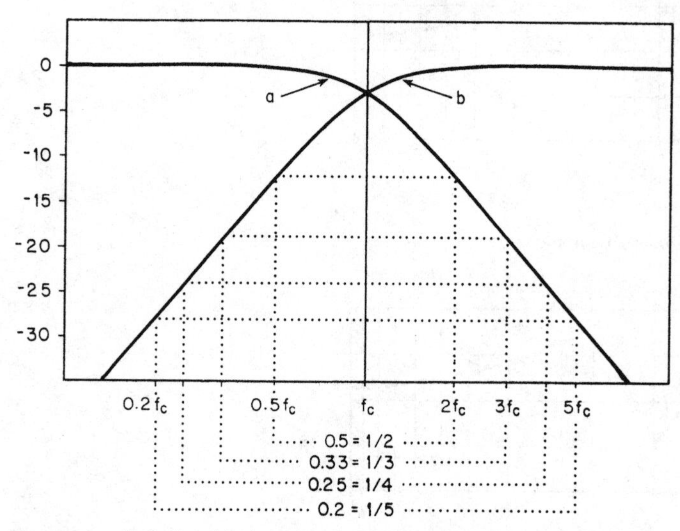

Figure 3.18 Relationship between low-pass and high-pass magnitude responses: (*a*) low-pass response and (*b*) high-pass response.

Bandpass filters

Bandpass filters are classified as wideband or narrowband based upon the relative width of their pass bands. Different methods are used for obtaining the transfer function for each type.

Wideband bandpass filters. Wideband bandpass filters can be realized by cascading a low-pass filter and a high-pass filter. This approach will be acceptable as long as the bandpass filters used exhibit relatively sharp transitions from the pass band to cutoff. Relatively narrow bandwidths and/or gradual rolloffs that begin within the pass band can cause a significant center-band loss as shown in Fig. 3.19. In situations where such losses are unacceptable, other bandpass filter realizations must be used. A general rule of thumb is to use narrowband techniques for pass bands that are an octave or smaller.

Narrowband bandpass filters. A normalized low-pass filter can be converted into a normalized narrowband bandpass filter by substituting $[s - (1/s)]$ for s in the low-pass transfer function. The center frequency of the resulting bandpass filter will be at the cutoff frequency of the original low-pass filter, and the pass band will be symmetric about the center frequency when plotted on a logarithmic frequency scale. At any particular attenuation level, the bandwidth of the bandpass filter will equal the frequency at which the low-pass filter exhibits the same attenuation (see Fig. 3.20). This particular bandpass transformation preserves the magnitude response shape of the lowpass prototype but distorts the transient responses.

Bandstop filters. A normalized low-pass filter can be converted into a normalized bandstop filter by substituting $s/(s^2 - 1)$ for s in the low-pass transfer function. The center frequency of the resulting bandstop filter will be at the cutoff

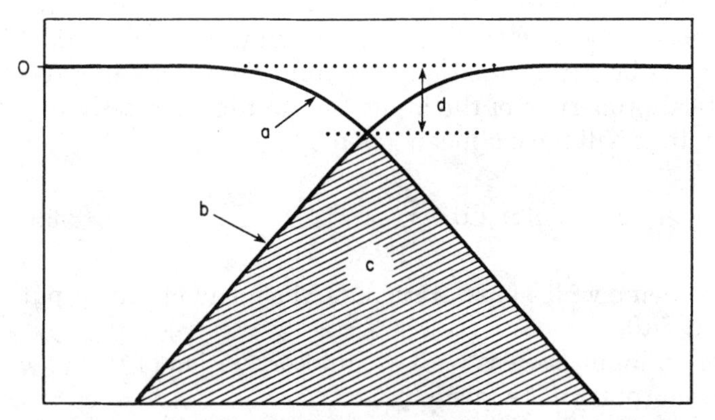

Figure 3.19 Center-band loss in a bandpass filter realized by cascading low-pass and high-pass filters: (*a*) low-pass response, (*b*) high-pass response, (*c*) pass band of BPF, and (*d*) center-band loss.

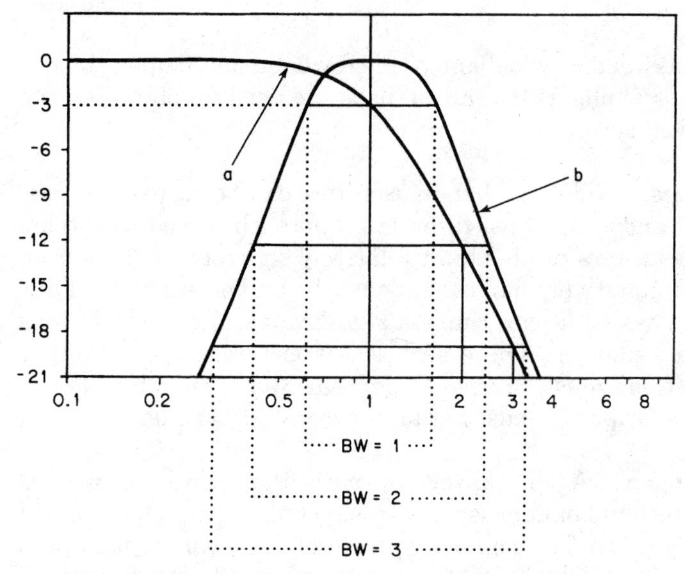

Figure 3.20 Relationship between low-pass and bandpass magnitude responses: (*a*) normalized low-pass response and (*b*) normalized bandpass response.

frequency of the original low-pass filter, and the stop band will be symmetrical about the center frequency when plotted on a logarithmic frequency scale. At any particular attenuation level, the width of the stop band will be equal to the reciprocal of the frequency at which the low-pass filter exhibits the same attenuation (see Fig. 3.21).

3.10 Linear Filtering of Noise Processes

Application of a noise process $x(t)$ to the input of a linear time-invariant filter will produce a different noise process $y(t)$ at the filter output. Some statistical properties of the output can be determined directly from the filter's impulse response and the statistical properties of the input. For an input process having a mean of $\mu_x(t)$, the output will have a mean given by

$$\mu_y(t) = \int_{-\infty}^{\infty} h(\tau)\, \mu_x(t - \tau)\, d\tau \tag{3.55}$$

For the special case of $x(t)$ being wide-sense stationary, the mean of the output can be simplified to $\mu_y = \mu_x H(0)$.

For the general case of an input process with an autocorrelation of $R_x(t_1, t_2)$, the autocorrelation of the output will be given by

$$R_y(t_1, t_2) = \int_{-\infty}^{\infty} h(\tau_1)\, d\tau_1 \int_{-\infty}^{\infty} h(\tau_2)\, R_x(t_1 - \tau_1, t_2 - \tau_2)\, d\tau_2 \tag{3.56}$$

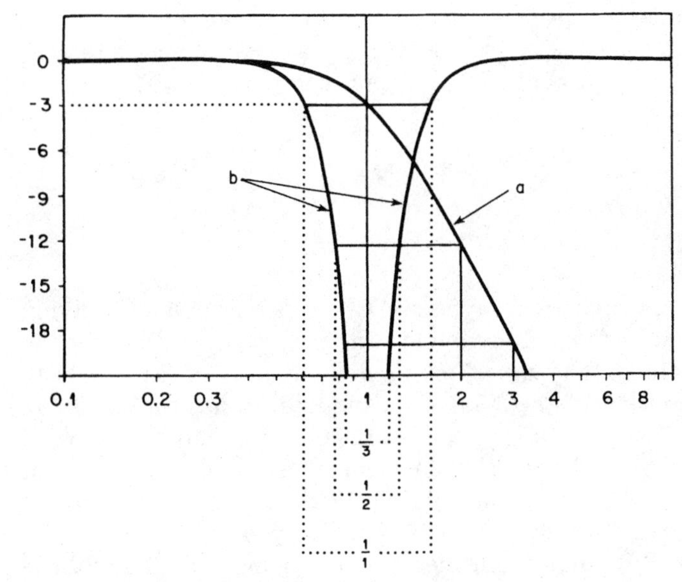

Figure 3.21 Relationship between low-pass and bandstop magnitude responses: (*a*) normalized low-pass response and (*b*) normalized bandstop response.

For the special case of $x(t)$ being wide-sense stationary, the autocorrelation can be simplified to

$$R_y(\tau) = \int_{-\infty}^{\infty} \int_{-\infty}^{\infty} h(\tau_1)\, h(\tau_2)\, R_x(t - \tau_1 + \tau_2)\, d\tau_1\, d\tau_2 \tag{3.57}$$

For an input with power spectral density of $S_x(f)$, the output will have a power spectral density given by

$$S_y(f) = |H(f)|^2\, S_x(f) \tag{3.58}$$

When the input noise process to a linear filter is a gaussian random process, the resulting output noise process is also gaussian.

3.11 Computer Representation of Polynomials and Transfer Functions

In the computer, any polynomial of degree N in sum of powers form can be represented using an array `double_complex c[ ]` to hold the coefficients c_n for $n = 0, 1, \ldots, N$. To multiply such a polynomial by a constant value, we only need to multiply each coefficient by this value as in

```
for( int n=0; n<=N; n++)
  { c[n] *= const_val; }
```

To multiply the polynomial by s, we only need to shift the contents of the array upwards by one location so that `c[N]` moves to `c[N+1]`, `c[N-1]` moves to `c[N]` and so on until `c[0]` moves to `c[1]`. The original contents of `c[0]` are then replaced by zero:

```
for( int n=N; n>=0; n--)
  { c[n+1] = c[n]: }
c[0] = double_complex(0.0, 0.0);
```

Using these rules for multiplying a polynomial by a constant and multiplying a polynomial in s by s, we can easily automate the process of performing the multiplications indicated in the numerator or denominator of Eq. (3.71) to obtain the sum-of-powers form of Eq. (3.59) or the biquadratic form of Eq. (3.70).

Let's define a class `CmplxPolynomial` for representing a polynomial with complex-valued coefficients. Clearly the data members of this class must include an integer (say, `Deg_Of_Poly`) for holding the degree of the polynomial and a complex-valued array (say, `Cmplx_Coeff[ ]`) of length `Deg_Of_Poly+1` for holding the coefficients. But what about member functions? What should the default constructor for this class do? Does it make any sense to have a polynomial of degree 0? Yes it does. A constant can be viewed as a polynomial of degree 0, and for complete generality our class should support this idea. Therefore, the default constructor will create a "zero" polynomial of degree 0 that has a single coefficient with a value of 0.

There should also be a copy constructor that can be used to make a duplicate of an existing `CmplxPolynomial` object. Binomial factors of the form $(s + a_n)$ or $(a_n s + b_n)$ occur so frequently that the `CmplxPolynomial` class should have a constructor specifically designed for creating and initializing binomials. The class will also need member functions for assignment, multiplication, and publishing the polynomial coefficients to an output stream. A class implementation that incorporates all of these features is shown in Listings 3.2 and 3.3.

In addition to `CmplxPolynomial`, it will be convenient to have a class, say, `Polynomial`, that can be used to represent polynomials with real-valued coefficients. Such polynomials are used in the biquadratic form of Eq. (3.70) and in the sum-of-powers form of Eq. (3.59). `Polynomial` should include real-valued versions of each of the functions in `CmplxPolynomial`.

`CmplxPolynomial` objects will often be used to multiply together terms with complex-valued coefficients to produce a result having all real-valued coefficients. This result will be in the form of a `CmplxPolynomial` object that has zero-valued imaginary parts for all of its coefficients. In simulations of analog filters, it will prove convenient to handle such a result as an object of type `Polynomial` rather than as an object of type `CmplxPolynomial`. Therefore, we need to provide a conversion constructor that will construct a `Polynomial` object and initialize it to be numerically equivalent to a `CmplxPolynomial` object that happens to have zero-valued imaginary parts for all of its coefficients. However, there is nothing to prevent a user from attempting to create a `Polynomial` object from a `CmplxPolynomial` object whose coefficients do not have zero-valued imaginary parts. There are two strategies for dealing with such an attempted misuse. We could blindly set each coefficient in the newly created `Polynomial` equal to the real part of the corresponding coefficient in `CmplxPolynomial`, without regard to the imaginary part of the coefficient. On the other hand, we could chose to check each coefficient in `CmplxPolynomial` and issue an error if the imaginary part of any coefficient is not very close to zero. (In theory, the imaginary parts should be exactly zero, but due to the effects of finite-precision arithmetic, they will rarely be exactly zero in any `CmplxPolynomial` that has been built up by multiplying together a number of binomial terms having complex coefficients.) The first approach is faster, and the second approach is safer. Since the polynomial conversions will only be done once or twice as part of the setup for a filter simulation, speed is not a driving concern. Therefore, the second approach was selected for the class implementation shown in Listings 3.4 and 3.5.

3.12 Computer Simulation of Analog Systems

Certain types of digital filters are obtained via transformations that are performed upon analog *prototype* filters. In assessing the performance of these digital filters it is often convenient to compare their responses to certain discrete-time input signals against the prototype filter's responses to the corresponding continuous-time input signals. Computer simulation of the analog prototype filters provides a convenient way to make such comparisons.

Sum-of-powers form

For all of the "traditional" analog filter families, the filter's transfer function can be expressed as a ratio of two polynomials in the complex-frequency variable s:

$$H(s) = H_0 \frac{\sum_{m=0}^{M} \alpha_m s^m}{\sum_{n=0}^{N} \beta_n s^n} \tag{3.59}$$

where the coefficients α_m and β_n are real.

Consider a filter with a transfer function given by

$$H(s) = \frac{Y(s)}{X(s)} = \frac{a_2 s^2 + a_1 s + a_0}{s^3 + b_2 s^2 + b_1 s + b_0} \tag{3.60}$$

Recalling that multiplication by s in the Laplace domain corresponds to differentiation with respect to time in the time domain, we could use Eq. (3.60) directly to build an implementation of the filter. However, this implementation would contain differentiators, which are difficult to build in hardware and which tend to be very noisy when implemented in software. Integration is a much easier operation to implement. Therefore, we can divide each term in the numerator and denominator of Eq. (3.60) by s^3 to obtain

$$H(s) = \frac{Y(s)}{X(s)} = \frac{a_2 s^{-1} + a_1 s^{-2} + a_0 s^{-3}}{1 + b_2 s^{-1} + b_1 s^{-2} + b_0 s^{-3}} \tag{3.61}$$

Now we make use of a well-known trick and split $H(s)$ into two parts:

$$H(s) = \frac{Y(s)}{U(s)} \cdot \frac{U(s)}{X(s)}$$

where

$$\frac{Y(s)}{U(s)} = a_2 s^{-1} + a_1 s^{-2} + a_0 s^{-3} \tag{3.62}$$

and

$$\frac{X(s)}{U(s)} = 1 + b_2 s^{-1} + b_1 s^{-2} + b_0 s^{-3} \tag{3.63}$$

Solving Eq. (3.62) for $Y(s)$ and Eq. (3.63) for $U(s)$, we obtain

$$Y(s) = a_2 s^{-1} U(s) + a_1 s^{-2} U(s) + a_0 s^{-3} U(s) \tag{3.64}$$

and

$$U(s) = X(s) - b_2 s^{-1} U(s) - b_1 s^{-2} U(s) - b_0 s^{-3} U(s) \tag{3.65}$$

If we were to take the inverse Laplace transform of Eqs. (3.64) and (3.65) [assuming that $u(t) = 0$ for $t < 0$] we would obtain

$$y(t) = a_2 \int_0^t u(\tau)\, d\tau + a_1 \int_0^t \int_0^{\tau_2} u(\tau_1)\, d\tau_1\, d\tau_2 + a_0 \int_0^t \int_0^{\tau_3} \int_0^{\tau_2} u(\tau_1)\, d\tau_1\, d\tau_2\, d\tau_3 \tag{3.66}$$

and

$$u(t) = x(t) - b_2 \int_0^t u(\tau)\, d\tau - b_1 \int_0^t \int_0^{\tau_2} u(\tau_1)\, d\tau_1\, d\tau_2 - b_0 \int_0^t \int_0^{\tau_3} \int_0^{\tau_2} u(\tau_1)\, d\tau_1\, d\tau_2\, d\tau_3 \tag{3.67}$$

The notation in these equations is becoming quite cumbersome—further manipulations will be made much easier if we substitute

$$w'''(t) \equiv \frac{d^3}{dt^3} w(t)$$

for $u(t)$ in Eqs. (3.66) and (3.67) to obtain

$$y(t) = a_2 w''(t) + a_1 w'(t) + a_0 w(t) \tag{3.68}$$

and

$$w'''(t) = x(t) - b_2 w''(t) - b_1 w'(t) - b_0 w(t) \tag{3.69}$$

Equation (3.69) now provides a recipe for generating $w'''(t)$ from $x(t)$ using only integrators, adders, and constant multipliers, as shown in Fig. 3.22. Likewise, Eq. (3.68) provides a recipe for generating $y(t)$ from $w'''(t)$ using only integrators, adders, and constant multipliers, as shown in Fig. 3.23. Notice that in both Fig. 3.22 and Fig. 3.23, the node corresponding to $w'''(t)$ is followed by three integrators in cascade. The node labeled 1 in Fig. 3.22 is equivalent to the node labeled 1 in Fig. 3.23. Likewise for the nodes labeled 2 and 3 in these two figures. What this means is that we can combine the two realizations so that they share a single string of integrators, as shown in Fig. 3.24. The filter may now be simulated in software using numerical integration techniques to implement each of these integrators.

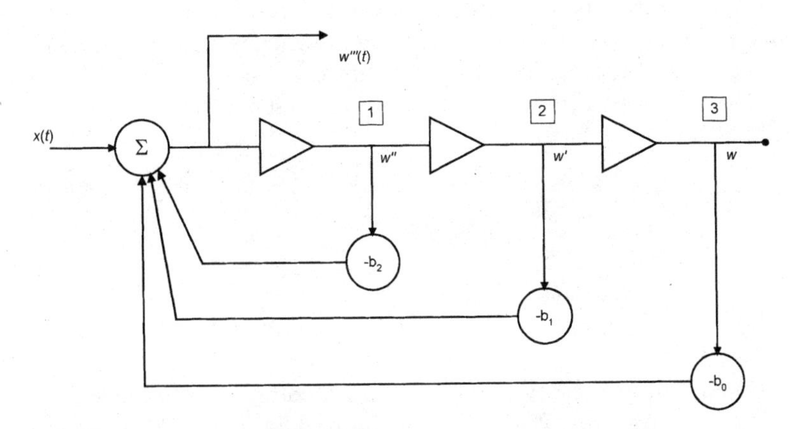

Figure 3.22 Realization of Eq. (3.64).

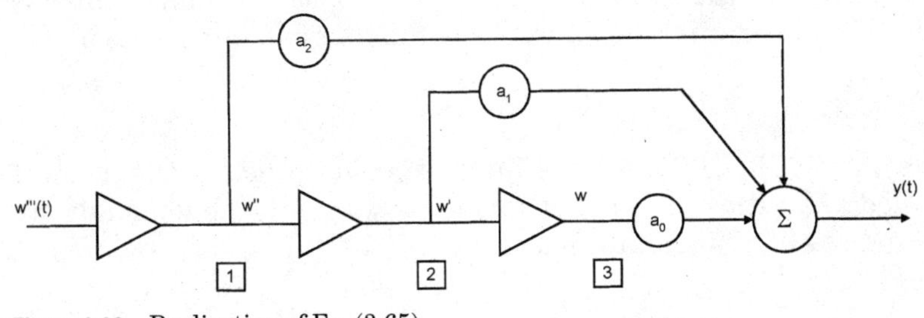

Figure 3.23 Realization of Eq. (3.65).

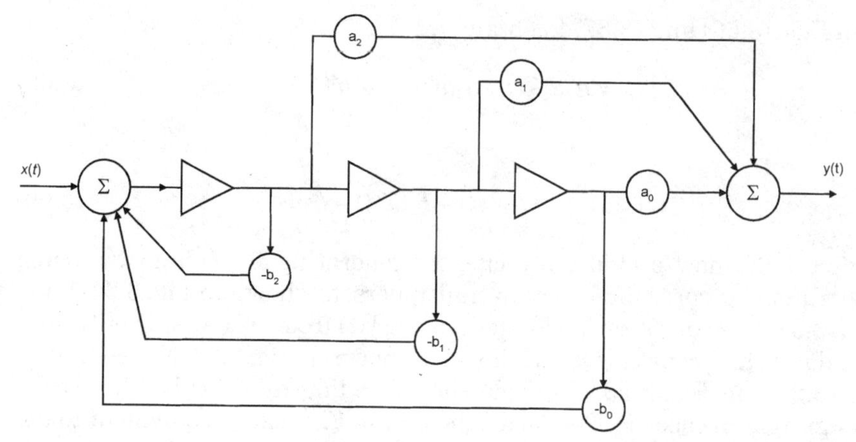

Figure 3.24 Realization of Eq. (3.61) formed by merging the realizations of Figs. 3.22 and 3.23.

Biquadratic form

The approach demonstrated in the preceding could be extended to filters with any number of poles and zeros, but it rarely is. It is usually more convenient to implement a high-order filter as a cascade of lower-order sections where each section has at most two poles and two zeros. Because the two polynomials in Eq. (3.59) have real coefficients, it can be shown that the roots of these polynomials either are real or occur in complex conjugate pairs. Therefore, it is possible to factor Eq. (3.59) into the form

$$H(s) = H_0 \prod_{k=1}^{N/2} \frac{a_{2k}s^2 + a_{1k}s + a_{0k}}{s^2 + b_{1k}s + b_{0k}} \qquad N \text{ even}$$

or

$$H(s) = \frac{H_0}{(s-d)} \prod_{k=1}^{(N-1)/2} \frac{a_{2k}s^2 + a_{1k}s + a_{0k}}{s^2 + b_{1k}s + b_{0k}} \qquad N \text{ odd} \tag{3.70}$$

where the roots of each quadratic polynomial form a complex conjugate pair and all of the a, b, and d are real. The form represented by Eq. (3.70) is called the *biquadratic* form of the filter. Each factor in Eq. (3.70) can be implemented using a *biquad section* of the form shown in Fig. 3.25. The complete filter is then implemented by cascading the appropriate number of biquad sections.

Polynomial expansions

For most of the analog filter families, the filter's transfer function $H(s)$ is most easily determined as a ratio of two polynomials in s where the polynomials are expressed as products of binomial terms

$$H(s) = H_0 \frac{\prod_{m=1}^{M} (s - q_m)}{\prod_{n=1}^{N} (s - p_n)} \tag{3.71}$$

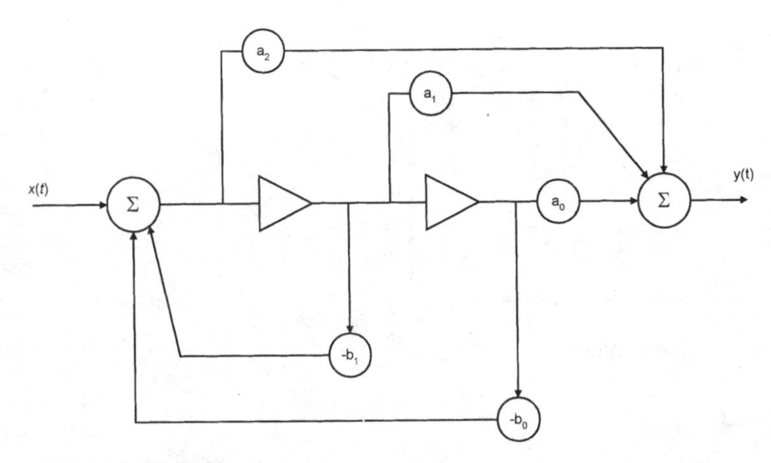

Figure 3.25 Biquad section.

where p_n and q_m denote, respectively, the filter's poles and zeros. However, to take advantage of the simulation approaches discussed previously, the transfer function needs to be in sum-of-powers form as in Eq. (3.59) or in the biquadratic form of Eq. (3.70). Expanding a product of binomials into a sum of powers by hand can be quite a tedious exercise—especially when the p_n and q_m are complex. Fortunately, it is relatively straightforward to create software that can perform this expansion. The class `CmplxPolynomial` described in Sec. 3.11 can be used for expanding products of binomials into sum-of-powers form.

Software for simulation of analog filters

A class `AnalogPoleZeroFilter` that can be used to simulate analog filters is provided in Listings 3.6 and 3.7. The heart of this class is its `Run` function, which uses numeric integration to implement Eqs. (3.68) and (3.69). The specifics of the numeric integration are isolated in a separate class, `NumericInteg`. The constructor for `AnalogPoleZeroFilter` will instantiate an array of `NumericInteg` objects, with the number of integrators being equal to the number of poles in the filter's transfer function.

Several common filter types—Butterworth, Chebyshev, and Bessel—are "all pole" filters having transfer functions of the form

$$H(s) = \frac{H_0}{X(s)}$$

An implementation for a third-order all-pole filter is shown in Fig. 3.26. Although `AnalogPoleZeroFilter` can be used with `A_Coef[k]` set to zero for all `k` other than zero, improved execution speed can be achieved by implementing a class specifically designed for simulating all-pole filters. Such a class, `AnalogAllPoleFilt`, is shown in Listings 3.8 and 3.9.

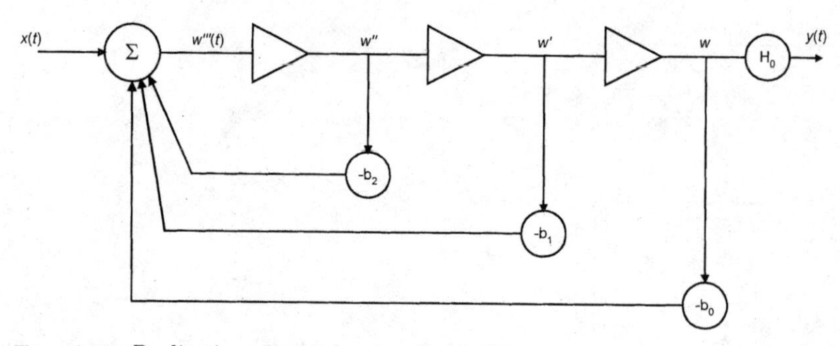

Figure 3.26 Realization of a third-order all-pole filter.

Listing 3.1 Laguerre Method

```
//+++++++++++++++++++++++++++++++++++++++++++++++++++++++++++++++++++
//
//   File = laguerre.cpp
//
//   Laguerre method for finding polynomial roots
//

#include <math.h>
#include <stdlib.h>
#include <iostream.h>
#include <fstream.h>
#include "mymath.h"
#include "laguerre.h"
#include "d_cmplx.h"
extern ofstream DebugFile;

int LaguerreMethod( int order,
                    double_complex *coef,
                    double_complex *root_ptr,
                    double epsilon,
                    double epsilon2,
                    int max_iter)
{
int iter, j;
double_complex p_eval, p_prime, p_double_prime;
double_complex root, f, f_sqrd, g, radical;
double_complex f_plus_rad, f_minus_rad, delta_root;
double old_delta_mag, root_mag, error;

root = *root_ptr;
old_delta_mag = 1000.0;

for(iter=1; iter<=max_iter; iter++)
  {
```

```
p_double_prime = double_complex(0.0,0.0);
p_prime = double_complex(0.0,0.0);
p_eval = coef[order];
error = mag(p_eval);
root_mag = mag(root);

for( j=order-1; j>=0; j--)
  {
  p_double_prime = p_prime + root * p_double_prime;
  p_prime = p_eval + root * p_prime;
  p_eval = coef[j] + root * p_eval;
  error = mag(p_eval) + root_mag * error;
  }
error = epsilon2 * error;
p_double_prime = 2.0 * p_double_prime;

if(mag(p_eval) < error)
  {
  *root_ptr = root;
  return(1);
  }
f = p_prime/p_eval;
f_sqrd = f * f;
g = f_sqrd - p_double_prime/p_eval;
radical = (order-1)*(order * g - f_sqrd);
radical = sqrt(radical);
f_plus_rad = f + radical;
f_minus_rad = f - radical;
if( mag(f_plus_rad) > mag(f_minus_rad) )
  {
  delta_root = double_complex(double(order), 0.0) /
               f_plus_rad;
  }
else
  {
  delta_root = double_complex(double(order), 0.0) /
               f_minus_rad;
  }
root = root - delta_root;
if( (iter > 6) && (mag(delta_root) > old_delta_mag) )
  {
  *root_ptr = root;
  return(2);
  }
if( mag(delta_root) < (epsilon * mag(root)))
  {
  *root_ptr = root;
  return(3);
```

```
    }
  old_delta_mag = mag(delta_root);
  }
DebugFile << "Laguerre method failed to converge" << endl;
return(-1);
}
```

Listing 3.2 Header for Class Implementation of Polynomials with Complex Coefficients

```
//
// File = cmpxpoly.h
//
#ifndef _CMPXPOLY_H_
#define _CMPXPOLY_H_

#include <fstream.h>
#include "d_cmplx.h"

class CmplxPolynomial
{
public:

  //  default constructor
  CmplxPolynomial( );

  //  copy constructor
  CmplxPolynomial( const CmplxPolynomial &original);

  // constructor for initializing a binomial
  CmplxPolynomial( const double_complex coeff_1,
                   const double_complex coeff_0);

  // assignment operator
  CmplxPolynomial& operator= (const CmplxPolynomial &right);

  //  multiply assign operator
  CmplxPolynomial& operator*= (const CmplxPolynomial &right);

  // dump polynomial to an output stream
  void DumpToStream( ofstream* output_stream);

  // get degree of polynomial
  int CmplxPolynomial::GetDegree(void);

  // return specified coefficient
  double_complex CmplxPolynomial::GetCoefficient(int k);
```

```
  friend class Polynomial;

private:

  int Degree;
  double_complex* Coefficient;
};
#endif
```

Listing 3.3 Class Implementation for Polynomials with Complex Coefficients

```
//++++++++++++++++++++++++++++++++++++++++++++++++++++++++++++++
//
//  File = cmpxpoly.cpp
//
//  class that implements a polynomial with
//  complex-valued coefficients
//

#include <math.h>
#include "mymath.h"
#include "cmpxpoly.h"
#include "d_cmplx.h"

//=====================================================
//  default constructor

CmplxPolynomial::CmplxPolynomial( )
{
 Degree = 0;
 Coefficient = (double_complex*) new double[2];
 Coefficient[0] = double_complex( 0.0, 0.0);
 return;
};

//==================================================================
//  copy constructor

CmplxPolynomial::CmplxPolynomial( const CmplxPolynomial& original )
{
 Degree = original.Degree;
 Coefficient = (double_complex*) new double[2*(Degree+1)];

 for( int i=0; i<=Degree; i++)
   {
    Coefficient[i] = original.Coefficient[i];
```

```
   }
 return;
};

//===========================================================================
//  constructor for initializing a binomial

CmplxPolynomial::CmplxPolynomial( const double_complex coeff_1,
                                  const double_complex coeff_0 )
{
 Degree = 1;
 Coefficient = (double_complex*) new double[4];

 Coefficient[0] = coeff_0;
 Coefficient[1] = coeff_1;

 return;
}

//===========================================================================
//  assignment operator

CmplxPolynomial& CmplxPolynomial::operator= (const CmplxPolynomial& right)
{
 if (Coefficient != right.Coefficient)
   {
    //-----------------------------------------------------------------
    // Get rid of old coefficient array to make way for a new one
    // of the correct length for the new polynomial being assigned

    delete [] Coefficient;

    Degree = right.Degree;
    Coefficient = (double_complex*) new double[2*(Degree+1)];
    for( int i=0; i<=Degree; i++)
      {
       Coefficient[i] = right.Coefficient[i];
      }
   }
 return *this;
}

//===========================================================================
// multiply assign operator

CmplxPolynomial& CmplxPolynomial::operator*= (const CmplxPolynomial &right)
{
 //-------------------------------------------------------
```

```
 // save pointer to original coefficient array so that
 // this array can be deleted once no longer needed

 double_complex *orig_coeff = Coefficient;
 int orig_degree = Degree;

 //-------------------------------------------------------
 //  create new longer array to hold the new coefficients

 Degree += right.Degree;
 Coefficient = (double_complex*) new double[2*(Degree+1)];

 for( int i=0; i<=Degree; i++)
    Coefficient[i] = double_complex(0.0, 0.0);

 //-------------------------------------
 //  perform multiplication

 for( int rgt_indx=0; rgt_indx<= right.Degree; rgt_indx++)
   {
    for( int orig_indx=0; orig_indx <= orig_degree; orig_indx++)
      {
       Coefficient[orig_indx+rgt_indx] +=
              (orig_coeff[orig_indx] * right.Coefficient[rgt_indx]);
      }
   }

 return *this;
}

//==============================================================
//  dump polynomial to an output stream

void CmplxPolynomial::DumpToStream( ofstream* output_stream)
{
 (*output_stream) << "Degree = " << Degree << endl;

 for(int i=Degree; i>=0; i--)
   {
    (*output_stream) << "Coeff[" << i << "] = "
                     << Coefficient[i] << endl;
   }
 return;
}

//=====================================================
//
```

```
int CmplxPolynomial::GetDegree(void)
{
return(Degree);
}

//=====================================================
//

double_complex CmplxPolynomial::GetCoefficient(int k)
{
return Coefficient[k];
}
```

Listing 3.4 Header for Class Implementation of Polynomials with Real Coefficients

```
//
// File = poly.h
//
#ifndef _POLY_H_
#define _POLY_H_

#include <fstream.h>
#include "cmpxpoly.h"

class Polynomial
{
public:

  //  default constructor
  Polynomial( );

  //  copy constructor
  Polynomial( const Polynomial &original);

  //  conversion constructor
  Polynomial( const CmplxPolynomial &original);

  // constructor for initializing a binomial
  Polynomial( const double coeff_1,
              const double coeff_0);

  // assignment operator
  Polynomial& operator= (const Polynomial &right);

  //  multiply assign operator
  Polynomial& operator*= (const Polynomial &right);
```

```
  // dump polynomial to an output stream
  void DumpToStream( ofstream* output_stream);

  // get degree of polynomial
  int Polynomial::GetDegree(void);

  // return specified coefficient
  double Polynomial::GetCoefficient(int k);

private:

  int Degree;
  double* Coefficient;
};
#endif
```

Listing 3.5 Class Implementation for Polynomials with Real Coefficients

```
//++++++++++++++++++++++++++++++++++++++++++++++++++++++++++++++
//
//  File = poly.cpp
//
//  class that implements a polynomial with
//  real-valued coefficients
//

#include <math.h>
#include "mymath.h"
#include "poly.h"
#include "f_cmplx.h"

//======================================================
//  default constructor

Polynomial::Polynomial( )
{
 Degree = 0;
 Coefficient = new double[1];
 Coefficient[0] = 0.0;
 return;
};

//===================================================================
//  copy constructor

Polynomial::Polynomial( const Polynomial& original )
{
```

```
 Degree = original.Degree;
 Coefficient = new double[Degree+1];

 for( int i=0; i<=Degree; i++)
   {
    Coefficient[i] = original.Coefficient[i];
   }
 return;
};

//====================================================================
//  conversion constructor

Polynomial::Polynomial( const CmplxPolynomial& original )
{
 Degree = original.Degree;
 Coefficient = new double[Degree+1];

 for( int i=0; i<=Degree; i++)
   {
    Coefficient[i] = real(original.Coefficient[i]);
   }
 return;
};

//====================================================================
//  constructor for initializing a binomial

Polynomial::Polynomial( const double coeff_1,
                        const double coeff_0 )
{
 Degree = 1;
 Coefficient = new double[2];

 Coefficient[0] = coeff_0;
 Coefficient[1] = coeff_1;

 return;
}

//==================================================================
//  assignment operator

Polynomial& Polynomial::operator= (const Polynomial& right)
{
 if (Coefficient != right.Coefficient)
   {
```

```
    //-------------------------------------------------------------
    // Get rid of old coefficient array to make way for a new one
    // of the correct length for the new polynomial being assigned

    delete [] Coefficient;

    Degree = right.Degree;
    Coefficient = new double[Degree+1];

    for( int i=0; i<=Degree; i++)
      {
       Coefficient[i] = right.Coefficient[i];
      }
    }
 return *this;
}

//=====================================================================
// multiply assign operator

Polynomial& Polynomial::operator*= (const Polynomial &right)
{
 //----------------------------------------------------
 // save pointer to original coefficient array so that
 // this array can be deleted once no longer needed

 double *orig_coeff = Coefficient;
 int orig_degree = Degree;

 //-------------------------------------------------------
 //  create new longer array to hold the new coefficients

 Degree += right.Degree;
 Coefficient = new double[Degree+1];

 for( int i=0; i<=Degree; i++)
    Coefficient[i] = 0.0;

 //--------------------------------
 //  perform multiplication

 for( int rgt_indx=0; rgt_indx<= right.Degree; rgt_indx++)
   {
    for( int orig_indx=0; orig_indx <= orig_degree; orig_indx++)
      {
       Coefficient[orig_indx+rgt_indx] +=
              (orig_coeff[orig_indx] * right.Coefficient[rgt_indx]);
```

```
      }
   }

 return *this;
}

//===========================================================
//  dump polynomial to an output stream

void Polynomial::DumpToStream( ofstream* output_stream)
{
 (*output_stream) << "Degree = " << Degree << endl;

 for(int i=Degree; i>=0; i--)
   {
    (*output_stream) << "Coeff[" << i << "] = "
                     << Coefficient[i] << endl;
   }
 return;
}

//======================================================
//

int Polynomial::GetDegree(void)
{
return(Degree);
}

//====================================================
//

double Polynomial::GetCoefficient(int k)
{
return Coefficient[k];
}
```

Listing 3.6 Header for Class Implementation of Analog Pole-Zero Filters

```
//
// File = pzfilt.h
//
#ifndef _PZFILT_H_
#define _PZFILT_H_

#include "f_cmplx.h"
#include "numinteg.h"
```

```
#include "anlgfilt.h"
#include "poly.h"

class AnalogPoleZeroFilter : public AnalogFilter
{
public:

  // constructors
  AnalogPoleZeroFilter( Polynomial numer_poly,
                        Polynomial denom_poly,
                        double h_sub_zero,
                        double delta_t);

  double Run( double input );

private:

  NumericInteg** Integrator;
  double* W_Prime;
  int Order;
  double* A_Coef;
  double* B_Coef;
  double H_Sub_Zero;
};
#endif
```

Listing 3.7 Class Implementation for Analog Pole-Zero Filters

```
//+++++++++++++++++++++++++++++++++++++++++++++++++++++++++++++++++++
//
//  File = pzfilt.cpp
//
//  simulation of analog pole-zero filter
//

#include <math.h>
#include "mymath.h"
#include "pzfilt.h"

//==========================================================
//  constructor that actually initializes filter model
//----------------------------------------------------------

AnalogPoleZeroFilter::AnalogPoleZeroFilter(
                            Polynomial numer_poly,
                            Polynomial denom_poly,
```

```
                                double h_sub_zero,
                                double delta_t)
                        : AnalogFilter()
{
 int k, order;

 order = denom_poly.GetDegree();

 Integrator = new NumericInteg*[order];
 W_Prime = new double[order+1];
 A_Coef = new double[order+1];
 B_Coef = new double[order];

 Order = order;

 for(k=0; k<order; k++)
   {
    Integrator[k] = new NumericInteg(delta_t);
    A_Coef[k] = numer_poly.GetCoefficient(k);
    B_Coef[k] = -(denom_poly.GetCoefficient(k));
    W_Prime[k] = 0.0;
    H_Sub_Zero = h_sub_zero;
   }
 return;
};
//+++++++++++++++++++++++++++++++++++++++++++++++++++++++++++++++++++

//=======================================================
//
//-------------------------------------------------------

double AnalogPoleZeroFilter::Run( double input )
{
double sum, output;
int k;

sum = H_Sub_Zero * input;

for( k=0; k<Order; k++)
  {
   sum += (W_Prime[k] * B_Coef[k]);
  }
W_Prime[Order] = sum;

output = 0.0;

for( k=Order-1; k>=0; k--)
  {
```

```
    W_Prime[k] = ((Integrator[k])->Integrate(W_Prime[k+1]));
    output += (W_Prime[k] * A_Coef[k]);
   }
return((float)output);
}
```

Listing 3.8 Header for Class Implementation of Analog All-Pole Filters

```
//
// File = polefilt.h
//
#ifndef _POLEFILT_H_
#define _POLEFILT_H_

#include "f_cmplx.h"
#include "numinteg.h"
#include "anlgfilt.h"
#include "poly.h"

class AnalogAllPoleFilt : public AnalogFilter
{
public:

  //  constructors
  AnalogAllPoleFilt( Polynomial denom_poly,
                     double h_sub_zero,
                     double delta_t);

  double Run( double input );

private:

  NumericInteg** Integrator;
  double* Y_Prime;
  int Order;
  double* B_Coef;
  double H_Sub_Zero;
};
#endif
```

Listing 3.9 Class Implementation for Analog All-Pole Filters

```
//+++++++++++++++++++++++++++++++++++++++++++++++++++++++++++++++++
//
//  File = polefilt.cpp
```

```
//
//  simulation of analog all-pole filter
//

#include <math.h>
#include "mymath.h"
#include "polefilt.h"

extern ofstream DebugFile;

//========================================================
//  constructor that actually initializes filter model
//--------------------------------------------------------

AnalogAllPoleFilt::AnalogAllPoleFilt( Polynomial denom_poly,
                                      double h_sub_zero,
                                      double delta_t)
                 : AnalogFilter()
{
 int k, order;

 order = denom_poly.GetDegree();

 Integrator = new NumericInteg*[order];
 Y_Prime = new double[order+1];
 B_Coef = new double[order];

 Order = order;
 H_Sub_Zero = h_sub_zero;

 for(k=0; k<order; k++)
   {
    Integrator[k] = new NumericInteg(delta_t);
    B_Coef[k] = -(denom_poly.GetCoefficient(k));
    DebugFile << "in AnalogAllPoleFilt, B_Coef["
              << k << "] = " << B_Coef[k] << endl;
    Y_Prime[k] = 0.0;
   }
 return;
};

//========================================================
//
double AnalogAllPoleFilt::Run( double input )
{
double sum;
int k;
```

```
sum = input;
for( k=0; k<Order; k++)
  {
   sum += (Y_Prime[k] * B_Coef[k]);
  }
Y_Prime[Order] = sum;

DebugFile << "in Run, input = "`<< input
          << "Y_Prime[" << Order << "] = "
          << sum << endl;

for( k=Order-1; k>=0; k--)
  {
   Y_Prime[k] = ((Integrator[k])->Integrate(Y_Prime[k+1]));
  }
return(H_Sub_Zero*Y_Prime[0]);
}
```

Chapter

4

Butterworth Filters

Butterworth low-pass filters (LPFs) are designed to have an amplitude response characteristic that is as flat as possible at low frequencies and that is monotonically decreasing with increasing frequency.

4.1 Transfer Function

The general expression for the transfer function of an nth-order Butterworth low-pass filter is given by

$$H(s) = \frac{1}{\prod_{i=1}^{n} (s - s_i)} = \frac{1}{(s - s_1)(s - s_2) \cdots (s - s_n)} \tag{4.1}$$

where

$$s_i = e^{j\pi[(2i + n - 1)/2n]} = \cos\left(\pi\frac{2i + n - 1}{2n}\right) + j \sin\left(\pi\frac{2i + n - 1}{2n}\right) \tag{4.2}$$

Example 4.1 Determine the transfer function for a low-pass third-order Butterworth filter.

solution The third-order transfer function will have the form

$$H(s) = \frac{1}{(s - s_1)(s - s_2)(s - s_3)}$$

The values for s_1, s_2, and s_3 are obtained from Eq. (4.2):

$$s_1 = \cos\left(\frac{2\pi}{3}\right) + j \sin\left(\frac{2\pi}{3}\right) = -0.5 + 0.866j$$

$$s_2 = e^{j\pi} = \cos(\pi) + j \sin(\pi) = -1$$

$$s_3 = \cos\left(\frac{4\pi}{3}\right) + j \sin\left(\frac{4\pi}{3}\right) = -0.5 - 0.866j$$

Thus,

$$H(s) = \frac{1}{(s + 0.5 - 0.866j)(s + 1)(s + 0.5 + 0.866j)}$$

$$= \frac{1}{s^3 + 2s^2 + 2s + 1}$$

The form of Eq. (4.1) indicates that an nth-order Butterworth filter will always have n poles and no finite zeros. Also true, but not quite so obvious, is the fact that these poles lie at equally spaced points on the left half of a circle in the s plane. As shown in Fig. 4.1 for the third-order case, any odd-order Butterworth LPF will have one real pole at $s = -1$, and all remaining poles will occur in complex conjugate pairs. As shown in Fig. 4.2 for the fourth-order case, the poles of any even-order Butterworth LPF will all occur in complex conjugate pairs. Pole values for orders 2 through 8 are listed in Table 4.1. A C++ class `ButterworthTransFunc( )` for generating Butterworth transfer functions is provided in Listing 4.1.

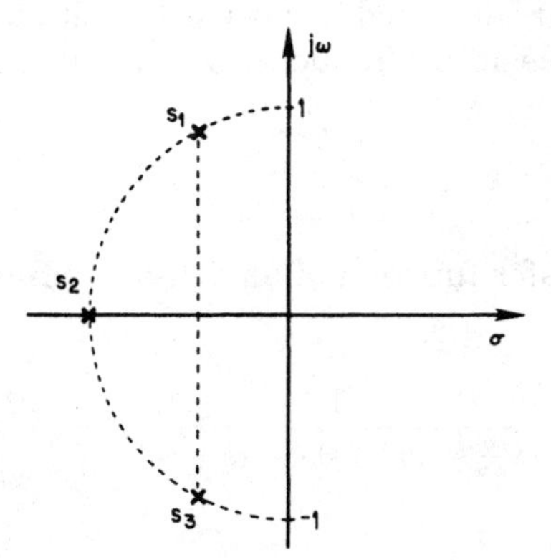

Figure 4.1 Pole locations for a third-order Butterworth LPF.

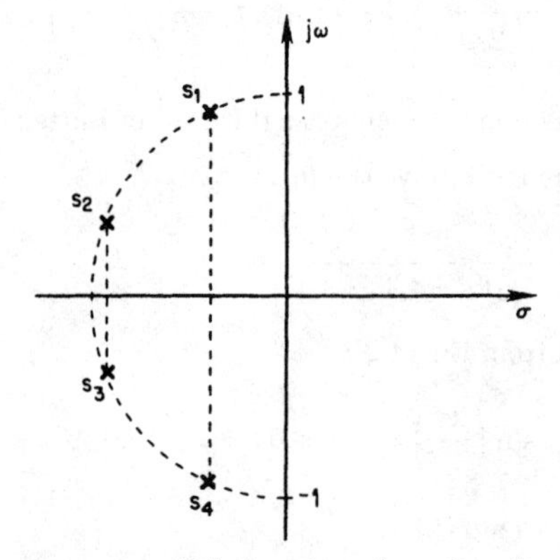

Figure 4.2 Pole locations for a fourth-order Butterworth LPF.

TABLE 4.1 Poles of Low-Pass Butterworth Filters

n	Pole values
2	$-0.707107 \pm 0.707107j$
3	-1.0 $-0.5 \pm 0.866025j$
4	$-0.382683 \pm 0.923880j$ $-0.923880 \pm 0.382683j$
5	-1.0 $-0.809017 \pm 0.587785j$ $-0.309017 \pm 0.951057j$
6	$-0.258819 \pm 0.965926j$ $-0.707107 \pm 0.707107j$ $-0.965926 \pm 0.258819j$
7	-1.0 $-0.900969 \pm 0.433884j$ $-0.623490 \pm 0.781831j$ $-0.222521 \pm 0.974928j$
8	$-0.195090 \pm 0.980785j$ $-0.555570 \pm 0.831470j$ $-0.831470 \pm 0.555570j$ $-0.980785 \pm 0.195090j$

4.2 Frequency Response

As shown in the following code fragment, frequency response data for Butterworth filters can be generated by creating an instance of `ButterworthTransFunc` and then using the function `FilterFrequencyResponse( )` belonging to the base class `FilterTransFunc` from which `ButterworthTransFunc` inherits:

```
filter_function = new ButterworthTransFunc(order);
filter_function->LowpassDenorm(passband_edge);
filter_function->FilterFrequencyResponse( );
```

Details of the `FilterFrequencyResponse( )` function are discussed in Chap. 3. Figures 4.3 through 4.5 show, respectively, the pass-band magnitude response, the stop-band magnitude response, and the phase response for Butterworth filters of various orders. These plots are normalized for a cutoff frequency of 1 Hz. To denormalize them, simply multiply the frequency axis by the desired cutoff frequency f_c.

Example 4.2 Use Figs. 4.4 and 4.5 to determine the magnitude and phase response at 800 Hz of a sixth-order Butterworth low-pass filter having a cutoff frequency of 400 Hz.

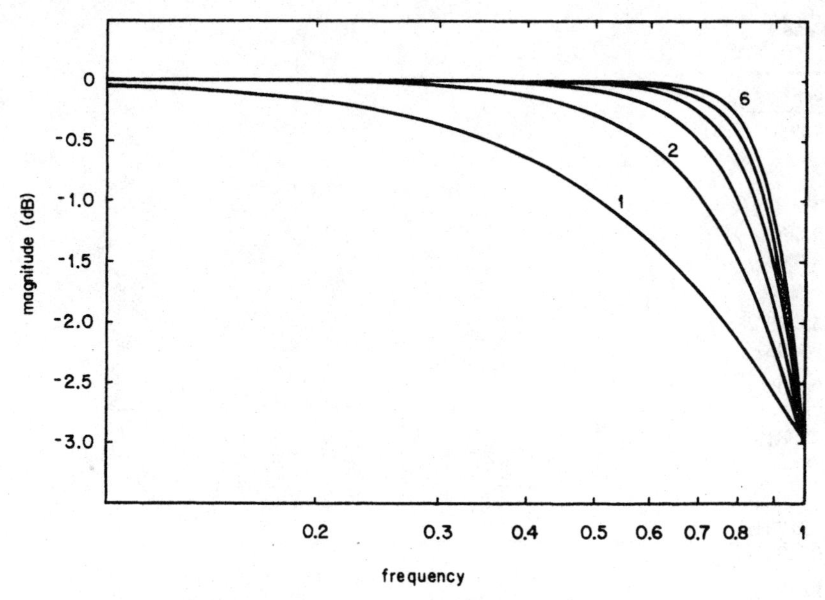

Figure 4.3 Passband amplitude response for low-pass Butterworth filters of orders 1 through 6.

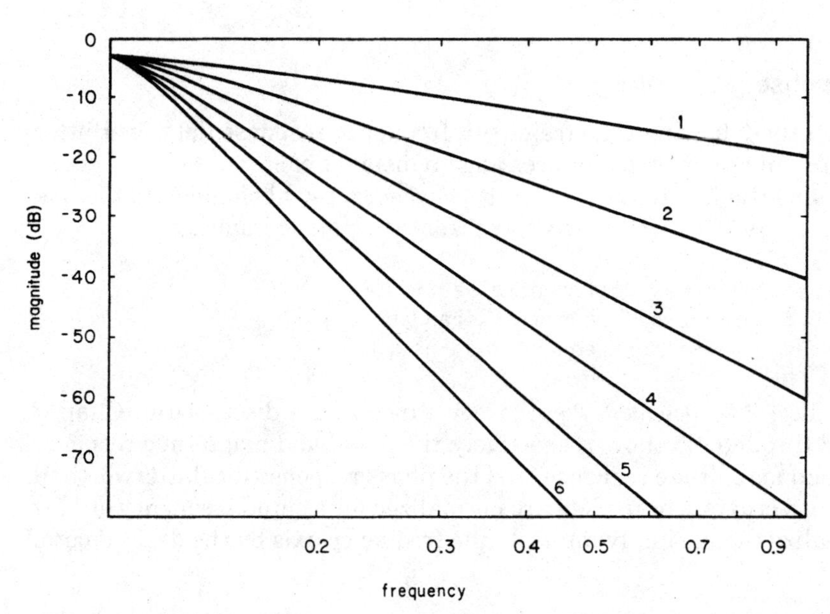

Figure 4.4 Stop-band amplitude response for low-pass Butterworth filters of orders 1 through 6.

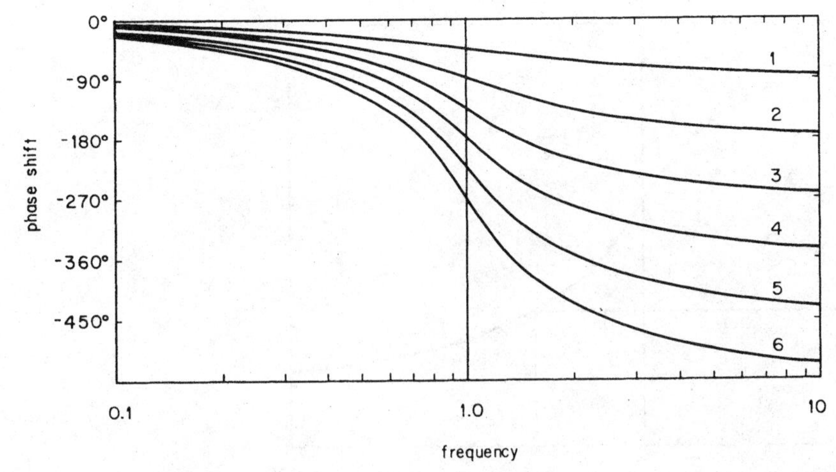

Figure 4.5 Phase response for low-pass Butterworth filters of orders 1 through 6.

solution By setting $f_c = 400$, the $n = 6$ response of Fig. 4.4 is denormalized to obtain the response shown in Fig. 4.6. This plot shows that the magnitude at 800 Hz is approximately –36 dB. The corresponding response calculated by `FilterFrequencyResponse` is –36.12466 dB. Likewise, the $n = 6$ response of Fig. 4.5 is denormalized to obtain the response shown in Fig. 4.7. This plot shows that the phase response at 800 Hz is approximately –425°. The corresponding value calculated by `FilterFrequencyResponse` is –65.475°, which "unwraps" to –425.475°.

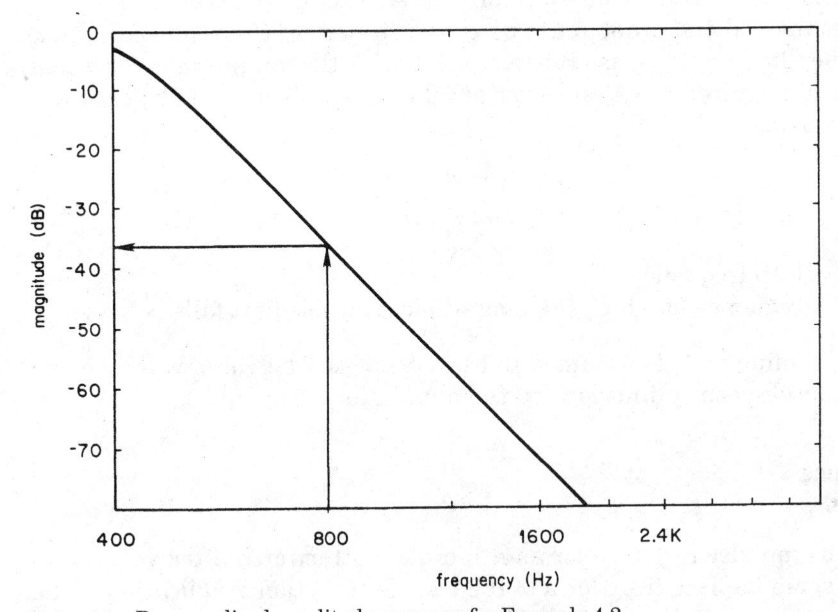

Figure 4.6 Denormalized amplitude response for Example 4.2.

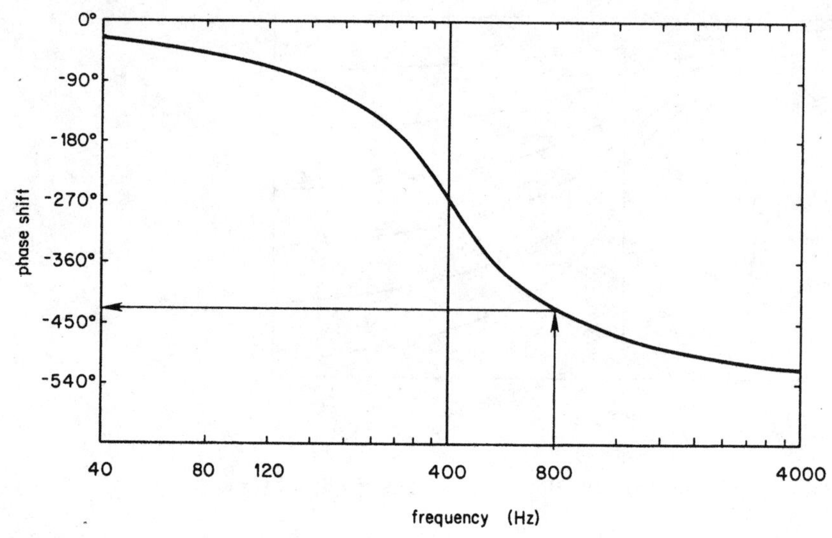

Figure 4.7 Denormalized phase response for Example 4.2.

4.3 Determination of Minimum Order for Butterworth Filters

Usually in the real world, the order of the desired filter is not given as in Example 4.2, but instead the order must be chosen based on the required performance of the filter. For low-pass Butterworth filters, the minimum order n that will ensure a magnitude of A_1 or lower at all frequencies ω_1 and above can be obtained by using

$$n = \frac{\log\left(10^{-A_1/10} - 1\right)}{2\log\left(\omega_1/\omega_c\right)} \tag{4.3}$$

where ω_c = 3-dB frequency
ω_1 = frequency at which the magnitude response first falls below A_1

(NOTE: The value of A_1 is assumed to be in decibels. The value will be negative, thus canceling the minus sign in the numerator exponent.)

4.4 Impulse Response of Butterworth Filters

To obtain the impulse response for an nth-order Butterworth filter, we need to take the inverse Laplace transform of the transfer function. Application of the Heaviside expansion to Eq. (4.1) produces

$$h(t) = \mathscr{L}^{-1}[H(s)] = \sum_{r=1}^{n} K_r\, e^{s_r t} \tag{4.4}$$

where

$$K_r = \left. \frac{(s - s_r)}{(s - s_1)(s - s_2) \cdots (s - s_n)} \right|_{s = s_r}$$

The values of both K_r and s_r are, in general, complex, but for the low-pass Butterworth case all the complex pole values occur in complex conjugate pairs. When the order n is even, this will allow Eq. (4.4) to be put in the form

$$h(t) = \sum_{r=1}^{n/2} [2\ \mathrm{Re}\ (K_r)\, e^{\sigma_r t} \cos (\omega_r t) - 2\ \mathrm{Im}\ (K_r)\, e^{\sigma_r t} \sin (\omega_r t)] \tag{4.5}$$

where $s_r = \sigma_r + j\omega_r$ and the roots s_r are numbered such that for $r = 1, 2, \ldots, n/2$ the s_r lie in the same quadrant of the s plane. [This last restriction prevents two members of the same complex conjugate pair from being used independently in evaluation of Eq. (4.5).] When the order n is odd, Eq. (4.4) can be put into the form

$$h(t) = Ke^{-t} + \sum_{r=1}^{(n-1)/2} [2\ \mathrm{Re}\ (K_r)\, e^{\sigma_r t} \cos (\omega_r t) - 2\ \mathrm{Im}\ (K_r)\, e^{\sigma_r t} \sin (\omega_r t)] \tag{4.6}$$

where no two of the roots s_r, $r = 1, 2, \ldots, (n-1)/2$ form a complex conjugate pair. Equations (4.5) and (4.6) are implemented in the `ImpulseResponse` class, which is provided in Listing 4.2. This class was used to generate the impulse responses for the low-pass Butterworth filters shown in Figs. 4.8 and 4.9. Calculation of the various K_r values in the constructor for `ImpulseResponse` has

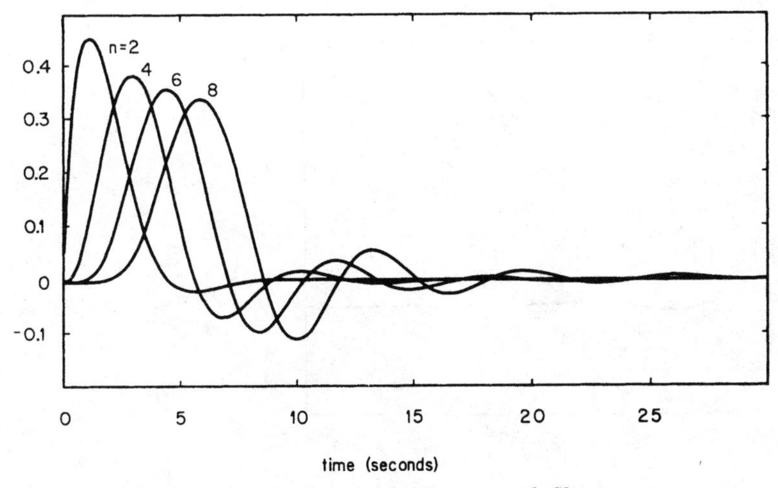

Figure 4.8 Impulse response of even-order Butterworth filters.

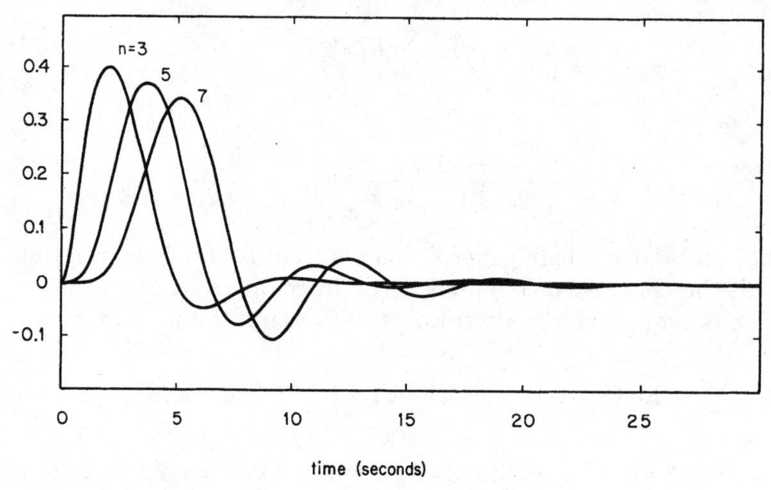

Figure 4.9 Impulse response of odd-order Butterworth filters.

been generalized to support pole-zero filters (such as elliptical filters) in addition to all-pole filters such as Butterworth. Therefore, the `ImpulseResponse` class can be used for any of the analog filter types presented in this book. These responses are normalized for low-pass filters having a cutoff frequency equal to 1 rad/s. To denormalize the response, divide the time axis by the desired cutoff frequency $\omega_c = 2\pi f_c$ and multiply the time axis by the same factor.

Example 4.3 Determine the instantaneous amplitude of the output 1.6 ms after a unit impulse is applied to the input of a fifth-order Butterworth LPF having $f_c = 250$ Hz.

solution The $n = 5$ response of Fig. 4.9 is denormalized as shown in Fig. 4.10. This plot shows that the response amplitude at $t = 1.6$ ms is approximately 378.

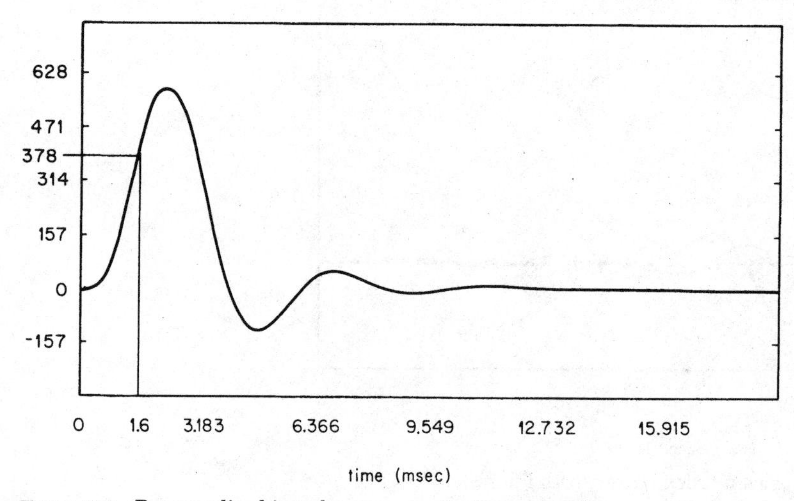

Figure 4.10 Denormalized impulse response for Example 4.3.

4.5 Step Response of Butterworth Filters

The step response can be obtained by integrating the impulse response. A C++ class `StepResponse` is provided in Listing 4.3. This class makes use of the `ImpulseResponse` class to generate samples of the impulse response, which are then integrated to produce the step response. The `StepResponse` class can be used with any of the analog filter types presented in this book. Step responses for low-pass Butterworth filters are shown in Figs. 4.11 and 4.12. These responses are normalized for low-pass filters having a cutoff frequency equal to 1 rad/s. To denormalize the response, divide the time axis by the desired cutoff frequency $\omega_c = 2\pi f_c$.

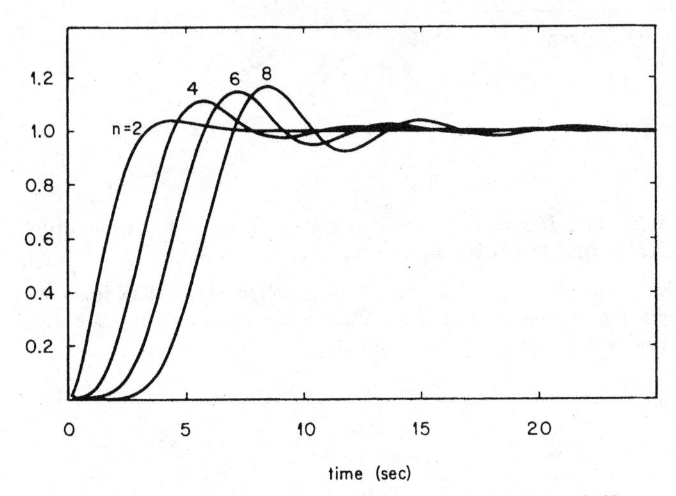

Figure 4.11 Step response of even-order low-pass Butterworth filters.

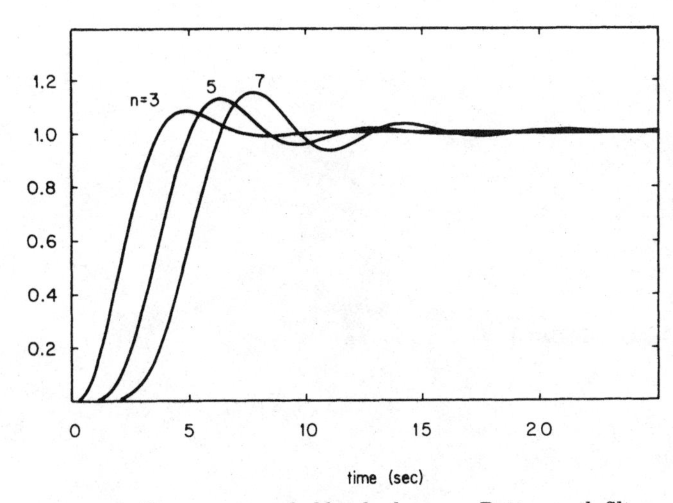

Figure 4.12 Step response of odd-order low-pass Butterworth filters.

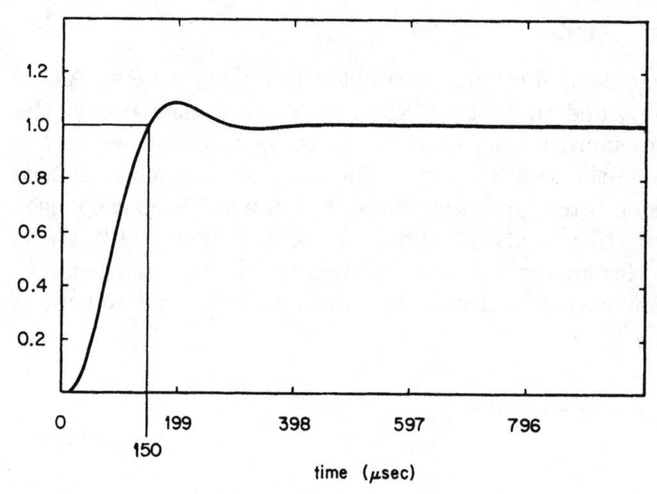

Figure 4.13 Denormalized step response for Example 4.4.

Example 4.4 Determine how long it will take for the step response of a third-order Butterworth LPF ($f_c = 4$ kHz) to first reach 100 percent of its final value.

solution By setting $\omega_c = 2\pi f_c = 8000\pi = 25{,}132.7$, the $n = 3$ response of Fig. 4.12 is denormalized to obtain the response shown in Fig. 4.13. This plot indicates that the step response first reaches a value of 1 in approximately 150 μs.

Listing 4.1 Transfer Function for Butterworth Filters

```
//+++++++++++++++++++++++++++++++++++++++++++++++++++++++++++
//
//  File = buttfunc.cpp
//
//  Butterworth Filter Response
//

#include <math.h>
#include "mymath.h"
#include "buttfunc.h"

extern ofstream DebugFile;

//==========================================================
//  constructor

ButterworthTransFunc::ButterworthTransFunc( int order )
                    :FilterTransFunc(order)
```

```
{
 double x;

 Prototype_Pole_Locs = new double_complex[order+1];
 Num_Prototype_Poles = order;
 Prototype_Zero_Locs = new double_complex[1];
 Num_Prototype_Zeros = 0;

 H_Sub_Zero = 1.0;

 for(int k=1; k<=order; k++)
   {
    x = PI * (order + (2*k)-1) / (2*order);
    Prototype_Pole_Locs[k] = double_complex( cos(x), sin(x) );
    DebugFile << "pole[" << k << "] = "
              << Prototype_Pole_Locs[k] << endl;
   }
 return;
};
```

Listing 4.2 Impulse Response for Analog Filters

```
//++++++++++++++++++++++++++++++++++++++++++++++++++++++++++++++++++++
//
//  File = impresp.cpp
//
//

#include <math.h>
#include <stdlib.h>
#include "mymath.h"
#include "impresp.h"
#include "d_cmplx.h"

extern ofstream DebugFile;

//==========================================================
//  constructors

ImpulseResponse::ImpulseResponse( FilterTransFunc *trans_func,
                                  int num_resp_pts,
                                  double delta_time)
 {
  double_complex k_sub_r_denom, k_sub_r_numer, s_sub_r;
  int r, n;
```

```
  Delta_Time = delta_time;
  Num_Resp_Pts = num_resp_pts;
  Trans_Func = trans_func;

  H_Sub_Zero = Trans_Func->GetHSubZero();
  Num_Poles = Trans_Func->GetNumPoles();
  Num_Zeros = Trans_Func->GetNumZeros();
  R_Max = (Num_Poles+1)>>1;
  Order_Is_Odd = Num_Poles%2;

  K_Sub_R = new double_complex[R_Max + 1];
  Sigma = new double[R_Max + 1];
  Omega = new double[R_Max + 1];

  //-----------------------------------
  //  compute Kr coefficients

  for(r=1; r<=R_Max; r++)
    {
    k_sub_r_denom = double_complex(1.0, 0.0);
    k_sub_r_numer = double_complex(1.0, 0.0);
    s_sub_r = Trans_Func->GetPole(r);
    Sigma[r] = real(s_sub_r);
    Omega[r] = imag(s_sub_r);
    for(n=1; n<=Num_Poles; n++)
      {
      if(n==r) continue;
        k_sub_r_denom *= (s_sub_r - (Trans_Func->GetPole(n)));
      }
    for(n=1; n<=Num_Zeros; n++)
      {
      k_sub_r_numer *= (s_sub_r - (Trans_Func->GetZero(n)));
      }
    K_Sub_R[r] = k_sub_r_numer/k_sub_r_denom;
    }

  return;
};

//=========================================================
void ImpulseResponse::GenerateResponse( void )
  {
  int resp_indx;
  double h_of_t, time, delta_t;

  Response_File = new ofstream("imp_anal.txt", ios::out);
```

```
  //-----------------------------------------------
  // compute samples of impulse response

  delta_t = Delta_Time;
  for(resp_indx=0; resp_indx<Num_Resp_Pts; resp_indx++)
    {
    time = delta_t * resp_indx;
    h_of_t = ComputeSample(time);
    (*Response_File) << time << ",  " << h_of_t << endl;
    }
  Response_File->close();
  return;
}

//=============================================================
double ImpulseResponse::ComputeSample( double time )
  {
  int r;
  double cos_part, sin_part;
  double h_of_t;

  h_of_t = 0.0;

  for(r=1; r<=(Num_Poles>>1); r++)
    {
    cos_part = 2 * real(K_Sub_R[r]) *
                exp(Sigma[r] * time) *
                cos(Omega[r] * time);
    sin_part = 2 * imag(K_Sub_R[r]) *
                exp(Sigma[r] * time) *
                sin(Omega[r] * time);
    h_of_t += (cos_part - sin_part);
    }
  //-----------------------------------------------
  //  add the real exponential component
  //  present in odd-order responses

  if(Order_Is_Odd == 1)
    {
    h_of_t += ( real(K_Sub_R[R_Max]) *
                  exp(Sigma[R_Max] * time) );
    }
  h_of_t *= H_Sub_Zero;

  return(h_of_t);
}
```

Listing 4.3 Step Response for Analog Filters

```
//+++++++++++++++++++++++++++++++++++++++++++++++++++++++++++++++++++++
//
//  File = stepresp.cpp
//
//

#include <math.h>
#include <stdlib.h>
#include "mymath.h"
#include "stepresp.h"
#include "d_cmplx.h"

extern ofstream DebugFile;

//=============================================================
//  constructors

StepResponse::StepResponse( FilterTransFunc *trans_func,
                            int num_resp_pts,
                            double delta_time)
{
  Delta_Time = delta_time;
  Num_Resp_Pts = num_resp_pts;
  Imp_Resp = new ImpulseResponse( trans_func,
                                  num_resp_pts,
                                  delta_time);

  return;
};

//=============================================================
void StepResponse::GenerateResponse( void )
  {
  int resp_indx;
  double h_of_t, time, delta_t;
  double u_of_t;

  Response_File = new ofstream("stp_anal.txt", ios::out);

  //--------------------------------------------
  // compute samples of impulse response

  delta_t = Delta_Time;
```

```
  for(resp_indx=0; resp_indx<Num_Resp_Pts; resp_indx++)
    {
    time = delta_t * resp_indx;
    h_of_t = Imp_Resp->ComputeSample(time);
    u_of_t += (delta_t * h_of_t);
    (*Response_File) << time << ",  " << u_of_t << endl;
    }
  Response_File->close();
  return;
}
```

Chapter

5

Chebyshev Filters

Chebyshev filters are designed to have an amplitude response characteristic that has a relatively sharp transition from the pass band to the stop band. This sharpness is accomplished at the expense of ripples that are introduced into the response. Specifically, Chebyshev filters are obtained as an equiripple approximation to the pass band of an ideal low-pass filter. This results in a filter characteristic for which

$$|H(j\omega)|^2 = \frac{1}{1 + \epsilon^2 T_n^2(\omega)} \tag{5.1}$$

where $\epsilon^2 = 10^{r/10} - 1$

$T_n(\omega)$ = Chebyshev polynomial of order n

r = passband ripple, dB

Chebyshev polynomials are listed in Table 5.1.

5.1 Transfer Function

The general shape of the Chebyshev magnitude response will be as shown in Fig. 5.1. This response can be normalized as in Fig. 5.2 so that the ripple bandwidth ω_r is equal to 1, or the response can be normalized as in Fig. 5.3 so that the 3-dB frequency ω_0 is equal to 1. Normalization based on the ripple bandwidth involves simpler calculations, but normalization based on the 3-dB point makes it easier to compare Chebyshev responses to those of other filter types.

The general expression for the transfer function of an nth-order Chebyshev low-pass filter is given by

$$H(s) = \frac{H_0}{\prod_{i=1}^{n} (s - s_i)} = \frac{H_0}{(s - s_1)(s - s_2) \cdots (s - s_n)} \tag{5.2}$$

TABLE 5.1 Chebyshev Polynomials

n	$T_n(\omega)$
0	1
1	ω
2	$2\omega^2 - 1$
3	$4\omega^3 - 3\omega$
4	$8\omega^4 - 8\omega^2 + 1$
5	$16\omega^5 - 20\omega^3 + 5\omega$
6	$32\omega^6 - 48\omega^4 + 18\omega^2 - 1$
7	$64\omega^7 - 112\omega^5 + 56\omega^3 - 7\omega$
8	$128\omega^8 - 256\omega^6 + 160\omega^4 - 32\omega^2 + 1$
9	$256\omega^9 - 576\omega^7 + 432\omega^5 - 120\omega^3 + 9\omega$
10	$512\omega^{10} - 1280\omega^8 + 1120\omega^6 - 400\omega^4 + 50\omega^2 + 1$

$$\text{where}\quad H_0 = \begin{cases} \displaystyle\prod_{i=1}^{n} (-s_i) & n \text{ odd} \\ \displaystyle 10^{r/20} \prod_{i=1}^{n} (-s_i) & n \text{ even} \end{cases} \tag{5.3}$$

$$s_i = \sigma_i + j\omega_i \tag{5.4}$$

$$\sigma_i = \left[\frac{(1/\gamma) - \gamma}{2}\right] \sin \frac{(2i-1)\pi}{2n} \tag{5.5}$$

$$\omega_i = \left[\frac{(1/\gamma) + \gamma}{2}\right] \cos \frac{(2i-1)\pi}{2n} \tag{5.6}$$

$$\gamma = \left(\frac{1 + \sqrt{1 + \epsilon^2}}{\epsilon}\right)^{1/n} \tag{5.7}$$

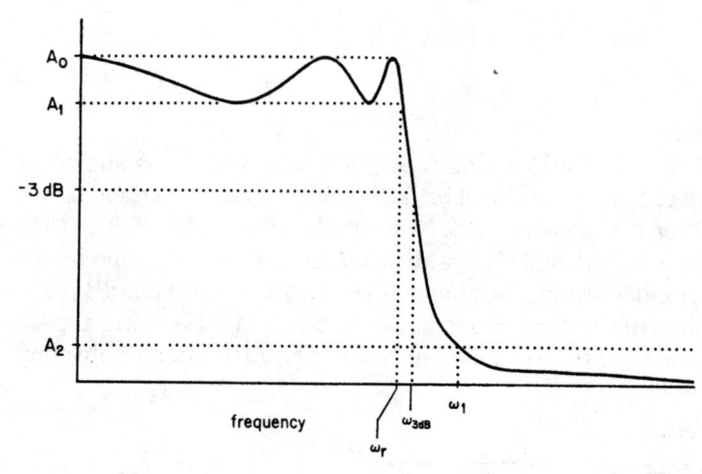

Figure 5.1 Magnitude response of a typical low-pass Chebyshev filter.

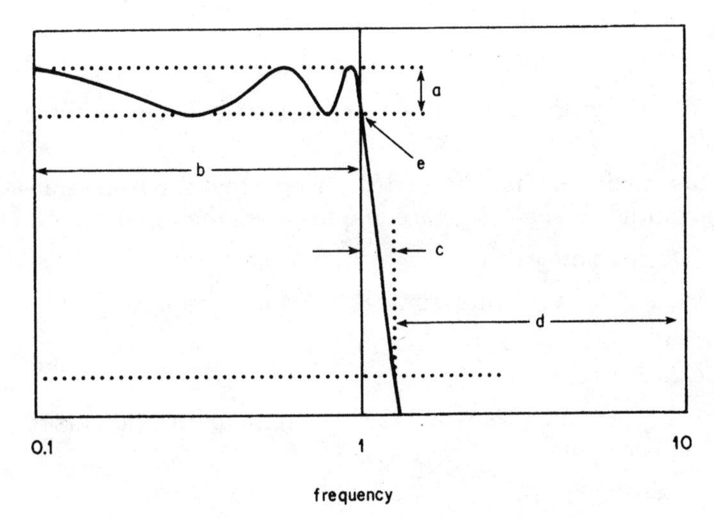

Figure 5.2 Chebyshev response normalized to have passband end at $\omega = 1$ rad/s. Features are: (a) ripple limits, (b) pass band, (c) transition band, (d) stop band, and (e) intersection of response and lower ripple limit at $\omega = 1$.

$$\epsilon = \sqrt{10^{r/10} - 1} \tag{5.8}$$

The pole formulas are somewhat more complicated than for the Butterworth filter examined in Chap. 4, and several parameters—ϵ, γ, and r—must be determined before the pole values can be calculated. Also, all the poles are involved in the calculation of the numerator H_0.

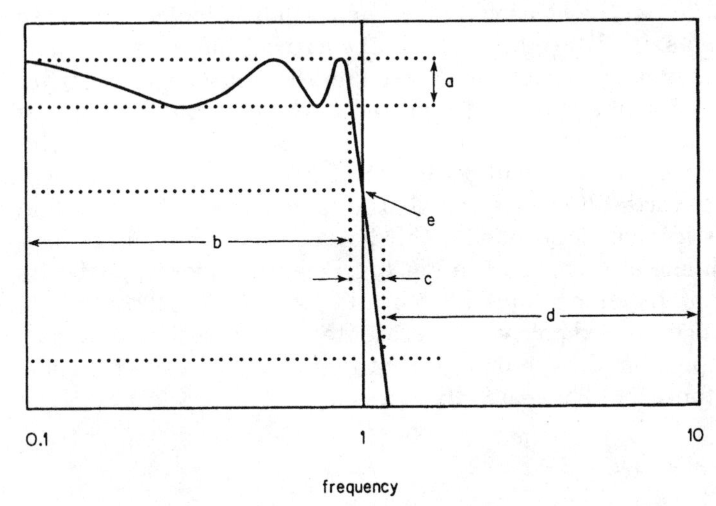

Figure 5.3 Chebyshev response normalized to have 3-dB point at $\hat{\omega} = 1$ rad/s. Features are: (a) ripple limits, (b) pass band, (c) transition band, (d) stop band, and (e) response that is 3 dB down at $\omega = 1$.

Algorithm 5.1 Determining poles of a Chebyshev filter

This algorithm computes the poles of an nth-order Chebyshev low-pass filter normalized for a ripple bandwidth of 1 Hz.

Step 1. Determine the maximum amount (in dB) of ripple that can be permitted in the passband magnitude response. Set r equal to or less than this value.

Step 2. Use Eq. (5.8) to compute ϵ.

Step 3. Select an order n for the filter that will ensure adequate performance.

Step 4. Use Eq. (5.7) to compute γ.

Step 5. For $i = 1, 2, \ldots, n$, use Eqs. (5.5) and (5.6) to compute the real part σ_i and imaginary part ω_i of each pole.

Step 6. Use Eq. (5.3) to compute H_0.

Step 7. Substitute the values of H_0 and s_1 through s_n into Eq. (5.2).

Example 5.1 Use Algorithm 5.1 to determine the transfer-function numerator and poles (normalized for ripple bandwidth equal to 1) for a third-order Chebyshev filter with 0.5-dB passband ripple.

solution Algorithm 5.1 produces the following results:

$$\epsilon = 0.349311 \qquad \gamma = 1.806477 \qquad s_1 = -0.313228 + 1.021928j$$

$$s_2 = -0.626457 \qquad s_3 = -0.313228 - 1.021928j \qquad H_0 = 0.715695$$

The form of Eq. (5.2) shows that an nth-order Chebyshev filter will always have n poles and no finite zeros. The poles will all lie on the left half of an ellipse in the s plane. The major axis of the ellipse lies on the $j\omega$ axis, and the minor axis lies on the σ axis. The dimensions of the ellipse and the locations of the poles will depend upon the amount of ripple permitted in the pass band. Values of passband ripple typically range from 0.1 to 1 dB. The smaller the passband ripple, the wider the transition band will be. In fact, for 0-dB ripple, the Chebyshev filter and Butterworth filter have exactly the same transfer-function and response characteristics. Pole locations for third-order Chebyshev filters having different ripple limits are compared in Fig. 5.4. Pole values for ripple limits of 0.1, 0.5, and 1 dB are listed in Tables 5.2, 5.3, and 5.4 for orders 2 through 8.

All the transfer functions and pole values presented so far are for filters normalized to have a ripple bandwidth of 1. Algorithm 5.2 can be used to renormalize the transfer function to have a 3-dB frequency of 1.

Algorithm 5.2 Renormalizing Chebyshev LPF transfer functions

This algorithm assumes that ϵ, H_0, and the pole values s_i have been obtained for the transfer function having a ripple bandwidth of 1.

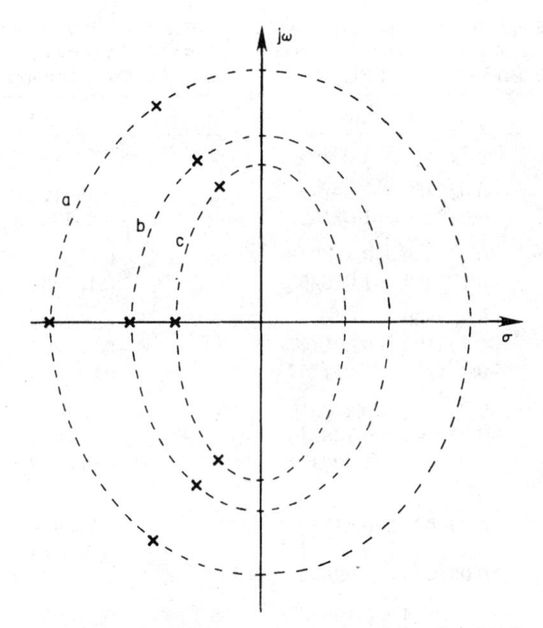

Figure 5.4 Comparison of pole locations for third-order low-pass Chebyshev filters with different amounts of passband ripple: (*a*) 0.01 dB, (*b*) 0.1 dB, and (*c*) 0.5 dB.

Step 1. Compute A using

$$A = \frac{\cosh^{-1}[(1/\epsilon)]}{n} = \frac{1}{n}\ln\left(\frac{1+\sqrt{1-\epsilon^2}}{\epsilon}\right)$$

Step 2. Using the value of A obtained in Step 1, compute R as

$$R = \cosh A = \frac{e^{A}+e^{-A}}{2}$$

(Table 5.5 lists R factors for various orders and ripple limits. If the required combination can be found in this table, Steps 1 and 2 can be skipped.)

Step 3. Use R to compute $H_{3\text{ dB}}(s)$ as

$$H_{3\text{ dB}}(s) = \frac{H_0/R^n}{\prod_{i=1}^{n}[s-(s_i/R)]}$$

A C++ class `ChebyshevTransFunc( )`, for generating Chebyshev transfer functions, is provided in Listing 5.1. This class inherits from the base class `FilterTransFunc` which, as dicussed in Chap. 3, provides several functions which are common to the transfer functions of all filter types.

TABLE 5.2 Pole Values for Low-Pass Chebyshev Filters with 0.1-dB Passband Ripple

n	Pole values
2	$-1.186178 \pm 1.380948j$
3	-0.969406 $-0.484703 \pm 1.206155j$
4	$-0.637730 \pm 0.465000j$ $-0.264156 \pm 1.122610j$
5	-0.538914 $-0.435991 \pm 0.667707j$ $-0.166534 \pm 1.080372j$
6	$-0.428041 \pm 0.283093j$ $-0.313348 \pm 0.773426j$ $-0.114693 \pm 1.056519j$
7	-0.376778 $-0.339465 \pm 0.463659j$ $-0.234917 \pm 0.835485j$ $-0.083841 \pm 1.041833j$
8	$-0.321650 \pm 0.205314j$ $-0.272682 \pm 0.584684j$ $-0.182200 \pm 0.875041j$ $-0.063980 \pm 1.032181j$

TABLE 5.3 Pole Values for Low-Pass Chebyshev Filters with 0.5-dB Passband Ripple

n	Pole values
2	$-0.712812 \pm 1.00402j$
3	-0.626457 $-0.313228 \pm 1.021928j$
4	$-0.423340 \pm 0.420946j$ $-0.175353 \pm 1.016253j$
5	-0.362320 $-0.293123 \pm 0.625177j$ $-0.111963 \pm 1.011557j$
6	$-0.289794 \pm 0.270216j$ $-0.212144 \pm 0.738245j$ $-0.077650 \pm 1.008461j$
7	-0.256170 $-0.230801 \pm 0.447894j$ $-0.159719 \pm 0.807077j$ $-0.057003 \pm 1.006409j$
8	$-0.219293 \pm 0.199907j$ $-0.185908 \pm 0.569288j$ $-0.124219 \pm 0.852000j$ $-0.043620 \pm 1.005002j$

TABLE 5.4 Pole Values for Low-Pass Chebyshev Filters with 1.0-dB Passband Ripple

n	Pole values
2	$-0.548867 \pm 0.895129j$
3	-0.494171 $-0.247085 \pm 0.965999j$
4	$-0.336870 \pm 0.407329j$ $-0.139536 \pm 0.983379j$
5	-0.289493 $-0.234205 \pm 0.611920j$ $-0.089458 \pm 0.990107j$
6	$-0.232063 \pm 0.266184j$ $-0.169882 \pm 0.727227j$ $-0.062181 \pm 0.993411j$
7	-0.205414 $-0.185072 \pm 0.442943j$ $-0.128074 \pm 0.798156j$ $-0.045709 \pm 0.995284j$
8	$-0.175998 \pm 0.198206j$ $-0.149204 \pm 0.564444j$ $-0.099695 \pm 0.844751j$ $-0.035008 \pm 0.996451j$

5.2 Frequency Response

As shown in the following code fragment, frequency response data for Chebyshev filters can be generated by creating an instance of `ChebyshevTransFunc` and then using the function `FilterFrequencyResponse( )` belonging to the base class `FilterTransFunc` from which `ChebyshevTransFunc` inherits:

```
filter_function = new ChebyshevTransFunc( order,
                                          passband_ripple,
                                          ripple_bw_norm);
filter_function->LowpassDenorm(passband_edge);
filter_function->FilterFrequencyResponse();
```

The variable `ripple_bw_norm` is set to 1 if the transfer function is to be normalized based upon its ripple bandwidth. Otherwise, the filter will be normalized based upon a 3-dB bandwidth. Details of the `FilterFrequencyResponse( )` function were discussed in Chap. 3.

TABLE 5.5 Factors for Renormalizing Chebyshev Transfer Functions

	Order						
Ripple	2	3	4	5	6	7	8
0.1	1.94322	1.38899	1.21310	1.13472	1.09293	1.06800	1.05193
0.2	1.67427	1.28346	1.15635	1.09915	1.06852	1.05019	1.03835
0.3	1.53936	1.22906	1.12680	1.08055	1.05571	1.04083	1.03121
0.4	1.45249	1.19348	1.10736	1.06828	1.04725	1.03464	1.02649
0.5	1.38974	1.16749	1.09310	1.05926	1.04103	1.03009	1.02301
0.6	1.34127	1.14724	1.08196	1.05220	1.03616	1.02652	1.02028
0.7	1.30214	1.13078	1.07288	1.04644	1.03218	1.02361	1.01806
0.8	1.26955	1.11699	1.06526	1.04160	1.02883	1.02116	1.01618
0.9	1.24176	1.10517	1.05872	1.03745	1.02596	1.01905	1.01457
1.0	1.21763	1.09487	1.05300	1.03381	1.02344	1.01721	1.01316
1.1	1.19637	1.08576	1.04794	1.03060	1.02121	1.01557	1.01191
1.2	1.17741	1.07761	1.04341	1.02771	1.01922	1.01411	1.01079
1.3	1.16035	1.07025	1.03931	1.02510	1.01741	1.01278	1.00978
1.4	1.14486	1.06355	1.03558	1.02272	1.01576	1.01157	1.00886
1.5	1.13069	1.05740	1.03216	1.02054	1.01425	1.01046	1.00801

Figures 5.5 through 5.8 show the magnitude and phase responses for Chebyshev filters with passband ripple limits of 0.5 dB. For comparison purposes, Figs. 5.9 and 5.10 show Chebyshev passband responses for ripple limits of 0.1 and 1.0 dB. These plots are normalized for a cutoff frequency of 1 Hz. To denormalize them, simply multiply the frequency axis by the desired cutoff frequency f_c.

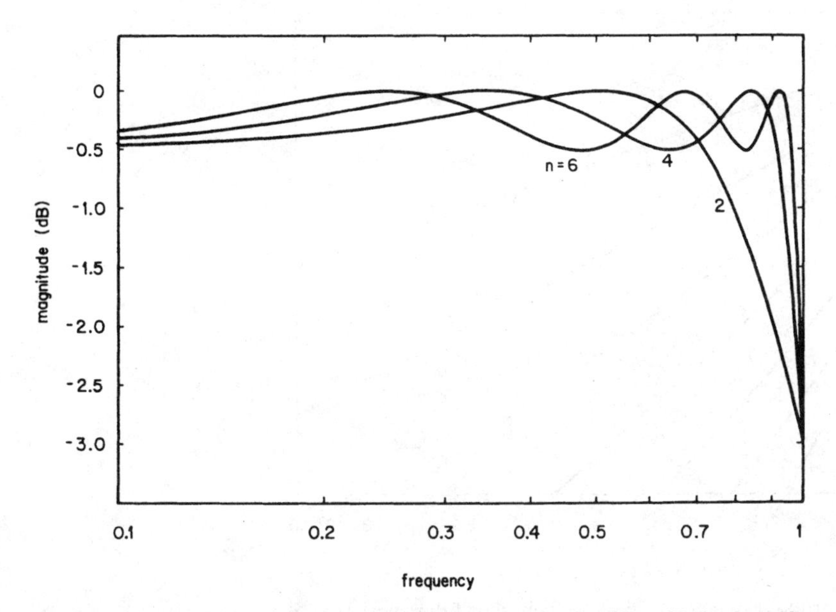

Figure 5.5 Passband magnitude response of even-order low-pass Chebyshev filters with 0.5-dB ripple.

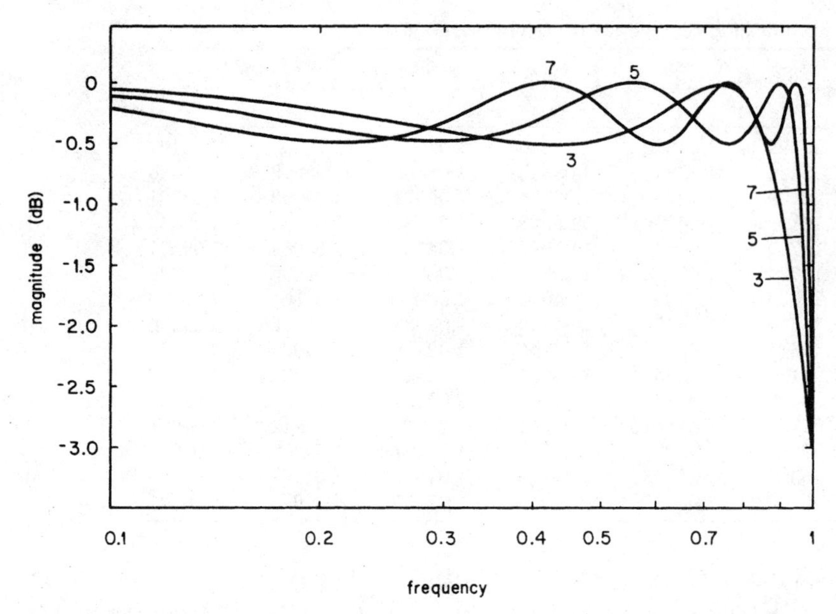

Figure 5.6 Passband magnitude response of odd-order low-pass Chebyshev filters with 0.5-dB ripple.

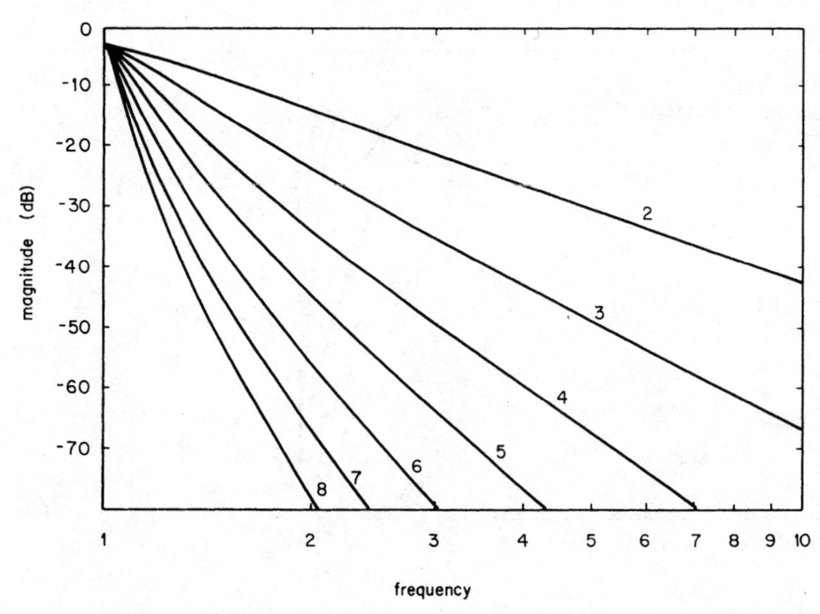

Figure 5.7 Stop-band magnitude response of low-pass Chebyshev filters with 0.5-dB ripple.

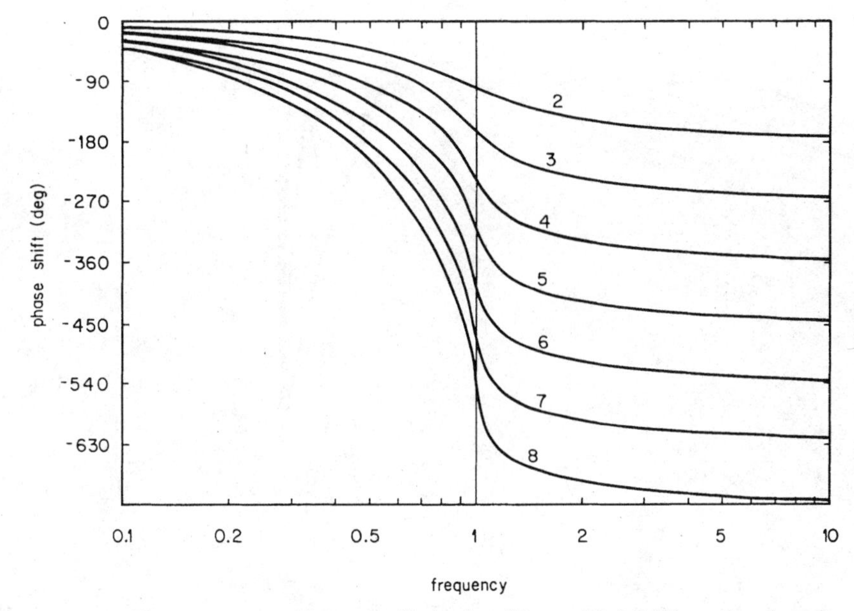

Figure 5.8 Phase response of low-pass Chebyshev filters with 0.5-dB passband ripple.

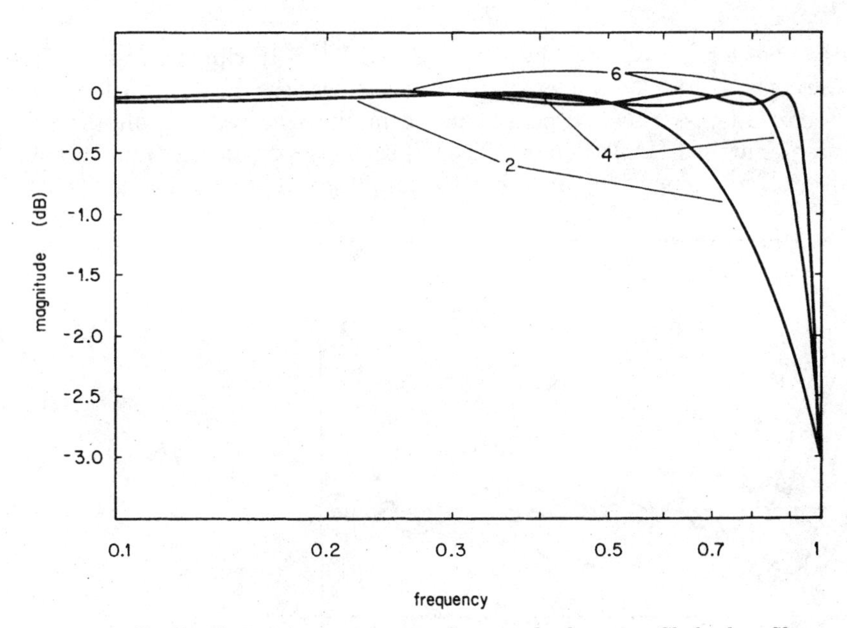

Figure 5.9 Passband magnitude response of even-order low-pass Chebyshev filters with 0.1-dB ripple.

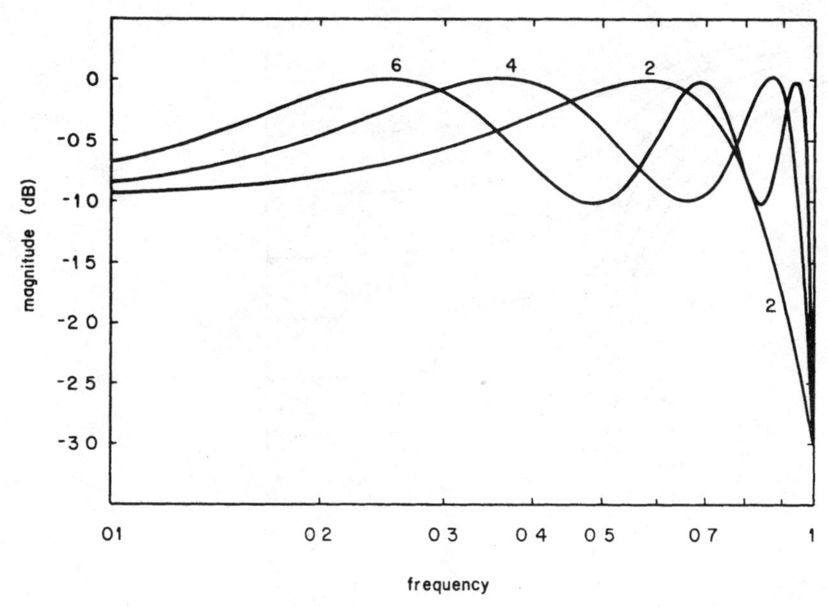

Figure 5.10 Pass-band magnitude response of even-order low-pass Chebyshev filters with 1.0-dB ripple.

5.3 Impulse Response

Impulse responses for low-pass Chebyshev filters with 0.5-dB ripple are shown in Fig. 5.11. The class `ImpulseResponse( )`, used to generate the data for these plots, was discussed in Chap. 4. These responses are normalized for low-pass filters having a 3-dB frequency of 1 Hz. To denormalize the response, divide the time axis by the desired cutoff frequency f_c and multiply the amplitude axis by the same factor.

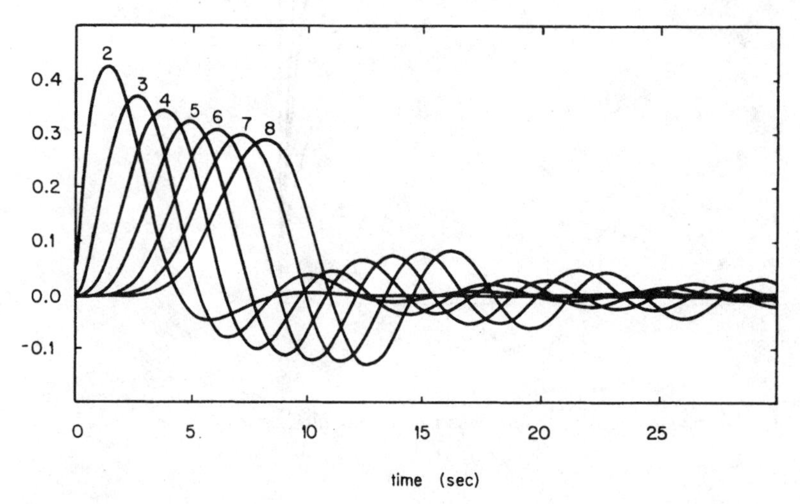

Figure 5.11 Impulse response of low-pass Chebyshev filters with 0.5-dB passband ripple.

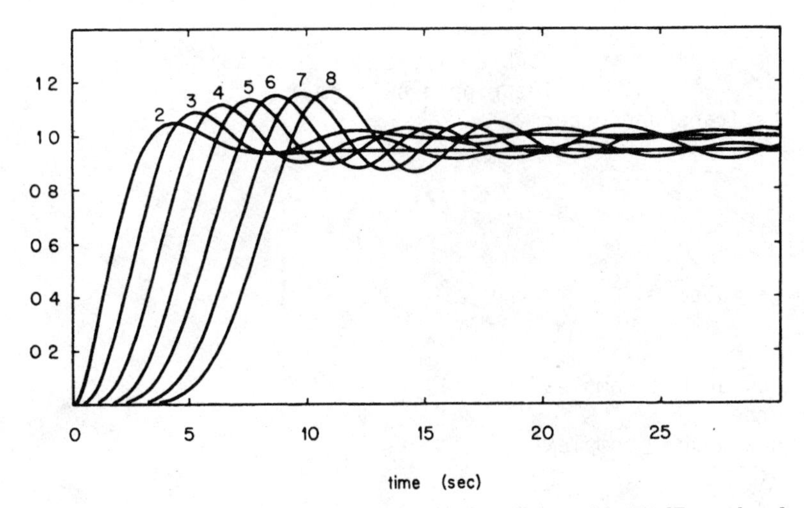

Figure 5.12 Step response of low-pass Chebyshev filters with 0.5-dB passband ripple.

5.4 Step Response

The step response can be obtained by integrating the impulse response. Step responses for low-pass Chebyshev filters with 0.5-dB ripple are shown in Fig. 5.12. These responses are normalized for low-pass filters having a cutoff frequency equal to 1 Hz. To denormalize the response, divide the time axis by the desired cutoff frequency f_c.

Listing 5.1 Transfer Function for Chebyshev Filters

```
//+++++++++++++++++++++++++++++++++++++++++++++++++++++++++++++++++++
//
//  File = chebfunc.cpp
//
//  Chebyshev Filter Function
//

#include <math.h>
#include "mymath.h"
#include "chebfunc.h"
#include "f_cmplx.h"
#include "d_cmplx.h"

//=======================================================
//  constructor
```

```
ChebyshevTransFunc::ChebyshevTransFunc( int order,
                                          double ripple,
                                          int ripple_bw_norm )
                   :FilterTransFunc(order)
{
 double x;
 int k;
 double epsilon, gamma;
 double big_r, big_a;
 double sigma_mult, omega_mult;
 double_complex work;

 Prototype_Pole_Locs = new double_complex[order+1];
 Num_Prototype_Poles = order;
 Prototype_Zero_Locs = new double_complex[1];
 Num_Prototype_Zeros = 0;

 epsilon = sqrt(pow(10.0, (double) (ripple/10.0)) -1.0);
 gamma = pow( (1+sqrt(1.0 + epsilon*epsilon))/epsilon,
              1.0/(double)order);
 if(ripple_bw_norm)
   {
    big_r = 1.0;
   }
 else
   {
    big_a = log((1.0+sqrt(1.0-epsilon*epsilon))/epsilon)/order;
    big_r = (exp(big_a)+exp(-big_a))/2.0;
    cout << "big_r = " << big_r << endl;
   }

 sigma_mult = ( (1.0/gamma) - gamma) / (2.0 * big_r);

 omega_mult = ( (1.0/gamma) + gamma) / (2.0 * big_r);

 for(k=1; k<=order; k++)
   {
    x = PI * ((2*k)-1) / (2*order);

    Prototype_Pole_Locs[k] = double_complex( sigma_mult * sin(x),
                                             omega_mult * cos(x) );
   }
 //---------------------------------------------
 //  compute gain factor Ho

 work = double_complex(1.0, 0.0);
 for(k=1; k<=order; k++)
```

```
   {
    work *= (-Prototype_Pole_Locs[k]);
   }

 H_Sub_Zero = real(work);

 if(order%2 == 0)  // if order is even
   {
    H_Sub_Zero /= sqrt(1.0 + epsilon*epsilon);
   }

 return;
};
```

Chapter

6

Elliptical Filters

By allowing ripples in the pass band, Chebyshev filters obtain better selectivity than Butterworth filters do. Elliptical filters improve upon the performance of Chebyshev filters by permitting ripples in *both* the pass band and stop band. The response of an elliptical filter satisfies

$$|H(j\omega)|^2 = \frac{1}{1 + \epsilon^2 R_n^2(\omega, L)}$$

where $R_n(\omega, L)$ is an nth-order *Chebyshev rational function* with ripple parameter L. Elliptical filters are sometimes called *Cauer filters.*

6.1 Parameter Specification

As shown in Chap. 4, determination of the (amplitude-normalized) transfer function for a Butterworth low-pass filter requires specification of just two parameters—cutoff frequency ω_c and filter order n. Determination of the transfer function for a Chebyshev filter requires specification of these two parameters plus a third—passband ripple (or stop-band ripple for inverse Chebyshev). Determination of the transfer function for an elliptical filter requires specification of the filter order n plus the following four parameters, which are depicted in Fig. 6.1:

A_p = maximum passband loss, dB

A_s = minimum stop-band loss, dB

ω_p = passband cutoff frequency

ω_s = stop-band cutoff frequency

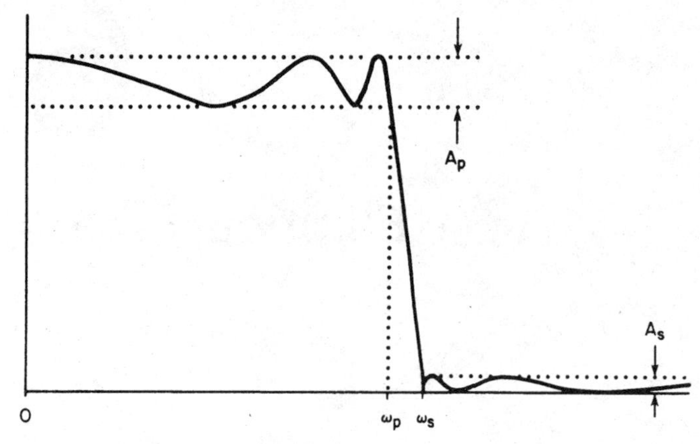

Figure 6.1 Frequency response showing parameters used to specify an elliptical filter.

The design procedures presented in this chapter assume that the maximum passband amplitude is unity. Therefore, A_p is the size of the passband ripples, and A_s is the size of the stop-band ripples. Any four of the five filter parameters can be specified independently, with the fifth then being fixed by the nature of the elliptical filter's response. The usual design strategy involves specifying A_p, A_s, ω_p, and ω_s based upon requirements of the intended application. Algorithm 6.1, as follows, can then be used to compute the minimum value of n for which an elliptical filter can yield the desired performance. Since n must be an integer, not all combinations of A_p, A_s, ω_p, and ω_s can be realized exactly. The design procedure presented in this chapter can yield a filter that meets the specified A_p, A_s, and ω_p and that meets *or exceeds* the specification on A_s.

Algorithm 6.1 Determining the required order for elliptical filters

Step 1. Based upon requirements of the intended application, determine the maximum stop-band loss A_p and minimum stop-band loss A_s in decibels.

Step 2. Based on requirements of the intended application, determine the passband cutoff frequency ω_p and stop-band cutoff frequency ω_s.

Step 3. Using ω_p and ω_s, compute *selectivity factor* k as $k = \omega_p/\omega_s$.

Step 4. Using the selectivity factor computed in Step 3, compute the *modular constant* q using

$$q = u + 2u^5 + 15u^9 + 150u^{13} \tag{6.1}$$

where

$$u = \frac{1 - \sqrt[4]{1 - k^2}}{2(1 + \sqrt[4]{1 - k^2})} \tag{6.2}$$

Step 5. Using the values of A_p and A_s, determined in Step 1, compute the *discrimination factor D* as

$$D = \frac{10^{A_s/10} - 1}{10^{A_p/10} - 1} \tag{6.3}$$

Step 6. Using the value of D from Step 5 and the value of q from Step 4, compute the minimum required order n as

$$n = \left\lceil \frac{\log 16D}{\log (1/q)} \right\rceil \tag{6.4}$$

where $\lceil x \rceil$ denotes the smallest integer equal to or greater than x.

The actual minimum stop-band loss provided by any given combination of A_p, ω_p, ω_s, and n is given by

$$A_s = 10 \log \left(1 + \frac{10^{A_p/10} - 1}{16q^n} \right) \tag{6.5}$$

where q is the modular constant given by Eq. (6.1).

Example 6.1 Use Algorithm 6.1 to determine the minimum order for an elliptical filter for which $A_p = 1$, $A_s \geq 50.0$, $\omega_p = 3000.0$, and $\omega_s = 3200.0$.

solution

$$k = \frac{3000}{3200} = 0.9375$$

$$u = 0.12897$$

$$q = 0.12904$$

$$D = \frac{10^5 - 1}{10^{0.01} - 1} = 4{,}293{,}093.82$$

$$n = \lceil 8.81267 \rceil = 9$$

6.2 Normalized-Transfer Function

The design of elliptical filters is greatly simplified by designing a frequency-normalized filter having the appropriate response characteristics, and then frequency-scaling this design to the desired operating frequency. The simplification comes about because of the particular type of normalizing that is performed. Instead of normalizing so that either a 3-dB bandwidth or the ripple bandwidth equals unity, an elliptical filter is normalized so that

$$\sqrt{\omega_{pN}\omega_{sN}} = 1 \tag{6.6}$$

where ω_{pN} and ω_{sN} are, respectively, the normalized passband cutoff frequency and the normalized stop-band cutoff frequency. If we let α represent the frequency-scaling factor such that

$$\omega_{pN} = \frac{\omega_p}{\alpha} \qquad \omega_{sN} = \frac{\omega_s}{\alpha} \tag{6.7}$$

then we can solve for the value of α by substituting Eq. (6.7) into Eq. (6.6) to obtain

$$\sqrt{\frac{\omega_p \omega_s}{\alpha^2}} = 1$$

$$\alpha = \sqrt{\omega_p \omega_s} \tag{6.8}$$

As it turns out, the only way that the frequencies ω_{pN} and ω_{sN} enter into the design procedure (given by Algorithm 6.2) is via the selectivity factor k that is given by

$$k = \frac{\omega_{pN}}{\omega_{sN}} = \frac{\omega_p/\alpha}{\omega_s/\alpha} = \frac{\omega_p}{\omega_s} \tag{6.9}$$

Since Eq. (6.9) indicates that k can be obtained directly from the desired ω_p and ω_s, we can design a *normalized* filter without having to determine the normalized frequencies ω_{pN} and ω_{sN}! However, once a normalized design is obtained, the frequency-scaling factor α as given by Eq. (6.8) *will* be needed to frequency-scale the design to the desired operating frequency.

Algorithm 6.2 Generating normalized-transfer functions for elliptical filters

Step 1. Use Algorithm 6.1 or any other equivalent method to determine a viable combination of values for A_p, A_s, ω_p, ω_s, and n.

Step 2. Using ω_p and ω_s, compute the *selectivity factor* k as $k = \omega_p/\omega_s$.

Step 3. Using the selectivity factor computed in Step 3, compute the *modular constant* q using

$$q = u + 2u^5 + 15u^9 + 150u^{13} \tag{6.10}$$

where

$$u = \frac{1 - \sqrt[4]{1 - k^2}}{2(1 + \sqrt[4]{1 - k^2})} \tag{6.11}$$

Step 4. Using the values of A_p and n from Step 1, compute V as

$$V = \frac{1}{2n} \ln \left(\frac{10^{A_p/20} + 1}{10^{A_p/20} - 1} \right) \tag{6.12}$$

Step 5. Using the value of q from Step 3 and the value of V from Step 4, compute p_0 as

$$p_0 = \left| \frac{q^{1/4} \sum_{m=0}^{\infty} (-1)^m q^{m(m+1)} \sinh [(2m+1)V]}{0.5 + \sum_{m=1}^{\infty} (-1)^m q^{m^2} \cosh 2mV} \right| \tag{6.13}$$

Step 6. Using the value of k from Step 2 and the value of p_0 from Step 5, compute W as

$$W = \left[\left(1 + \frac{p_0^2}{k} \right) (1 + kp_0^2) \right]^{1/2} \tag{6.14}$$

Step 7. Determine r, the number of quadratic sections in the filter, as $r = n/2$ for even n, and $r = (n-1)/2$ for odd n.

Step 8. For $i = 1, 2, \ldots, r$, compute X_i as

$$X_i = \frac{2q^{1/4} \sum_{m=0}^{\infty} (-1)^m q^{m(m+1)} \sin [(2m+1)\mu\pi/n]}{1 + 2 \sum_{m=1}^{\infty} (-1)^m q^{m^2} \cos (2m\mu\pi/n)} \tag{6.15}$$

where $\mu = \begin{cases} i & n \text{ odd} \\ i - \dfrac{1}{2} & n \text{ even} \end{cases}$

Step 9. For $i = 1, 2, \ldots, r$, compute Y_i as

$$Y_i \left[\left(1 - \frac{X_i^2}{k} \right) (1 - kX_i^2) \right]^{1/2} \tag{6.16}$$

Step 10. For $i = 1, 2, \ldots, r$, use the W, X_i, and Y_i from Steps 6, 8, and 9; compute the coefficients a_i, b_i, and c_i as

$$a_i = \frac{1}{X_i^2} \tag{6.17}$$

$$b_i = \frac{2p_0 Y_i}{1 + p_0^2 X_i^2} \tag{6.18}$$

$$c_i = \frac{(p_0 Y_i)^2 + (X_i W)^2}{(1 + p_0^2 X_i^2)^2} \tag{6.19}$$

Step 11. Using a_i and c_i, compute H_0 as

$$H_0 = \begin{cases} p_0 \prod_{i=1}^{r} \dfrac{c_i}{a_i} & n \text{ odd} \\ 10^{-A_p/20} \prod_{i=1}^{r} \dfrac{c_i}{a_i} & n \text{ even} \end{cases} \tag{6.20}$$

Step 12. Finally, compute the normalized transfer function $H_N(s)$ as

$$H_N(s) = \frac{H_0}{d} \prod_{i=1}^{r} \frac{s^2 + a_i}{s^2 + b_i s + c_i} \tag{6.21}$$

where

$$d = \begin{cases} s + p_0 & n \text{ odd} \\ 1 & n \text{ even} \end{cases}$$

A C++ class `EllipticalTransFunc( )`, which implements Steps 1 through 11 of Algorithm 6.2, is provided in Listing 6.1. Step 12 is implemented separately by creating an instance of `EllipticalTransFunc` and then using the function `FilterFrequencyResponse( )` belonging to the base class `FilterTransFunc` from which `EllipticalTransFunc` inherits:

```
filter_function = new EllipticalTransFunc( order,
                                           passband_ripple,
                                           stopband_ripple,
                                           passband_edge,
                                           stopband_edge,
                                           upper_summation_limit);
filter_function->LowpassDenorm( sqrt( passband_edge * stopband_edge) );
filter_function->FilterFrequencyResponse();
```

The variable `upper_summation_limit` is the number of terms to be included in the evaluations of the infinite summations in Eqs. (6.13) and (6.15). Details of the `FilterFrequencyResponse( )` function were discussed in Chap. 3.

Example 6.2 Use Algorithm 6.2 to obtain the coefficients of the normalized-transfer function for the ninth-order elliptical filter having $A_p = 0.1$ dB, $\omega_p = 3000$ rad/s, and $\omega_s = 3200$ rad/s. Determine the actual minimum stop-band loss.

solution Using the formulas from Algorithm 6.2 plus Eq. (6.5), we obtain

$$q = 0.129041 \qquad V = 0.286525 \qquad p_0 = 0.470218$$

$$W = 1.221482 \qquad r = 4 \qquad A_s = 51.665651$$

The coefficients X_i, Y_i, a_i, b_i, and c_i obtained via Steps 8 through 10 for $i = 1, 2, 3, 4$ are listed in Table 6.1. Using Eq. (6.20), we obtain $H_0 = 0.015317$. The normalized-frequency

TABLE 6.1 Coefficients for Example 6.2

i	X_i	Y_i	a_i	b_i	c_i
1	0.4894103	0.7598211	4.174973	0.6786235	0.4374598
2	0.7889940	0.3740371	1.606396	0.3091997	0.7415493
3	0.9196814	0.1422994	1.182293	0.1127396	0.8988261
4	0.9636668	0.0349416	1.076828	0.0272625	0.9538953

response of this filter is shown in Figs. 6.2, 6.3, and 6.4. (The phase response shown in Fig. 6.4 may seem a bit peculiar. At first glance, the discontinuities in the phase response might be taken for jumps of 2π caused by the $+\pi$ to $-\pi$ "wraparound" of the arctangent operation. However, this is not the case. The discontinuities in Fig. 6.4 are jumps of π that coincide with the nulls in the magnitude response.

6.3 Denormalized-Transfer Function

As noted in Sec. 3.9, if we have a response normalized for $\omega_{cN} = 1$, we can frequency-scale the transfer function to yield an identical response for $\omega_c = \alpha$ by multiplying each pole and each zero by α and dividing the overall transfer function by $\alpha^{(n_z - n_p)}$ where n_z is the number of zeros and n_p is the number of poles. An elliptical filter has a transfer function of the form given by Eq. (6.20). For odd n, there is a real pole at $s = p_0$ and r can conjugate pairs of poles that are roots of

$$s^2 + b_i s + c_i = 0 \qquad i = 1, 2, \ldots, r$$

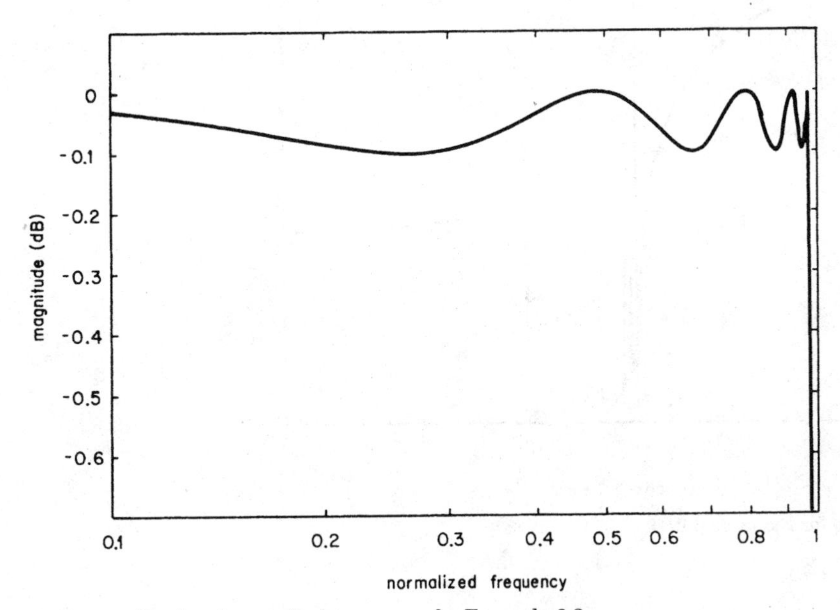

Figure 6.2 Passband magnitude response for Example 6.2.

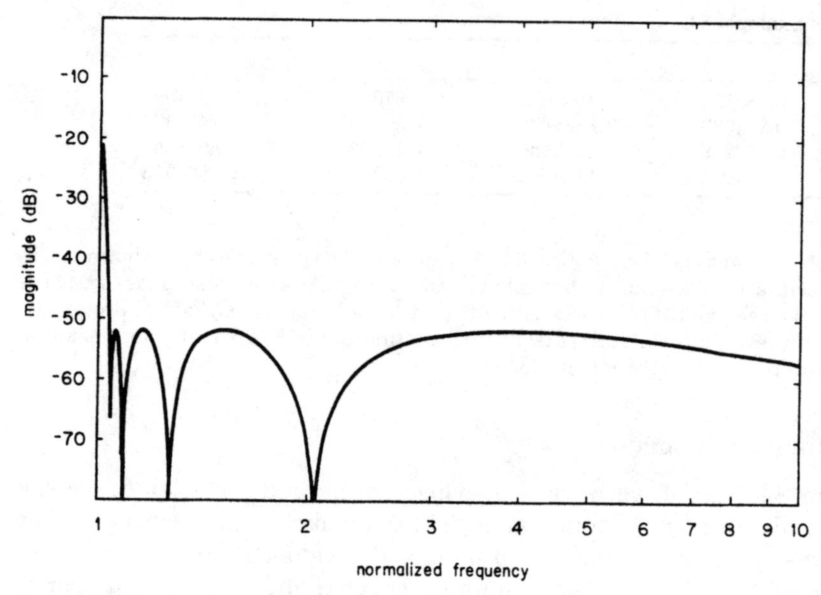

Figure 6.3 Stop-band magnitude response for Example 6.2.

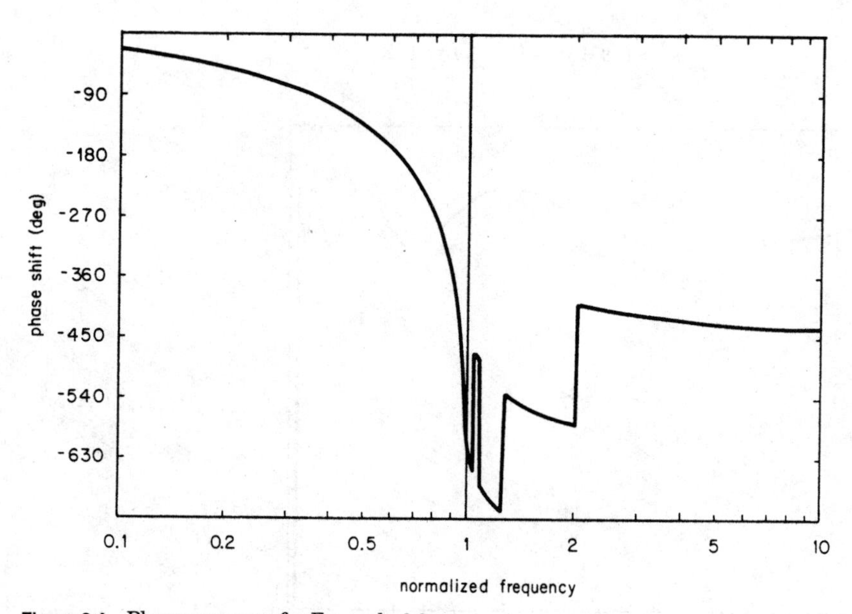

Figure 6.4 Phase response for Example 6.2.

Using the quadratic formula, the ith pair of complex pole values can be expressed as

$$p_i = \frac{-b_i \pm \sqrt{b_i^2 - 4c_i}}{2}$$

The zeros of the normalized-transfer function occur at $s = \pm j\sqrt{a_i}$, $i = 1, 2, \ldots, r$. For even n, the number of poles equals the number of zeros so $\alpha^{(nz - np)} = 1$. For odd n, $n_z - n_p = -1$, so the transfer function must be divided by $1/\alpha$ or multiplied by α. If we multiply the poles and zeros by α and multiply the overall transfer function by 1 or α as appropriate, we obtain the frequency-scaled transfer function $H(s)$ as

$$H(s) = K \prod_{i=1}^{r} \frac{s^2 + \alpha^2 a_i}{s^2 + \alpha b_i s + \alpha^2 c_i} \tag{6.22}$$

where

$$K = \begin{cases} \dfrac{H_0 \alpha}{s + \alpha p_0} & n \text{ odd} \\ H_0 & n \text{ even} \end{cases}$$

Comparison of Eqs. (6.21) and (6.22) indicates that the frequency rescaling consists of making the following substitutions in Eq. (6.21):

$\alpha^2 a_i$ replaces a_i

$\alpha^2 c_j$ replaces c_i

αb_i replaces b_i

$H_0\alpha$ replaces H_0 (n odd)

αp_0 replaces p_0 (n odd)

Listing 6.1 Transfer Function for Elliptical Filters

```
//+++++++++++++++++++++++++++++++++++++++++++++++++++++++++++++
//
//  File = elipfunc.cpp
//
//  Elliptical Filter Function
//

#include <math.h>
#include <stdlib.h>
#include "mymath.h"
```

```
#include "elipfunc.h"
#include "f_cmplx.h"
#include "d_cmplx.h"
extern ofstream DebugFile;

//=========================================================
//  constructor

EllipticalTransFunc::EllipticalTransFunc(
                                    int order,
                                    double passband_ripple,
                                    double stopband_ripple,
                                    double passband_edge,
                                    double stopband_edge,
                                    int upper_summation_limit )
                        :FilterTransFunc(order)
{
 int m;
 int min_order;
 double u, u4, x;
 double modular_const;
 double selec_factor;
 double double_temp;
 double discrim_factor;
 double term, sum;
 double numer, denom;
 double vv, ww, xx, yy;
 double p_sub_zero;
 double mu;
 int i, i_mirror, r;
 double aa, bb, cc;
 double_complex cmplx_work, work2;

 //-------------------------------------
 // Check viability of parameter set

 selec_factor = passband_edge/stopband_edge;

 x = pow( (1.-selec_factor*selec_factor), 0.25);
 u = (1.0 - x)/(2.0*(1+x));
 u4 = u*u*u*u;

 //  compute:
 // modular_const = u + 2u**5 + 15u**9 + 150u**13

 modular_const = u*(1.+(2*u*u4*(1.+(7.5*u4*(1+(10.*u4))))));

 discrim_factor = (pow(10.0, stopband_ripple/10.0) - 1.0)/
                  (pow(10.0, passband_ripple/10.0) - 1.0);
```

```
min_order = (int)ceil( log10(16.0*discrim_factor)/
                       log10(1.0/modular_const));

if(order < min_order)
  {
   cout << "Fatal error -- minimum order of "
        << min_order << " required"
        << endl;
   exit(1);
  }

//-------------------------------------------------------
// compute transfer function

Num_Prototype_Poles = order;
Prototype_Pole_Locs = new double_complex[order+1];

if(order%2)      //order is odd
  {Num_Prototype_Zeros = order-1;}
else            //order is even
  {Num_Prototype_Zeros = order;}
Prototype_Zero_Locs =
               new double_complex[Num_Prototype_Zeros+1];

//---------------------------------------------------
//  step 7 Algorith 6.2

r = (order - (order%2))/2;
Num_Biquad_Sects = r;

A_Biquad_Coef = new double[r+1];
B_Biquad_Coef = new double[r+1];
C_Biquad_Coef = new double[r+1];

//-------------------------------------------------------
//  Eq. (6.12)

numer = pow(10.0, passband_ripple/20.0) + 1.0;

vv = log(numer/(pow(10.0, passband_ripple/20.0)-1.))/(2.*order);

//-------------------------------------------------------
//  Eq. (6.13)

sum = 0.0;
for( m=0; m<upper_summation_limit; m++)
  {
   term = ipow(-1.0, m);
   term *= ipow(modular_const, m*(m+1));
```

```
    term *= sinh((2.*m+1)*vv);
    sum = sum + term;
  }
numer = sum * sqrt(sqrt(modular_const));

sum = 0.0;
for( m=1; m<upper_summation_limit; m++)
  {
    term = ipow(-1.0, m);
    term *= ipow(modular_const, m*m);
    term *= cosh(2.0 * m * vv);
    sum = sum + term;
  }
p_sub_zero = fabs(numer/(0.5 + sum));

//---------------------------------------------
//  Eq. (5.14)

ww = 1.0 + selec_factor * p_sub_zero * p_sub_zero;
ww = sqrt(ww*(1.0 + p_sub_zero * p_sub_zero / selec_factor));

//------------------------------------------
//  loop for steps 8, 9, 10, of Alg 6.2

H_Sub_Zero = 1.0;

for(i=1; i<=r; i++)
  {
   if(order%2)  // if order is odd
     {
      mu = i;
     }
   else  // order is even
     {
      mu = i - 0.5;
     }
   //-------------------------------
   //  Eq. (6.15)

   sum = 0.0;
   for(m=0; m<upper_summation_limit; m++)
     {
      term = ipow(-1.0, m);
      term *= ipow(modular_const, m* (m+1));
      term *= sin( (2*m+1) * PI * mu /order);
      sum += term;
     }
   numer = 2.0 * sum * sqrt(sqrt(modular_const));
```

```
//----------------------------------------
//  Eq. (6.15)

sum = 0.0;
for(m=1; m<upper_summation_limit; m++)
  {
   term = ipow(-1.0,m);
   term *= ipow(modular_const, m*m);
   term *= cos(2.0 * PI * m * mu/order);
   sum += term;
  }
xx = numer/(1.+2. * sum);

//----------------------------------------
//  Eq. (6.15)

yy = 1.0 - selec_factor * xx * xx;
yy = sqrt(yy * (1.0-(xx*xx/selec_factor)));

//----------------------------------------
//  Eq. (6.17)

aa = 1.0/ (xx * xx);
aa *= (passband_edge * passband_edge);
A_Biquad_Coef[i] = aa;

//----------------------------------------
//  Eq. (6.18)

denom = 1.0 + ipow(p_sub_zero * xx, 2);
bb = 2.0 * p_sub_zero * yy/denom;
bb *= passband_edge;
B_Biquad_Coef[i] = bb;

//----------------------------------------
//  Eq. (6.19)

denom = ipow(denom, 2);
numer = ipow(p_sub_zero * yy, 2) + ipow(xx*ww, 2);
cc = numer/denom;
cc *= (passband_edge * passband_edge);
C_Biquad_Coef[i] = cc;

//----------------------------------------
//
H_Sub_Zero *= (cc/aa);

//----------------------------------------
```

```
//  compute pair of pole locations
//  by finding roots of s**2 + bb*s + cc = 0

//-----------------------------------------------------
//  we need to compute:
//  cmplx_work = sqrt((double_complex) (bb*bb - 4.*cc));
//
//  work around for missing sqrt(double_complex) function
//
//  (bb*bb - 4.0*cc) will always be real and negative
//  so sqrt(bb*bb -4.0*cc) will always be pure imaginary
//  equal to sqrt(-1)*sqrt(4.0*cc - bb*bb)
//  therefore:

double_temp = sqrt(4.0*cc - bb*bb);
cmplx_work = double_complex(0.0, double_temp);

Prototype_Pole_Locs[i] = (double_complex(-bb, 0.0) - cmplx_work)/2.0;
DebugFile << "in ellip response, pole[" << i << "] = "
          << Prototype_Pole_Locs[i] << endl;
Prototype_Pole_Locs[order+1-i] =
                    (double_complex(-bb, 0.0) + cmplx_work)/2.0;
//----------------------------------------------------------
// compute pair of zero locations
// by finding roots of s**2 + a = 0
//
//  roots = +/- sqrt(-a)
//

if(order%2)
  {
   i_mirror = order-i;
  }
else
  {
   i_mirror = order+1-i;
  }
if(aa < 0.0)
  {
   double_temp = sqrt(-aa);
   Prototype_Zero_Locs[i] = double_complex(double_temp, 0.0);
   Prototype_Zero_Locs[i_mirror] =
                      double_complex((-double_temp), 0.0);
  }
else
  {
   double_temp = sqrt(aa);
   Prototype_Zero_Locs[i] = double_complex(0.0, double_temp);
```

```
      Prototype_Zero_Locs[i_mirror] =
                              double_complex(0.0, (-double_temp));
      }
    DebugFile << "in ellip response, zero[" << i << "] = "
              << Prototype_Zero_Locs[i] << endl;
  }
//----------------------------
//  Finish up Ho

if(order%2)
  {
   p_sub_zero *= passband_edge;
   H_Sub_Zero *= p_sub_zero;
   Prototype_Pole_Locs[(order+1)/2] = double_complex(-p_sub_zero, 0.0);
   DebugFile << "p_sub_zero = " << p_sub_zero << endl;
   DebugFile << "in ellip, H_Sub_Zero = "
             << H_Sub_Zero << endl;
  }
else
  {
   H_Sub_Zero *= pow(10.0, passband_ripple/(-20.0));
  }
return;
};
```

Chapter

7

Bessel Filters

Bessel filters are designed to have maximally flat group-delay characteristics. As a consequence, there is no ringing in the impulse and step responses.

7.1 Transfer Function

The general expression for the transfer function of an nth-order Bessel lowpass filter is given by

$$H(s) = \frac{b_0}{q_n(s)} \tag{7.1}$$

where

$$q_n(s) = \sum_{k=1}^{n} b_k s^k$$

$$b_k = \frac{(2n-k)!}{2^{n-k}\, k!(n-k)!}$$

The following recursion can be used to determine $q_n(s)$ from $q_{n-1}(s)$ and $q_{n-2}(s)$:

$$q_n = (2n-1)q_{n-1} + s^2 q_{n-2} \tag{7.2}$$

Table 6.1 lists $q_n(s)$ for $n = 2$ through $n = 8$.

Unlike the transfer function for Butterworth and Chebyshev filters, Eq. (7.1) does not provide an explicit expression for the poles of the Bessel filter. The numerator of Eq. (7.1) will be a polynomial in s, upon which numerical root-finding methods (such as Algorithm 3.1) must be used to determine the pole locations for $H(s)$. Table 7.2 lists approximate pole locations for $n = 2$ through $n = 8$.

TABLE 7.1 Denominator Polynomials for Transfer Functions of Bessel Filters Normalized to Have Unit Delay at $\omega = 0$

n	$q_n(s)$
2	$s^2 + 3s + 3$
3	$s^3 + 6s^2 + 15s + 15$
4	$s^4 + 10s^3 + 45s^2 + 105s + 105$
5	$s^5 + 15s^4 + 105s^3 + 420s^2 + 945s + 945$
6	$s^6 + 21s^5 + 210s^4 + 1260s^3 + 4725s^2 + 10{,}395s + 10{,}395$
7	$s^7 + 28s^6 + 378s^5 + 3150s^4 + 17{,}325s^3 + 62{,}370s^2 + 135{,}135s + 135{,}135$
8	$s^8 + 36s^7 + 630s^6 + 6930s^5 + 9450s^4 + 270{,}270s^3 + 945{,}945s^2 + 2{,}027{,}025s + 2{,}027{,}025$

The transfer functions given by Eq. (7.1) are for Bessel filters normalized to have unit delay at $\omega = 0$. The poles p_k and denominator coefficients b_k can be renormalized for a 3-dB frequency of $\omega = 1$ using

$$p'_k = Ap_k \qquad b'_k = A^{n-k}\, b_k \tag{7.3}$$

where the value of A appropriate for n is selected from Table 7.3.

A C++ class `BesselTransFunc( )`, for generating Bessel-filter transfer functions, is provided in Listing 7.1. The constructor for this class uses the recursion given in Eq. (7.2) to generate the coefficients for the transfer function's

TABLE 7.2 Poles of Bessel Filter Normalized to Have Unit Delay at $\omega = 0$

n	Pole values
2	$-1.5 \pm 0.8660j$
3	-2.3222
	$-1.8390 \pm 1.7543j$
4	$-2.1039 \pm 2.6575j$
	$-2.8961 \pm 0.8672j$
5	-3.6467
	$-2.3247 \pm 3.5710j$
	$-3.3520 \pm 1.7427j$
6	$-2.5158 \pm 4.4927j$
	$-3.7357 \pm 2.6263j$
	$-4.2484 \pm 0.8675j$
7	-4.9716
	$-2.6857 \pm 5.4206j$
	$-4.0701 \pm 3.5173j$
	$-4.7584 \pm 1.7393j$
8	$-5.2049 \pm 2.6162j$
	$-4.3683 \pm 4.4146j$
	$-2.8388 \pm 6.3540j$
	$-5.5878 \pm 0.8676j$

TABLE 7.3 Factors for Renormalizing Bessel Filter Poles from Unit Delay at $\omega = 0$ to 3-dB Attenuation at $\omega = 1$

n	A
2	1.35994
3	1.74993
4	2.13011
5	2.42003
6	2.69996
7	2.95000
8	3.17002

denominator polynomials. If the third input parameter is set TRUE, the transfer function will be normalized to have unit delay at zero frequency. If the third input parameter is set FALSE, the transfer function will be normalized to have a 3 attenuation at the passband edge. `BesselTransFunc` uses the Laguerre method from Chap. 2 to find the roots of the denominator polynomial and thereby determine the filter's pole locations.

7.2 Frequency Response

As shown in the following code fragment, frequency response data for Bessel filters can be generated by creating an instance of `BesselTransFunc` and then using the function `FilterFrequencyResponse( )` belonging to the base class `FilterTransFunc` from which `BesselTransFunc` inherits:

```
filter_function = new BesselTransFunc( order,
                                       passband_edge,
                                       normalize_for_unit_delay);
filter_function->LowpassDenorm( passband_edge );
filter_function->FilterFrequencyResponse();
```

Details of the `FilterFrequencyResponse( )` function were presented in Chap. 3. Figures 7.1 and 7.2 show the magnitude responses for Bessel filters of several different orders.

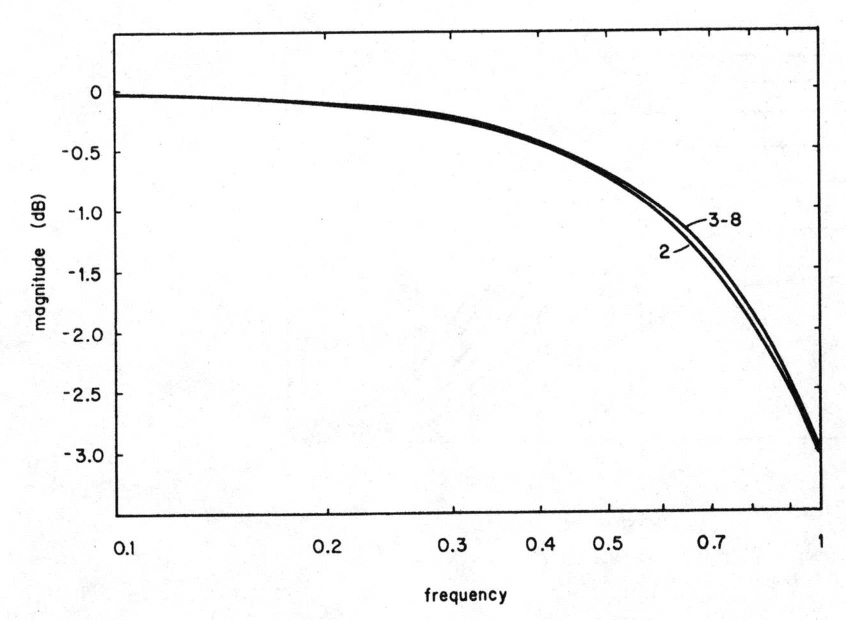

Figure 7.1 Passband magnitude response of low-pass Bessel filters.

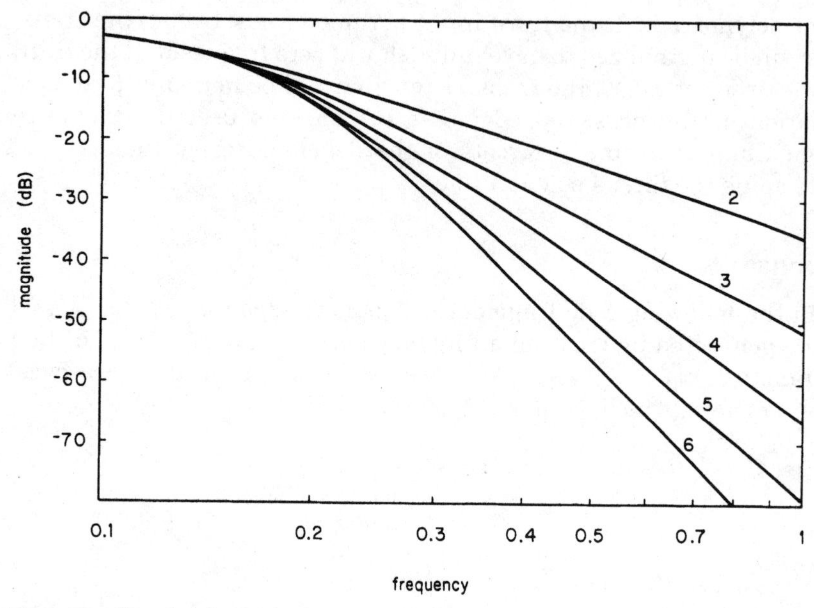

Figure 7.2 Stop-band magnitude response of low-pass Bessel filters.

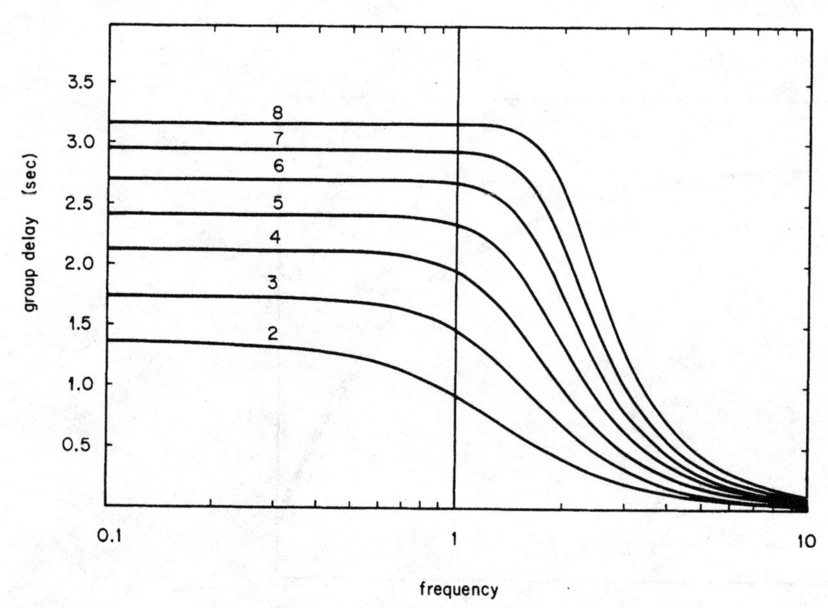

Figure 7.3 Group-delay response of low-pass Bessel filters.

7.3 Group Delay

Group delays for low-pass Bessel filters of several different orders are plotted in Fig. 7.3. The data for these plots was generated by the `FilterFrequencyResponse` function, which performs numerical differentiation of the phase response to evaluate the group delay.

Listing 7.1 Transfer Function for Bessel Filters

```
//+++++++++++++++++++++++++++++++++++++++++++++++++++++++++++++++
//
//  File = bessfunc.cpp
//
//  Bessel Filter Function
//

#include <math.h>
#include <stdlib.h>
#include "mymath.h"
#include "bessfunc.h"
#include "elipfunc.h"
#include "laguerre.h"
#include "f_cmplx.h"
#include "d_cmplx.h"
extern ofstream DebugFile;

//=======================================================
//  constructor

BesselTransFunc::BesselTransFunc( int order,
                                  double passband_edge,
                                  int norm_for_delay)
                :FilterTransFunc(order)
{
  int indx, indx_m1, indx_m2;
  int i, n, ii, work_order;
  double epsilon, epsilon2;
  int max_iter, laguerre_status;
  long q_poly[3][MAX_BESSEL_ORDER];
  double_complex *denom_poly, *work_poly;
  double_complex root, work1, work2;
  double renorm_val, smallest;
  //---------------------------------------------------
  //  these values are reciprocals of values in Table 7.3

  double renorm_factor[9] = { 0.0,     0.0,     0.72675,
                              0.57145, 0.46946, 0.41322,
                              0.37038, 0.33898, 0.31546};
```

```
Prototype_Pole_Locs = new double_complex[order+1];
Num_Prototype_Poles = order;
Prototype_Zero_Locs = new double_complex[1];
Num_Prototype_Zeros = 0;

H_Sub_Zero = 1.0;
 denom_poly = new double_complex[MAX_BESSEL_ORDER];
 work_poly = new double_complex[MAX_BESSEL_ORDER];

 indx = 1;
 indx_m1 = 0;
 indx_m2 = 2;
 renorm_val = renorm_factor[order];

 //-----------------------------------------
 // initialize polynomials for n=0 and n=1

 for( i=0; i<(3*MAX_BESSEL_ORDER) ; i++)
     q_poly[0][i] = 0;

 q_poly[0][0] = 1;
 q_poly[1][0] = 1;
 q_poly[1][1] = 1;

 //---------------------------------------------
 //  compute polynomial using recursion from n=2
 //  up through n=order

 for( n=2; n<=order; n++)
   {
   indx = (indx+1)%3;
   indx_m1 = (indx_m1+1)%3;
   indx_m2 = (indx_m2+1)%3;
   for( i=0; i<n; i++)
     {
     q_poly[indx][i] = (2*n-1) *
                             q_poly[indx_m1][i];
     }
   for( i=2; i<=n; i++)
     {
     q_poly[indx][i] = q_poly[indx][i] +
                             q_poly[indx_m2][i-2];
     }
   }
 if(norm_for_delay)
   {
   for( i=0; i<=order; i++)
     {
```

```
      denom_poly[i] = double_complex(
                      double(q_poly[indx][i]), 0.0);
      }
    }
  else
    {
    for( i=0; i<=order; i++)
      denom_poly[i] = double_complex(
                      (double(q_poly[indx][i]) *
                      ipow(renorm_val, (order-i))), 0.0);
    }
  //-----------------------------------------------
  // use Laguerre method to find roots of the
  // denominator polynomial -- these roots are the
  // poles of the filter

  epsilon = 1.0e-6;
  epsilon2 = 1.0e-6;
  max_iter = 10;

  for(i=0; i<=order; i++) work_poly[i] = denom_poly[i];

  for(i=order; i>1; i--)
    {
    root = double_complex(0.0,0.0);
    work_order = i;
    laguerre_status = LaguerreMethod( work_order,
                                      work_poly,
                                      &root,
                                      epsilon,
                                      epsilon2,
                                      max_iter);
    if(laguerre_status <0)
      {
      DebugFile << "FATAL ERROR - \n"
                << "Laguerre method failed to converge.\n"
                << "Unable to find poles for desired Bessel filter."
                << endl;
      exit(-1);
      }

    //------------------------------------------
    // if imaginary part of root is very small
    // relative to real part, set it to zero

    if(fabs(imag(root)) < epsilon*fabs(real(root)))
      {
      root = double_complex(real(root), 0.0);
```

```
      }
    Prototype_Pole_Locs[order+1-i] = root;

    //-----------------------------------------------
    // deflate working polynomial by removing
    // (s - r) factor where r is newly found root

    work1 = work_poly[i];
    for(ii=i-1; ii>=0; ii--)
      {
      work2 = work_poly[ii];
      work_poly[ii] = work1;
      work1 = work2 + root * work1;
      }
    } // end of loop over i
  Prototype_Pole_Locs[order] = -work_poly[0];
  //-----------------------------------------------
  // sort poles so that imaginary parts are in
  // ascending order.  This order is critical for
  // successful operation of ImpulseResponse().

  for(i=1; i<order; i++)
    {
    smallest = imag(Prototype_Pole_Locs[i]);
    for( ii=i+1; ii<=order; ii++)
      {
      if(smallest <= imag(Prototype_Pole_Locs[ii])) continue;
        work1 = Prototype_Pole_Locs[ii];
        Prototype_Pole_Locs[ii] = Prototype_Pole_Locs[i];
        Prototype_Pole_Locs[i] = work1;
        smallest = imag(work1);
      }
    }
  return;
}
```

Chapter

8

Fundamentals of Digital Signal Processing

Digital signal processing (*DSP*) is based on the fact that an analog signal can be digitized and input to a general-purpose digital computer or special-purpose digital processor. Once this is accomplished, we are free to perform all sorts of mathematical operations on the sequence of digital data samples inside the processor. Some of these operations are simply digital versions of classical analog techniques, while others have no counterpart in analog circuit devices or processing methods. This chapter covers digitization and introduces the various types of processing that can be performed on the sequence of digital values once they are inside the processor.

8.1 Digitization

Digitization is the process of converting an analog signal such as a time-varying voltage or current into a sequence of digital values. Digitization actually involves two distinct parts—*sampling* and *quantization*—which are usually analyzed separately for the sake of convenience and simplicity. Three basic types of sampling, shown in Fig. 8.1, are *ideal, instantaneous,* and *natural.* From the illustration we can see that the sampling process converts a signal that is defined over a continuous time interval into a signal that has nonzero amplitude values only at discrete instants of time (as in ideal sampling) or over a number of discretely separate but internally continuous subintervals of time (as in instantaneous and natural sampling). The signal that results from a sampling process is called a *sampled-data signal.* The signals resulting from ideal sampling are also referred to as *discrete-time signals.*

Each of the three basic sampling types occurs at different places within a DSP system. The output from a sample-and-hold amplifier or a digital-to-analog converter (DAC) is an instantaneously sampled signal. In the output of a practical analog-to-digital converter (ADC) used to sample a signal, each sample will, of

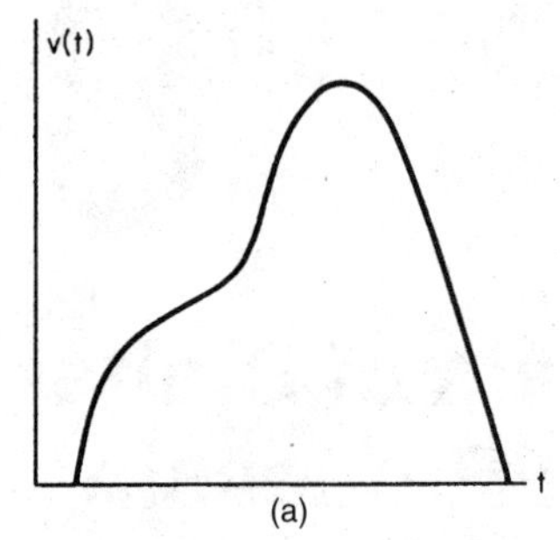

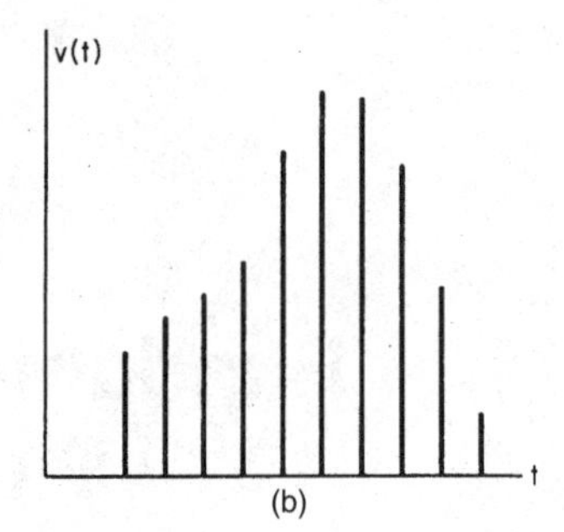

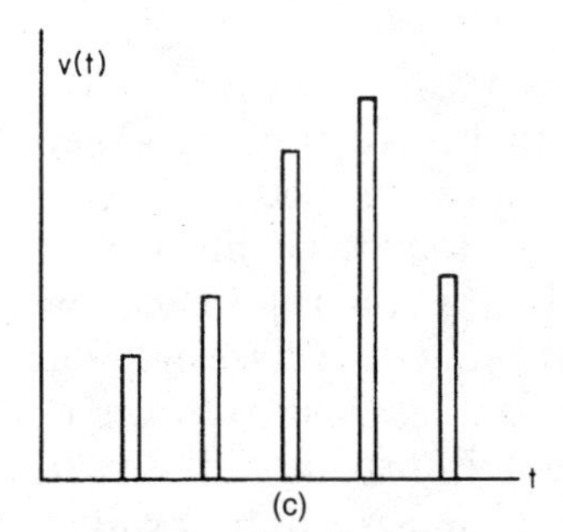

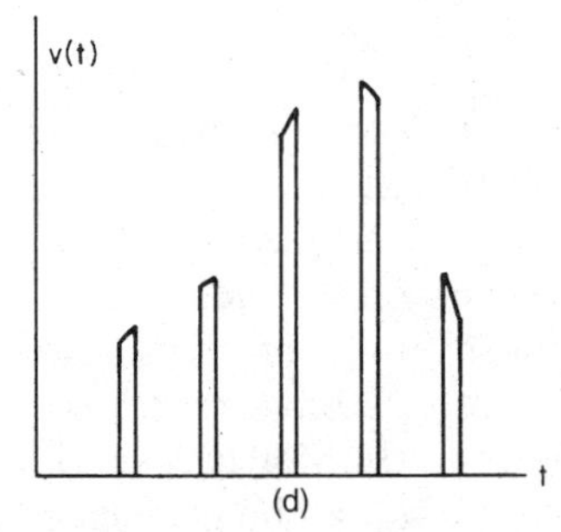

Figure 8.1 An analog signal (*a*) and three different types of sampling: (*b*) ideal, (*c*) instantaneous, and (*d*) natural.

course, exist for some nonzero interval of time. However, within the software of the digital processor, these values can still be interpreted as the amplitudes for a sequence of ideal samples. In fact, this is almost always the best approach, since the ideal sampling model results in the simplest processing for most applications. Natural sampling is encountered in the analysis of the analog multiplexing that is often performed prior to A/D conversion in multiple-signal systems. In all three of the sampling approaches presented, the sample values are free to assume any appropriate value from the continuum of possible analog signal values.

Quantization is the part of digitization that is concerned with converting the amplitudes of an analog signal into values that can be represented by binary numbers having some finite number of bits. A quantized, or *discrete-valued,* signal is shown in Fig. 8.2. The sampling and quantization processes will introduce some significant changes in the spectrum of a digitized signal. The details of the changes will depend upon both the precision of the quantization operation and the particular sampling model that most aptly fits the actual situation.

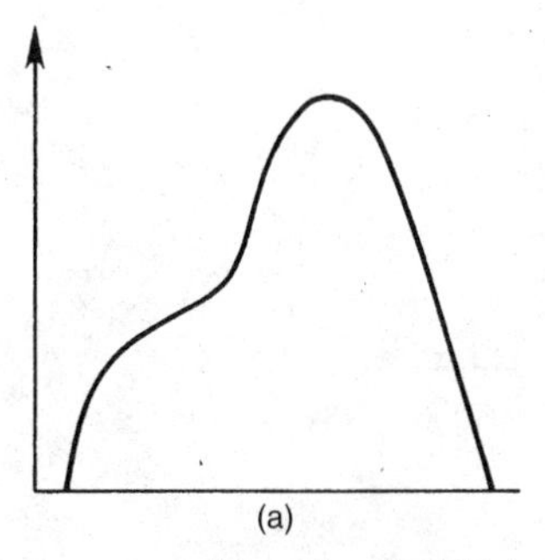

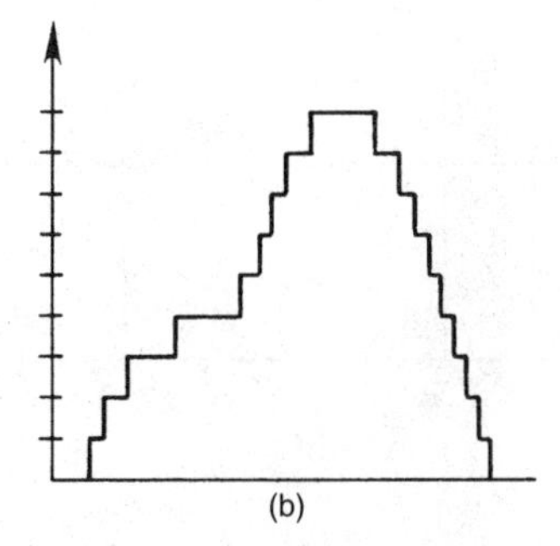

Figure 8.2 An analog signal (*a*) and the corresponding quantized signal (*b*).

Ideal sampling

In *ideal sampling,* the sampled-data signal, as shown in Fig. 8.3, comprises a sequence of uniformly spaced impulses, with the weight of each impulse equal to the amplitude of the analog signal at the corresponding instant in time. Although not mathematically rigorous, it is convenient to think of the sampled-data signal as the result of multiplying the analog signal $x(t)$ by a periodic train of unit impulses:

$$x_s(\cdot) = x(t) \sum_{n=-\infty}^{\infty} \delta(t - nT)$$

Based upon Property 11 from Table 1.2, this means that the spectrum of the sampled-data signal could be obtained by convolving the spectrum of the analog signal with the spectrum of the impulse train:

$$\mathcal{F}\left[x(t) \sum_{n=-\infty}^{\infty} \delta(t - nT)\right] = X(f) * \left[f_s \sum_{m=-\infty}^{\infty} \delta(f - mf_s)\right]$$

As illustrated in Fig. 8.4, this convolution produces copies, or *images,* of the original spectrum that are periodically repeated along the frequency axis. Each

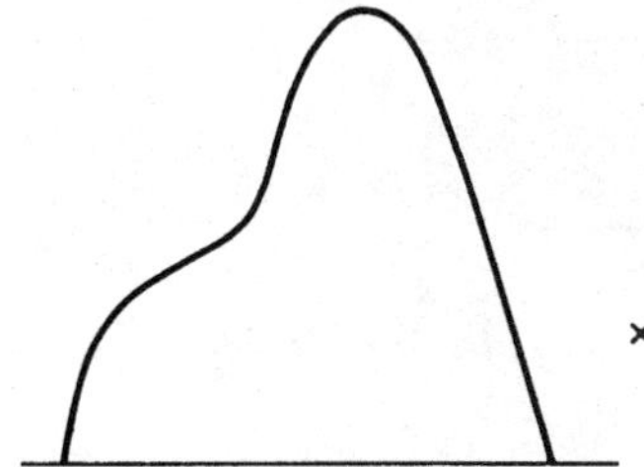

×

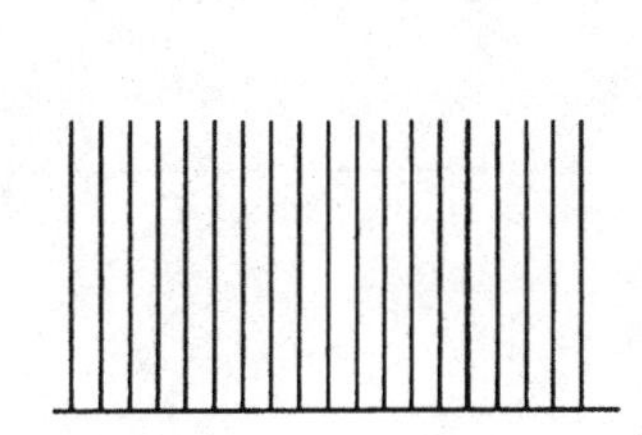

=

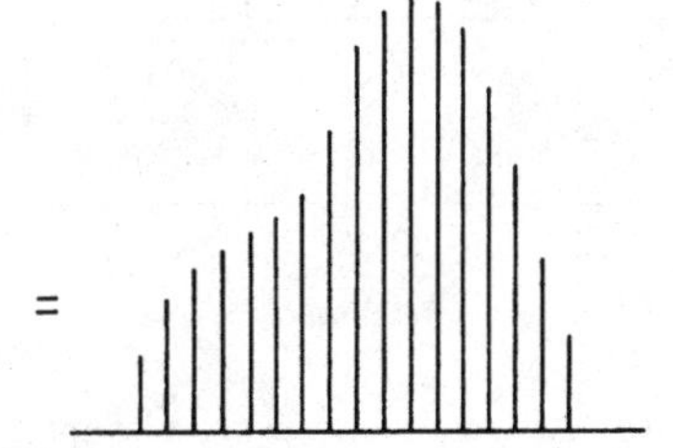

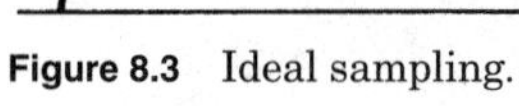

Figure 8.3 Ideal sampling.

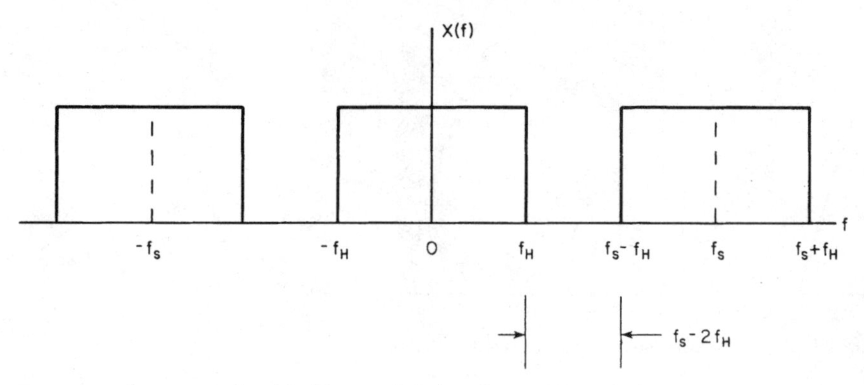

Figure 8.4 Spectrum of an ideally sampled signal.

of the images is an exact (to within a scaling factor) copy of the original spectrum. The center-to-center spacing of the images is equal to the sampling rate f_s, and the edge-to-edge spacing is equal to $f_s - 2f_H$. As long as f_s is greater than 2 times f_H, the original signal can be recovered by a low-pass filtering operation that removes the extra images introduced by the sampling.

Sampling rate selection

If f_s is less than $2f_H$, the images will overlap, or *alias,* as shown in Fig. 8.5, and recovery of the original signal will not be possible. The minimum alias-free sampling rate of $2f_H$ is called the *Nyquist rate.* A signal sampled exactly at its Nyquist rate is said to be *critically sampled.*

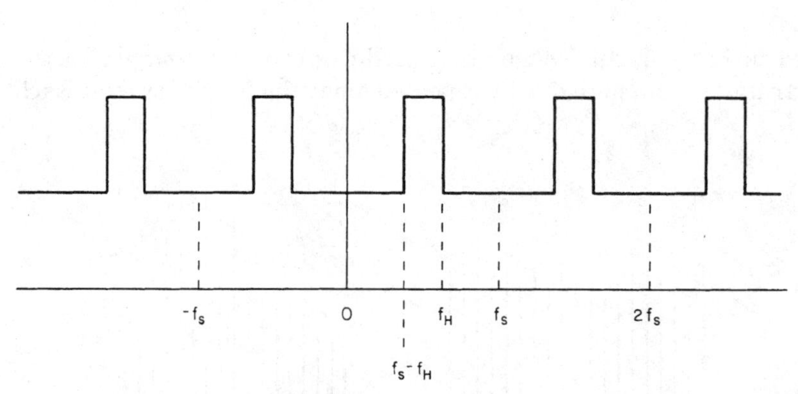

Figure 8.5 Aliasing due to overlap of spectral images.

Uniform sampling theorem. If the spectrum $X(f)$ of a function $x(t)$ vanishes beyond an upper frequency of f_H Hz or ω_H rad/s, then $x(t)$ can be completely determined by its values at uniform intervals of less than $1/(2f_H)$ or π/ω. If sampled within these constraints, the original function $x(t)$ can be reconstructed from the samples by

$$x(t) = \sum_{n=-\infty}^{\infty} x(nT) \frac{\sin [2f_s(t - nT)]}{2f_s(t - nT)}$$

where T is the sampling interval.

Since practical signals cannot be strictly band-limited, sampling of a real-world signal must be performed at a rate greater than $2f_H$ where the signal is known to have negligible (that is, typically less than 1 percent) spectral energy above the frequency of f_H. When designing a signal processing system, we will rarely, if ever, have reliable information concerning the exact spectral occupancy of the noisy real-world signals that our system will eventually face. Consequently, in most practical design situations, a value is selected for f_H based upon the requirements of the particular application, and then the signal is low-pass filtered prior to sampling. Filters used for this purpose are called *antialiasing filters* or *guard filters.* The sample-rate selection and guard filter design are coordinated so that the filter provides attenuation of 40 dB or more for all frequencies above $f_s/2$. The spectrum of an ideally sampled practical signal is shown in Fig. 8.6. Although some aliasing does occur, the aliased components are suppressed at least 40 dB below the desired components. Antialias filtering must be performed prior to sampling. In general, there is no way to eliminate aliasing once a signal has been improperly sampled. The particular type (Butterworth, Chebyshev, Bessel, Cauer, and so on) and order of the filter should be chosen to provide the necessary stop-band attenuation while preserving the passband characteristics most important to the intended application.

Instantaneous sampling

In instantaneous sampling, each sample has a nonzero width and a flat top. As shown in Fig. 8.7, the sampled-data signal resulting from instantaneous sampling can be viewed as the result of convolving a sample pulse $p(t)$ with an ideally sampled version of the analog signal. The resulting sampled-data signal can thus be expressed as

$$x_s(\cdot) = p(t) * \left[x(t) \sum_{n=-\infty}^{\infty} \delta(t - nT) \right]$$

where $p(t)$ is a single rectangular sampling pulse and $x(t)$ is the original analog signal. Based upon Property 10 from Table 1.2, this means that the spectrum

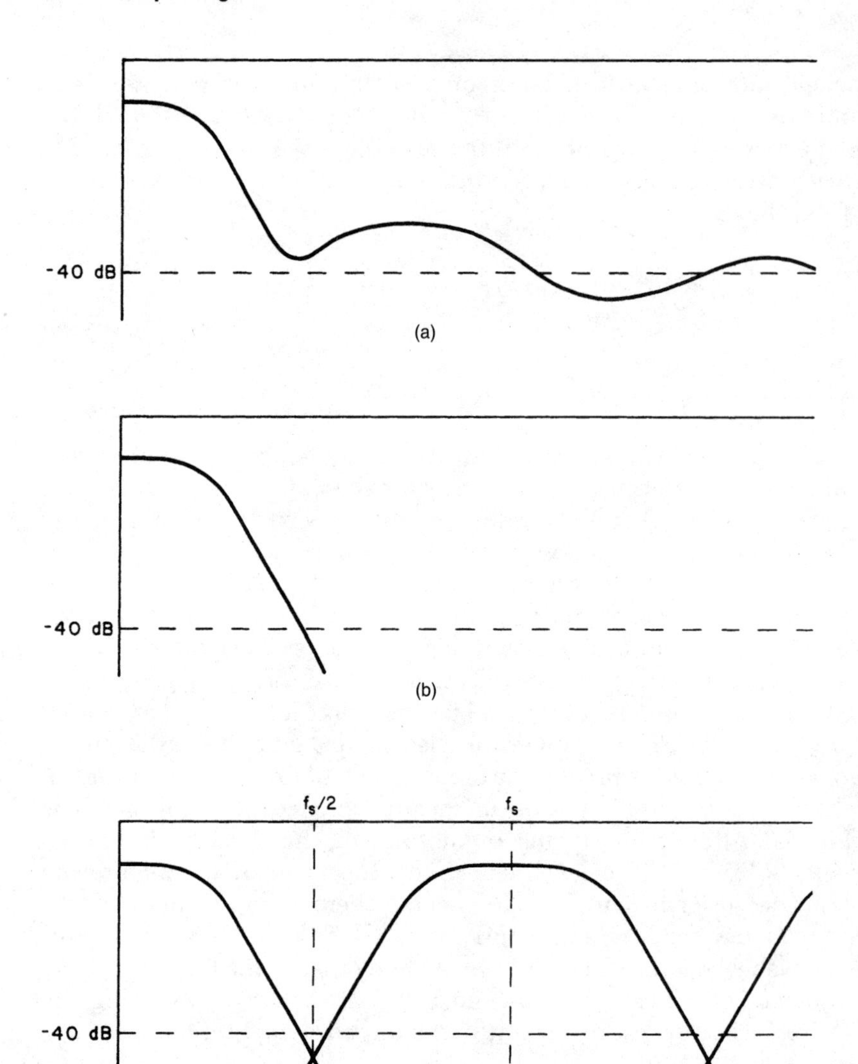

Figure 8.6 Spectrum of an ideally sampled practical signal: (*a*) spectrum of raw analog signal, (*b*) spectrum after low-pass filtering, and (*c*) spectrum after sampling.

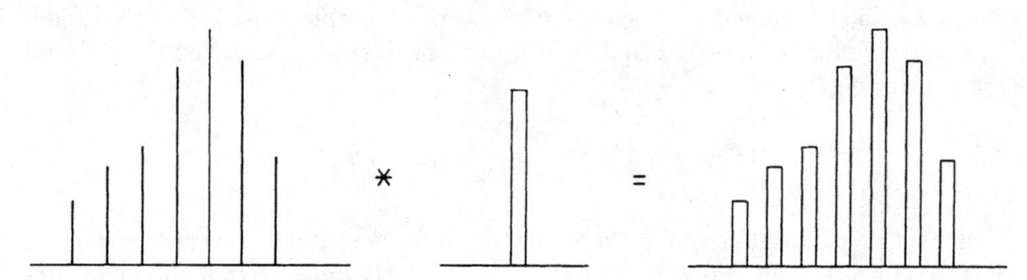

Figure 8.7 Instantaneous sampling.

of the instantaneous sampled-data signal can be obtained by multiplying the spectrum of the sample pulse with the spectrum of the ideally sampled signal:

$$\mathcal{F}\left\{p(t) * \left[x(t) \sum_{n=-\infty}^{\infty} \delta(t - nT)\right]\right\} = P(f) \cdot \left\{X(f) * \left[f_s \sum_{m=-\infty}^{\infty} \delta(f - mf_s)\right]\right\}$$

As shown in Fig. 8.8, the resulting spectrum is similar to the spectrum produced by ideal sampling. The only difference is the amplitude distortion introduced by the spectrum of the sampling pulse. This distortion is sometimes called the *aperture effect.* Notice that distortion is present in all the images, including the one at baseband. The distortion will be less severe for narrow sampling pulses. As the pulses become extremely narrow, instantaneous sampling begins to look just like ideal sampling, and distortion due to the aperture effect all but disappears.

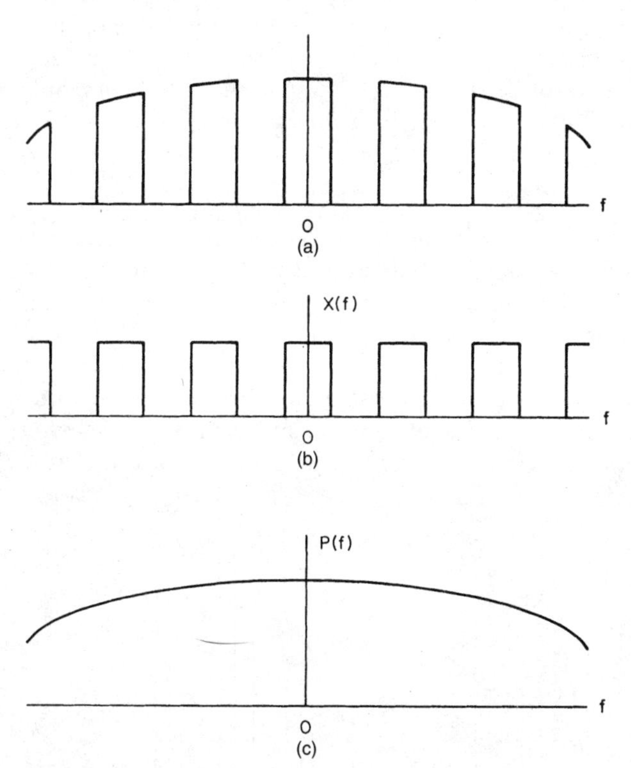

Figure 8.8 Spectrum (a) of an instantaneously sampled signal is equal to the spectrum (b) of an ideally sampled signal multiplied by the spectrum (c) of 1 sampling pulse.

Natural sampling

In natural sampling, each sample's amplitude follows the analog signal's amplitude throughout the sample's duration. As shown in Fig. 8.9, this is mathematically equivalent to multiplying the analog signal by a periodic train of rectangular pulses:

$$x_s(\cdot) = x(t) \cdot \left\{ p(t) * \left[\sum_{n=-\infty}^{\infty} \delta(t - nT) \right] \right\}$$

The spectrum of a naturally sampled signal is found by convolving the spectrum of the analog signal with the spectrum of the sampling pulse train:

$$\mathcal{F}[x_s(\cdot)] = X(f) * \left[P(f)\, f_s \sum_{m=-\infty}^{\infty} \delta(f - mf_s) \right]$$

As shown in Fig. 8.10, the resulting spectrum will be similar to the spectrum produced by instantaneous sampling. In instantaneous sampling, all frequencies of the sampled signal's spectrum are attenuated by the spectrum of the sampling pulse, while in natural sampling each image of the basic spectrum will be attenuated by a factor that is equal to the value of the sampling pulse's spectrum at the center frequency of the image. In communications theory, natural sampling is called *shaped-top pulse amplitude modulation.*

Discrete-time signals

In the discussion so far, weighted impulses have been used to represent individual sample values in a discrete-time signal. This was necessary in order to use continuous mathematics to connect continuous-time analog signal representations with their corresponding discrete-time digital representations. However, once we are operating strictly within the digital or discrete-time realms, we can dispense with the Dirac delta impulse and adopt in its place the unit sample function, which is much easier to work with. The unit sample function is also referred to as a *Kronecker delta impulse* (Cadzow 1973). Figure 8.11 shows both the Dirac

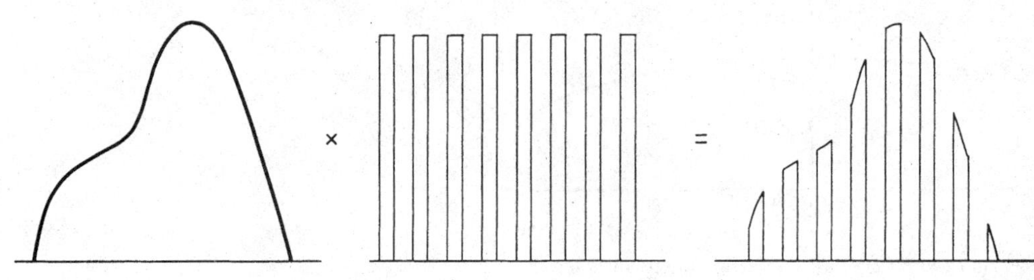

Figure 8.9 Natural sampling.

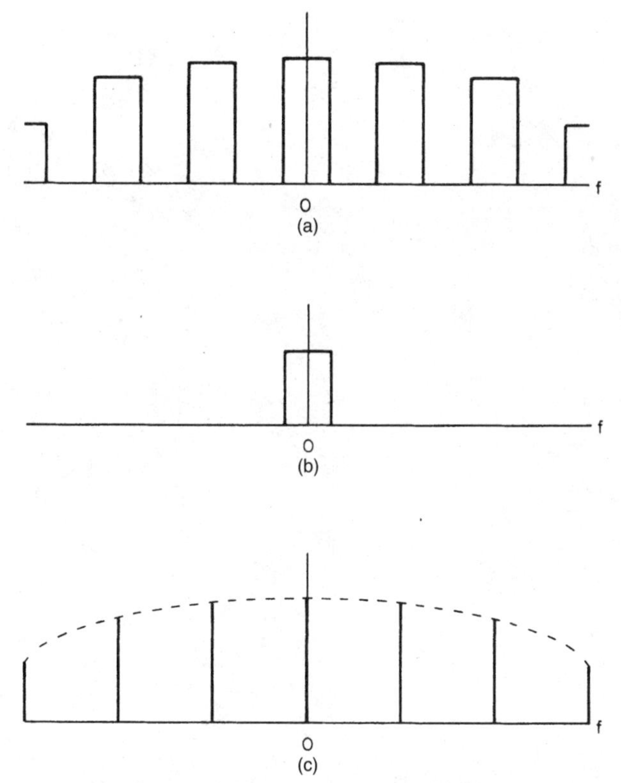

Figure 8.10 Spectrum (*a*) of a naturally sampled signal is equal to the spectum (*b*) of the analog signal convolved with the spectrum (*c*) of the sampling pulse train.

delta and Kronecker delta representations for a typical signal. In the function sampled using a Dirac impulse train, the independent variable is continuous time t and integer multiples of the sampling interval T are used to explicitly define the discrete sampling instants. On the other hand, the Kronecker delta notation assumes uniform sampling with an implicitly defined sampling interval. The independent variable is the integer-valued index n whose values correspond to the discrete instants at which samples can occur. In most theoretical work, the implicitly defined sampling interval is dispensed with completely by treating all the discrete-time functions as though they have been normalized by setting $T = 1$.

Notation

Writers in the field of digital-signal processing are faced with the problem of finding a convenient notational way to distinguish between continuous-time functions and discrete-time functions. Since the early 1970s, a number of different approaches have appeared in the literature, but none of the schemes

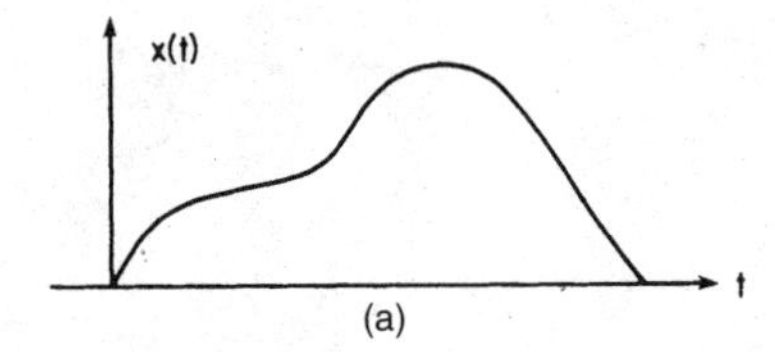

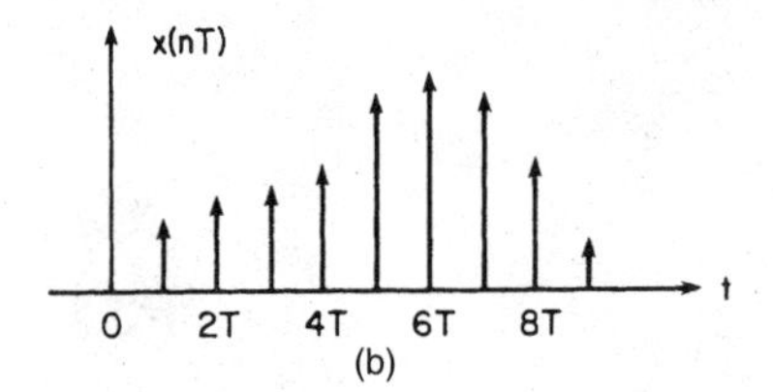

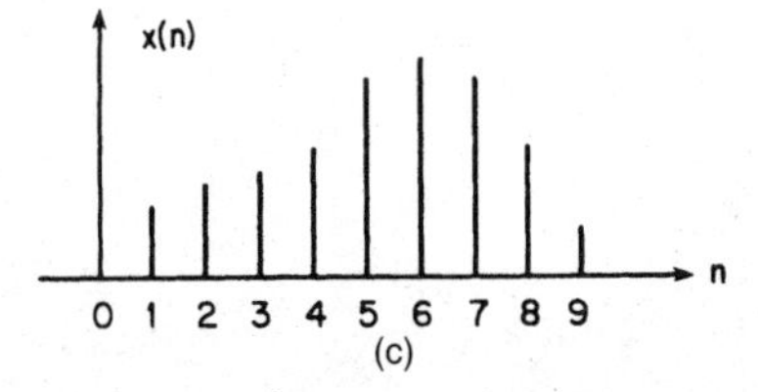

Figure 8.11 Sampling with Dirac and Kronecker impulses: (*a*) continuous signal, (*b*) sampling with Dirac impulses, and (*c*) sampling with Kronecker impulses.

advanced so far have been perfectly suited for all situations. In fact, some authors use two or more different notational schemes within different parts of the same book. In keeping with long-established mathematical practice, functions of a continuous variable are almost universally denoted with the independent variable enclosed in parentheses: $x(t)$, $H(e^{j\omega})$, $\phi(f)$ and so on. Many authors, such as Oppenheim and Schafer (1975), Rabiner and Gold (1975), and Roberts and Mullis (1987), make no real notational distinction between functions of continuous variables and functions of discrete variables, and instead rely on context to convey the distinction. This approach, while easy for the writer, can be very confusing for the reader. Another approach involves using subscripts for functions of a discrete variable:

$$x_k \triangleq x(kT)$$

$$H_n \triangleq H(e^{jn\theta})$$

$$\phi_m \triangleq \phi(mF)$$

This approach quickly becomes typographically unwieldy when the independent variable is represented by a complicated expression. A fairly recent practice (Oppenheim and Schafer 1989) uses parentheses ( ) to enclose the independent variable of continuous-variable functions and brackets [ ] to enclose the independent variable of discrete-variable functions:

$$x[k] = x(kT)$$

$$H[n] = H(e^{jn\theta})$$

$$\phi[m] = \phi(mF)$$

For the remainder of this book, we will adopt this practice and just remind ourselves to be careful in situations where the bracket notation for discrete-variable functions could be confused with the bracket notation used for arrays in C++.

8.2 Discrete-Time Fourier Transform

The Fourier series given by Eq. (1.10) can be rewritten to make use of the discrete sequence notation that was introduced in Sec. 8.1:

$$x(t) = \sum_{n=-\infty}^{\infty} X[n] e^{j2\pi nFt}$$

where $F = \dfrac{1}{t_0}$ = sample spacing in the frequency domain

t_0 = period of $x(t)$

Likewise, Eq. (1.11) can be written as

$$X[n] = \frac{1}{t_0} \int_{t_0} x(t)\, e^{-jn2\pi Ft}\, dt$$

The fact that the signal $x(t)$ and sequence $F[n]$ form a Fourier series pair with a frequency domain sampling interval of F can be indicated as

$$x(t) \overset{\text{FS};\,F}{\longleftrightarrow} X[n]$$

In Sec. 8.1 the results concerning the impact of sampling upon a signal's spectrum were obtained using the *continuous-time* Fourier transform in conjunction with a periodic train of Dirac impulses to model the sampling of the continuous-time signal $x(t)$. Once we have defined a discrete-time sequence $x[n]$, the *discrete-time Fourier transform* (*DTFT*) can be used to obtain the corresponding spectrum directly from the sequence without having to resort to impulses and continuous-time Fourier analysis.

The discrete-time Fourier transform, which links the discrete-time and continuous-frequency domain, is defined by

$$X(e^{j\omega T}) = \sum_{n=-\infty}^{\infty} x[n]\, e^{-j\omega nT} \tag{8.1}$$

and the corresponding inverse is given by

$$x[n] = \frac{1}{2\pi} \int_{-\pi}^{\pi} X(e^{j\omega})\, e^{j\omega nT}\, d\omega \tag{8.2}$$

If Eqs. (8.1) and (8.2) are compared to the DTFT definitions given by certain texts (Oppenheim and Schafer 1975; Oppenheim and Schafer 1989; Rabiner and Gold 1975), an apparent disagreement will be found. The cited texts define the DTFT and its inverse as

$$X(e^{j\omega}) = \sum_{n=-\infty}^{\infty} x[n]\, e^{-j\omega n} \tag{8.3}$$

$$x[n] = \frac{1}{2\pi} \int_{-\pi}^{\pi} X(e^{j\omega})\, e^{j\omega nT}\, d\omega \tag{8.4}$$

The disagreement is due to the notation used by these texts, in which ω is used to denote the *digital* frequency given by

$$\omega = \frac{\Omega}{F_s} = \Omega T$$

where Ω = analog frequency
F_s = sampling frequency
T = sampling interval

In most DSP books other than the three previously cited, the analog frequency is denoted by ω rather than by Ω. Whether ω or Ω is the "natural" choice for denoting analog frequency depends upon the overall approach taken in developing Fourier analysis of sequences. Books that begin with sequences, then proceed on to Fourier analysis of sequences, and finally tie sequences to analog signals via sampling tend to use ω for the first frequency variable encountered, which is *digital* frequency. Other books that begin with analog theory and then move on to sampling and sequences tend to use ω for the first frequency variable encountered, which is *analog* frequency. In this book, we will adopt the convention used by Peled and Liu (1976), denoting analog frequency by ω and digital frequency by $\lambda = \omega T$. The function $X(e^{j\omega T})$ is periodic with a period of $\omega_p = 2\pi/T$, and $X(e^{j\lambda})$ is periodic with a period of $\lambda_p = 2\pi$.

Independent of the ω versus Ω controversy, the notation $X(e^{j\omega T})$ or $X(e^{j\lambda})$ is commonly used rather than $X(\omega)$ or $X(\lambda)$ so that the form of Eq. (8.1) remains similar to the form of the z transform given in Chap. 10, which is

$$X(z) = \sum_{n=-\infty}^{\infty} x[n]\, z^{-n} \tag{8.5}$$

If $e^{j\omega}$ is substituted for z in Eq. (8.5), the result is identical to Eq. (8.1). This indicates that the DTFT is nothing more than the z transform evaluated on the unit circle. [NOTE: $e^{j\omega} = \cos\omega + j\sin\omega$, $0 \le \omega \le 2\pi$, does in fact define the unit circle in the z plane since $|e^{j\omega}| = (\cos^2\omega + \sin^2\omega)^{1/2} \equiv 1$].

Convergence conditions

If the time sequence $x[n]$ satisfies

$$\sum_{n=-\infty}^{\infty} |x[n]| < \infty$$

then $X(e^{j\omega T})$ exists and the series in Eq. (8.1) converges uniformly to $X(e^{j\omega T})$. If $x[n]$ satisfies

$$\sum_{n=-\infty}^{\infty} |x[n]|^2 < \infty$$

then $X(e^{j\omega T})$ exists and the series in Eq. (8.1) converges in a mean-square sense to $X(e^{j\omega T})$, that is,

$$\lim_{M \to \infty} \int_{-\pi}^{\pi} |X(e^{j\omega T}) - X_M(e^{j\omega T})|^2\, d\omega = 0$$

where

$$X_M(e^{j\omega T}) = \sum_{n=-M}^{M} x[n]\, e^{-j\omega nT}$$

The function $X_M(e^{j\omega T})$ is a form of the Dirichlet kernel discussed in Sec. 14.2.

Relationship to Fourier series

Since the Fourier series represents a periodic continuous-time function in terms of a discrete-frequency function, and the DTFT represents a discrete-time function in terms of a periodic continuous-frequency function, we might suspect that some sort of duality exists between the Fourier series and DTFT. It turns out that such a duality does indeed exist. Specifically if

$$f[k] \overset{\text{DTFT}}{\longleftrightarrow} F(e^{j\omega T})$$

and we set

$$\omega_0 = T$$

$$x(t) = F(e^{j\omega T})\,|_{\,\omega = T}$$

$$X[n] = f[k]\,|_{\,k=-n}$$

then

$$x(t) \overset{\text{FS};\,\omega_0}{\longleftrightarrow} X[n]$$

8.3 Discrete-Time Systems

In Chap. 3 we saw how continuous-time systems such as filters and amplifiers can accept analog input signals and operate upon them to produce different analog output signals. *Discrete-time systems* perform essentially the same role for digital or discrete-time signals.

Difference equations

Although I have deliberately avoided discussing differential equations and their accompanying headaches in the analysis of analog systems, *difference* equations are much easier to work with, and they play an important role in the analysis and synthesis of discrete-time systems. A discrete-time, linear, time-invariant (or if you prefer, shift-invariant) DTLTI or DTLSI system, which accepts an input sequence $x[n]$ and produces an output sequence $y[n]$, can be described by a linear difference equation of the form

$$y[n] + a_1 y[n-1] + a_2 y[n-2] + \cdots + a_k y[n-k]$$
$$= b_0 x[n] + b_1 x[n-1] + b_2 x[n-2] + \cdots + b_k x[n-k] \quad (8.6)$$

Such a difference equation can describe a DTLTI system having any initial conditions as long as they are specified. This is in contrast to the discrete-convolution and discrete-transfer functions that are limited to describing digital filters that are initially relaxed (that is, all inputs and outputs are initially zero). In general, the computation of the output $y[n]$ at point n using Eq. (8.6) will involve previous outputs $y[n-1], y[n-2], y[n-3]$, and so on. However, in some filters all of the coefficients $a_1, a_2, \ldots, a_k$ are equal to zero, thus yielding

$$y[n] = b_0 x[n] + b_1 x[n-1] + b_2 x[n-2] + \cdots + b_k x[n-k] \quad (8.7)$$

in which the computation of $y[n]$ does not involve previous output values. Difference equations involving previous output values are called *recursive differ-*

ence equations, and equations in the form of Eq. (8.7) are called *nonrecursive difference equations.*

Example 8.1 Determine a nonrecursive difference equation for a simple moving-average low-pass filter in which the output at $n = i$ is equal to the arithmetic average of the five inputs from $n = i - 4$ through $n = i$.

solution The desired difference equation is given by

$$y[n] = \frac{x[n] + x[n-1] + x[n-2] + x[n-3] + x[n-4]}{5}$$

$$= 0.2x[n] + 0.2x[n-1] + 0.2x[n-2] + 0.2x[n-3] + 0.2x[n-4] \qquad (8.8)$$

Relating this to the standard form of Eq. (8.7), we find $k = 4$, $b_i = 0$ for all i, and $a_0 = a_1 = a_2 = a_3 = a_4 = 0.2$.

Discrete convolution

A discrete-time system's impulse response is the output response produced when a unit sample function is applied to the input of the previously relaxed system. As we might expect from our experiences with continuous systems, we can obtain the output $y[n]$ due to any input by performing a *discrete convolution* of the input signal $x[n]$ and the impulse response $h[n]$. This discrete convolution is given by

$$y[n] = \sum_{m=0}^{\infty} h[m]\, x[n-m]$$

If the impulse response has nonzero values at an infinite number of points along the discrete-time axis, a digital filter having such an impulse response is called an *infinite-impulse response (IIR)* filter. On the other hand, if $h[m] = 0$ for all $m \geq M$, the filter is called a *finite-impulse response* (*FIR*) filter, and the convolution summation can be rewritten as

$$y[n] = \sum_{m=0}^{M-1} h[m]\, x[n-m]$$

FIR filters are also called *transversal filters.*

Example 8.2 For the moving-average filter described in Example 8.1, obtain the filter's impulse response.

solution The filter's impulse response $h[n]$ can be obtained by direct evaluation of Eq. (8.8) for the case of $x[n]$ equal to the unit sample function:

$$h[n] = y[n] \qquad \text{for} \qquad x[n] = \begin{cases} 1 & n = 0 \\ 0 & n \neq 0 \end{cases}$$

Thus,

$$h[n] = \begin{cases} 0.2 & 0 \le n \le 4 \\ 0 & \text{otherwise} \end{cases}$$

The following summation identities will often prove useful in the evaluation of convolution summations:

$$\sum_{n=0}^{N} \alpha^n = \frac{1 - \alpha^{N+1}}{1 - \alpha} \qquad \alpha \neq 1 \tag{8.9}$$

$$\sum_{n=0}^{N} n\alpha^n = \frac{\alpha}{(1-\alpha)^2}(1 - \alpha^N - N\alpha^N + N\alpha^{N+1}) \qquad \alpha \neq 1 \tag{8.10}$$

$$\sum_{n=0}^{N} n^2\alpha^n = \frac{\alpha}{(1-\alpha)^3}[(1+\alpha)(1-\alpha^N) - 2(1-\alpha)N\alpha^N - (1-\alpha)^2 N^2\alpha^N] \qquad \alpha \neq 1 \tag{8.11}$$

8.4 Diagramming Discrete-Time Systems

Block diagrams

As is the case for continuous-time systems, block diagrams are useful in the design and analysis of discrete-time systems. Construction of block diagrams for discrete-time systems involves three basic building blocks: the unit-delay element, multiplier, and summer.

Unit-delay element. As its name implies, a *unit-delay element* generates an output that is identical to its input delayed by one sample interval:

$$y[k] = x[k-1]$$

The unit-delay element is usually drawn as shown in Fig. 8.12. The term z^{-1} is used to denote a unit delay because delaying a discrete-time signal by one sample time multiplies the signal's z transform by z^{-1}. (See Property 5 in Table 10.4.) Delays of p sample times may be depicted as p unit delays in series or as a box enclosing z^{-p}.

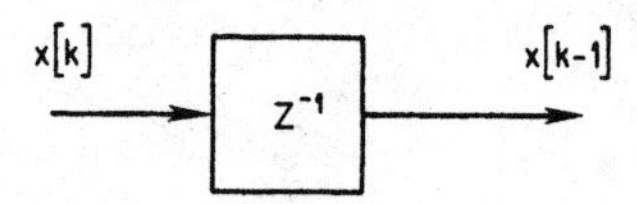

Figure 8.12 Block diagram representation of a unit-delay element.

Multiplier. A *multiplier* generates as output the product of a fixed constant and the input signal

$$y[k] = ax[k]$$

A multiplier can be drawn in any of the ways shown in Fig. 8.13. The form shown in Fig. 8.13c is usually reserved for adaptive filters and other situations where the factor a is not constant. [Note that a system containing multiplication by a nonconstant factor would not be a *linear time-invariant* (*LTI*) system!]

Summer. A *summer* adds two or more discrete-time signals to generate the discrete-time output signal:

$$y[k] = x_1[k] + x_2[k] + \cdots + x_n[k]$$

A summer is depicted using one of the forms shown in Fig. 8.14. A negative sign can be placed next to a summer's input paths as required to indicate a signal that is to be subtracted rather than added.

Example 8.3 Draw a block diagram for a simple moving-average low-pass filter in which the output at $k = i$ is equal to the arithmetic average of the three inputs for $k = i - 2$ through $k = i$.

solution The difference equation for the desired filter is

$$y[k] = \frac{1}{3}x[k] + \frac{1}{3}x[k-1] + \frac{1}{3}x[k-2]$$

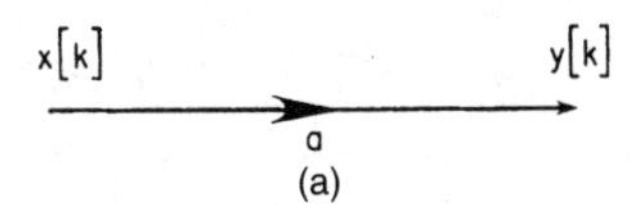

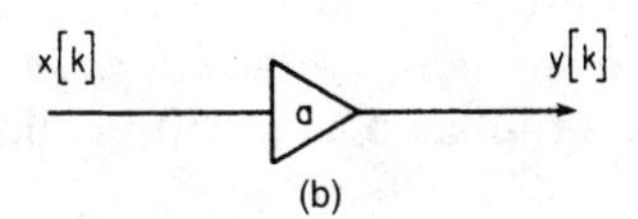

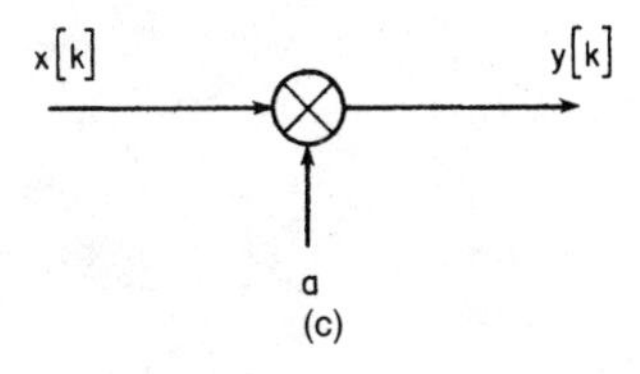

Figure 8.13 Block diagram representations of a multiplier.

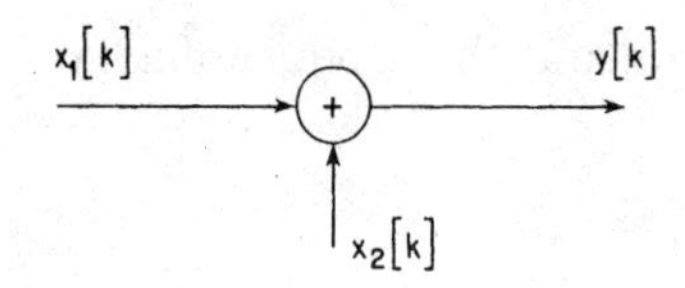

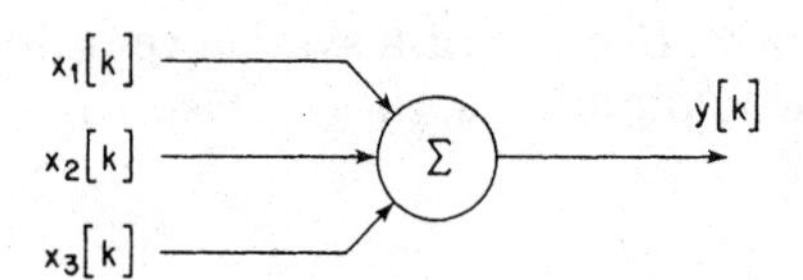

Figure 8.14 Block diagram representations of a summer.

The block diagram for this filter will be as shown in Fig. 8.15. It should be noted that block diagram representations are in general not unique and that a given system can be represented in several different ways.

Example 8.4 Draw alternative block diagrams for the filter of Example 8.3.

solution Since multiplication distributes over addition, the difference equation can be rewritten as

$$y[k] = \frac{1}{3}\{x[k] + x[k-1] + x[k-2]\}$$

and the block diagram can be redrawn as shown in Fig. 8.16.

Signal flow graphs

A modified form of a directed graph, called a *signal flow graph* (*SFG*), can be used to depict all the same information as a block diagram but in a more compact form. Consider the block diagram in Fig. 8.17, which has some labeled points added for ease of reference. The *oriented graph,* or *directed graph,* for this system is obtained by replacing each multiplier, each connecting branch, and each delay element with a directed line segment called an *edge.* Furthermore, each branching point and each adder is replaced by a point called a *node.*

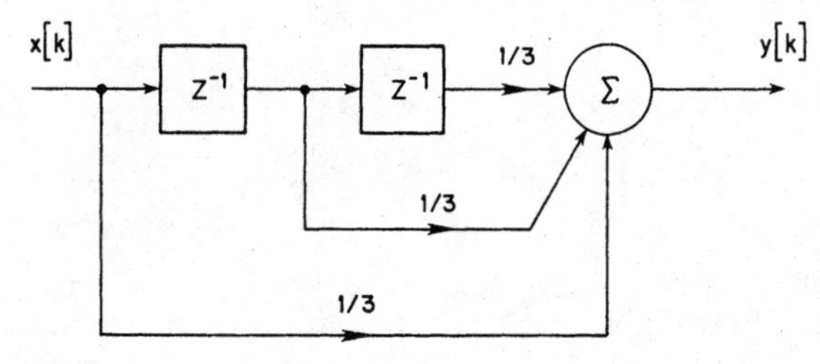

Figure 8.15 Block diagram for Example 8.3.

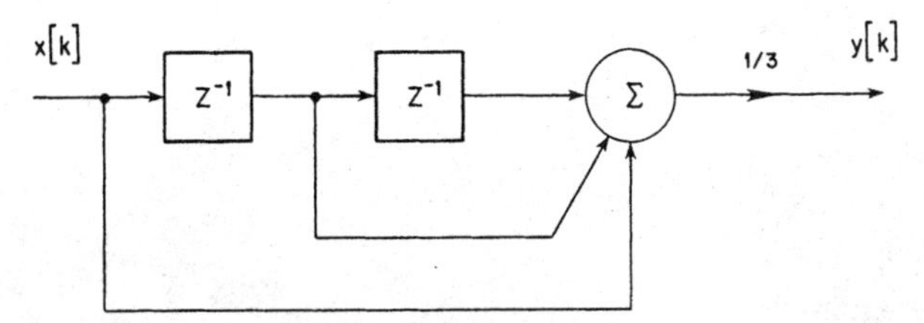

Figure 8.16 Block diagram for Example 8.4.

The resulting graph is shown in Fig. 8.18. A signal flow graph is obtained by associating a signal with each node and a linear operation with each edge of the directed graph. The node weights correspond to signals present within the discrete-time system. Associated with each edge is the linear operation (delay or constant gain) that must be performed upon the signal associated with the edge's *from* node in order to obtain the signal associated with the edge's *to* node. For a node which is the *to* node for two or more edges, the signal associated with the node is the sum of all the signals produced by the incoming edges. For the graph shown in Fig. 8.18, the following correspondences can be identified:

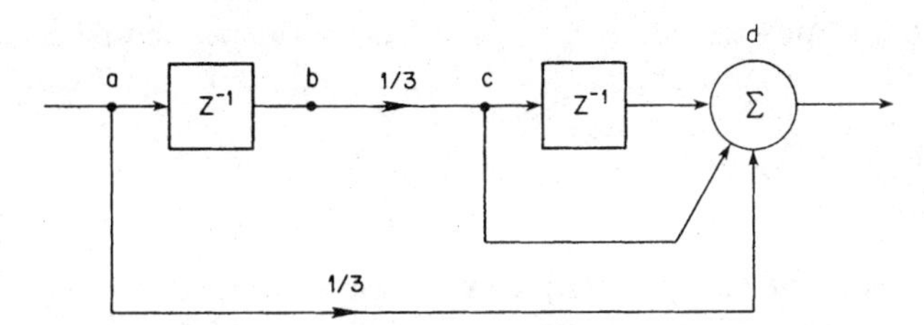

Figure 8.17 Block diagram of a discrete-time system.

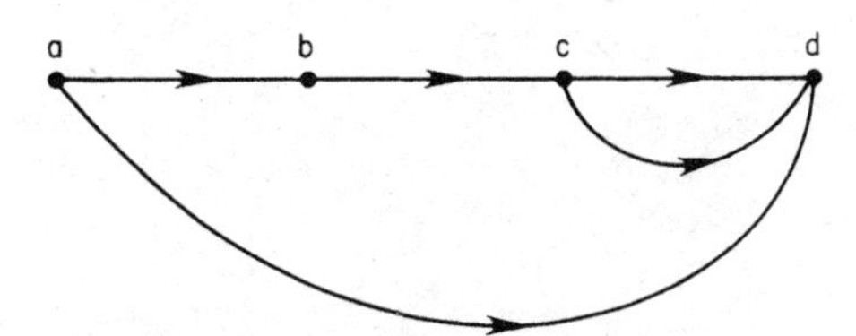

Figure 8.18 Directed graph corresponding to the block diagram of Fig. 8.17.

Node a	$x[k]$
Node b	$x[k-1]$
Node c	$\frac{1}{3}x[k-1]$
Node d	Summer producing $y[k]$
Edge (a, b)	First delay element
Edge (c, d)	Second delay element
Edge (a, d)	Bottom multiplier
Edge (b, c)	Top multiplier
Edge (c, d)	Unity gain connection from point c to summer

The resulting signal flow graph is shown in Fig. 8.19. It is customary to use multiplication by z^{-1} as a shorthand notation for unit delay, even though the signals in an SFG are time domain signals, and multiplication by z^{-1} is a frequency domain operation.

8.5 Quantization

Although floating-point formats are used in some digital filters, cost and speed considerations will often dictate the use of fixed-point formats having a relatively short word length. Such formats will force some precision to be lost in representations of the signal samples, filter coefficients, and computation results. A digital filter designed under the infinite-precision assumption will not perform up to design expectations if implemented with short word-length, fixed-point arithmetic. In many cases, the degradations can be so severe as to make the filter unusable. This chapter examines the various types of degradations caused by finite-precision implementations and explores what can be done to achieve acceptable filter performance in spite of the degradations.

Fixed-point numeric formats

Binary fixed-point representation of numbers enjoys widespread use in digital signal-processing applications where there is usually some control over the range of values that must be represented. Typically, all of the coefficients $h[n]$ for a digital filter will be scaled such that

$$|h[n]| \leq 1.0 \qquad \text{for} \quad n = 1, 2, \ldots, N \tag{8.12}$$

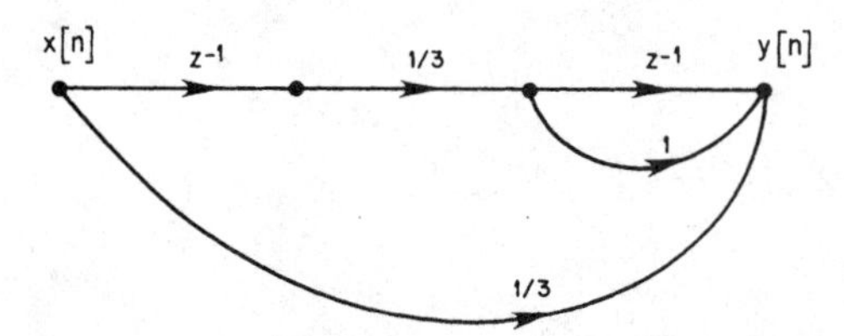

Figure 8.19 Signal flow graph derived from the directed graph of Fig. 8.18.

Once scaled in this way, each coefficient can be expressed as

$$h = b_0 2^0 + b_1 2^{-1} + b_2 2^{-2} + \cdots \tag{8.13}$$

where each of the b_n is a single bit; that is, $b_n \in \{0, 1\}$. If we limit our representation to a length of $L + 1$ bits, the coefficients can be represented as a fixed-point binary number of the form shown in Fig. 8.20. As shown in the figure, a small triangle is often used to represent the binary point so that it cannot be easily confused with a decimal point. The expansion of Eq. (8.13) can then be written as

$$h = \sum_{k=0}^{L} b_k \, 2^{-k} \tag{8.14}$$

The bit shown to the left of the binary point in Fig. 8.20 is necessary to represent coefficients for which the equality in Eq. (8.12) holds, but its presence complicates the implementation of arithmetic operations. If we eliminate the need to exactly represent coefficients that equal unity, we can use the fixed-point fractional format shown in Fig. 8.21. Using this scheme, some values are easy to write:

$$\frac{1}{2} = {}_{\Delta}1000$$

$$\frac{3}{8} = {}_{\Delta}01100$$

$$\frac{5}{64} = {}_{\Delta}000101$$

Some other values are not so easy. Consider the case of 1/10, which expands as

$$\frac{1}{10} = 2^{-4} + 2^{-5} + 2^{-8} + 2^{-9} + 2^{-12} + 2^{-13} + \cdots$$

$$= \sum_{k=1}^{\infty} \left(2^{-4k} + 2^{-4k-1}\right)$$

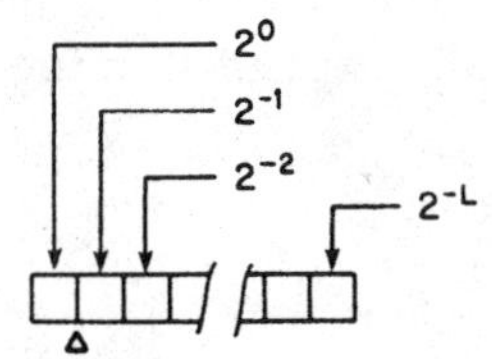

Figure 8.20 Fixed-point binary number format.

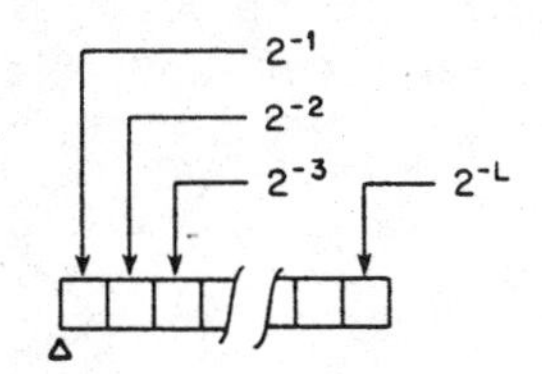

Figure 8.21 Alternative fixed-point binary number format.

The corresponding fixed-point binary representation is a repeating fraction given by

$$\frac{1}{10} = {}_{\Delta}000\overline{1100}11\cdots$$

If we are limited to a 16-bit fixed-point binary representation, we can truncate the fraction after 16 bits to obtain

$$\frac{1}{10} \cong {}_{\Delta}0001100110011001$$

The actual value of this 16-bit representation is

$$2^{-4} + 2^{-5} + 2^{-8} + 2^{-9} + 2^{-12} + 2^{-13} + 2^{-16} = \frac{6553}{65{,}536} \cong 0.099990845$$

Thus, the value represented in 16 bits is too small by approximately 9.155×10^{-6}.

Instead of truncating, we could use a rounding approach. Rounding a binary value is easy—just add 1 to the first (leftmost) bit that is not being retained in the rounded format. In the current example we add 1 to bit 16. This generates a carry into b_{15} which propagates into b_{14} to yield

$${}_{\Delta}0001100110011010 = \frac{6554}{65{,}536} \cong 0.100006104$$

This value is too big by approximately 6.1×10^{-6}.

In many DSP applications where design simplicity, low cost, or high speed is important, the word length may be significantly shorter than 16 bits, and the error introduced by either truncating or rounding the coefficients can be quite severe.

Floating-point numeric formats

A fixed-point fractional format has little use in a general-purpose computer where there is little or no a priori control over the range of values that may need to be represented. Clearly, any time a value equals or exceeds 1.0, it cannot be represented in the format of Fig. 8.21. Floating-point formats remove this limitation by effectively allowing the binary point to shift position as needed. For floating-point representations, a number is typically expanded in the form

$$h = 2^{a} \sum_{k=0}^{L} b_k 2^{-k}$$

A typical floating-point numeric format is shown in Fig. 8.22. The fields denoted i and f contain a fixed-point value of the form shown in Fig. 8.20 where the

Figure 8.22 A typical floating-point numeric format.

binary point is assumed to lie between i and the most significant bit of f. This fixed-point value is referred to as the *mantissa.* If the bits in field f are designated from left to right as $f_1, f_2, \ldots, f_{63}$, the value of the mantissa is given by

$$m = \mathrm{i} + \sum_{k=1}^{63} f_k \, 2^{-k}$$

The field denoted as e is a 15-bit integer value used to indicate the power of 2 by which the numerator must be multiplied in order to obtain the value being represented. This can be a positive or negative power of 2, but rather than using a sign in conjunction with the exponent, most floating-point formats use an offset. A 15-bit binary field can have values ranging from 0 to 32,767. Values from 0 to 16,382 are interpreted as negative powers of 2, and values from 16,384 to 32,766 are interpreted as positive powers of 2. The value 16,383 is interpreted as $2^0 = 1$, and the value 32,767 is reserved for representing infinity and specialized values called NaN (*not-a-number*). The sign bit denoted by s is the sign of the overall number. Thus the value represented by a floating-point number in the format of Fig. 8.22 can be obtained as

$$v = (-1)^s \, 2^{(e - 16{,}383)} \left(i + \sum_{k=1}^{63} f_k 2^{-k} \right)$$

provided $e \neq 32{,}767$.

Suppose we wish to represent 1/10 in the floating-point format of Fig. 8.22. One way to accomplish this is to set the mantissa equal to a 64-bit fixed-point representation of 1/10 and set $e = 16{,}383$ to indicate a multiplier of unity. Using the hexadecimal notation discussed previously, we can write the results of such an approach as

$$s = 0$$

$$e = \mathrm{0x3fff}$$

$$i = 0$$

$$f = \mathrm{0x0cccccccccccccccc}$$

With the various fields packed together, the resulting 80-bit floating-point representation of 1/10 is W = 0x3fff0cccccccccccccccc. Slightly more precision can be squeezed into the representation if we shift f four places to the left and modify e to indicate multiplication by 2^{-4}. Such an approach yields

$$W = \text{0x3ffbcccccccccccccccc}$$

Numbers greater than 1.0 present no problem for this format. The value 57 is represented as

$$s = 0$$

$$e = \text{0x4004} \qquad \text{(that is, } 2^5\text{)}$$

$$i = 1$$

$$f = \text{0x6400000000000000}$$

$$W = \text{0x4004e400000000000000}$$

In other words, this representation stores 57 by making use of the fact that

$$57 = 2^5(2^0 + 2^{-1} + 2^{-2} + 2^{-5})$$

Quantized coefficients

When the coefficients of a digital filter are quantized, the filter becomes a different filter. The resulting filter is still a discrete-time linear time-invariant system—it's just not the system we set out to design. Consider the 21-tap low-pass filter having the coefficients listed in Table 8.1. The values given in the table, having 15 decimal digits in the fractional part, will be used as the baseline approximation to the coefficients' infinite-precision values. Let's force the coefficient values into a fixed-point fractional format having a 16-bit magnitude plus 1 sign bit. After truncating the bits in excess of 16, the coefficient values listed in Table 8.2 are obtained. The magnitude response of a filter using such coefficients

TABLE 8.1 Coefficients for 21-Tap Low-Pass Filter

n	$h[n]$
0, 20	0.000
1, 19	−0.000823149720361
2, 18	−0.002233281959082
3, 17	0.005508892585759
4, 16	0.017431813641454
5, 17	−0.000000000000050
6, 16	−0.049534952531101
7, 15	−0.049511869643024
8, 14	0.084615800641299
9, 13	0.295322344140975
10	0.40

TABLE 8.2 Truncated 16-Bit Coefficients for 21-Tap Low-Pass Filter

n	Sign	Hex value	Decimal value
0, 20	+	0000	0.0
1, 19	–	0035	–0.000808715820312
2, 18	–	0092	–0.002227783203125
3, 17	+	0169	0.005508422851562
4, 16	+	0476	0.017425537109375
5, 15	+	0000	0.0
6, 14	–	0cae	–0.049530029296875
7, 13	–	0cac	–0.049499511718750
8, 12	+	15a9	0.084609985351562
9, 11	+	4b9a	0.295318603515625
10	+	6666	0.399993896484375

is virtually identical to the response obtained using the floating-point coefficients of Table 8.1. If the coefficients are further truncated to 14- or 12-bit magnitudes, slight degradations in stop-band attenuation can be observed.

The degradations in filter response are really quite significant for the 10-bit coefficients listed in Table 8.3. As shown in Fig. 8.23, the fourth sidelobe is narrowed, and the fifth sidelobe peaks at –50.7 dB—a value significantly worse than the –68.2 dB of the baseline case. The filter response for 8- and 6-bit coefficients are shown in Figs. 8.24 and 8.25, respectively.

Quantization noise

The finite digital word lengths used to represent numeric values within a digital filter limit the precision of other quantities besides the filter coefficients. Each sample of the input and output, as well as all intermediate results of mathematical operations, must be represented with finite precision. As we saw in the previous section, the effects of coefficient quantization are straightforward and easy to characterize. The effects of signal quantization are somewhat different.

TABLE 8.3 Truncated 10-Bit Coefficients for 21-Tap Low-Pass Filter

n	Sign	Hex value	Decimal value
0, 20	+	000	0.0
1, 19	–	000	0.0
2, 18	–	008	–0.001953125
3, 17	+	014	0.0048828125
4, 16	+	044	0.0166015625
5, 15	+	000	0.0
6, 14	–	0c8	–0.048828125
7, 13	–	0c8	–0.048828125
8, 12	+	158	0.083984375
9, 11	+	4b8	0.294921875
10	+	664	0.3994140625

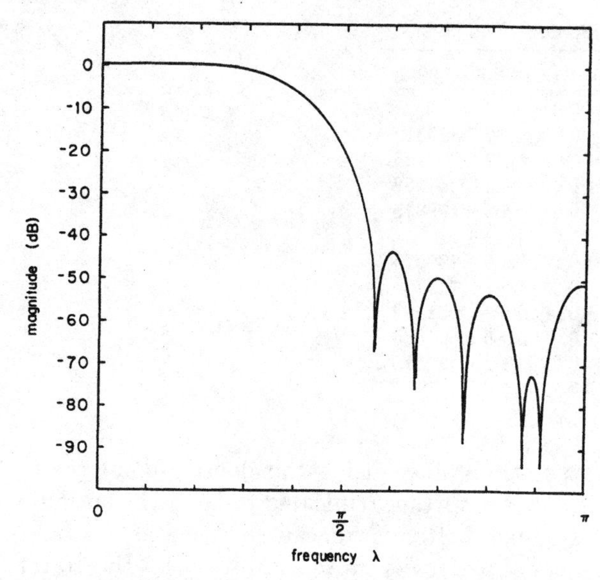

Figure 8.23 Magnitude response for 21-tap low-pass filter with coefficients quantized to 10 bits plus sign.

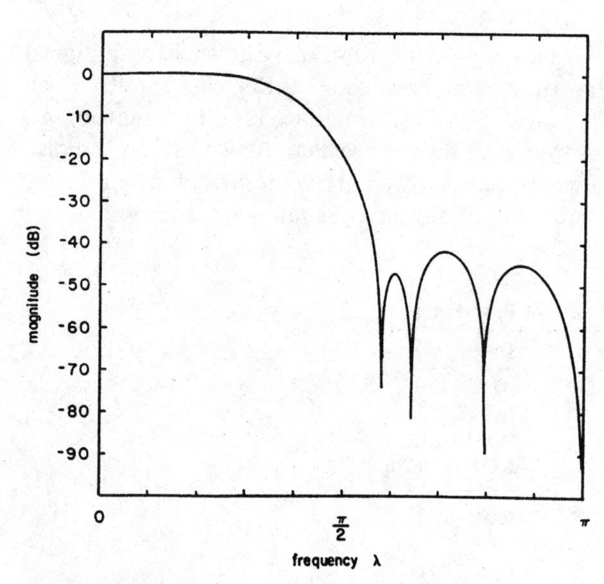

Figure 8.24 Magnitude response for 21-tap low-pass filter with coefficients quantized to 8 bits plus sign.

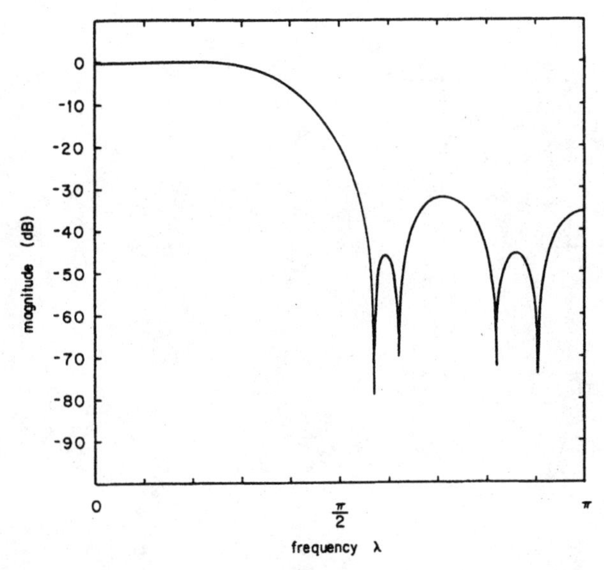

Figure 8.25 Magnitude response for 21-tap low-pass filter with coefficients quantized to 6 bits plus sign.

Typically, an *analog-to-digital converter* (*ADC*) is used to sample and quantize an analog signal that can be thought of as a continuous amplitude function of continuous time. The ADC can be viewed as a sampler and quantizer in cascade. The transfer characteristic of a typical quantizer is shown in Fig. 8.26. This particular quantizer *rounds* the analog value to the nearest "legal" quantized value. The resulting sequence of quantized signal values $y[n]$ can be viewed as the sampled continuous-time signal $x[n]$ plus an error sequence $e[n]$ whose values are equal to the errors introduced by the quantizer:

$$y[n] = x[n] + e[n]$$

A typical discrete-time signal along with the corresponding quantized sequence and error sequence are shown in Fig. 8.27. Because the quantizer rounds to the nearest quantizer level, the magnitude of the error will never exceed $Q/2$, where Q is the increment between two consecutive legal quantizer output levels, that is,

$$\frac{-Q}{2} \leq e(t) \leq \frac{Q}{2} \qquad \text{for all } t$$

The error is usually assumed to be uniformly distributed between $-Q/2$ and $Q/2$ and, consequently, to have a mean and variance of 0 and $Q^2/12$, respectively. For

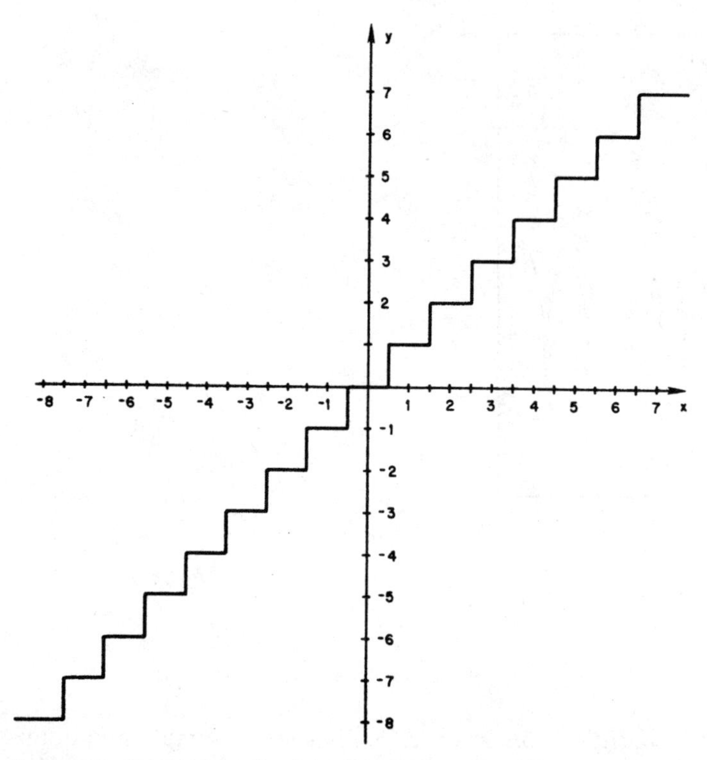

Figure 8.26 Typical transfer characteristic for a rounding quantizer.

most practical applications, this assumption is reasonable. The quantization interval Q can be related to the number of bits in the digital word. Assume a word length of $L + 1$ bits with 1 bit used for the sign and L bits for the magnitude. For the fixed-point format of Fig. 8.21, the relationship between Q and L is then given by $Q = 2^{-L}$.

It is often useful to characterize the quantization noise by means of a *signal-to-noise ratio* (*SNR*). In order to accomplish this characterization, the following additional assumptions are usually made:

1. The error sequence is assumed to be a sample sequence of a stationary random process; that is, the statistical properties of the error sequence do not change over time.

2. The error is a white-noise process; or, equivalently, the error signal is uncorrelated.

3. The error sequence $e[n]$ is uncorrelated with the sequence of unquantized samples $x[n]$.

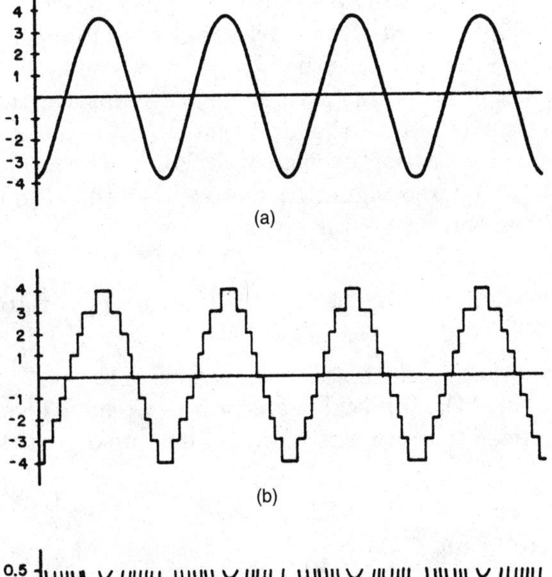

Figure 8.27 (*a*) Discrete-time continuous amplitude signal, (*b*) corresponding quantized signal, and (*c*) error sequence.

Based on these assumptions, the power of the quantization noise is equal to the error variance that was given previously as

$$\sigma_e^2 = \frac{Q^2}{12} = \frac{2^{-2L}}{12}$$

If we let σ_x^2 denote the signal power, then the SNR is given by

$$\frac{\sigma_x^2}{\sigma_e^2} = \frac{\sigma_x^2}{2^{-2L}/12} = (12 \cdot 2^{2L})\sigma_x^2$$

Expressed in decibels, this SNR is

$$10 \log \left(\frac{\sigma_x^2}{\sigma_e^2} \right) = 10 \log 12 + 20L \log 2 + 10 \log \sigma_x^2$$

$$= 10.792 + 6.021L + 10 \log \sigma_x^2 \tag{8.15}$$

The major insight to be gained from Eq. (8.15) is that the SNR improves by 6.02 dB for each bit added to the digital word format. We are not yet in a position to compute an SNR using Eq. (8.15), because the term σ_x^2 needs some further examination. How do we go about obtaining a value for σ_x^2? Whatever the value of σ_x^2 may be originally, we must realize that in practical systems, the input signal is subjected to some amplification prior to digitization. For a constant amplifier gain of A, the unquantized signal becomes $Ax[n]$, the signal power becomes $A^2\sigma_x^2$, and the corresponding SNR is given by

$$\text{SNR} = 10 \log\left(\frac{A^2\sigma_x^2}{\sigma_e^2}\right) = 10.792 + 6.021L + 10 \log (A^2\sigma_x^2) \tag{8.16}$$

A general rule of thumb often used in practical DSP applications is to set A so that $A\sigma_x$ is equal to 25 percent of the ADC full-scale value. Since we have been treating full scale as being normalized to unity, this indicates a value of A such that

$$A\sigma_x = 0.25 \qquad \text{or} \qquad A = \frac{1}{4\sigma_x}$$

Substituting this value of A into Eq. (8.16) yields

$$\begin{aligned}\text{SNR} &= 10.79 + 6.02L + 10 \log\left(\frac{1}{16}\right)\\ &= 6.02L - 1.249 \text{ dB}\end{aligned}$$

Using a value of $A = 1/(4\sigma_x)$ means that the ADC will introduce clipping any time the unquantized input signal exceeds $4\sigma_x$. Increasing A improves the SNR but decreases the *dynamic range,* that is, the range of signal values that can be accommodated without clipping. Thus, for a fixed word length, we can improve the SNR at the expense of degraded dynamic range. Conversely, by decreasing A, we could improve dynamic range at the expense of degraded SNR. The only way to simultaneously improve both dynamic range and quantization SNR is to increase the number of bits in the digital word length.

Chapter

9

Discrete Fourier Transform (DFT)

The *Fourier series* (*FS*), introduced in Chap. 1, links the continuous-time domain to the discrete-frequency domain; and the *Fourier transform* (*FT*) links the continuous-time domain to the continuous-frequency domain. The *discrete-time Fourier transform* (*DTFT*), introduced in Sec. 8.2, links the discrete-time domain to the continuous-frequency domain. In this chapter, we examine the *discrete Fourier transform* (*DFT*) which links the discrete-time and discrete-frequency domains. A complete treatment of the design and coding of DFT algorithms can fill volumes (see Brigham 1974; Burrus and Parks 1984; Nussbaumer 1981). Rather than attempt complete coverage of DFTs, this chapter presents only those aspects that are germane to the design of digital filters. Coverage of the so-called fast algorithms for implementation of the DFT is limited to one specific type of algorithm along with an examination of the computational savings that fast algorithms can provide.

9.1 Discrete Fourier Transform

The discrete Fourier transform and its inverse are given by

$$X[m] = \sum_{n=0}^{N-1} x[n]\, e^{-j2\pi mnFT} \qquad m = 0, 1, \ldots, N-1 \tag{9.1a}$$

$$= \sum_{n=0}^{N-1} x[n] \cos(2\pi mnFT) + j \sum_{n=0}^{N-1} x[n] \sin(2\pi mnFT) \tag{9.1b}$$

$$x[n] = \sum_{m=0}^{N-1} X[m]\, e^{j2\pi mnFT} \qquad n = 0, 1, \ldots, N-1 \tag{9.2a}$$

$$= \sum_{m=0}^{N-1} X[m] \cos(2\pi mnFT) + j \sum_{m=0}^{N-1} X[m] \sin(2\pi mnFT) \tag{9.2b}$$

It is a common practice in the DSP literature to "bury the details" of Eqs. (9.1) and (9.2) by defining $W_N = e^{j2\pi/N} = e^{j2\pi FT}$ and rewriting Eqs. (9.1*a*) and (9.2*a*) as

$$X[m] = \sum_{n=0}^{N-1} x[n]\, W_N^{-mn} \tag{9.3}$$

$$x[n] = \sum_{m=0}^{N-1} X[m]\, W_N^{mn} \tag{9.4}$$

Since the exponents in Eqs. (9.3) and (9.4) differ only in sign, another common practice in writing DFT software is to write only a single routine that can evaluate either Eq. (9.3) or Eq. (9.4) depending upon the value of an input flag being equal to +1 or −1. Back in the "olden days," when memory and disk space were expensive, this was a big deal; but these days, having two separate routines may pay for itself in terms of clarity, execution speed, and simplified calling sequences.

Parameter selection

In designing a DFT for a particular application, values must be chosen for the parameters N, T, and F. N is the number of time sequence values $x[n]$ over which the DFT summation is performed to compute each frequency sequence value. It is also the total number of frequency sequence values $X[m]$ produced by the DFT. For convenience, the complete set of N consecutive time sequence values is referred to as the *input record,* and the complete set of N consecutive frequency sequence values is called the *output record.* T is the time interval between two consecutive samples of the input sequence, and F is the frequency interval between two consecutive samples of the output sequence. The selection of values for N, F, and T is subject to the following constraints, which are a consequence of the sampling theorem and the inherent properties of the DFT:

1. The inherent properties of the DFT require that $FNT = 1$.
2. The sampling theorem requires that $T \leq 1/(2f_H)$, where f_H is the highest significant frequency component in the continuous-time signal.
3. The record length in time is equal to NT or $1/F$.
4. Many fast DFT algorithms (such as those discussed in Chap. 11) require that N be an integer power of 2.

Example 9.1 Choose values of N, F, and T given that F must be 5 Hz or less, N must be an integer power of 2, and the bandwidth of the input signal is 300 Hz. For the values chosen, determine the longest signal that can fit into a single input record.

solution From constraint 2 preceding, $T \leq 1/(2f_H)$. Since $f_H = 300$ Hz, $T \leq 1.66$ ms. If we select $F = 5$ and $T = 0.0016$, then $N \geq 125$. Since N must be an integer power of 2, then we choose $N = 128 = 2^7$, and F becomes 4.883 Hz. Using these values, the input record will span $NT = 204.8$ ms.

Example 9.2 Assuming that $N = 256$ and F must be 5 Hz or less, determine the highest input-signal bandwidth that can be accommodated without aliasing.

solution Since $FNT = 1$, then $T \geq 781.25$ μs. This corresponds to a maximum f_H of 640 Hz.

Periodicity

A periodic function of time will have a discrete-frequency spectrum, and a discrete-time functon will have a spectrum that is periodic. Since the DFT relates a discrete-time function to a corresponding discrete-frequency function, this implies that both the time function and frequency function are periodic as well as discrete. This means that some care must be exercised in selecting DFT parameters and in interpreting DFT results, but it does not mean that the DFT can be used only on periodic digital signals. Based on the DFT's inherent periodicity, it is a common practice to regard the points from $n = 1$ through $n = N/2$ as positive and the points from $n = N/2$ through $n = N - 1$ as negative. Since both the time and frequency sequences are periodic, the values at points $n = N/2$ through $n = N - 1$ are in fact equal to the values at points $n = N/2$ through $n = -1$. Under this convention, it is convenient to redefine the concept of even and odd sequences: If $x[N - n] = x[n]$, the $x[n]$ is even symmetric, and if $x[N - n] = -x[n]$, then $x[n]$ is odd symmetric or antisymmetric.

9.2 Properties of the DFT

The DFT exhibits a number of useful properties and operational relationships that are similar to the properties of the continuous Fourier transform discussed in Chap. 1.

Linearity

The DFT relating $x[n]$ and $X[m]$:

$$x[n] \underset{\text{IDFT}}{\overset{\text{DFT}}{\rightleftarrows}} X[m]$$

is homogeneous

$$aX[n] \underset{\text{IDFT}}{\overset{\text{DFT}}{\rightleftarrows}} aX[m]$$

additive

$$x[n] + y[n] \underset{\text{IDFT}}{\overset{\text{DFT}}{\rightleftarrows}} X[m] + Y[m]$$

and therefore linear

$$ax[n] + by[n] \underset{\text{IDFT}}{\overset{\text{DFT}}{\rightleftarrows}} aX[m] + bY[m]$$

Symmetry

A certain symmetry exists between a time sequence and the corresponding frequency sequence produced by the DFT. Given that $x[n]$ and $X[m]$ constitute a DFT pair, that is,

$$x[n] \underset{\text{IDFT}}{\overset{\text{DFT}}{\rightleftarrows}} X[m]$$

then

$$\frac{1}{N} X[n] \underset{\text{IDFT}}{\overset{\text{DFT}}{\rightleftarrows}} x[-m]$$

Time shifting

A time sequence $x[n]$ can be shifted in time by subtracting an integer from n. Shifting the time sequence will cause the corresponding frequency sequence to be phase-shifted. Specifically, given

$$x[n] \underset{\text{IDFT}}{\overset{\text{DFT}}{\rightleftarrows}} X[m]$$

then

$$x[n-k] \underset{\text{IDFT}}{\overset{\text{DFT}}{\rightleftarrows}} X[m]\, e^{-j2\pi mk/N}$$

Frequency shifting

Time sequence modulation is accomplished by multiplying the time sequence by an imaginary exponential term $e^{j2\pi nk/N}$. This will cause a frequency shift of the corresponding spectrum. Specifically, given

$$x[n] \underset{\text{IDFT}}{\overset{\text{DFT}}{\rightleftarrows}} X[m]$$

then

$$x[n]\, e^{j2\pi mk/N} \underset{\text{IDFT}}{\overset{\text{DFT}}{\rightleftarrows}} X[m-k]$$

Even and odd symmetry

Consider a time sequence $x[n]$ and the corresponding frequency sequence $X[m] = X_R[m] + jX_I[m]$, where $X_R[m]$ and $X_I[m]$ are real valued. If $x[n]$ is even, then $X[m]$ is real valued and even:

$$x[-n] = x[n] \Leftrightarrow X[m] = X_R[m] = X_R[-m]$$

If $x[n]$ is odd, then $X[m]$ is imaginary and odd:

$$x[-n] = -x[n] \Leftrightarrow X[m] = jX_I[m] = -jX_I[-m]$$

Real and imaginary properties

In general, the DFT of a real-valued time sequence will have an even real component and an odd imaginary component. Conversely, an imaginary-valued time sequence will have an odd real component and an even imaginary component. Given a time sequence $x[n] = x_R[n] + jx_I[n]$ and the corresponding frequency sequence $X[m] = X_R[m] + jX_I[m]$, then

$$x[n] = x_R[n] \Leftrightarrow X_R[m] = X_R[-m] \qquad X_I[m] = -X_I[-m]$$

$$x[n] = jx_I[n] \Leftrightarrow X_R[m] = -X_R[-m] \qquad X_I[m] = X_I[-m]$$

9.3 Implementing the DFT

The function `Dft( )` shown in Listing 9.1 is the "brute-force" implementation of Eq. (9.1). This function is an example of grossly inefficient code. The sine and cosine operations are each performed N^2 times to compute an N-point DFT. Since

$$\exp\left(\frac{-2\pi jk}{N}\right) = \exp\left[\frac{-2\pi j(k \bmod N)}{N}\right]$$

it follows that there are only N different values of `phi` that need to be computed in `Dft( )`. We can trade space for speed by precomputing and storing the values of `sin(phi)` and `cos(phi)` for `phi` $= 2\pi k/N$, $k = 0, 1, \ldots, N-1$. The resulting modified function `Dft2( )` is shown in Listing 9.2.

9.4 Applying the DFT

Short time-limited signals

Consider the time-limited continuous-time signal and its continuous spectrum shown in Figs. 9.1*a* and 9.1*b*. (Remember that a signal cannot be both strictly time limited and strictly band limited.) We can sample this signal to produce the time sequence shown in Fig. 9.1*c* for input to a DFT. If the input record length N is chosen to be longer than the length of the input time sequence, the entire sequence can fit within the input record as shown. As discussed in Sec. 9.2, the DFT will treat the input sequence as though it is the periodic sequence shown in Fig. 9.1*d*. This will result in a periodic discrete-frequency spectrum as shown in Fig. 9.1*e*. The actual output produced by the DFT algorithm will be the sequence of values from $m = 0$ to $m = N - 1$. Of course, there will be some aliasing due to the time-limited nature (and consequently unlimited bandwidth) of the input-signal pulse.

Periodic signals

Consider the band-limited and periodic continuous-time signal and its spectrum shown in Fig. 9.2. We can sample this signal to produce the time sequence

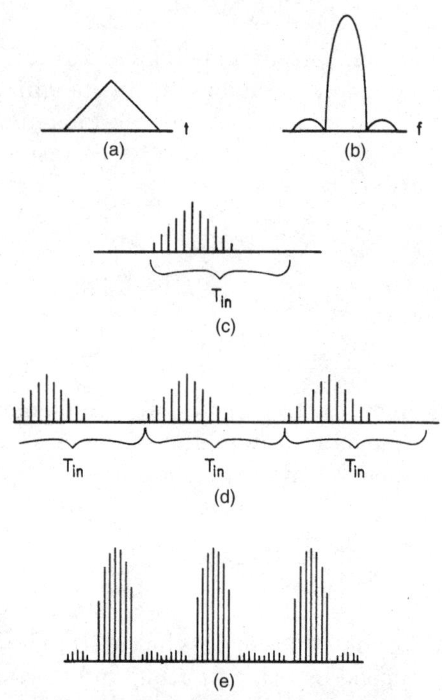

Figure 9.1 Signals and sequences for the DFT of a short time-limited signal: (*a*) the continuous signal, (*b*) its continuous spectrum, (*c*) sampled sequence for input to DFT, (*d*) periodic sequence the DFT will treat it as, and (*e*) the resulting periodic discrete-frequency spectrum.

shown in Fig. 9.2*c* for input to the DFT. If the input record length N of the DFT is chosen to be exactly equal to the length of one period of this sequence, the periodic assumption implicit in the DFT will cause the DFT to treat the single input record as though it were the complete sequence. The corresponding periodic discrete-frequency spectrum is shown in Fig. 9.2*d*. The DFT output sequence will actually consist of just one period that matches *exactly* the spectrum of Fig. 9.2*b*. We could not hope for (or find) a more convenient situation. Unfortunately, this relationship exists only in an N-point DFT where the input signal is both band limited and periodic with a period of exactly N.

Long aperiodic signals

So far we have covered the use of the DFT under relatively favorable conditions that are not likely to exist in many important signal-processing applications.

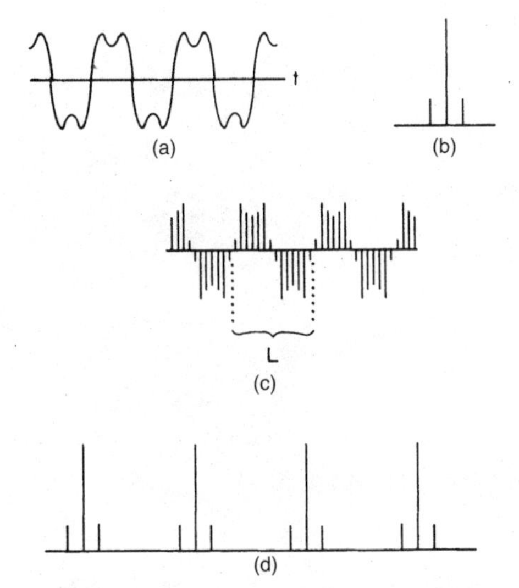

Figure 9.2 Signal and sequences for the DFT of a periodic signal. The length L of the DFT input record equals the period of the signal. (*a*) The band-limited signal. (*b*) The signal's spectrum. (*c*) The resulting time sequence for DFT input. (*d*) The corresponding discrete-frequency spectrum.

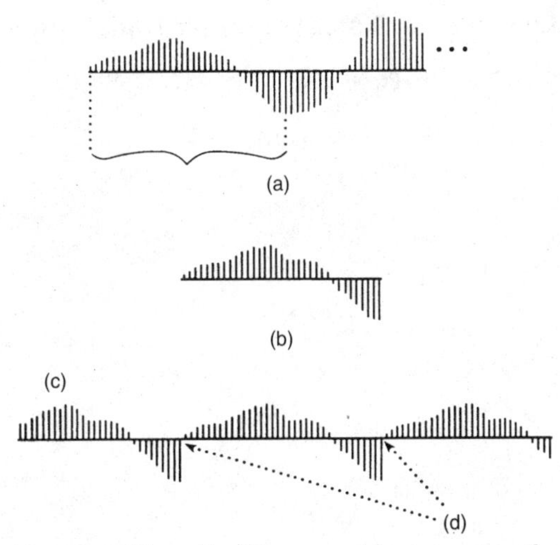

Figure 9.3 Discontinuities caused by truncating the input sequence of a DFT: (*a*) long input sequence, (*b*) truncated input sequence, (*c*) input sequence as interpreted by the DFT, and (*d*) resulting discontinuities.

Often the signal to be analyzed will be neither periodic nor reasonably time-limited. The corresponding sequence of digitized-signal values will be longer than the DFT input record and will therefore have to be truncated to just N samples before the DFT can be applied. The periodic nature of the DFT will cause the truncated sequence of Fig. 9.3*b* to be interpreted as though it were the sequence shown in Fig. 9.3*c*. Notice that in this sequence there is a large discontinuity in the signal at the points corresponding to the ends of the input record. This will introduce additional high-frequency components into the spectrum produced by the DFT. This phenomenon is called *leakage*. To reduce the leakage effects, it is a common practice to multiply the truncated input sequence by a tapering window prior to application of the DFT. A good window shape will taper off at the ends of the input record but still have a reasonably compact and narrow spectrum. This is important, since multiplying the time sequence by the window will cause the corresponding frequency sequence to be convolved with the spectrum of the window. A narrow window spectrum will cause minimum smearing of the signal spectrum. Several popular windowing functions and their spectra are treated at length in Chap. 14.

Listing 9.1 Discrete Fourier Transform

```
const double TWO_PI = 6.283185308;

void dft( double_complex *x_in,
          double_complex *y_out,
          int num_samps)
{
 int n, m;
 int k;
 double phi;
 double sum_real, sum_imag;

 for( m =0; m<num_samps; m++)
   {
    sum_real = 0.0;
    sum_imag = 0.0;

    for( n =0; n<num_samps; n++)
      {
       phi = TWO_PI * m * n /num_samps;
       sum_real += (real(x_in[n]) * cos(phi) - imag(x_in[k]) * sin(phi));
       sum_imag += (imag(x_in[n]) * cos(phi) + real(x_in[k]) * sin(phi));
      }
    y_out[m] = double_complex(sum_real, sum_imag);
   }
 return;
}
```

Listing 9.2 Improved Implementation of the Discrete Fourier Transform

```
const double TWO_PI = 6.283185308;

void dft2( double_complex *x_in,
           double_complex *y_out,
           int num_samps)
{
 int n, m;
 int k;
 double *cos_val, *sin_val;
 double w_factor;
 double sum_real, sum_imag;

 cos_val = new double[num_samps];
 sin_val = new double[num_samps];
 w_factor = TWO_PI/num_samps;
```

```
 for( k=0; k<num_samps; k++)
   {
    cos_val[k] = (double)cos(w_factor * k);
    sin_val[k] = (double)sin(w_factor * k);
   }

 for( m =0; m<num_samps; m++)
   {
    sum_real = 0.0;
    sum_imag = 0.0;

    for( n =0; n<num_samps; n++)
      {
       k = (m*n) % num_samps;
       sum_real += (real(x_in[n]) * cos_val[k] + imag(x_in[n]) * sin_val[k]);
       sum_imag += (imag(x_in[n]) * cos_val[k] - real(x_in[n]) * sin_val[k]);
      }
    y_out[m] = double_complex(sum_real, sum_imag);
   }
 delete [] cos_val;
 delete [] sin_val;
 return;
}
```

Chapter

10

The z Transform

The *two-sided,* or *bilateral,* z transform of a discrete-time sequence $x[n]$ is defined by

$$X(z) = \sum_{n=-\infty}^{\infty} x[n]\, z^{-n} \tag{10.1}$$

and the *one-sided,* or *unilateral,* z transform is defined by

$$X(z) = \sum_{n=0}^{\infty} x[n]\, z^{-n} \tag{10.2}$$

Some authors (for example, Rabiner and Gold 1975) use the unqualified term *z transform* to refer to Eq. (10.1), while others (for example, Cadzow 1973) use the unqualified term to refer to Eq. (10.2). In this book, *z transform* refers to the two-sided transform, and the one-sided transform is explicitly identified as such. For causal sequences (that is, $x[n] = 0$ for $n < 0$) the one-sided and two-sided transforms are equivalent. Some of the material presented in this chapter may seem somewhat abstract, but rest assured that the z transform and its properties play a major role in many of the design and realization methods that appear in later chapters.

10.1 Region of Convergence

For some values of z, the series in Eq. (10.1) does not converge to a finite value. The portion of the z plane for which the series does converge is called the *region of convergence* (*ROC*). Whether or not Eq. (10.1) converges depends upon the magnitude of z rather than a specific complex value of z. In other words, for a given sequence $x[n]$, if the series in Eq. (10.1) converges for a value of $z = z_1$, then the series will converge for all values of z for which $|z| = |z_1|$. Conversely, if the series diverges for $z = z_2$, then the series will diverge for all values of z for which

$|z| = |z_2|$. Because convergence depends on the magnitude of z, the region or convergence will always be *bounded* by circles centered at the origin of the z plane. This is not to say that the region of convergence is always a circle—it can be the interior of a circle, the exterior of a circle, an annulus, or the entire z plane as shown in Fig. 10.1. Each of these four cases can be loosely viewed as an annulus—a circle's interior being an annulus with an inner radius of zero and a finite outer radius, a circle's exterior being an annulus with nonzero inner radius and infinite outer radius, and the entire z plane being an annulus with an inner radius of zero and an infinite outer radius. In some cases, the ROC has an inner radius of zero, but the origin itself is not part of the region. In other cases, the ROC has an infinite outer radius, but the series diverges *at* $|z| = \infty$.

By definition, the ROC cannot contain any poles, since the series becomes infinite at the poles. The ROC for a z transform will always be a simply connected region in the z plane. If we assume that the sequence $x[n]$ has a finite magnitude for all finite values of n, the nature of the ROC can be related to the nature of the sequence in several ways, as discussed in the paragraphs that follow and as summarized in Table 10.1.

Finite-duration sequences

If $x[n]$ is nonzero over only a finite range of n, then the z transform can be rewritten as

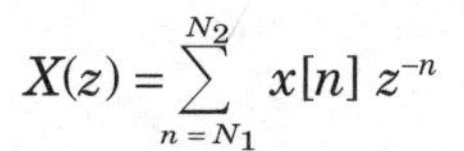

$$X(z) = \sum_{n=N_1}^{N_2} x[n]\, z^{-n}$$

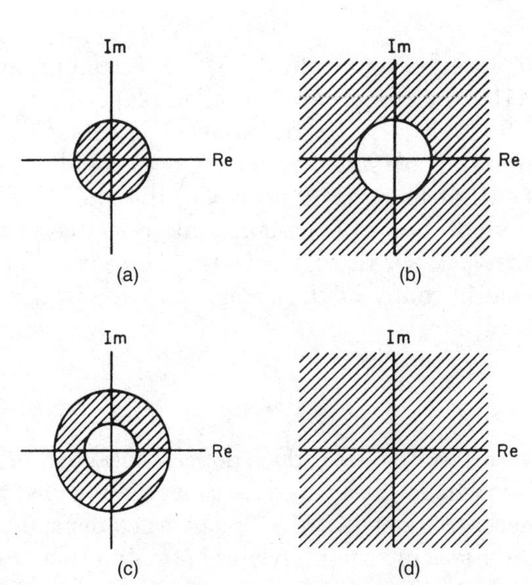

Figure 10.1 Possible configurations of the region of convergence for the z transform: (*a*) interior of a circle, (*b*) exterior of a circle, (*c*) an annulus, and (*d*) the entire plane.

TABLE 10.1 Properties of the Region of Convergence for the z Transform

$x[n]$	ROC for $X(z)$
All	Includes no poles
All	Simply connected region
Single sample at $n = 0$	Entire z plane
Finite-duration, causal, $x[n] = 0$ for all $n < 0$, $x[n] \neq 0$ for some $n > 0$	z plane except for $z = 0$
Finite-duration, with $x[n] \neq 0$ for some $n < 0$, $x[n] = 0$ for all $n > 0$	z plane except for $z = \infty$
Finite-duration, with $x[n] \neq 0$ for some $n < 0$, $x[n] \neq 0$ for some $n > 0$	z plane except for $z = 0$ and $z = \infty$
Right-sided, $x[n] = 0$ for all $n < 0$	Outward from outermost pole
Right-sided, $x[n] \neq 0$ for some $n < 0$	Outward from outermost pole, $z = \infty$ is excluded
Left-sided, $x[n] = 0$ for all $n > 0$	Inward from innermost pole
Left-sided, $x[n] \neq 0$ for some $n > 0$	Inward from innermost pole, $z = 0$ is excluded
Two-sided	Annulus

This series will converge provided that $|x[n]| < \infty$ for $N_1 \leq n \leq N_2$ and $|z^{-n}| < \infty$ for $N_1 \leq n \leq N_2$. For negative values of n, $|z^{-n}|$ will be infinite for $z = \infty$; and for positive values of n, $|z^{-n}|$ will be infinite for $z = 0$. Therefore, a sequence having nonzero values only for $n = N_1$ through $n = N_2$ will have a z transform that converges everywhere in the z plane except for $z = \infty$ when $N_1 < 0$ and $z = 0$ when $N_2 > 0$. Note that a single sample at $n = 0$ is the only finite-duration sequence defined over the entire z plane.

Infinite-duration sequences

The sequence $x[n]$ is a *right-sided sequence* if $x[n]$ is zero for all n less than some finite value N_1. It can be shown (see Oppenheim and Schafer 1975 or 1989) that the z transform $X(z)$ of a right-sided sequence will have an ROC that extends outward from the outermost finite pole of $X(z)$. In other words, the ROC will be the area outside a circle whose radius equals the magnitude of the pole of $X(z)$ having the largest magnitude (see Fig. 10.2). If $N_1 < 0$, this ROC will not include $z = \infty$.

The sequence $x[n]$ is a *left-sided sequence* if $x[n]$ is zero for all n greater than some finite value N_2. The z transform $X(z)$ of a left-sided sequence will have an ROC that extends inward from the innermost pole of $X(z)$. The ROC will be the interior of a circle whose radius equals the magnitude of the pole of $X(z)$ having the smallest magnitude (see Fig. 10.3). If $N_2 > 0$, this ROC will not include $z = 0$.

The sequence $x[n]$ is a *two-sided sequence* if $x[n]$ has nonzero values extending to both $-\infty$ and $+\infty$. The ROC for the z transform of a two-sided sequence will be an annulus.

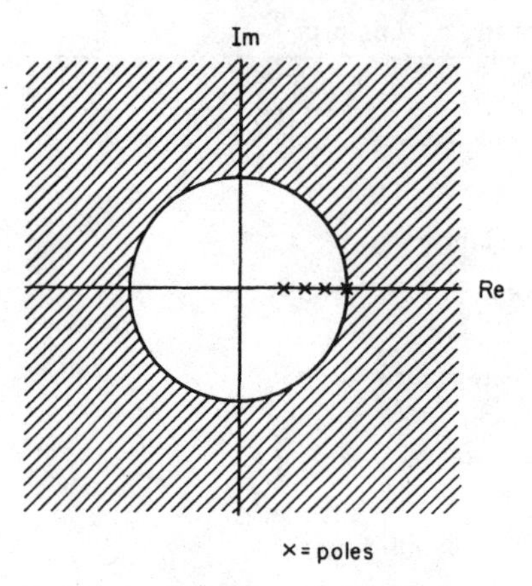

Figure 10.2 Region of convergence for the z transform of a right-sided sequence.

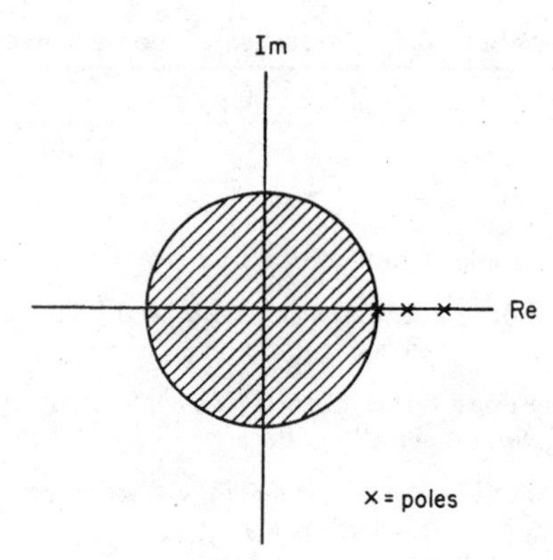

Figure 10.3 Region of convergence for the z transform of a left-sided sequence.

Convergence of the unilateral *z* transform

Note that all of the properties discussed in the preceding are for the two-sided z transform defined by Eq. (10.1). Since the one-sided z transform is equivalent to the two-sided transform when $x[n] = 0$ for $n < 0$, the ROC for a one-sided transform will always look like the ROC for the two-sided transform of either a causal finite-duration sequence or a causal right-sided sequence. For all causal systems, the ROC for the bilateral transform always consists of the area outside a circle of radius $R \geq 0$. Therefore, for two-sided transforms of causal sequences and for all one-sided transforms, the ROC can be (and frequently is) specified in terms of a *radius of convergence* R such that the transform converges for $|z| > R$.

10.2 Relationship between the Laplace and *z* Transforms

The z transform can be related to both the Laplace and Fourier transforms. As noted in Chap. 8, a sequence can be obtained by sampling a function of continuous time. Specifically, for a causal sequence

$$x[n] = \sum_{n=0}^{\infty} x_a(nT)\,\delta(t - nT) \tag{10.3}$$

the Laplace transform is given by

$$X(s) = \sum_{n=0}^{\infty} x_a(nT)\, e^{-nTs} \tag{10.4}$$

Let $X_a(s)$ denote the Laplace transform of $x_a(t)$. The pole-zero pattern for $X(s)$ consists of the pole-zero pattern for $X_a(s)$ replicated at intervals of $\omega_s = 2\pi/T$ along the $j\omega$ axis in the s plane. If we modify Eq. (10.4) by substituting

$$z = e^{sT} \tag{10.5}$$

$$x[n] = x_a(nT) \tag{10.6}$$

we obtain the z transform defined by Eq. (10.1).

Relationships between features in the s plane and features in the z plane can be established using Eq. (10.5). Since $s = \sigma + j\omega$ with σ and ω real, we can expand Eq. (10.5) as

$$z = e^{sT} = e^{\sigma T} e^{j\omega T} = e^{\sigma T}(\cos \omega T + j \sin \omega T)$$

Because $|e^{j\omega T}| = (\cos^2 \omega T + \sin^2 \omega T)^{1/2} = 1$, and $T > 0$, we can conclude that $|z| < 1$ for $\sigma < 0$. Or, in other words, the left half of the s plane maps into the interior of the unit circle in the z plane. Likewise, $|z| = 1$ for $\sigma = 0$, so the $j\omega$ axis of the s plane maps onto the unit circle in the z plane. The "extra" replicated copies of the pole-zero pattern for $X(s)$ will all map into a single pole-zero pattern in the z plane. When evaluated around the unit circle (that is, $z = e^{j\lambda}$), the z transform yields the discrete-time Fourier transform (DTFT) (see Sec. 8.2).

10.3 System Functions

Given the relationships between the Laplace transform and the z transform that were noted in the previous section, we might suspect that the z transform of a discrete-time system's unit sample response (that is, digital impulse response) plays a major role in the analysis of the system in much the same way that the Laplace transform of a continuous-time system's impulse response yields the system's transfer function. This suspicion is indeed correct. The z transform of a discrete-time system's unit sample response is called the *system function,* or *transfer function,* of the system and is denoted by $H(z)$.

The system function can also be derived from the linear difference equation that describes the filter. If we take the z transform of each term in Eq. (8.6), we obtain

$$Y(z) + a_1 z^{-1} Y(z) + a_2 z^{-2} Y(z) + \cdots + a_k z^{-k} Y(z)$$

$$= b_0 X(z) + b_1 z^{-1} X(z) + b_2 z^{-2} X(z) + b_k z^{-k} X(z)$$

Factoring out $Y(z)$ and $X(z)$ and then solving for $H(z) = Y(z)/X(z)$ yields

$$H(z) = \frac{Y(z)}{X(z)} = \frac{b_0 + b_1 z^{-1} + b_2 z^{-2} + \cdots + b_k z^{-k}}{1 + a_1 z^{-1} + a_2 z^{-2} + \cdots + a_k z^{-k}}$$

Both the numerator and denominator of $H(z)$ can be factored to yield

$$H(z) = \frac{b_0(z - q_1)(z - q_2) \cdots (z - q_k)}{(z - p_1)(z - p_2)(z - p_3) \cdots (z - p_k)}$$

The poles of $H(z)$ are $p_1, p_2, \ldots, p_k$, and the zeros are $q_1, q_2, \ldots, q_m$.

10.4 Common *z*-Transform Pairs and Properties

The use of the unilateral z transform by some authors and the use of the bilateral transform by others does not present as many problems as we might expect, because in the field of digital filters, most of the sequences of interest are causal sequences or sequences that can easily be made causal. As we noted previously, for causal sequences the one-sided and two-sided transforms are equivalent. It really just comes down to a matter of being careful about definitions. An author using the unilateral default (that is, "z transform" means "unilateral z transform") might say that the z transform of $x[n] = a^n$ is given by

$$X(z) = \frac{z}{z - a} \qquad \text{for} \quad |z| > |a| \tag{10.7}$$

On the other hand, an author using the bilateral default might say that Eq. (10.7) represents the z transform of $x[n] = a^n u[n]$, where $u[n]$ is the unit step sequence. Neither author is concerned with the values of a^n for $n < 0$—the first author is eliminating these values by the way the transform is defined, and the second author is eliminating these values by multiplying them with a unit step sequence that is zero for $n < 0$. There are a few useful bilateral transform pairs that consider values of $x[n]$ for $n < 0$. These pairs are listed in Table 10.2. However, the majority of the most commonly used z-transform pairs involve values of $x[n]$ only for $n \geq 0$. These pairs are most conveniently tabulated as unilateral transforms with the understanding that any unilateral transform pair can be converted into a bilateral transform pair by replacing $x[n]$ with $x[n]\,u[n]$. Some common unilateral z-transform pairs are listed in Table 10.3. Some useful

TABLE 10.2 Common Bilateral *z*-Transform Pairs

$x[n]$	$X(z)$	ROC
$\delta[n]$	1	All z
$\delta[n - m],\ m > 0$	z^{-m}	$z \neq 0$
$\delta[n - m],\ m < 0$	z^{-m}	$z \neq \infty$
$u[n]$	$\dfrac{z}{z - 1}$	$\lvert z \rvert > 1$
$-u[-n - 1]$	$\dfrac{z}{z - 1}$	$\lvert z \rvert < 1$
$-a^n u[-n - 1]$	$\dfrac{z}{z - a}$	$\lvert z \rvert < \lvert a \rvert$
$-na^n u[-n - 1]$	$\dfrac{az}{(z - a)^2}$	$\lvert z \rvert < \lvert a \rvert$

TABLE 10.3 Common Unilateral z-Transform Pairs

$x[n]$	$X(z)$	R
1	$\dfrac{z}{z-1}$	1
$u_1[n]$	$\dfrac{z}{z-1}$	1
$\delta[n]$	1	0 (z = 0 included)
nT	$\dfrac{Tz}{(z-1)^2}$	1
$(nT)^2$	$\dfrac{T^2z(z+1)}{(z-1)^3}$	1
$(nT)^3$	$\dfrac{T^3z(z^2+4z+1)}{(z-1)^4}$	1
a^n	$\dfrac{z}{z-a}$	$\lvert a \rvert$
$(n+1)a^n$	$\dfrac{z^2}{(z-a)^2}$	$\lvert a \rvert$
$\dfrac{(n+1)(n+2)}{2!}a^n$	$\dfrac{z^3}{(z-a)^3}$	$\lvert a \rvert$
$\dfrac{(n+1)(n+2)(n+3)}{3!}a^n$	$\dfrac{z^4}{(z-a)^4}$	$\lvert a \rvert$
$\dfrac{(n+1)(n+2)(n+3)(n+4)}{4!}a^n$	$\dfrac{z^5}{(z-a)^5}$	$\lvert a \rvert$
na^n	$\dfrac{az}{(z-a)^2}$	$\lvert a \rvert$
n^2a^n	$\dfrac{az(z+a)}{(z-a)^3}$	$\lvert a \rvert$
n^3a^n	$\dfrac{az(z^2+4az+a^2)}{(z-a)^4}$	$\lvert a \rvert$
$\dfrac{a^n}{n!}$	$e^{a/z}$	0
e^{-anT}	$\dfrac{z}{z-e^{-aT}}$	$\lvert e^{-aT} \rvert$
$a^n \sin n\omega T$	$\dfrac{az \sin \omega T}{z^2 - 2az \cos \omega T + a^2}$	$\lvert a \rvert$
$a^n \cos n\omega T$	$\dfrac{z^2 - za \cos \omega T}{z^2 - 2az \cos \omega T + a^2}$	$\lvert a \rvert$
$e^{-anT} \sin \omega_0 nT$	$\dfrac{ze^{-aT} \sin \omega_0 T}{z^2 - 2ze^{-aT} \cos \omega_0 T + e^{-2aT}}$	$\lvert e^{-aT} \rvert$
$e^{-anT} \cos \omega_0 nT$	$\dfrac{z^2 - ze^{-aT} \cos \omega_0 T}{z^2 - 2ze^{-aT} \cos \omega_0 T + e^{-2aT}}$	$\lvert e^{-aT} \rvert$

NOTE: R = radius of convergence.

properties exhibited by both the unilateral and bilateral z transforms are listed in Table 10.4.

10.5 Inverse z Transform

The inverse z transform is given by the contour integral

$$x[n] = \frac{1}{2\pi j} \oint_C X(z)\, z^{n-1}\, dz \tag{10.8}$$

where the integral notation indicates a counterclockwise closed contour that encircles the origin of the z plane and that lies within the region of convergence for $X(z)$. If $X(z)$ is rational, the residue theorem can be used to evaluate Eq. (10.8). However, direct evaluation of the inversion integral is rarely performed in actual practice. In practical situations, inversion of the z transform is usually performed indirectly, using established transform pairs and transform properties.

10.6 Inverse z Transform via Partial Fraction Expansion

Consider a system function of the general form given by

$$H(z) = \frac{b_0 z^m + b_1 z^{m-1} + \cdots + b_{m-1} z^1 + b_m}{z_m + a_1 z^{m-1} + \cdots + a_{m-1} z^1 + a_m} \tag{10.9}$$

Such a system function can be expanded into a sum of simpler terms that can be more easily inverse-transformed. Linearity of the z transform allows us to

TABLE 10.4 Properties of the z Transform

Property no.	Time function	Transform
	$x[n]$	$X(z)$
	$y[n]$	$Y(z)$
1	$ax[n]$	$aX(z)$
2	$x[n] + y[n]$	$X(z) + Y(z)$
3	$e^{-anT}\, x[n]$	$X(e^{at}z)$
4	$\alpha^n x[n]$	$X\left(\frac{z}{\alpha}\right)$
5	$x[n-m]$	$z^{-m}\, X(z)$
6	$x[n] * y[n]$	$X(z)\, Y(z)$
7	$nx[n]$	$-z\frac{d}{dz} X(z)$
8	$x[-n]$	$X(z^{-1})$
9	$x^*[n]$	$X^*(z^*)$

then sum the simpler inverse transforms to obtain the inverse of the original system function. The method for generating the expansion differs slightly depending upon whether the system function's poles are all distinct or if some are multiple poles. Since most practical filter designs involve system functions with distinct poles, the more complicated multiple-pole procedure is not presented. For a discussion of the multiple-pole case, see Cadzow (1973).

Algorithm 10.1 Partial fraction expansion for $H(z)$ having simple poles

Step 1. Factor the denominator of $H(z)$ to produce

$$H(z) = \frac{b_0 z^m + b_1 z^{m-1} + \cdots + b_{m-1} z^1 + b_m}{(z - p_1)(z - p_2)(z - p_3) \cdots (z - p_k)}$$

Step 2. Compute c_0 as given by

$$c_0 = H(z)\big|_{z=0} = \frac{b_m}{(-p_1)(-p_2)(-p_3) \cdots (-p_m)}$$

Step 3. Compute c_i for $1 \le i \le m$ using

$$c_i = \frac{z - p_i}{z} H(z)\big|_{z=p_i}$$

Step 4. Formulate the discrete-time function $h[n]$ as given by

$$h(n) = c_0 \delta(n) + c_1 (p_1)^n + c_2 (p_2)^n + \cdots + c_m (p_m)^n \qquad \text{for} \quad n = 0, 1, 2, \ldots$$

The function $h[n]$ is the inverse z transform of $H(z)$.

Example 10.1 Use the partial fraction expansion to determine the inverse z transform of

$$H(z) = \frac{z^2}{z^2 + z - 2}$$

solution

Step 1. Factor the denominator of $H(z)$ to produce

$$H(z) = \frac{z^2}{(z-1)(z+2)}$$

Step 2. Compute c_0 as

$$c_0 = H(z)\big|_{z=0} = 0$$

Step 3. Compute c_1, c_2 as

$$c_1 = \left[\frac{(z-1)}{z} \frac{z^2}{(z-1)(z+2)} \right] \Bigg|_{z=1} = \frac{z^2}{z^2+2z} \Bigg|_{z=1} = \frac{1}{3}$$

$$c_2 = \left[\frac{(z+2)}{z} \frac{z^2}{(z-1)(z+2)} \right] \Bigg|_{z=-2} = \frac{z^2}{z^2-z} \Bigg|_{z=-2} = \frac{2}{3}$$

Step 4. The inverse transform $h[n]$ is given by

$$h[n] = \frac{1}{3}(1)^n + \frac{1}{3}(-2)^n$$

$$= 1 + \frac{1}{3}(-2)^n \qquad n = 0, 1, 2, \ldots$$

Chapter

11

Fast Fourier Transforms

The discrete Fourier transform has many potential uses in the design and implementation of digital filters. However, for all but the smallest transforms, the direct computation of the DFT in the form presented in Chap. 9 is prohibitively expensive in terms of required computer operations. Fortunately, a number of "fast" transforms have been developed that are mathematically equivalent to the DFT, but which require significantly fewer computer operations for their implementation. This chapter examines some of the more useful of these fast algorithms.

11.1 Computational Complexity of the DFT

Consider the basic form of the DFT given by

$$X[m] = \sum_{n=0}^{N-1} x[n] e^{-j2\pi mn/N}$$

It is readily apparent that computation of $X[m]$ for any single value of m will require (in general) N complex multiplications and N complex additions. Therefore, computing a complete set of N values for $X[m]$ will entail N^2 complex multiplications and N^2 complex additions. (This total includes some trivial multiplications by 1 as well as some nearly trivial multiplications by j.) Furthermore, values of $e^{-j2\pi mn/N}$ need to be computed for various combinations of m and n.

11.2 Decimation-in-Time Algorithms

Start with the usual DFT for an N-point sequence

$$X[m] = \sum_{n=0}^{N-1} x[n] W_N^{mn} \qquad m = 0, 1, \ldots, N-1$$

where

$$W_N = \exp\left(\frac{-2\pi j}{N}\right)$$

Then break the summation into two separate summations—one for the even-indexed samples of $x[n]$ and one for the odd-indexed samples of $x[n]$,

$$\begin{aligned} X[m] &= \sum_{\substack{n=0 \\ n \text{ even}}}^{N-1} x[n]W_N^{nm} + \sum_{\substack{n=0 \\ n \text{ odd}}}^{N-1} x[n]W_N^{nm} \\ &= \sum_{n=0}^{N/2-1} x[2n]W_N^{2nm} + \sum_{n=0}^{N/2-1} x[2n+1]W_N^{(2n+1)m} \\ &= \sum_{n=0}^{N/2-1} x[2n]W_N^{2nm} + W_N^m \sum_{n=0}^{N/2-1} x[2n+1]W_N^{2nm} \end{aligned} \tag{11.1}$$

The factor W_N^{2mn} is equal to $W_{N/2}^{mn}$. Therefore, we can represent Eq. (11.1) as

$$X[m] = \sum_{n=0}^{N/2-1} x[2n]W_{N/2}^{nm} + W_N^m \sum_{n=0}^{N/2-1} x[2n+1]W_{N/2}^{nm} \tag{11.2}$$

Each of the summations in Eq. (11.2) has the form of an ($N/2$)-point DFT. Therefore, we can define x_{even} and x_{odd} as

$$x_{\text{even}}[n] = x[2n] \qquad n = 0, 1, \ldots, N/2 - 1$$

$$x_{\text{odd}}[n] = x[2n+1] \qquad n = 0, 1, \ldots, N/2 - 1$$

and rewrite Eq. (11.2) as

$$X[m] = X_{\text{even}}[m] + W_N^m X_{\text{odd}}[m]$$

where $X_{\text{even}}[m]$ and $X_{\text{odd}}[m]$ are the ($N/2$)-point DFTs of $x_{\text{even}}[n]$ and $x_{\text{odd}}[n]$ respectively. What all this means is that any N-point DFT (where N is even) can be broken into two ($N/2$)-point DFTs. In turn, if $N/2$ is even, each of these ($N/2$)-point DFTs can be broken into two ($N/4$)-point DFTs, allowing us to express the original N-point DFT in terms of four ($N/4$)-point DFTs. If N is an integer power of 2 (i.e., $N = 2^\nu$) the process of breaking each DFT into two smaller DFTs can be repeated until the original DFT can be computed as a combination of 2^ν 1-point DFTs. Computing the DFT in this indirect manner results in a very significant computational savings.

Example 11.1 Let's do the complete breakdown for the case of an 8-point DFT originally defined by

$$X[m] = \sum_{n=0}^{7} x[n]W^{nm} \qquad m = 0, 1, \ldots, 7$$

(The subscript N has been omitted from W for convenience.) Splitting this into separate DFTs for even and odd n as in Eq. (11.1) yields

$$X[m] = \sum_{n=0}^{3} x[2n]W^{2mn} + W^m \sum_{n=0}^{3} x[2n+1]W^{2mn} \tag{11.3}$$

If we let $A[m]$ denote the DFT of the even-indexed samples and $B[m]$ denote the DFT of the odd-indexed samples, then we can rewrite Eq. (11.3) as

$$X[m] = A[m] + W^m B[m] \tag{11.4}$$

$X[m]$ is an 8-point frequency sequence, but $A[m]$ and $B[m]$ are only 4-point frequency sequences. What happens for $m = 4, 5, 6,$ and 7? As discussed in Chap. 9, an N-point DFT is periodic with a period of N samples, that is,

$$A[4] = A[0], B[4] = B[0], A[5] = A[1], B[5] = B[1], \text{etc.}$$

Therefore,

$$X[4] = A[0] + W^4 B[0]$$

$$X[5] = A[1] + W^5 B[1]$$

$$X[6] = A[2] + W^6 B[2]$$

$$X[7] = A[3] + W^7 B[3]$$

The operations represented by Eq. (11.4) are depicted in the signal flow graph (SFG) of Fig. 11.1. In an SFG there are *nodes* and *edges.* Each *node* represents a signal that is obtained by summing together all of the signals represented by the edges directed into the node. Each *edge* represents the multiplication of a weight times the signal that is represented by the edge's source node. An edge's weight is indicated by an annotation near the arrowhead used to indicate the edge's direction. An edge weight of 1 is assumed if no weight is indicated. For example, the node marked $X[5]$ in the figure has two incident edges. The upper incident edge, (coming from $A[1]$) has no weight indicated. The lower incident edge (coming from $B[1]$) has a weight of W^5. All of this is interpreted to mean that $X[5] = A[1] + W^5 B[1]$.

Each of the two 4-point DFTs in Eq. (11.4) can be broken into two 2-point DFTs as follows:

$$A[m] = \sum_{n=0}^{1} x[4n]W^{4nm} + \sum_{n=0}^{1} x[4n+2]W^{(4n+2)m}$$

$$= C[m] + W^{2m}D[m] \tag{11.5}$$

$$W^m B[m] = \sum_{n=0}^{1} x[4n+1]W^{(4n+1)m} + \sum_{n=0}^{1} x[4n+3]W^{(4n+3)m}$$

$$= W^m(E[m] + W^{2m}F[m]) \tag{11.6}$$

The operations represented by Eqs. (11.5) and (11.6) are depicted in the signal flow graph (SFG) of Fig. 11.2. Notice that in going from the second term of Eq. (11.4) to Eq. (11.6), the multiplier W^m has not been distributed over the terms inside the parentheses of Eq. (11.6). If W^m were distributed over the terms within the parentheses to yield

$$W^m B[m] = W^m E[m] + W^{3m} F[m]$$

it would not be possible to simply extend the SFG of Fig. 11.1 to obtain the SFG of Fig. 11.2 without having to change some of the existing edges between nodes for $B[m]$ and nodes for

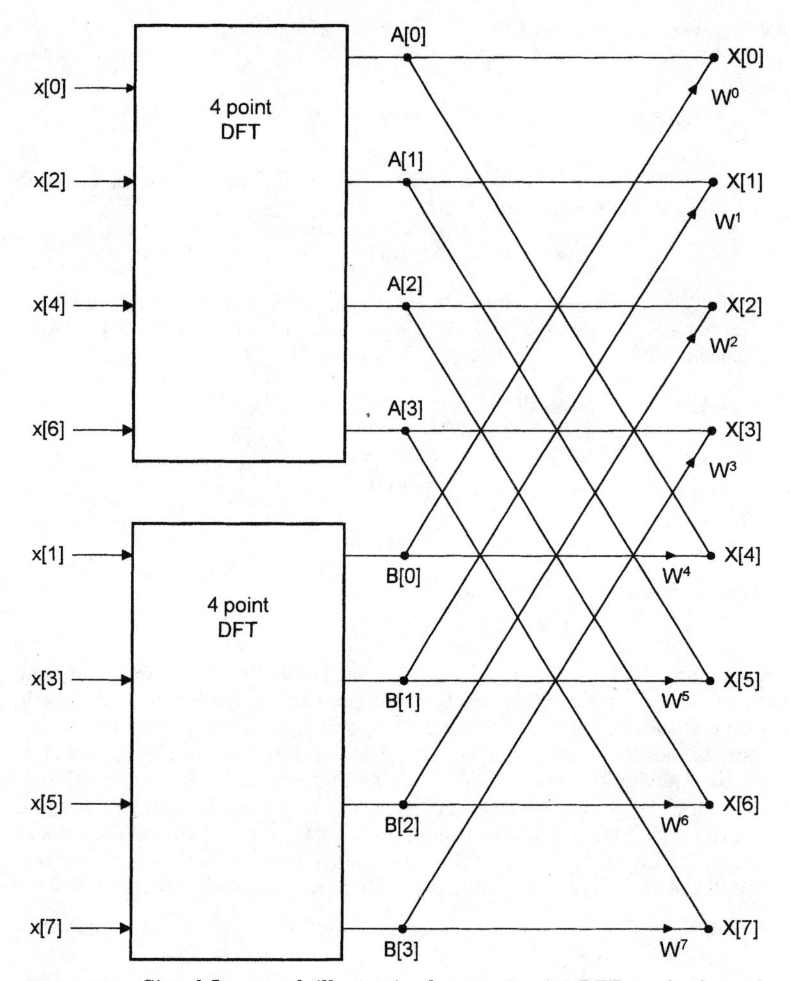

Figure 11.1 Signal flow graph illustrating how an 8-point DFT can be formed in terms of two 4-point DFTs.

$X[m]$. Keeping the various multipliers factored is the key to maximizing the reuse of interim results and thereby minimizing the total computational burden.

Finally, each of the 2-point DFTs $C[m], D[m], E[m]$, and $F[m]$ can be broken into two single-point DFTs

$$\begin{aligned} C[m] &= \sum_{n=0}^{0} x[8n]W^{8nm} + \sum_{n=0}^{0} x[8n+4]W^{(8n+4)m} \\ &= x[0]W^0 + x[4]W^{4m} \\ W^{2m}D[m] &= \sum_{n=0}^{0} x[8n+2]W^{(8n+2)m} + \sum_{n=0}^{0} x[8n+6]W^{(8n+6)m} \\ &= x[2]W^{2m} + x[6]W^{6m} \end{aligned} \tag{11.7}$$

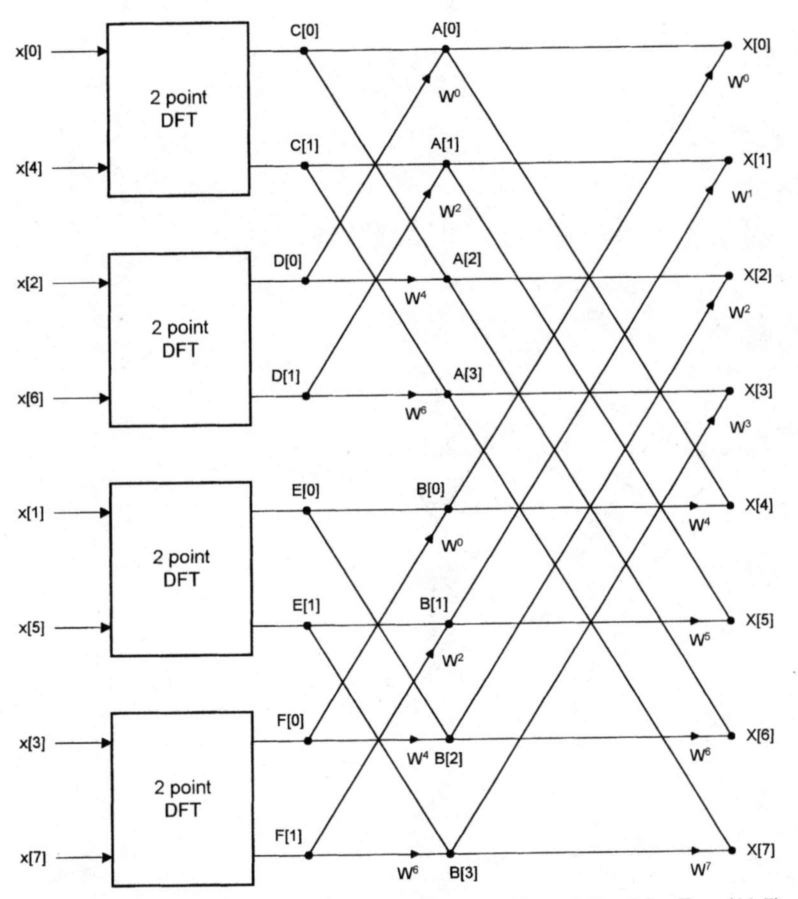

Figure 11.2 Signal flow graph depicting the operations defined by Eqs. (11.5) and (11.6).

$$= W^{2m}(x[2] + x[6]W^{4m}) \tag{11.8}$$

$$W^m E[m] = \sum_{n=0}^{0} x[8n+1]W^{(8n+1)m} + \sum_{n=0}^{0} x[8n+5]W^{(8n+5)m}$$

$$= x[1]W^m + x[5]W^{5m}$$

$$= W^m(x[1] + x[5]W^{4m}) \tag{11.9}$$

$$W^m W^{2m} F[m] = \sum_{n=0}^{0} x[8n+3]W^{(8n+3)m} + \sum_{n=0}^{0} x[8n+7]W^{(8n+7)m}$$

$$= x[3]W^{3m} + x[7]W^{7m}$$

$$= W^m W^{2m}(x[3] + x[7]W^{4m}) \tag{11.10}$$

The operations represented by Eqs. (11.7) through (11.10) are depicted in the SFG of Fig. 11.3.

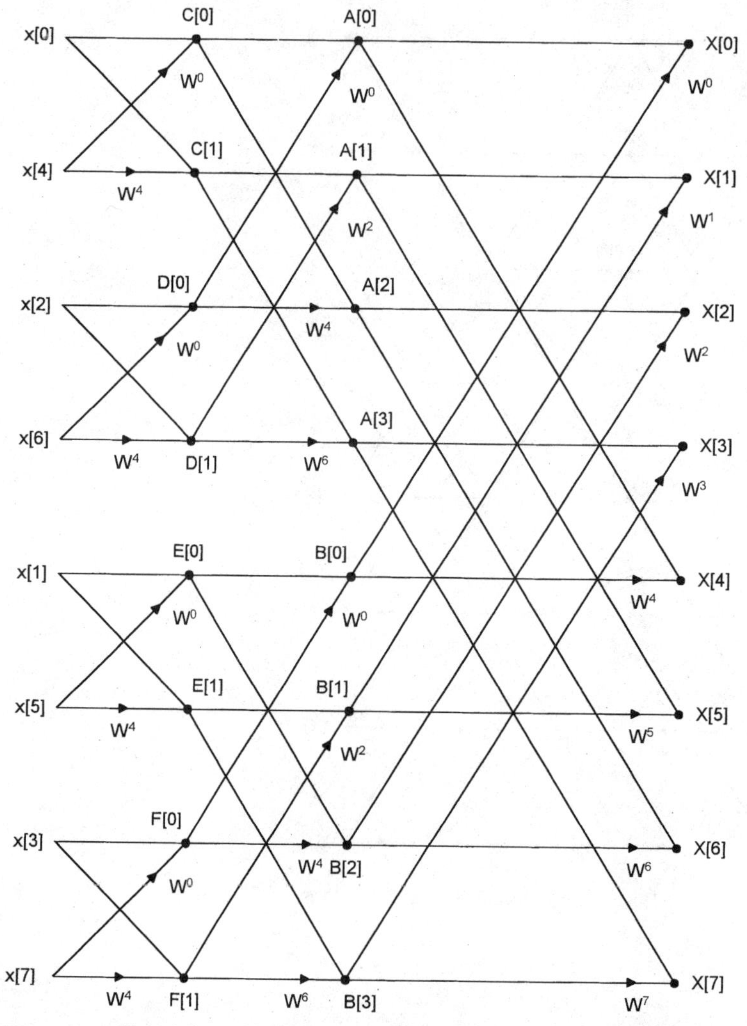

Figure 11.3 Signal flow graph depicting the operations defined by Eqs. (11.7) through (11.10).

How do we go about writing software to implement the 8-point FFT algorithm represented by the SFG of Fig. 11.3? More important, how do we extract the salient features of the algorithm so that we can devise software that will work for any value of N that is a power of 2?

Let's take a closer look at the figure. The nodes in the leftmost column of the graph are samples of the input sequence. Moving down the column, these samples are not in the "natural" order $x_0, x_1, x_2, \ldots$ These inputs are in *bit-reversed* order—so named because of the way in which naturally ordered indices are mapped into scrambled indices. For a 2^ν-point FFT, the natural index of each sample is represented as a ν-bit binary value. For any particular natural index, the corresponding scrambled index is obtained by simply reversing the order of the ν-bit representation. The mapping for an 8-point FFT is given in Table 11.1. Listing 11.1 contains a function `ComplexBitReverse( )` that can be used for in-place scrambling of a naturally ordered complex-valued array. (As we will see shortly, this same function can also be used for in-place descrambling of an array that is already in bit-reversed scrambled order.)

The input nodes in the first column are in pairs, with each pair being used to compute exactly one pair of nodes in the second column. For example, x_0 and x_4 are both used to compute C_0 and C_1, and neither x_0 nor x_4 is used in the calculation of any other second-column nodes. Once x_0 and x_4 have been used to calculate C_0 and C_1 they are not needed again. This means that the calculation can be done in place, with the resulting C_0 and C_1 being written into the memory locations that originally held x_0 and x_4.

The set of calculations that produces a pair of column $k + 1$ nodes from a pair of column k nodes is sometimes called a *butterfly* because of the shape that the four nodes and the edges between them form in the SFG. We will refer to the butterflies between the first column of nodes and the second column of nodes as *first stage butterflies.*

In going from the second column of nodes to the third column of nodes, the second-stage butterflies will each involve two pairs of nodes, but the pairing is different than for the first-stage butterflies. For example, C_0 and C_1 were produced by the same first-stage butterfly, but in the second stage they are split up, with C_0 being paired with D_0 to produce A_0 and A_2, while C_1 is paired with D_1 to produce A_1 and A_3. Despite the changes in pairing, the in-place relationship still holds—node A_0 is in the same row of the SFG as node C_0, so A_0 can be written into the memory location that held C_0. Likewise, A_2 can be written into the memory location that held D_0.

In the third stage of butterflies, the pair (A_0, A_2) is split up, with A_0 being paired with B_0 to produce X_0 and X_4 while A_2 is paired with B_2 to produce X_2 and X_6.

Let's redraw Fig. 11.3 to show the boundaries of the 2-point and 4-point DFTs that are nested within the overall 8-point DFT. As shown in Fig. 11.4, the

TABLE 11.1 Bit-Reversed Index Values for an 8-Point FFT

Natural index	Binary value	Reversed binary	Scrambled index
0	000	000	0
1	001	100	4
2	010	010	2
3	011	110	6
4	100	001	1
5	101	101	5
6	110	011	3
7	111	111	7

third-stage butterflies operate on outputs of 4-point DFTs to their left to produce outputs of the 8-point DFT to their right. The second-stage butterflies operate on outputs of 2-point DFTs to their left to produce outputs of the 4-point DFTs to their right. The first-stage butterflies operate on outputs of 1-point DFTs to their left to produce outputs of 2-point DFTs to their right. In general, for an N-point DFT with $N = 2^M$, the stage k butterflies will operate on

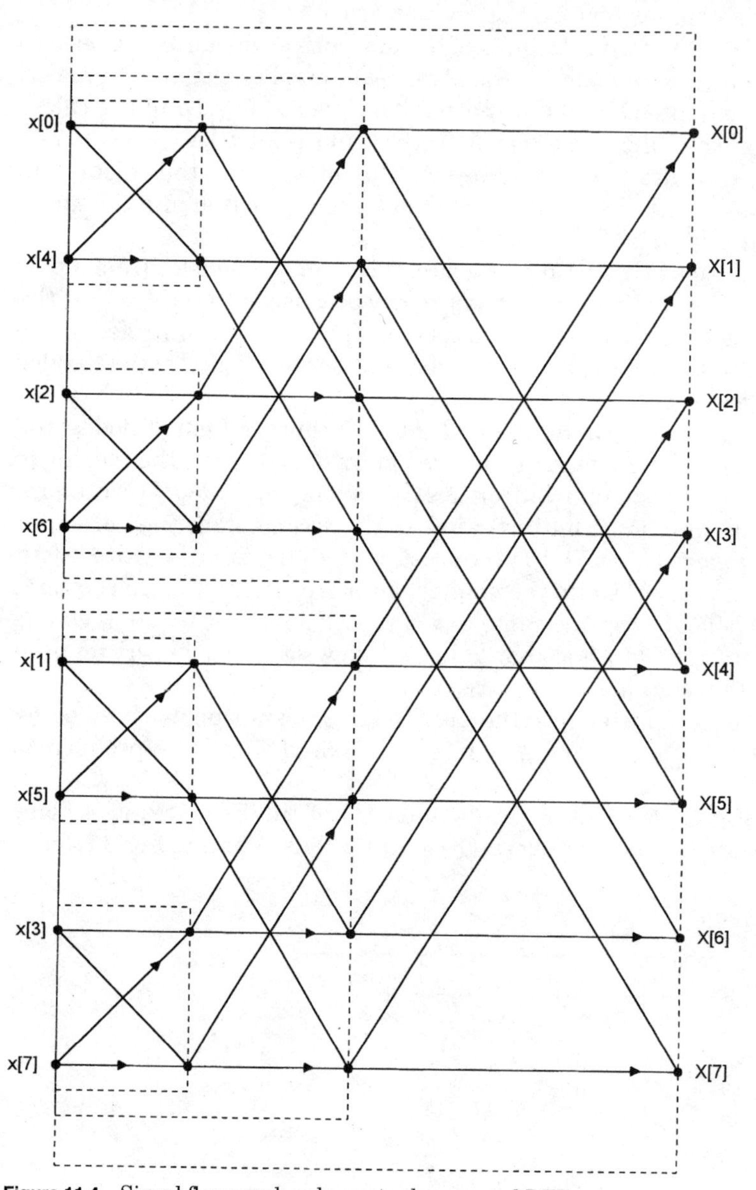

Figure 11.4 Signal flow graph redrawn to show nested DFTs.

outputs of 2^{k-1}-point DFTs to their left to produce outputs of the 2^k-point DFTs to their right. Notice that every butterfly straddles the gap between two adjacent left-hand DFTs, but none of the butterflies straddles the gap between two right-hand DFTs.

The top edge of each butterfly in stage k begins at one of the 2^{k-1} outputs from the top DFT in the left-hand pair. The bottom edge of each butterfly begins at the corresponding output from the bottom DFT in this pair. (Because for stage k each left-hand DFT has 2^{k-1} outputs, the top and bottom edges of each butterfly will always be exactly 2^{k-1} locations apart in the array used to store the results of stage $k-1$.

In Fig. 11.4, there are 4 second-stage butterflies. Two of these butterflies operate on the C and D nodes to produce the A nodes, and the other two operate on the E and F nodes to produce the B nodes. Corresponding butterflies in these two sets involve the same multipliers on corresponding edges. For example, the upper edges into both A_1 and B_1 have a multiplier of unity, and the lower edges into both A_1 and B_1 have a multiplier of W^2. Because of this correspondence, it is more efficient to compute the butterfly beginning at C_0, then compute the butterfly beginning at E_0 before computing the butterfly beginning at C_1. Computing the corresponding butterflies across all groups before computing a different butterfly within the same group avoids the need for recomputing identical values of W^p for each of the $N/2^k$ DFTs to the right of the butterflies. Hence, in Listing 11.2, the inner loop over values of `top_node` is exhausted for a given value of `bfly_pos`, before `bfly_pos` is incremented in the middle loop.

Other variations of decimation-in-time FFT algorithms

The nodes of an SFG can be reordered, and so long as the connections between nodes are preserved, the algorithm represented by the reordered SFG is equivalent to the algorithm represented by the original SFG. Specifically, we can reorder the input nodes in the SFG of Fig. 11.3 to obtain the SFG of Fig. 11.5, which now has naturally-ordered inputs and scrambled outputs. A function for implementing this form of FFT is given in Listing 11.3. Notice that the sequence in which the powers of W are used has been changed. Therefore, a different looping strategy is needed to minimize repeated calculation of the same powers of W.

11.3 Decimation-in-Frequency Algorithms

Start with the usual DFT for an N-point sequence

$$X[m] = \sum_{n=0}^{N-1} x[n] W_N^{mn} \qquad m = 0, 1, \ldots, N-1 \tag{11.11}$$

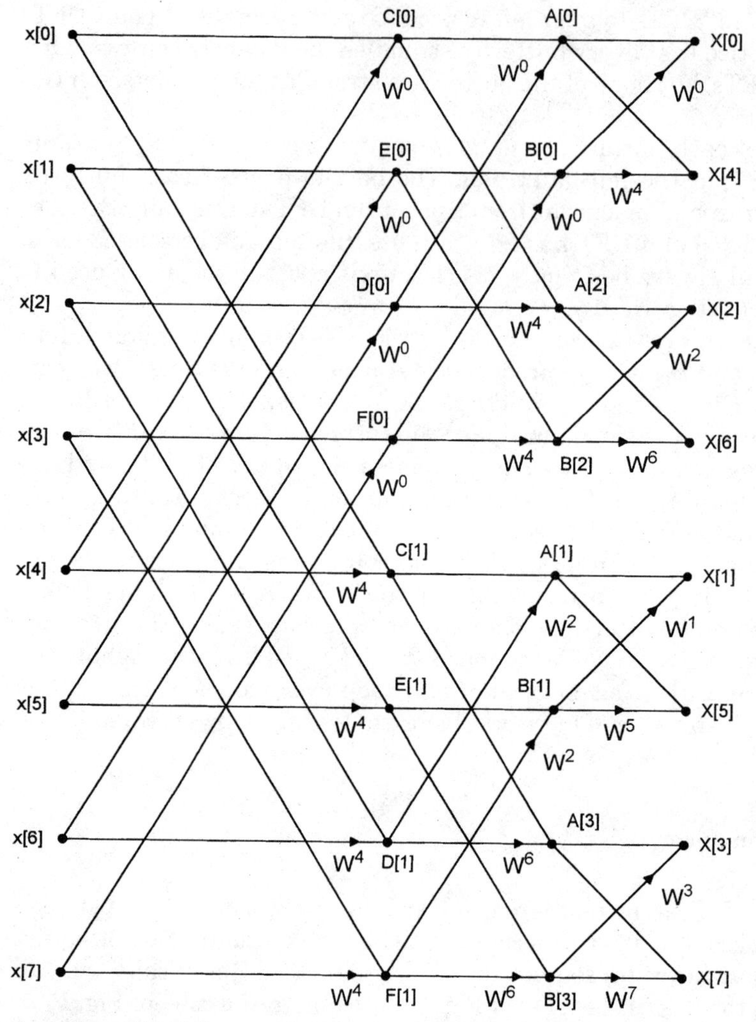

Figure 11.5 Signal flow graph for decimation-in-time FFT with naturally ordered inputs and scrambled outputs.

where

$$W_N = \exp\left(\frac{-2\pi j}{N}\right)$$

Now specialize Eq. (11.11) into two different forms—one form tailored for computing the even-numbered frequency samples and one form tailored for computing the odd-numbered frequency samples. First let's consider the specialization for even-numbered samples:

$$X[2r] = \sum_{n=0}^{N-1} x[n] W_N^{2nr} \qquad r = 0, 1, \ldots, (N/2) - 1$$

This summation can be split into two pieces:

$$X[2r] = \sum_{n=0}^{(N/2)-1} x[n] W_N^{2nr} + \sum_{n=N/2}^{N-1} x[n] W_N^{2nr}$$

$$= \sum_{n=0}^{(N/2)-1} x[n] W_N^{2nr} + \sum_{n=0}^{(N/2)-1} x\left[n + \frac{N}{2}\right] W_N^{2r[n+(N/2)]}$$

The factor $W_N^{2r[n+(N/2)]}$ is equal to $W_{N/2}^{rn}$ Therefore,

$$X[2r] = \sum_{n=0}^{(N/2)-1} x[n] W_N^{2nr} + \sum_{n=0}^{(N/2)-1} x\left[n + \frac{N}{2}\right] W_{N/2}^{nr}$$

$$= \sum_{n=0}^{(N/2)-1} \left(x[n] + x\left[n + \frac{N}{2}\right] \right) W_{N/2}^{nr} \qquad r = 0, 1, \ldots, (N/2) - 1 \tag{11.12}$$

Let's set this result aside for a moment and consider the specialization for odd-numbered frequency samples:

$$X[2r+1] = \sum_{n=0}^{N-1} x[n] W_N^{n(2r+1)} \qquad r = 0, 1, \ldots, (N/2) - 1 \tag{11.13}$$

Using manipulations similar to the even-sample case, Eq. (11.13) can be reduced to

$$X[2r+1] = \sum_{n=0}^{(N/2)-1} \left(x[n] - x\left[n + \frac{N}{2}\right] \right) W_N^n W_{N/2}^{nr} \tag{11.14}$$

We can define two new $(N/2)$-point time sequences $a[n]$ and $b[n]$

$$a[n] = x[n] + x\left[n + \frac{N}{2}\right] \qquad n = 0, 1, \ldots, (N/2) - 1$$

$$b[n] = x[n] - x\left[n + \frac{N}{2}\right] \qquad n = 0, 1, \ldots, (N/2) - 1$$

Then Eq. (11.12) can be seen as the $(N/2)$-point DFT of the sequence $a[n]$

$$X[2r] = \sum_{n=0}^{(N/2)-1} a[n] W_{N/2}^{nr} \qquad r = 0, 1, \ldots, (N/2) - 1$$

and Eq. (11.14) can be seen as the $(N/2)$-point DFT of the sequence $W_N^n b[n]$

$$X[2r+1] = \sum_{n=0}^{(N/2)-1} b[n] W_N^n W_{N/2}^{nr} \qquad r = 0, 1, \ldots, (N/2) - 1$$

If N is a power of 2, this decomposition process can be continued until the original N-point DFT has been decomposed into N 1-point DFTs.

Example 11.2 Let's do the complete decimation-in-frequency decomposition for the case of an 8-point DFT originally defined by

$$X[m] = \sum_{n=0}^{7} x[n] W^{nm} \qquad m = 0, 1, \ldots, 7$$

Splitting this into separate DFTs for even and odd m as in Eqs. (11.12) and (11.14) yields

$$X[2r] = \sum_{n=0}^{3} (x[n] + x[n+4]) W_N^{2rn} \tag{11.15}$$

$$X[2r+1] = \sum_{n=0}^{3} (x[n] - x[n+4]) W_N^{(2r+1)n} \tag{11.16}$$

The operations represented by Eqs. (11.15) and (11.16) are depicted in the signal flow graph (SFG) of Fig. 11.6.

Each of the two 4-point DFTs can be decomposed into two 2-point DFTs as follows:

$$X[4r] = \sum_{n=0}^{1} (a[n] + a[n+2]) W_N^{4rn} \tag{11.17}$$

$$X[4r+2] = \sum_{n=0}^{1} (a[n] - a[n+2]) W_N^{(4r+2)n}$$

$$= \sum_{n=0}^{1} (a[n] - a[n+2]) W_N^{2n} W_N^{4rn} \tag{11.18}$$

$$X[4r+1] = \sum_{n=0}^{1} (b[n] + b[n+2]) W_N^{(4r+1)n}$$

$$= \sum_{n=0}^{1} (b[n] + b[n+2]) W_N^{n} W_N^{4rn} \tag{11.19}$$

$$X[4r+3] = \sum_{n=0}^{1} (b[n] - b[n+2]) W_N^{(4r+3)n}$$

$$= \sum_{n=0}^{1} (b[n] - b[n+2]) W_N^{3n} W_N^{4rn} \tag{11.20}$$

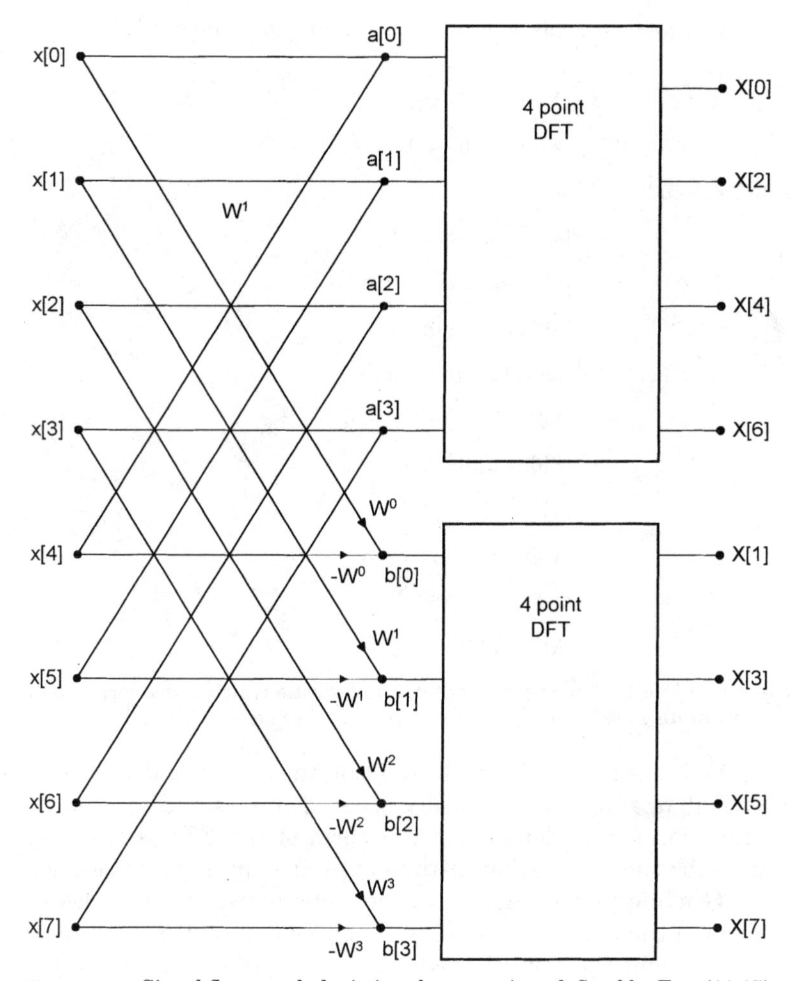

Figure 11.6 Signal flow graph depicting the operations defined by Eqs. (11.15) and (11.16).

Each of the four 2-point DFTs can then be decomposed into two 1-point DFTs. If we let $c[n] = a[n] + a[n+2]$ then Eq. (11.17) becomes

$$X[4r] = \sum_{n=0}^{1} c[n] W_N^{4rn} \qquad r = 0, 1 \tag{11.21}$$

The frequency sequence produced by Eq. (11.21) consists of just two samples, $X[0]$ and $X[4]$, but we can still perform an even-odd decomposition to obtain

$$X[8r] = \sum_{n=0}^{0} (c[n] + c[n+1]) W_N^{8rn}$$

$$X[8r+4] = \sum_{n=0}^{0} (c[n] - c[n+1]) W_N^{(8r+4)n}$$

Since each of these two equations holds only for $r = 0$, we can immediately simplify them to obtain

$$X[0] = c[0] + c[1]$$

$$X[4] = c[0] - c[1]$$

In a similar fashion we can let

$$d[n] = a[n] - a[n+2]$$

$$f[n] = b[n] + b[n+2]$$

$$g[n] = b[n] - b[n+2]$$

and decompose Eqs. (11.18), (11.19), and (11.20) to obtain

$$X[2] = d[0] + d[1]$$

$$X[6] = d[0] - d[1]$$

$$X[1] = f[0] + f[1]$$

$$X[5] = f[0] - f[1]$$

$$X[3] = g[0] + g[1]$$

$$X[7] = g[0] - g[1]$$

The signal flow graph in Fig. 11.7 has been annotated to indicate which nodes correspond to the various intermediate working sequences $a[n]$, $b[n]$, and so on.

As shown in Fig. 11.7, the result of this decimation-in-frequency decomposition is a *NISO* FFT algorithm with naturally ordered inputs and scrambled order outputs. A function for implementing this form of the FFT is given in Listing 11.4. Just as for the decimation-in-time case, it is possible to reorder the nodes of the SFG while preserving the connections between the nodes to produce a SINO form of the decimation-in-frequency FFT in which the inputs are in scrambled order and the outputs are in natural order. A function for implementing a DIF-SINO FFT is given in Listing 11.5.

11.4 Prime Factor Algorithms

The *prime factor algorithm* (*PFA*) for computing the DFT can be viewed as a generalization of the radix 2 FFT algorithms developed in prior sections. In a radix 2 FFT, a DFT containing $N = 2^m$ points is computed as an m-stage combination of 2-point DFTs. If, instead of being a power of 2, the size of the DFT is some other composite number $N = N_1 N_2$ [where $\mathrm{GCF}(N_1, N_2) = 1$], it is possible to express the original N-point DFT in the form of an N_1 by N_2 two-dimensional DFT.

Consider a DFT of length $N = N_1 N_2$ with $\mathrm{GCF}(N_1, N_2) = 1$. The one-dimensional input sequence $x[n]$ must be mapped into a two-dimensional sequence $\hat{x}[n_1, n_2]$. This mapping can be accomplished via the index transformation

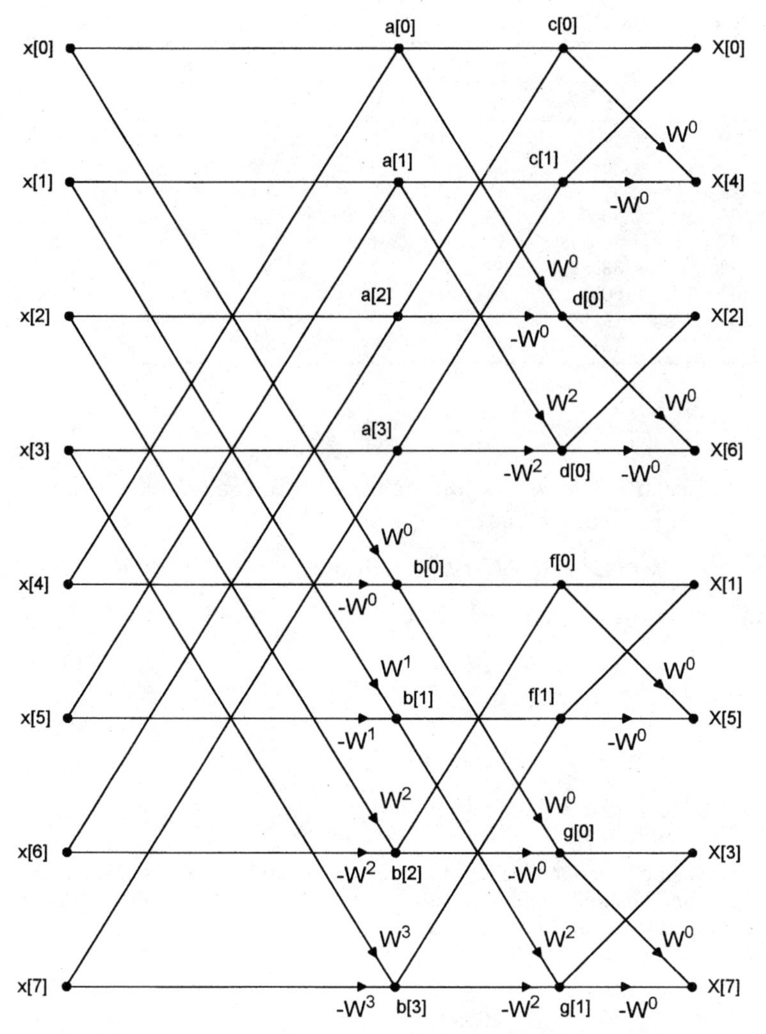

Figure 11.7 Signal flow graph depicting the operations defined by Eqs. (11.17) through (11.21).

$$n \equiv (N_1 n_2 + N_2 n_1) \text{ modulo } N \tag{11.22}$$

where $n_1 = 0, 1, \ldots N_1 - 1$
$n_2 = 0, 1, \ldots N_2 - 1$

The sequence $\hat{x}[n_1, n_2]$ can be used as the input to a two-dimensional DFT defined by

$$\hat{X}[k_1, k_2] = \sum_{n_2=0}^{N_2-1} W_2^{n_2 k_2} \sum_{n_1=0}^{N_1-1} \hat{x}[n_1, n_2] W_1^{n_1 k_1}$$

TABLE 11.2 Input Index Mapping for Example 11.3

		n_1						
		0	1	2	3	4	5	6
	0	0	9	18	27	36	45	54
	1	7	16	25	34	43	52	61
	2	14	23	32	41	50	59	5
	3	21	30	39	48	57	3	12
n_2	4	28	37	46	55	1	10	19
	5	35	44	53	62	8	17	26
	6	42	51	60	6	15	24	33
	7	49	58	4	13	22	31	40
	8	56	2	11	20	29	38	47

where $W_1 = \exp(-j2\pi/N_1)$
$W_2 = \exp(-j2\pi/N_2)$

The two-dimensional result $\hat{X}[k_1, k_2]$ is then mapped into the one-dimensional result $X[k]$ using the index transformation

$$k \equiv (N_1 t_1 k_2 + N_2 t_2 k_1) \text{ modulo } N \tag{11.23}$$

The values t_1 and t_2 must be chosen such that

$$N_2 t_2 \equiv 1 \text{ modulo } N_1 \tag{11.24}$$

and

$$N_1 t_1 \equiv 1 \text{ modulo } N_2 \tag{11.25}$$

Example 11.3 Determine the index mappings needed to apply the PFA to compute a 63-point DFT with $N_1 = 7$ and $N_2 = 9$.

solution The index transformation for the input sequence is readily enumerated by simply evaluating Eq. (11.22) for all possible combinations of n_1 and n_2. The results are listed in Table 11.2. Before we can use Eq. (11.23) to enumerate the index transformation for the output sequence, we need to use Eqs. (11.24) and (11.25) to determine values for t_2 and t_1. Equation (11.24) is satisfied for $t_2 = 4$, and Eq. (11.25) is satisfied for $t_1 = 4$. Thus, Eq. (11.23) becomes

$$k \equiv (28k_2 + 36k_1) \text{ modulo } 63 \tag{11.26}$$

The index mapping produced by Eq. (11.26) is listed in Table 11.3.

TABLE 11.3 Output Index Mapping for Example 11.3

		k_1						
		0	1	2	3	4	5	6
	0	0	36	9	45	18	54	27
	1	28	1	37	10	46	19	55
	2	56	29	2	38	11	47	20
	3	21	57	30	3	39	12	48
k_2	4	49	22	58	31	4	40	13
	5	14	50	23	59	32	5	41
	6	42	15	51	24	60	33	6
	7	7	43	16	52	25	61	34
	8	35	8	44	17	53	26	62

Listing 11.1 Bit-Reversed Addressing of a Complex-Valued Array

```
//
//  File = cbitrev.cpp
//

#include "f_cmplx.h"
#include "cbitrev.h"

void ComplexBitReverse( float_complex *array, int size)
{
 float_complex tt;
 int nv2, nm1, i, j, k;

 nv2 = size/2;
 nm1 = size - 1;

 j=0;
 for (i=0; i<nm1; i++)
   {
    if (i<j)
      {
       tt = array[j];
       array[j] = array[i];
       array[i] = tt;
      }
    k = nv2;
    while (k<=j)
      {
       j -= k;
       k /= 2;
      }
    j += k;
   }
}
```

Listing 11.2 Decimation-in-Time Fast Fourier Transform with Scrambled Inputs and Naturally Ordered Outputs

```
//
//  File = dit_sino.cpp
//
//  Decimation-In-Time FFT
//
//  Scrambled Input / Naturally-ordered Output
//
```

```
#include <math.h>
#include "mymath.h"
#include "dit_sino.h"

void FftDitSino( float_complex *array,
                 int fft_size)
{
double trig_arg;
int log2_size;
float_complex twiddle, w_fact;
float_complex temp;
int pts_in_left_dft, pts_in_right_dft;
int stage, bfly_pos;
int top_node, bot_node;

log2_size = ilog2(fft_size);

ComplexBitReverse(array, fft_size);

pts_in_right_dft = 1;
for( stage=1; stage <=log2_size; stage++)
  {
   pts_in_left_dft = pts_in_right_dft;  // set pts_in_left_dft = 2**(stage-1)
   pts_in_right_dft *= 2;               // set pts_in_right_dft = 2**stage

   twiddle = float_complex(1.0, 0.0);
   trig_arg = PI/pts_in_left_dft;
   w_fact = float_complex(cos(trig_arg), -sin(trig_arg));

   for( bfly_pos =0; bfly_pos < pts_in_left_dft; bfly_pos++)
     {
      for( top_node = bfly_pos; top_node<fft_size; top_node += pts_in_right_dft)
        {
         bot_node = top_node + pts_in_left_dft;
         temp = array[bot_node] * twiddle;
         array[bot_node] = array[top_node] - temp;
         array[top_node] += temp;
        }  // end of loop over top_node
       twiddle *= w_fact;

     } // end of loop over bfly_pos
  } // end of loop over stage

return;
}
```

Listing 11.3 Decimation-in-Time Fast Fourier Transform with Naturally Ordered Inputs and Scrambled Outputs

```
//
//  File = dit_niso.cpp
//
//  Decimation-In-Time FFT
//
//  Naturally-ordered Input / Scrambled Output
//

#include <math.h>
#include "mymath.h"
#include "dit_niso.h"

void FftDitNiso( float_complex *array,
                 int fft_size)
{
double trig_arg;
int log2_size;
float_complex twiddle;
float_complex temp;
int pts_in_lft_grp, pts_in_rgt_grp;
int stage, grp_pos, grp_cntr;
int top_node, bot_node;

log2_size = ilog2(fft_size);

pts_in_rgt_grp = fft_size;
for( stage=1; stage <=log2_size; stage++)
  {
   grp_cntr = -1;

   pts_in_lft_grp = pts_in_rgt_grp;  // set pts_in_left_dft = N/(2**(stage-1))
   pts_in_rgt_grp /= 2;               // set pts_in_right_dft = N/(2**stage)

   for( grp_pos =0; grp_pos < fft_size; grp_pos += pts_in_lft_grp)
     {
      grp_cntr++;

      trig_arg = (TWO_PI*bitrev(grp_cntr, log2_size-1))/fft_size;
      twiddle = float_complex(cos(trig_arg), -sin(trig_arg));

      for( top_node = grp_pos; top_node < grp_pos+pts_in_rgt_grp;
                                top_node++)
```

```
        {
         bot_node = top_node + pts_in_rgt_grp;
         temp = array[bot_node] * twiddle;
         array[bot_node] = array[top_node] - temp;
         array[top_node] += temp;
        }  // end of loop over top_node

      } // end of loop over grp_pos
   } // end of loop over stage

ComplexBitReverse(array, fft_size);

return;
}
```

Listing 11.4 Decimation-in-Frequency Fast Fourier Transform with Naturally Ordered Inputs and Scrambled Outputs

```
//+++++++++++++++++++++++++++++++++++++++++++++++++++++++++++++++
//
//   File = dif_niso.cpp
//
//   Decimation-In-Frequency FFT
//
//   Naturally-ordered Input / Scrambled Output
//

#include <math.h>
#include "mymath.h"
#include "dif_niso.h"

void FftDifNiso( float_complex *array,
                 int fft_size)
{
double trig_arg;
int log2_size;
float_complex twiddle, w_fact;
float_complex temp;
int pts_in_left_dft, pts_in_right_dft;
int stage, bfly_pos;
int top_node, bot_node;

log2_size = ilog2(fft_size);

 pts_in_right_dft = fft_size;
 for( stage=1; stage <=log2_size; stage++)
```

```
    {
     pts_in_left_dft = pts_in_right_dft;  // set pts_in_left_dft = N/(2**(stage-
                                              1))
     pts_in_right_dft /= 2;               // set pts_in_right_dft = N/(2**stage)

     twiddle = float_complex(1.0, 0.0);
     trig_arg = PI/pts_in_right_dft;
     w_fact = float_complex(cos(trig_arg), -sin(trig_arg));

     for( bfly_pos = 0; bfly_pos < pts_in_right_dft; bfly_pos++)
       {
        for( top_node = bfly_pos; top_node<fft_size; top_node += pts_in_left_dft)
          {
           bot_node = top_node + pts_in_right_dft;
           temp = array[top_node] + array[bot_node];
           array[bot_node] = (array[top_node] - array[bot_node]) * twiddle;
           array[top_node] = temp;
          }  // end of loop over top_node

        twiddle *= w_fact;

       } // end of loop over bfly_pos
    } // end of loop over stage

  ComplexBitReverse(array, fft_size);

  return;
}
//+++++++++++++++++++++++++++++++++++++++++++++++++++++++++++++++++++++
```

Listing 11.5 Decimation-in-Frequency Fast Fourier Transform with Scrambled Inputs and Naturally Ordered Outputs

```
//++++++++++++++++++++++++++++++++++++++++++++++++++++++++++++++++
//
//  File = dif_sino.cpp
//
//  Decimation-In-Frequency FFT
//
//  Scrambled Input / Naturally-ordered Output
//

#include <math.h>
#include "mymath.h"
#include "dif_sino.h"

void FftDifSino( float_complex *array,
                 int fft_size)
```

```
{
 double trig_arg;
 int log2_size;
 float_complex twiddle;
 float_complex temp;
 int pts_in_lft_grp, pts_in_rgt_grp;
 int stage, grp_pos, grp_cntr;
 int top_node, bot_node;

 log2_size = ilog2(fft_size);

 ComplexBitReverse(array, fft_size);

 pts_in_rgt_grp = 1;
 for( stage=1; stage <=log2_size; stage++)
   {
    pts_in_lft_grp = pts_in_rgt_grp;  // set pts_in_lft_grp = 2**(stage-1)
    pts_in_rgt_grp *= 2;              // set pts_in_rgt_grp = 2**stage

    grp_cntr = -1;

    for( grp_pos =0; grp_pos < fft_size; grp_pos +=pts_in_rgt_grp)
      {
       grp_cntr++;
       trig_arg = (TWO_PI*bitrev(grp_cntr, log2_size-1))/fft_size;
       twiddle = float_complex(cos(trig_arg), -sin(trig_arg));

       for( top_node = grp_pos; top_node< grp_pos+pts_in_lft_grp;
                                top_node ++)
         {
          bot_node = top_node + pts_in_lft_grp;
          temp = array[top_node] + array[bot_node];
          array[bot_node] = (array[top_node] - array[bot_node]) * twiddle;
          array[top_node] = temp;
         }  // end of loop over top_node

      } // end of loop over grp_pos
   } // end of loop over stage

 return;
}
//+++++++++++++++++++++++++++++++++++++++++++++++++++++++++++++++++++
```

Chapter

12

Introduction to Digital Filter Design

Digital filters are usually classified by duration of impulse response, which can be either finite or infinite. The methods for designing and implementing these two filter classes differ considerably. *Finite impulse response* (*FIR*) filters are digital filters that have a unit impulse response (unit sample function) that is finite in duration. This is in contrast to *infinite impulse response* (*IIR*) filters, which have a unit impulse response that is infinite in duration. FIR and IIR filters each have advantages and disadvantages, and neither is best in all situations. FIR filters can be implemented using either recursive or nonrecursive techniques, but usually nonrecursive techniques are used.

12.1 FIR Filters

A nonrecursive implementation of an FIR digital filter forms each output sample as a weighted sum of a finite number of input samples, as depicted in the block diagram of Fig. 12.1. FIR filters have the following advantages:

- FIR filters can easily be designed to have constant phase delay and/or constant group delay.
- FIR filters implemented with nonrecursive techniques will always be stable.
- Round-off noise (which is due to finite-precision arithmetic performed in the digital processor) can be made relatively small for nonrecursive implementations.
- FIR filters can also be implemented using recursive techniques if this is desired.

Despite their advantages, FIR filters still exhibit some significant disadvantages:

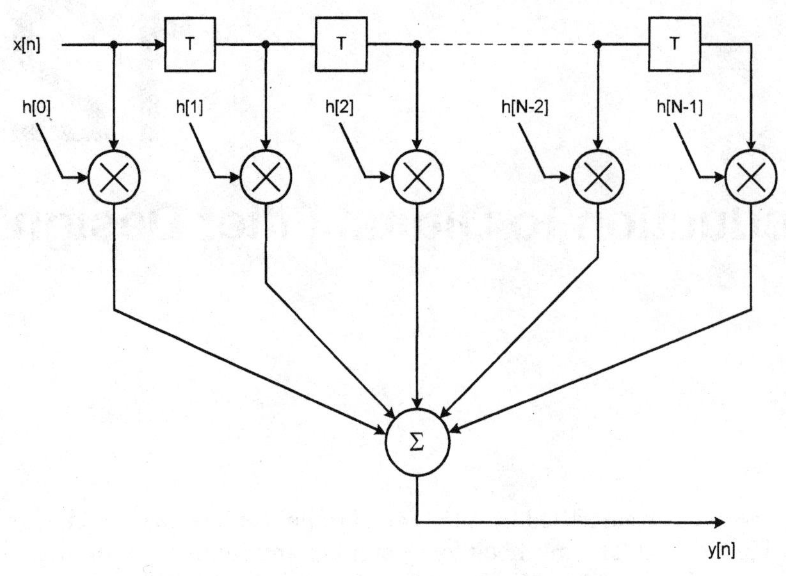

Figure 12.1 Nonrecursive implementation of an FIR digital filter.

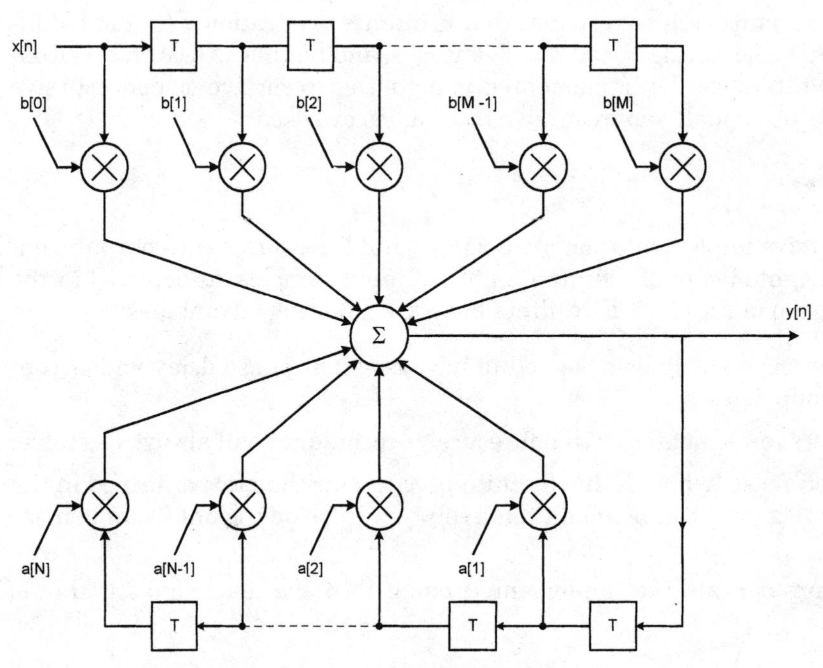

Figure 12.2 Recursive implementation of an IIR digital filter.

- An FIR filter's impulse response duration, although finite, may have to be very long to obtain sharp cutoff characteristics.
- The design of FIR filters to meet specific performance objectives is generally more difficult than the design of IIR filters for similar applications.

12.2 IIR Filters

A recursive implementation of an FIR digital filter forms each output sample as a weighted sum of a finite number of input samples and a finite number of previous output samples, as depicted in the block diagram of Fig. 12.2. IIR filters have the following advantages:

- IIR filters can be used in digital simulations to approximate the behavior of traditional analog filter families such as Butterworth, Chebyshev, and so on.
- IIR filters will generally require fewer coefficients than an FIR filter to satisfy the same set of performance specifications.

IIR filters exhibit the following disadvantages:

- IIR filters are generally more sensitive to the effects of finite-precision arithmetic and unless special precautions are taken they will often exhibit limit-cycle oscillations.
- Except for the special case in which all the poles of the transfer function $H(z)$ lie on the unit circle, it is not possible to design stable, realizable IIR filters having an exactly linear phase response.

Chapter

13

FIR Filter Design: Fundamentals

13.1 Introduction to FIR Filters

The general form for a linear time-invariant FIR system's output $y[k]$ at time k is given by

$$y[k] = \sum_{n=0}^{N-1} h[n]\, x[k-n] \qquad (13.1)$$

where $h[n]$ is the system's impulse response. As Eq. (13.1) indicates, the output is a linear combination of the present input and the N previous inputs. The remainder of this chapter is devoted to basic properties and realization issues for FIR filters. Specific design approaches for selecting the coefficients b_n are covered in Chaps. 14 through 17.

Software design

The essential data components for representing an FIR filter consist of just an integer for the number of taps and a real-valued array for the coefficient values. Member functions for the class `FirFilterDesign` are provided in Listing 13.1. The data portion of the class definition for `FirFilterDesign` consists of just two items:

```
int Num_Taps;
double *Imp_Resp_Coeff;
```

Examination of the listing reveals that the default constructor contains no executable statements, and invoking this constructor simply causes storage to be allocated for these two data items. The default constructor will be used in later chapters when `FirFilterDesign` is used as a base class for more specialized derived classes that are used to represent specific types of FIR filters. For many of these applications, `FirFilterDesign` must be allocated before the number of filter taps is known—hence, the need for a default constructor. Whenever an `FirFilterDesign` object is instantiated via the default constructor, the `Initialize` method must subsequently be used to set the value of `Num_Taps` and allocate space on the heap for holding the array of filter coefficients.

When the number of taps is known prior to instantiation of `FirFilterDesign`, the constructor form `FirFilterDesign(int num_taps)` can be used to set `Num_Taps` and allocate the coefficient array from within the constructor. A third form of the constructor, `FirFilterDesign(int num_taps, double *coeff)`, can be used to both allocate and initialize the coefficient array. The method `CopyCoefficients(double *coeff)` can be used to initialize the coefficients in instances of `FirFilterDesign` that are created via either of the first two constructors. This method could also be used to reinitialize the coefficients in any instance of `FirFilterDesign`, provided that the number of coefficients is held constant. Additional housekeeping functions provided in `FirFilterDesign` include `GetNumTaps( )`, `GetCoefficients( )` and `DumpCoefficients(ofstream* )`.

13.2 Evaluating the Frequency Response of FIR Filters

A digital filter's impulse response $h[n]$ is related to the frequency response $H(e^{j\lambda})$ via the DTFT:

$$H(e^{j\lambda}) = \sum_{n=-\infty}^{\infty} h[n]\, e^{-jn\lambda} \tag{13.2}$$

For an FIR filter, $h[n]$ is nonzero only for $0 \le n < N$. Therefore, the limits of the summation can be changed to yield

$$H(e^{j\lambda}) = \sum_{n=0}^{N-1} h[n]\, e^{-jn\lambda} \tag{13.3}$$

Equation (13.3) can be evaluated directly at any desired value of λ.

We now take note of the fact that $\lambda = \omega T$ and that the value of continuous-radian frequency ω_m corresponding to the discrete-frequency index m is given by

$$\omega_m = 2\pi m F \tag{13.4}$$

Substituting $2\pi mFT$ for λ, and $H[m]$ for $H(e^{j\lambda})$ in Eq. (13.2) yields the discrete Fourier transform:

$$H[m] = \sum_{n=0}^{N-1} h[n] \exp(-2\pi jnmFT) \tag{13.5}$$

Thus, the DTFT can be evaluated at a set of discrete frequencies $\omega = \omega_m$, $0 \leq m < N$, by using the DFT, which in turn may be evaluated in a computationally efficient fashion using one of the various FFT algorithms.

Software design

From a theoretical perspective, we could easily view the continuous-frequency response of an FIR filter as being an intrinsic property or *attribute* of the filter itself, and, therefore, we might conclude that the software for producing a filter's frequency response should be made part of the class `FirFilterDesign` that implements the filter. However, once we begin to think about the details of designing software to calculate a filter's frequency response, we quickly discover that, in practice, this response possesses a number of attributes which are most definitely not attributes of the filter itself. In theory, the frequency response is a function of continuous frequency defined over all frequencies. In practice, we can evaluate the response at only a finite number of discrete frequencies over a finite range. Therefore, to define a practical response plot we need to know the answers to a number of questions:

- At how many frequencies is the response to be evaluated?
- What is the minimum frequency at which the response is to be evaluated?
- What is the maximum frequency at which the response is to be evaluated?
- How are the evaluation frequencies to be spaced between the minimum and the maximum? The obvious choice of uniform spacing may not always be the correct answer—for responses to be plotted against a logarithmic frequency axis, we may want to space the frequency values so that they are uniformly spaced in the plot.
- Should values of phase response be produced in degrees or in radians?
- Should values of magnitude response be produced in linear numeric units or in decibels?
- Should the raw magnitude response be left as is, or should the values be normalized so that the peak passband value is either 1.0 (linear) or 0.0 (dB)?

Because the software that implements the frequency response must "know" or obtain the answers to all of these questions, this software has been implemented in the separate class `FirFilterResponse`. The member functions for this class are provided in Listing 13.2, and the data member definitions are listed in Table 13.1.

The `FirFilterResponse` class has been designed with two different constructors. The first constructor takes all the necessary configuration parameters plus a pointer to an `FirFilterDesign` object as input arguments. The second constructor's input arguments are limited to a pointer to an `FirFilterDesign` object plus references to an input stream `(&uin)` and an output stream `(&uout)`.

TABLE 13.1 Data Members for Class `FirFilterResponse`

```
FirFilterDesign *Filter_Design;
int Num_Resp_Pts;
logical Db_Scale_Enabled
logical Normalize_Enabled
ofstream *Response_File
int Num_Taps
double *Mag_Resp
```

These streams are used to conduct a short interactive exchange with the user to obtain the necessary configuration parameters. (Questions are inserted into `uout` and user responses are extracted from `uin`.) Typically, this constructor would be called with `cout` as the output stream and `cin` as the input stream.

The method `ComputeMagResp` will compute the desired magnitude response, and if `Normalize_Enabled` is set TRUE, call the method `NormalizeResponse`. Both `ComputeMagResp` and `NormalizeResponse` are provided as separate public methods so that the filter's magnitude response can be recomputed if the coefficients in `FirFilterDesign` are changed. The "pure" object-oriented approach for dealing with changes to `FirFilterDesign` would be to delete the obsolete `FirFilterResponse` object and construct a new one using the updated coefficients from `FirFilterDesign`. This approach was not taken here because `FirFilterResponse` will be used in Chap. 15 as part of an iterative design procedure that will make *many* small changes to `FirFilterDesign`'s coefficients and then recompute the magnitude spectrum after each change. Continued deletion and allocation of new `FirFilterResponse` objects would excessively fragment heap memory and possibly cause an out-of-memory condition on many smaller computers. As long as none of the basic configuration parameters are changed, it is perfectly safe to change coefficients in `FirFilterDesign` and then recompute the magnitude response without constructing a new `FirFilterResponse` object each time. However, attempting to change `Num_Taps` will most likely lead to disaster.

Another advantage in making `ComputeMagResp` a separate function is that when `FirFilterResponse` is used as a base class, it will be easier for a derived class to redefine the method that is used to compute the magnitude response. As we will see in Sec. 13.3, there are ways to compute the magnitude response of a linear phase FIR filter which require less computation than the general method implemented in `FirFilterResponse`. These methods will be implemented in a derived class that inherits from `FirFilterResponse`.

Examination of the class design in Listing 13.2 reveals that the questions posed earlier are answered in the following ways:

- The number of evaluation frequencies is a user-supplied input—either passed in as an argument to the first constructor or read in from stream `uin` by the interactive constructor.

- The minimum evaluation frequency is assumed to be 0. This assumption is hard-coded into the method `ComputeMagResp`.
- The maximum evaluation frequency is assumed to be π rad/s. This assumption is hard-coded into the method `ComputeMagResp`.
- The spacing of the evaluation frequencies is assumed to be uniform between the minimum and the maximum.
- A user-supplied input `db_scale_enabled` is used to select between linear numeric units or decibels for magnitude response values. This flag is either passed in as an argument to the first constructor or read in from stream `uin` by the interactive constructor.
- A user-supplied input `normalize_enabled` is used to select between raw magnitude response values or magnitude responses that are normalized to have a peak passband value of 1.0 (for `db_scale_enabled==FALSE`) or 0.0 (for `db_scale_enabled==TRUE`).

13.3 Linear Phase FIR Filters

As discussed in Sec. 3.8, constant group delay is a desirable property for filters to have since nonconstant group delay will cause envelope distortion in modulated-carrier signals and pulse-shape distortion in baseband digital signals. A filter's frequency response $H(e^{j\omega})$ can be expressed in terms of amplitude response $A(\omega)$ and phase response $\theta(\omega)$ as

$$H(e^{j\omega}) = A(\omega)\, e^{j\theta(\omega)}$$

If a filter has a linear phase response of the form

$$\theta(\omega) = -\alpha\omega \qquad -\pi \le \omega \le \pi \tag{13.6}$$

it will have both constant phase delay τ_p and constant group delay τ_g. In fact, in this case $\tau_p = \tau_g = \alpha$. It can be shown (for example, Rabiner and Gold 1975) that for $\alpha = 0$, the impulse response is an impulse of arbitrary strength:

$$h[n] = \begin{cases} c & n = 0 \\ 0 & n \ne 0 \end{cases}$$

For nonzero α, it can be shown that Eq. (13.6) is satisfied if and only if

$$\alpha = \frac{N-1}{2} \tag{13.7a}$$

$$h[n] = h[N-1-n] \qquad 0 \le n \le N-1 \tag{13.7b}$$

Within the constraints imposed by Eq. (13.7), the possible filters are usually separated into two types. Type 1 filters satisfy Eq. (13.7) with N odd, and type

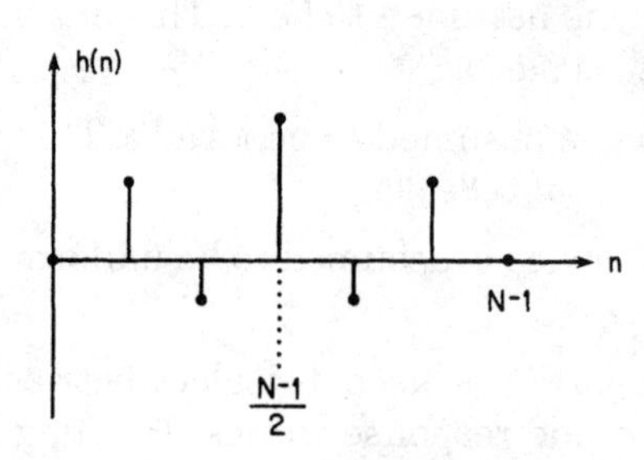

Figure 13.1 Impulse response for a type 1 linear phase FIR filter showing even symmetry about $n = (N-1)/2$.

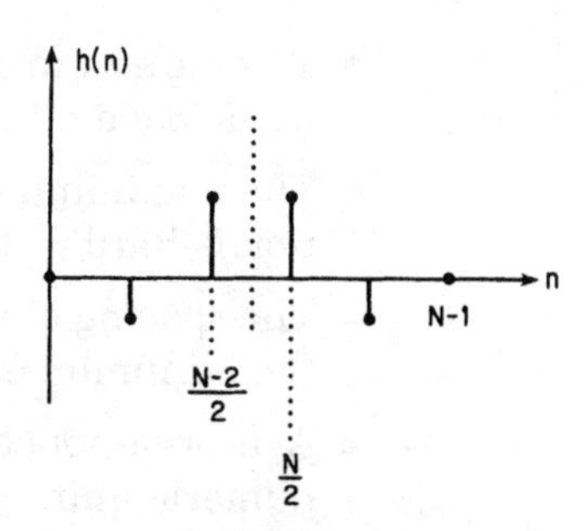

Figure 13.2 Impulse response for a type 2 linear phase FIR filter showing even symmetry about the abscissa midway between $n = (N-2)/2$ and $n = N/2$.

2 filters satisfy Eq. (13.7) with N even. For type 1 filters, the axis of symmetry for $h[n]$ lies at $n = (N-1)/2$ as shown in Fig. 13.1. For type 2 filters, the axis of symmetry lies midway between $n = N/2$ and $n = (N-2)/2$ as shown in Fig. 13.2.

Filters can have constant group delay without having constant phase delay if the phase response is a straight line that does not pass through the origin. Such a phase response is defined as

$$\theta(\omega) = \beta + \alpha\omega \tag{13.8}$$

The phase response of a filter will satisfy Eq. (13.8) if

$$\alpha = \frac{N-1}{2} \tag{13.9a}$$

$$\beta = \pm\frac{\pi}{2} \tag{13.9b}$$

$$h[n] = -h[N-1-n] \qquad 0 \le n \le N-1 \tag{13.9c}$$

An impulse response satisfying Eq. (13.9c) is said to be *odd symmetric,* or *antisymmetric.* Within the constraints imposed by Eq. (13.9), the possible filters can be separated into two types that are commonly referred to as type 3 and type 4 *linear phase* filters despite the fact that the phase response is *not truly linear.* [The phase response is a straight line, but it does not pass through the origin, and consequently $\theta(\omega_1 + \omega_2)$ does not equal $\theta(\omega_1) + \theta(\omega_2)$.] Type 3 filters satisfy Eq. (13.9) with N odd, and type 4 filters satisfy Eq. (13.9) with N even. For type 3 filters, the axis of antisymmetry for $h[n]$ lies at $n = (N-1)/2$ as shown in Fig. 13.3. When $n = (N-1)/2$, with N even, Eq. (13.9c) gives

$$h\left[\frac{N-1}{2}\right] = -h\left[\frac{N-1}{2}\right]$$

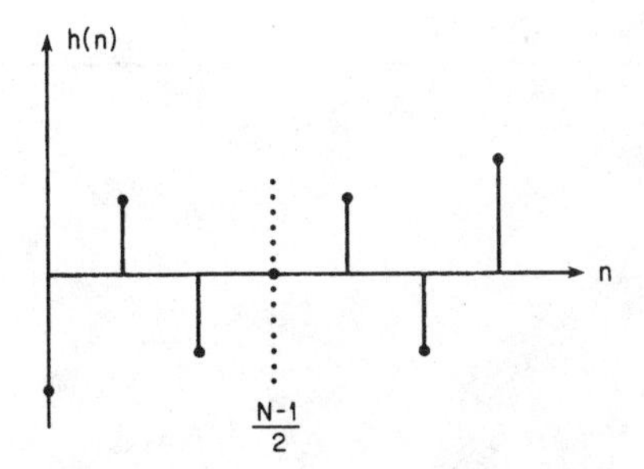

Figure 13.3 Impulse response for a type 3 linear phase FIR filter showing odd symmetry about $n = (N - 1)/2$.

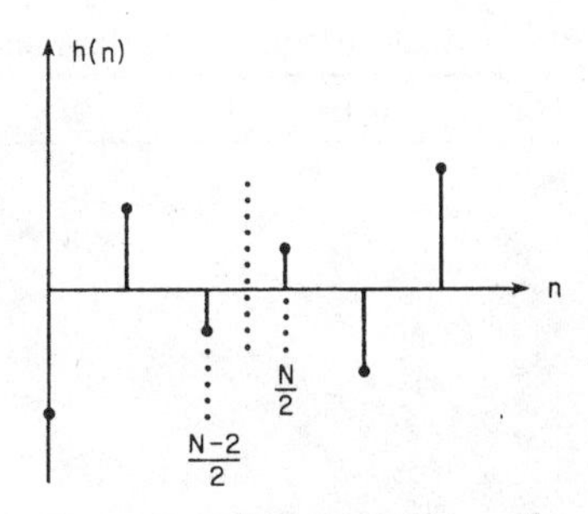

Figure 13.4 Impulse response for a type 4 linear phase FIR filter showing odd symmetry about the abscissa midway between $n = (N - 2)/2$ and $n = N/2$.

Therefore, $h[(N - 1)/2]$ must always equal zero in type 3 filters. For type 4 filters, the axis of antisymmetry lies midway between $n = N/2$ and $n = (N - 2)/2$ as shown in Fig. 13.4.

Software design

The definition for derived class `LinearPhaseFirDesign` is provided in Listing 13.3, and the member function bodies are provided in Listing 13.4. This class doesn't really add much functionality to that already provided in the base class `FirFilterDesign`. In fact, this class isn't really meant to be instantiated as an object on its own. It was created simply to provide a common base from which several specific types of linear phase FIR filter classes can be derived. (In Chap. 14, we derive a class `FirIdealFilter` for representing linear phase FIR approximations to ideal filters, and in Chap. 15 we derive the class `FreqSampFirDesign` for representing a type of linear phase FIR that is designed by optimizing the value of samples in the transition band of the filter's magnitude response.) The important additions provided by `LinearPhaseFirFilter` are the two new data members `Band_Config` and `Fir_Type`. These are two attributes of linear phase FIR filters that are not included in the base class `FirFilterDesign`. (NOTE: The type `BAND_CONFIG_TYPE` is an enumeration that is defined in file `typedefs.h`.)

Frequency response of linear phase FIR filters

The discrete-time Fourier transform (DTFT) can be used directly, as it is in Listing 13.2, to obtain the frequency response of any FIR filter. However, for the special case of linear phase FIR filters, the symmetry and "realness" properties of the impulse response can be used to modify the general DTFT to obtain dedicated formulas having reduced computational burdens.

The frequency response $H(e^{j\omega T})$ and amplitude response $A(e^{j\omega T})$ are listed in Table 13.2 for the four types of linear phase FIR filters. The properties of these four types are summarized in Table 13.3.

TABLE 13.2 Frequency Response Formulas for Linear Phase FIR Filters

$h(nT)$ symmetry	N	$H(e^{j\omega T})$	$A(e^{j\omega T})$
Even	Odd	$e^{-j\omega(N-1)T/2}\,A(e^{j\omega T})$	$\sum_{k=0}^{(N-1)/2} a_k \cos \omega k T$
Even	Even	$e^{-j\omega(N-1)T/2}\,A(e^{j\omega T})$	$\sum_{k=1}^{N/2} b_k \cos\left[\omega\left(k-\frac{1}{2}\right)T\right]$
Odd	Odd	$e^{-j[\omega(N-1)T/2-\pi/2]}\,A(e^{j\omega T})$	$\sum_{k=1}^{(N-1)/2} a_k \sin \omega k T$
Odd	Even	$e^{-j[\omega(N-1)T/2-\pi/2]}\,A(e^{j\omega T})$	$\sum_{k=1}^{N/2} b_k \sin\left[\omega\left(k-\frac{1}{2}\right)T\right]$

NOTE: $a_0 = h\left[\frac{(N-1)T}{2}\right]$ $a_k = 2h\left[\left(\frac{N-1}{2}-k\right)T\right]$ $b_k = 2h\left[\left(\frac{N}{2}-k\right)T\right]$

At first glance, the fact that $A(\omega)$ is periodic with a period of 4π for type 2 and type 4 filters seems to contradict the fundamental relationship between sampling rate and folding frequency that was established in Chap. 8. The difficulty lies in how we have defined $A(\omega)$. The frequency response $H(\omega)$ is, in fact, periodic in 2π for all four types, as we would expect. Both $\mathrm{Re}[H(\omega)]$ and $\mathrm{Im}[H(\omega)]$ are periodic in 2π, but factors of -1 are allocated between $A(\omega)$ and $\theta(\omega)$ differently over the intervals $(0, 2\pi)$ and $(2\pi, 4\pi)$ so that $\theta(\omega)$ can be made linear [and $A(\omega)$ can be made analytic].

Some of the properties listed in Table 13.3 have an impact on which types can be used in particular applications. As a consequence of odd symmetry about $\omega = 0$, types 3 and 4 always have $A(0) = 0$ and should therefore not be used for low-pass or bandstop filters. As a consequence of their odd symmetry about $\omega = \pi$, types 2 and 3 always have $A(\pi) = 0$ and should therefore not be used for high-pass or bandstop filters. Within the bounds of these restrictions, the choice between an odd-length or even-length filter is often made so that the desired transition frequency falls as close as possible to the midpoint between two sampled frequencies. The phase response of types 3 and 4 includes a constant component of 90° in addition to the linear component. Therefore, these types are suited for use as differentiators and Hilbert transformers (see Rabiner and Gold 1975).

TABLE 13.3 Properties of FIR Filters Having Constant Group Delay

	Type			
	1	2	3	4
Length, N	Odd	Even	Odd	Even
Symmetry about $\omega = 0$	Even	Even	Odd	Odd
Symmetry about $\omega = \pi$	Even	Odd	Odd	Even
Periodicity	2π	4π	2π	4π

Software design

The equations of Table 13.2 are implemented in the class `LinearPhaseFirResponse`. The two member functions for this derived class are provided in Listing 13.5. The constructor simply invokes the constructor for the base class `FirFilterResponse` using initializer syntax. The member function `ComputeMagResp` redefines the like-named function that is declared virtual in the base class. This redefined function will compute the magnitude response using the appropriate equation from Table 13.2, and if `Normalize_Enabled` is set TRUE, call the base class method `NormalizeResponse`.

13.4 Structures for FIR Realizations

There are a number of different structures that can be used to realize FIR filters. For any given set of filter coefficients, all of these different structures are equivalent, assuming that they are implemented with infinite-precision arithmetic. However, when implemented using finite-precision arithmetic with quantized coefficients and quantized signals, the different structures can exhibit vastly different behavior. Therefore, some care needs to be exercised in the selection of a structure for implementing a particular filter. This section will explore several of the most common implementation structures used for FIR filters.

Direct form

As revealed in prior sections, an FIR filter can be represented by a difference equation of the form

$$y[n] = \sum_{k=0}^{N-1} h[k]\, x[n-k] \tag{13.10}$$

where $h[k]$ is the impulse response of the filter. Equation (13.10) maps directly into the *direct form* FIR structure shown in Fig. 13.5. Recall that the interpretation of a signal flow graph such as Fig. 13.5 is subject to the following rules:

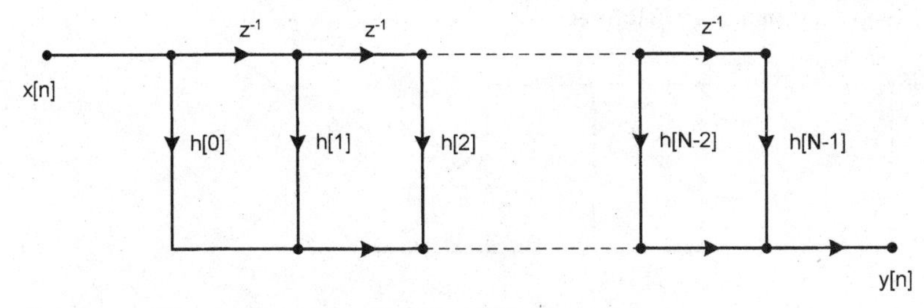

Figure 13.5 Direct form realization of an FIR filter.

- The gain of each branch is indicated near an arrowhead in the center of the branch.
- An unlabeled branch is assumed to have unity gain.
- An indicated gain of z^{-M} is used to denote a delay of M sample times; hence, an indicated gain of z^{-1} denotes a unit delay.
- All of the branch signals going into a node are added together to obtain the signal out of the node.

In some of the literature that discusses applications such as adaptive equalization, the structure of Fig. 13.5 is referred to as a *tapped delay line* or *transversal filter* and is drawn in the form shown in Fig. 13.6.

Transposed direct form

The transposition theorem can be applied to the direct form structure of Fig. 13.5 to obtain the *transposed direct form* structure shown in Fig. 13.7.

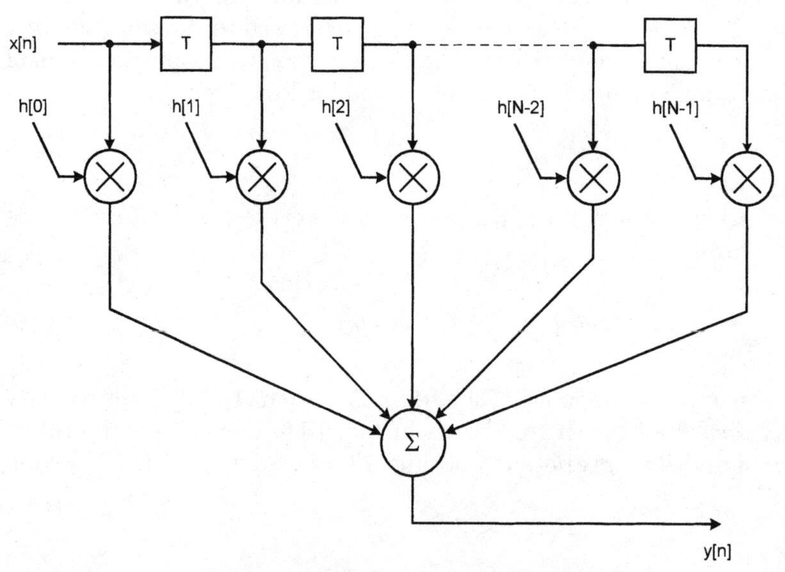

Figure 13.6 Tapped delay line representation of an FIR filter.

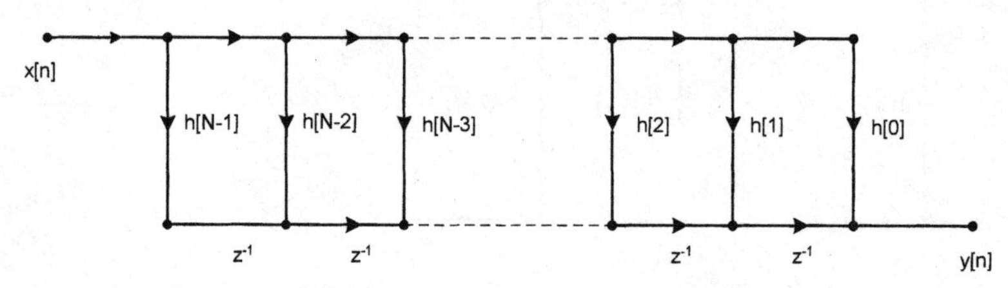

Figure 13.7 Transposed direct form realization of an FIR filter.

Cascade form

The polynomial system function $H(z)$ for an FIR filter can be factored into a product of first- and second-order polynomials to yield:

$$H(z) = \sum_{n=0}^{N} h[n]z^{-n} = \prod_{k=1}^{N_1} (\beta_{0k} + \beta_{1k}z^{-1}) \prod_{k=1}^{N_2} (b_{0k} + b_{1k}z^{-1} + b_{2k}z^{-2}) \qquad (13.11)$$

where each of the first-order polynomials has as its root a *real* root of $H(z)$, each of the second-order polynomials has as its root a complex-conjugate pair of roots from $H(z)$, and N_1, N_2 satisfy $N = N_1 + 2N_2$. For all of the even-order FIR filters examined in this book, the roots of $H(z)$ will always occur in complex-conjugate pairs. For all of the odd-order FIR filters examined in this book, $H(z)$ will have a single real root (usually at $z = -1$), and all of the remaining roots will occur in complex-conjugate pairs. Therefore, we can rewrite Eq. (13.11) as

$$H(z) = \begin{cases} \displaystyle\prod_{n=1}^{N/2} (b_{0k} + b_{1k}z^{-1} + b_{2k}z^{-2}) & N \text{ even} \\ \displaystyle(b_{00} + b_{10}z^{-1}) \prod_{n=1}^{(N-1)/2} (b_{0k} + b_{1k}z^{-1} + b_{2k}z^{-2}) & N \text{ odd} \end{cases} \qquad (13.12)$$

The form of Eq. (13.12) suggests that the corresponding filter can be implemented as a cascade of second-order sections plus, for odd-order filters, one first-order section. Cascade implementations that use direct form sections are shown in Figs. 13.8 and 13.9. Notice that the single first-order section in Fig. 13.9 is equivalent to one of the second-order sections with the coefficient b_{2k} set to zero. Often this fact is exploited to collapse the two cases in Eq. (13.12) into the following single case

$$H(z) = \prod_{n=1}^{N_S} (b_{0k} + b_{1k}z^{-1} + b_{2k}z^{-2})$$

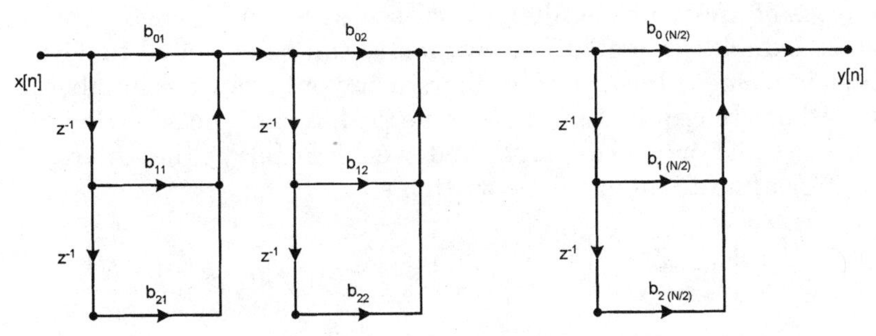

Figure 13.8 Cascade form realization of an even-length FIR filter.

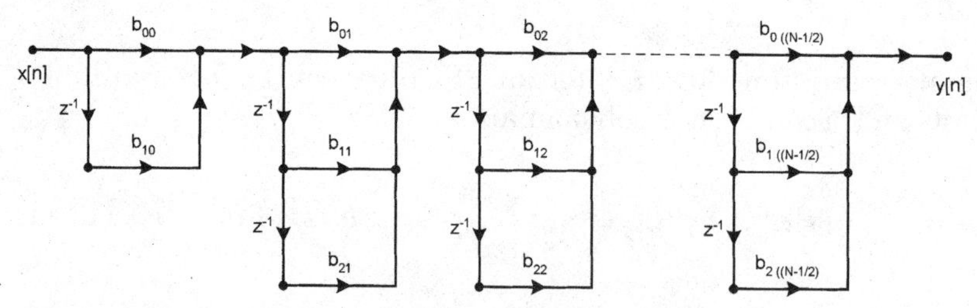

Figure 13.9 Cascade form realization of an odd-length FIR filter.

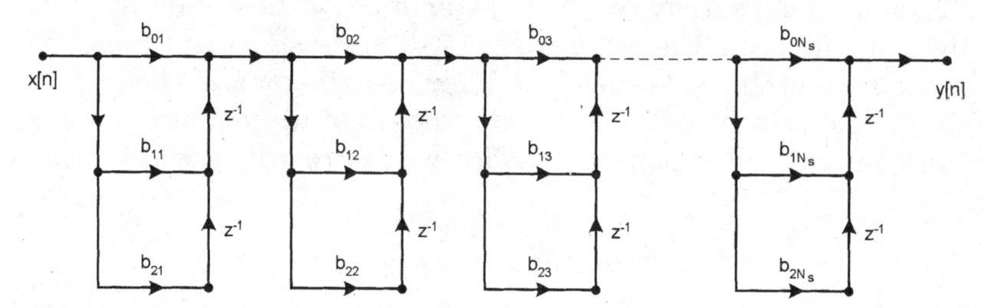

Figure 13.10 Cascade form realization of FIR filter with individual sections implemented in transposed direct form.

where $N_S = \lfloor (N+1)/2 \rfloor$, and it is understood that for odd-order filters one of the b_{2k} is zero. (The notation $\lfloor x \rfloor$ represents the floor of x, which is the largest integer that does not exceed x.)

It is possible to obtain additional cascade forms by using the transpose direct form for the second-order sections as in Fig. 13.10, or by applying the transpose theorem to the entire structure of Fig. 13.8. If this second approach is used, each of thc sections will be like the sections in Fig. 13.10, but the sequence of the sections will be reversed, with b_{0N_S} coming right after the input and b_{01} coming right before the output.

Structures for linear phase FIR filters

The various types of linear phase filters discussed in Sec. 13.3 have impulse responses which exhibit symmetry. This symmetry can be exploited to devise structures that implement linear phase filters using only half the number of multiplications that are required for nonsymmetric filters of the same length. For type 1 filters (which have odd length and even symmetry), the difference equation relating output to input can be written as

$$y[n] = h\left[\frac{N-1}{2}\right] x\left[n - \frac{N-1}{2}\right] + \sum_{k=0}^{(N-3)/2} h[k]\,(x[n-k] + x[n+k+1-N])$$

The corresponding implementation structure is shown in Fig. 13.11.

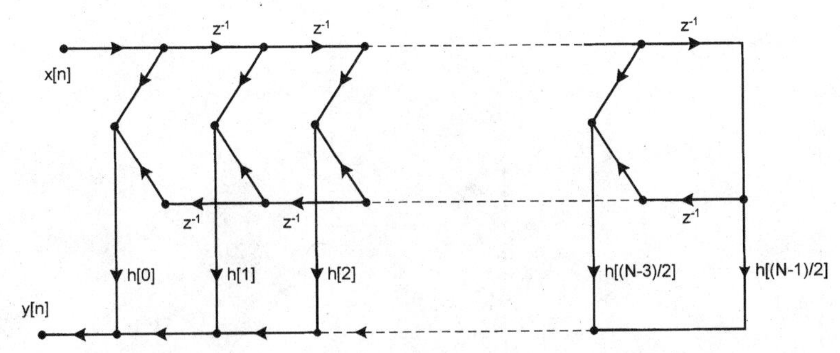

Figure 13.11 Direct form structure for type 1 linear phase FIR filter.

For type 2 filters (which have even length and even symmetry), the difference equation relating output to input can be written as

$$y[n] = \sum_{k=0}^{N/2-1} h[k]\,(x[n-k] + x[n+k+1-N])$$

The corresponding implementation structure is shown in Fig. 13.12.

For type 3 filters (which have odd length and odd symmetry), the difference equation relating output to input can be written as

$$y[n] = \sum_{k=0}^{(N-3)/2} h[k]\,(x[n-k] - x[n+k+1-N])$$

The corresponding implementation structure is shown in Fig. 13.13.

Finally, for type 4 filters (which have even length and odd symmetry), the difference equation relating output to input can be written as

$$y[n] = \sum_{k=0}^{N/2-1} h[k]\,(x[n-k] - x[n+k+1-N])$$

The corresponding implementation structure is shown in Fig. 13.14.

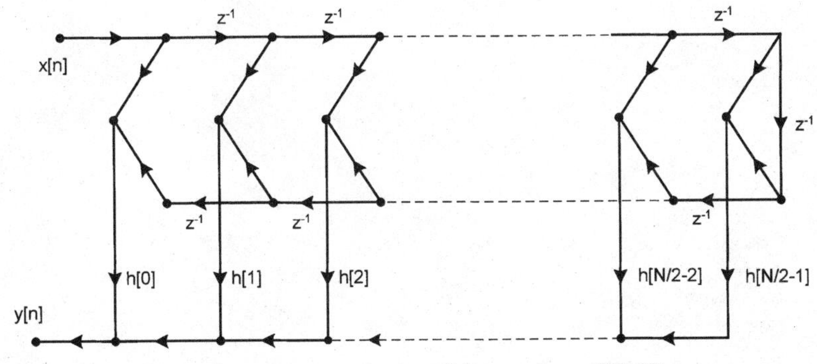

Figure 13.12 Direct form structure for type 2 linear phase FIR filter.

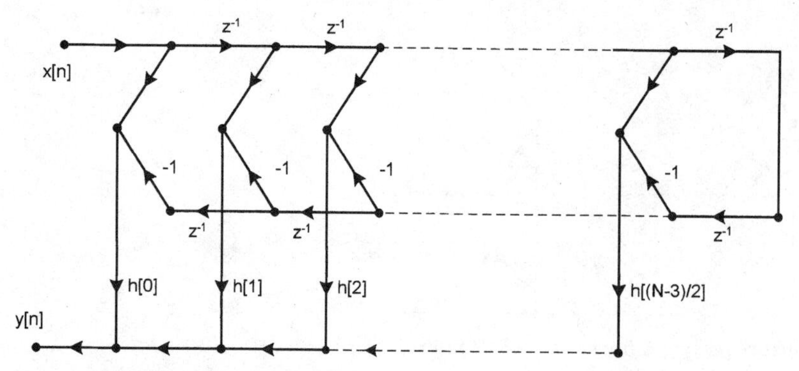

Figure 13.13 Direct form structure for type 3 linear phase FIR filter.

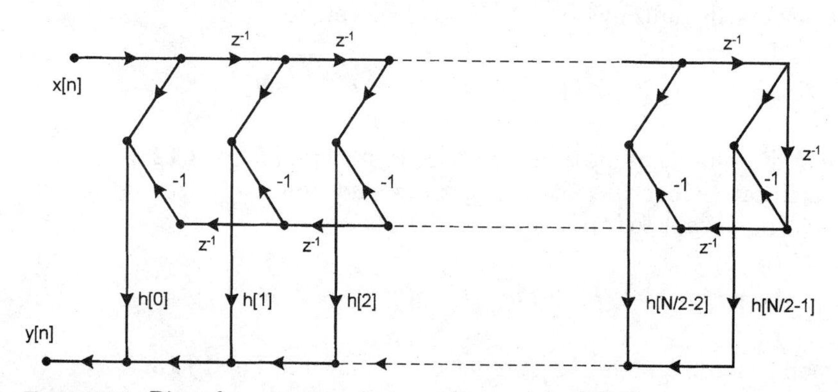

Figure 13.14 Direct form structure for type 4 linear phase FIR filter.

Listing 13.1 Member Functions for FIR Filter Design Class

```
//
//  File = fir_dsgn.cpp
//

#include <math.h>
#include <stdlib.h>
#include <iomanip.h>
#include "misdefs.h"
#include "fir_dsgn.h"

//==========================================
// default constructor
//------------------------------------------

FirFilterDesign::FirFilterDesign( void )
```

```
{
 return;
}

//================================================
//  constructor that allocates array of
//  length num_taps to hold coefficients
//------------------------------------------------

FirFilterDesign::FirFilterDesign( int num_taps )
{
 Num_Taps = num_taps;
 Imp_Resp_Coeff = new double[num_taps];
 Original_Coeff = new double[num_taps];
}

//============================================================
// constructor that allocates array of length num_taps
// and initializes this array to values contained in
// input array *imp_resp_coeff
//------------------------------------------------------------

FirFilterDesign::FirFilterDesign( int num_taps,
                                  double *imp_resp_coeff)
{
 Num_Taps = num_taps;
 Imp_Resp_Coeff = new double[num_taps];
 Original_Coeff = new double[num_taps];

 for(int n=0; n<num_taps; n++)
   {
    Imp_Resp_Coeff[n] = imp_resp_coeff[n];
    Original_Coeff[n] = imp_resp_coeff[n];
   }
 return;
}

//================================================
// method to allocate coefficient array
// after default constructor has been used
//------------------------------------------------

void FirFilterDesign::Initialize( int num_taps )
{
 Num_Taps = num_taps;
 Imp_Resp_Coeff = new double[num_taps];
 Original_Coeff = new double[num_taps];
}
```

```
//==========================================================
// copy coefficient values from array *Imp_Resp_Coeff
// to output array *coeff
//----------------------------------------------------------

void FirFilterDesign::CopyCoefficients( double *coeff)
{
 for(int n=0; n<Num_Taps; n++)
   {
    coeff[n] = Imp_Resp_Coeff[n];
   }
 return;
}

//=====================================
//  get number of filter taps
//-------------------------------------

int FirFilterDesign::GetNumTaps(void)
{
 return(Num_Taps);
}

//==================================================================
// dump complete set of coefficients to output_stream
//------------------------------------------------------------------

void FirFilterDesign::DumpCoefficients( ofstream* output_stream)
{
 output_stream->setf(ios::fixed, ios::floatfield);
 output_stream->precision(11);
 for(int n=0; n<Num_Taps; n++)
   {
    (*output_stream) << "h[" << n << "] = "
                     << Imp_Resp_Coeff[n] << endl;
   }
 output_stream->precision(0);
 output_stream->setf(0, ios::floatfield);
 return;
}

//==============================================
//  get pointer to coefficient array
//----------------------------------------------
double* FirFilterDesign::GetCoefficients(void)
{
 cout << "in fs_dsgn, Imp_Resp_Coeff = " << (void*)Imp_Resp_Coeff << endl;
```

```
 return(Imp_Resp_Coeff);
}
```

Listing 13.2 Member Functions for FIR Filter Response Class

```
//
//  File = fir_resp.cpp
//
//  Member functions for class FirFilterResponse
//

#include <math.h>
#include <stdlib.h>
#include "d_cmplx.h"
#include "fir_resp.h"
#include "typedefs.h"
#include "misdefs.h"

//======================================================
//  constructor with all configuration parameters
//  passed in as arguments
//------------------------------------------------------

FirFilterResponse::FirFilterResponse( FirFilterDesign *filter_design,
                                      int num_resp_pts,
                                      int db_scale_enabled,
                                      int normalize_enabled,
                                      char* resp_file_name )
{
 Filter_Design = filter_design;
 Num_Resp_Pts = num_resp_pts;
 Db_Scale_Enabled = db_scale_enabled;
 Normalize_Enabled = normalize_enabled;

 if( resp_file_name == NULL)
   { Response_File = new ofstream("win_resp.txt", ios::out);}
 else
   { Response_File = new ofstream(resp_file_name, ios::out);}

 Num_Taps = Filter_Design->GetNumTaps();
 Mag_Resp = new double[Num_Resp_Pts];

 return;
}
```

```
//=====================================================================
// alternate constructor with interactive setting of
// configuration parameters
//---------------------------------------------------------------------
FirFilterResponse::FirFilterResponse( FirFilterDesign *filter_design,
                                       istream& uin,
                                       ostream& uout )
{
 logical default_file_ok;
 Filter_Design = filter_design;

 uout << "number of points in plot of frequency response?" << endl;
 uin >> Num_Resp_Pts;

 uout << "scaling?\n"
      << "  0 = linear, 1 = dB" << endl;
 uin >> Db_Scale_Enabled;

 if( Db_Scale_Enabled != 0) Db_Scale_Enabled = 1;
 Normalize_Enabled = 1;

 uout << "default name for magnitude response output\n"
      << "file is win_resp.txt\n\n"
      << "is this okay?"
      << "  0 = NO, 1 = YES"
      << endl;
 uin >> default_file_ok;

 if( default_file_ok)
    {
     Response_File = new ofstream("win_resp.txt", ios::out);
    }
  else
    {
     char *file_name;
     file_name = new char[31];

     uout << "enter complete name for output file (30 chars max)"
          << endl;
     uin >> file_name;
     Response_File = new ofstream(file_name, ios::out);
     delete []file_name;
    }

Num_Taps = Filter_Design->GetNumTaps();
Mag_Resp = new double[Num_Resp_Pts];
```

```
 return;
}

//==================================================
//  method to compute magnitude response
//--------------------------------------------------
void FirFilterResponse::ComputeMagResp( void )
{
 int resp_indx, tap_indx;
 double lambda;
 double_complex work;

 cout << " in FirFilterResponse::ComputeMagResp" << endl;
 double* coeff = Filter_Design->GetCoefficients();

 for( resp_indx=0; resp_indx<Num_Resp_Pts; resp_indx++)
   {
   lambda = resp_indx * PI / (double) Num_Resp_Pts;
   work = double_complex(0.0, 0.0);

   for( tap_indx=0; tap_indx<Num_Taps; tap_indx++)
     {
      work = work + (coeff[tap_indx] *
             double_complex( cos(tap_indx*lambda),
                            -sin(tap_indx*lambda)));
     }

   if(Db_Scale_Enabled)
     {Mag_Resp[resp_indx] = 20.0 * log10(norm(work));}
   else
     {Mag_Resp[resp_indx] = norm(work);}
   }

 if(Normalize_Enabled) NormalizeResponse();

 return;
}

//=======================================================
//  method to normalize magnitude response
//-------------------------------------------------------

void FirFilterResponse::NormalizeResponse( void )
{
 int n;
 double biggest;
```

```
 if(Db_Scale_Enabled)
   {
    biggest = -100.0;

    for( n=0; n < Num_Resp_Pts; n++)
      {if(Mag_Resp[n]>biggest) biggest = Mag_Resp[n];}
    for( n=0; n < Num_Resp_Pts; n++)
      {Mag_Resp[n] = Mag_Resp[n] - biggest;}
   }
 else
   {
    biggest = 0.0;

    for( n=0; n < Num_Resp_Pts; n++)
      {if(Mag_Resp[n]>biggest) biggest = Mag_Resp[n];}
    for( n=0; n < Num_Resp_Pts; n++)
      {Mag_Resp[n] = Mag_Resp[n] / biggest;}
   }
 return;
}
//==================================================
//  method to return a pointer to the magnitude
//  response that is stored inside this class
//--------------------------------------------------

double* FirFilterResponse::GetMagResp( void)
{
 return(Mag_Resp);
}

//============================================================
//  method to dump magnitude response to the stream
//  designated by Response_File
//------------------------------------------------------------

void FirFilterResponse::DumpMagResp( void )
{
 double freq;

 Response_File->setf(ios::fixed, ios::floatfield);
 for(int n=0; n<Num_Resp_Pts; n++)
   {
    freq = (n*PI)/double(Num_Resp_Pts);
    (*Response_File) << freq << ", "
                     << Mag_Resp[n] << endl;
   }
 Response_File->setf(0, ios::floatfield);
```

```
 return;
}
//===========================================================
//  searches the magnitude response over the interval
//  from sample intrvl_beg thru the sample intrvl_end
//  and then returns the largest value found in this
//  interval.
//-----------------------------------------------------------
double FirFilterResponse::GetIntervalPeak( int nBeg,
                                            int nEnd)
{
 double peak;
 int n, indexOfPeak;

 peak = -9999.0;
 for(n=nBeg; n<nEnd; n++)
   {
    if(Mag_Resp[n]>peak)
      {
       peak=Mag_Resp[n];
       indexOfPeak = n;
      }
   }
 return(peak);
}
```

Listing 13.3 Header for Linear Phase FIR Filter Design Class

```
//
//  File = lin_dsgn.h
//

#ifndef _LIN_DSGN_H_
#define _LIN_DSGN_H_

#include "typedefs.h"

class LinearPhaseFirDesign : public FirFilterDesign
{
 public:

  //---------------------
  // default constructor

  LinearPhaseFirDesign( );
```

```
  //-----------------------------------------------
  // constructor that allocates (via base class)
  // an array of length num_taps to hold
  // filter coefficients

  LinearPhaseFirDesign::LinearPhaseFirDesign( int num_taps );

  //---------------------------------------------------
  //  method to return band configuration
  //  ( lowpass, bandpass, highpass, or bandstop )

  BAND_CONFIG_TYPE GetBandConfig(void);

  //------------------------------------------------
  // method to return type of linear phase filter

  int GetFirType(void);

 protected:

  BAND_CONFIG_TYPE Band_Config;

  int Fir_Type;
};

#endif
```

Listing 13.4 Member Functions for Linear Phase FIR Filter Design Class

```
//
//  File = lin_dsgn.cpp
//

#include "misdefs.h"
#include "typedefs.h"
#include "fir_dsgn.h"
#include "lin_dsgn.h"

//==============================================
// default constructor
//----------------------------------------------

LinearPhaseFirDesign::LinearPhaseFirDesign( )
                    :FirFilterDesign()
{
}
```

```
//==============================================
// constructor that allocates (via base class)
// an array of length num_taps to hold
// filter coefficients
//----------------------------------------------

LinearPhaseFirDesign::LinearPhaseFirDesign( int num_taps )
                     :FirFilterDesign( num_taps )
{
}

//=========================================================
//  method to return band configuration
//  ( lowpass, bandpass, highpass, or bandstop )
//---------------------------------------------------------

BAND_CONFIG_TYPE LinearPhaseFirDesign::GetBandConfig(void)
{ return(Band_Config); }

//================================================
// method to return type of linear phase filter
//------------------------------------------------

int LinearPhaseFirDesign::GetFirType(void)
{ return(Fir_Type); }
```

Listing 13.5 Member Functions for Linear Phase FIR Filter Response Class

```
//
//  File = lin_resp.cpp
//

#include <math.h>
#include <stdlib.h>
#include "fs_spec.h"
#include "lin_resp.h"
#include "typedefs.h"
#include "misdefs.h"
extern ofstream DebugFile;

//==================================================================
// constructor with interactive setting of configuration parameters
//------------------------------------------------------------------
LinearPhaseFirResponse::LinearPhaseFirResponse( LinearPhaseFirDesign *filter_
                                                design,
                                                istream& uin,
                                                ostream& uout )
```

```
                    :FirFilterResponse( filter_design,
                                        uin,
                                        uout)
{
}

//===========================================================
//  method to compute magnitude response
//
//  note: this function redefines the virtual function
//        ComputeMagResp that is defined in the base
//        class FirFilterResponse
//-----------------------------------------------------------

void LinearPhaseFirResponse::ComputeMagResp( void )
{
int index, resp_indx, tap_indx;
double lambda, work;

double* coeff = Filter_Design->GetCoefficients();
int fir_type = ((LinearPhaseFirDesign*)Filter_Design)->GetFirType();

for( resp_indx=0; resp_indx<Num_Resp_Pts; resp_indx++)
  {
  lambda = resp_indx * PI / (double) Num_Resp_Pts;

  switch (fir_type) {

    case 1:     /* symmetric and odd */
      work = coeff[(Num_Taps-1)/2];
      for( tap_indx=1; tap_indx<=((Num_Taps-1)/2); tap_indx++)
        {
        index = (Num_Taps-1)/2 - tap_indx;
        work = work + 2.0 * coeff[index] * cos(tap_indx*lambda);
        }
      break;

    case 2:     /* symmetric and even */
      work = 0.0;
      for( tap_indx=1; tap_indx<=(Num_Taps/2); tap_indx++)
        {
        index = Num_Taps/2-tap_indx;
        work = work + 2.0 * coeff[index] * cos((tap_indx-0.5)*lambda);
        }
      break;

    case 3:     /* antisymmetric and odd */
```

```
      work = 0.0;
      for( tap_indx=1; tap_indx<=((Num_Taps-1)/2); tap_indx++)
        {
        index = (Num_Taps-1)/2 - tap_indx;
        work = work + 2.0 * coeff[index] * sin(tap_indx*lambda);
        }
      break;

    case 4:     /* symmetric and even */
      work = 0.0;
      for( tap_indx=1; tap_indx<=(Num_Taps/2); tap_indx++)
        {
        index = Num_Taps/2-tap_indx;
        work = work + 2.0 * coeff[index] * sin((tap_indx-0.5)*lambda);
        }
      break;
    }

  if(Db_Scale_Enabled)
    {Mag_Resp[resp_indx] = 20.0 * log10(fabs(work));}
  else
    {Mag_Resp[resp_indx] = fabs(work);}
  }
return;
}
```

Chapter 14

FIR Filter Design: Window Method

The window method of FIR filter design is built upon a more fundamental approach that is usually called the *Fourier series method.* Therefore, this chapter begins with an exploration of the Fourier series method before moving on to discuss windowing issues in subsequent sections.

14.1 Basis of the Fourier Series Method

This Fourier series method of FIR filter design is based on the fact that the frequency response of a digital filter is periodic and is therefore representable as a Fourier series. A desired target frequency response is selected and expanded as a Fourier series. This expansion is truncated to a finite number of terms that are then used as the filter coefficients or tap weights. The resulting filter has a frequency response that approximates the original desired target response.

Algorithm 14.1 Designing FIR filters via the Fourier series method

Step 1. Specify a desired frequency response $H_d(\lambda)$.

Step 2. Specify the desired number of filter taps N.

Step 3. Compute the filter coefficients $h[n]$ for $n = 0, 1, 2, \ldots, N-1$ using

$$h[n] = \frac{1}{2\pi} \int_{2\pi} H_d(\lambda)[\cos(m\lambda) + j \sin(m\lambda)]\, d\lambda \tag{14.1}$$

where $m = n - (N-1)/2$.

[Simplifications of Eq. (14.1) are presented following for the cases in which H_d is the magnitude response of ideal low-pass, high-pass, bandpass, or bandstop filters.]

Step 4. Using the techniques presented in Secs. 12.2 and 12.3, compute the actual frequency response of the resulting filter. If the performance is not adequate, change N or $H_d(\lambda)$ and go back to Step 3.

Example 14.1 Use the Fourier series method to design a 21-tap FIR filter that approximates the amplitude response of an ideal low-pass filter with a cutoff frequency of 2 kHz assuming a sampling frequency of 5 kHz.

solution The normalized cutoff is $\lambda = 2\pi/5$. The desired frequency response is depicted in Fig. 14.1. Using Eq. (14.1), we can immediately write

$$h[n] = \frac{1}{2\pi}\int_{-2\pi/5}^{2\pi/5} \cos(m\lambda)\, d\lambda + j\frac{1}{2\pi}\int_{-2\pi/5}^{2\pi/5} \sin(m\lambda)\, d\lambda$$

Since the second integrand is an odd function and the limits of integration are symmetric about zero, the second integral equals zero. Therefore,

$$h[n] = \left.\frac{\sin(m\lambda)}{2m\pi}\right|_{\lambda=-2\pi/5}^{2\pi/5}$$

$$= \frac{\sin(2m\pi/5)}{m\pi} \tag{14.2}$$

where $m = n - 10$.

L'Hospital's rule can be used to evaluate Eq. (14.2) for the case of $m = 0$ (that is, $n = 10$):

$$h[10] = \left.\frac{(d/dm)\sin(2m\pi/5)}{(d/dm)m\pi}\right|_{m=0}$$

$$= \left.\frac{(2\pi/5)\cos(2m\pi/5)}{\pi}\right|_{m=0}$$

$$= \frac{2}{5} = 0.4$$

Evaluation of Eq. (14.2) for $m \neq 0$ is straightforward. The values of $h[n]$ are listed in Table 14.1, and the corresponding magnitude response is shown in Figs. 14.2 and 14.3. Usually, the passband ripples are more pronounced when the vertical axis is in linear units such as numeric magnitude or percentage of peak magnitude, as in Fig. 14.2. On the other hand, details of the stopband response are usually more clearly displayed when the vertical axis is in decibels, as in Fig. 14.3.

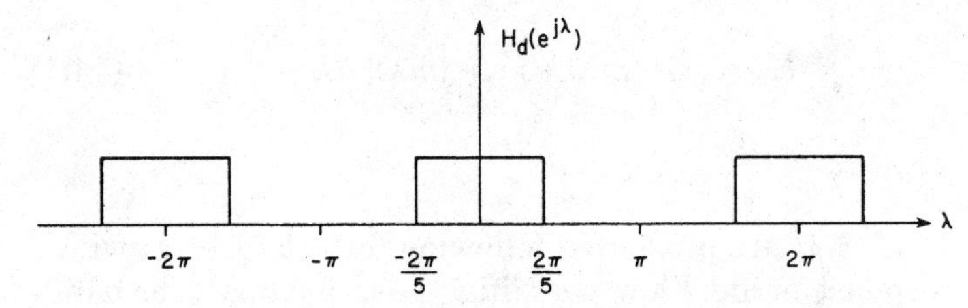

Figure 14.1 Desired frequency response for Example 14.1.

TABLE 14.1 Impulse Response Coefficients for the 21-Tap Low-Pass Filter of Example 14.1

$h[0] = h[20] = 0.000000$
$h[1] = h[19] = -0.033637$
$h[2] = h[18] = -0.023387$
$h[3] = h[17] = 0.026728$
$h[4] = h[16] = 0.050455$
$h[5] = h[15] = 0.000000$
$h[6] = h[14] = -0.075683$
$h[7] = h[13] = -0.062366$
$h[8] = h[12] = 0.093549$
$h[9] = h[11] = 0.302731$
$h[10] = 0.400000$

Properties of the Fourier series method

1. Filters designed using Algorithm 14.1 will exhibit the linear phase property discussed in Sec. 13.3, provided that the target frequency response $H_d(\lambda)$ is either symmetric or antisymmetric.
2. As a consequence of the Gibbs phenomenon, the frequency response of filters designed with Algorithm 14.1 will contain undershoots and overshoots at the band edges as exhibited by the responses shown in Figs. 14.2 and 14.3. As long as the number of filter taps remains finite, these disturbances cannot be elim-

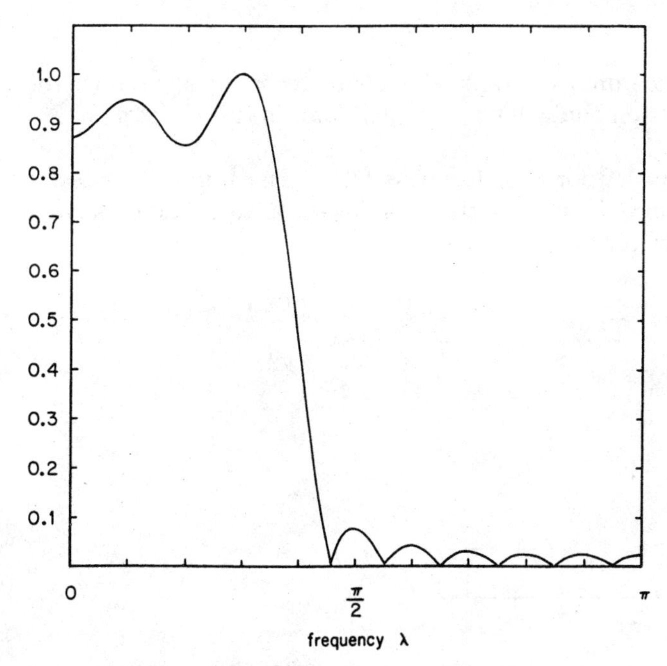

Figure 14.2 Magnitude response (as a percentage of peak) obtained from the 21-tap low-pass filter of Example 14.1.

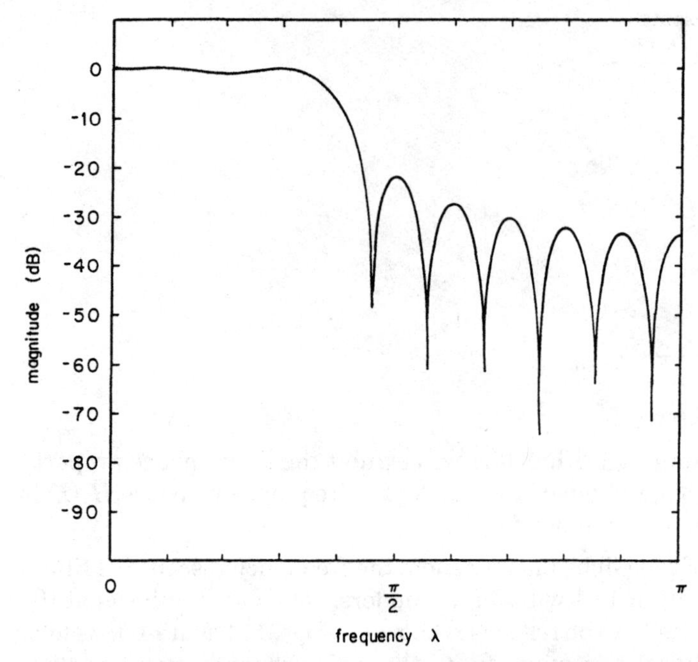

Figure 14.3 Magnitude response (in dB) obtained from the 21-tap low-pass filter of Example 14.1.

inated by increasing the number of taps. Windowing techniques to reduce the effects of the Gibbs phenomena will be presented later in this chapter.

Result 14.1 FIR approximation for ideal low-pass filter. The impulse response coefficients for an FIR approximation to the ideal low-pass amplitude response shown in Fig. 14.4 are given by

$$h[n] = \frac{\sin (m\lambda_U)}{m\pi} \qquad \begin{aligned} n &= 0, 1, \ldots, N-1 \\ m &= n - (N-1)/2 \end{aligned}$$

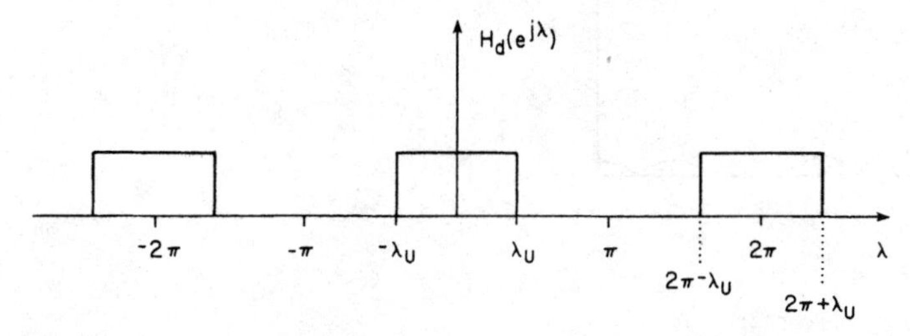

Figure 14.4 Frequency response of ideal low-pass digital filter.

For odd-length filters, the coefficient at $n = (N - 1)/2$ is obtained by application of L'Hospital's rule to yield

$$h\left[\frac{N-1}{2}\right] = \frac{\lambda_U}{\pi}$$

where

$$m = \begin{cases} n - (N-1)/2 & n \text{ odd} \\ n - N/2 & n \text{ even} \end{cases}$$

Software for FIR approximations to ideal filters

An FIR approximation to an ideal filter can be represented in software by the class `FirIdealFilter`, which is defined in Listing 14.1. This class is derived from the class `LinearPhaseFirDesign`, which in turn is derived from base class `FirFilterDesign` that was described in Chap. 13. The data portion of the derived class is very simple, consisting of just two `double` values that hold the ideal filter's cutoff frequencies. (For low-pass and high-pass configurations only one of the frequency values is actually used—both are used for bandpass and bandstop.) The derived class also uses two data items that are members of the base class: an `int` value for holding the number of filter taps, and a pointer to a `double` array that will hold the filter coefficients. The base class constructor allocates the array of `double` for the filter coefficients, and then the derived class constructor calls the appropriate method for computing the coefficients according to the input argument `band_config`. Each of these four different methods—low-pass, high-pass, bandpass, and bandstop—will assume that the specified cutoff frequencies are normalized such that the folding frequency will be π rad/s [in other words, the frequencies are normalized for a sampling interval of $1/(2\pi)$]. The method `IdealLowpass` provided in Listing 14.2 implements Result 14.1.

Result 14.2 FIR approximation for ideal high-pass filter. The impulse response coefficients for an FIR approximation to the ideal high-pass amplitude response shown in Fig. 14.5 are given by

$$h[n] = \begin{cases} 1 - \dfrac{\lambda_L}{\pi} & m = 0 \\ \dfrac{-\sin(m\lambda_L)}{m\pi} & m \neq 0 \end{cases}$$

where m is as defined for Result 14.1.

The coefficients given by Result 14.2 can be computed using the method `IdealHighpass` provided in Listing 14.3.

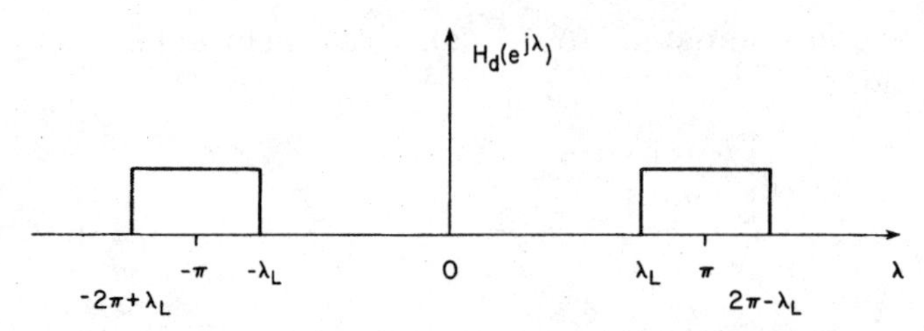

Figure 14.5 Frequency response of ideal high-pass digital filter.

Example 14.2 Use Result 14.2 to design a 21-tap FIR filter that approximates the amplitude response of an ideal high-pass filter with a normalized cutoff frequency of $\lambda_U = 3\pi/5$.

solution The coefficients $h(n)$ are listed in Table 14.2, and the resulting frequency response is shown in Figs. 14.6 and 14.7.

Result 14.3 FIR approximation for ideal bandpass filter. The impulse response coefficients for an FIR approximation to the ideal bandpass amplitude response shown in Fig. 14.8 are given by

$$h[n] = \begin{cases} \dfrac{\lambda_U - \lambda_L}{\pi} & m = 0 \\ \dfrac{1}{m\pi}[\sin(m\lambda_U) - \sin(m\lambda_L)] & m \neq 0 \end{cases}$$

where m is as defined for Result 14.1.

The coefficients given by Result 14.3 can be computed using the method `IdealBandpass` provided in Listing 14.4.

Example 14.3 Use Result 14.3 to design a 21-tap FIR filter that approximates the amplitude response of an ideal bandpass filter with a pass band that extends from $\lambda_L = 2\pi/5$ to $\lambda_U = 3\pi/5$.

solution The coefficients $h(n)$ are listed in Table 14.3, and the resulting frequency response is shown in Fig. 14.9.

TABLE 14.2 Impulse Response Coefficients for the 21-Tap High-Pass Filter of Example 14.2

$h[0] = h[20] =$	0.000000
$h[1] = h[19] =$	0.033637
$h[2] = h[18] =$	−0.023387
$h[3] = h[17] =$	−0.026728
$h[4] = h[16] =$	0.050455
$h[5] = h[15] =$	0.000000
$h[6] = h[14] =$	−0.075683
$h[7] = h[13] =$	0.062366
$h[8] = h[12] =$	0.093549
$h[9] = h[11] =$	−0.302731
$h[10] =$	0.400000

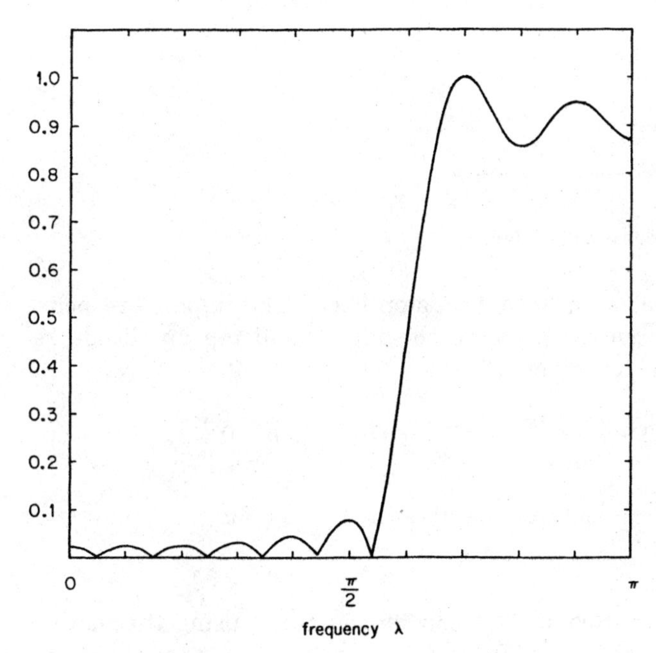

Figure 14.6 Magnitude response (as a percentage of peak) obtained from the 21-tap high-pass filter of Example 14.2.

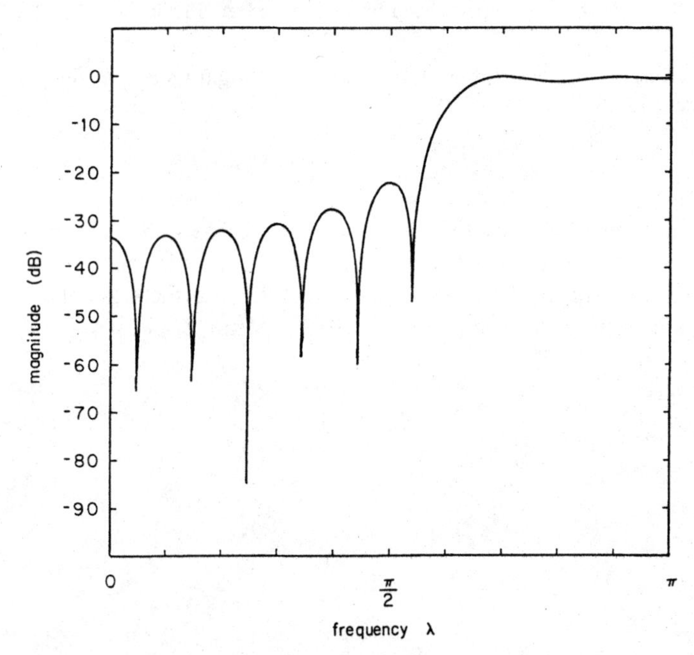

Figure 14.7 Magnitude response (in dB) obtained from 21-tap high-pass filter of Example 14.2.

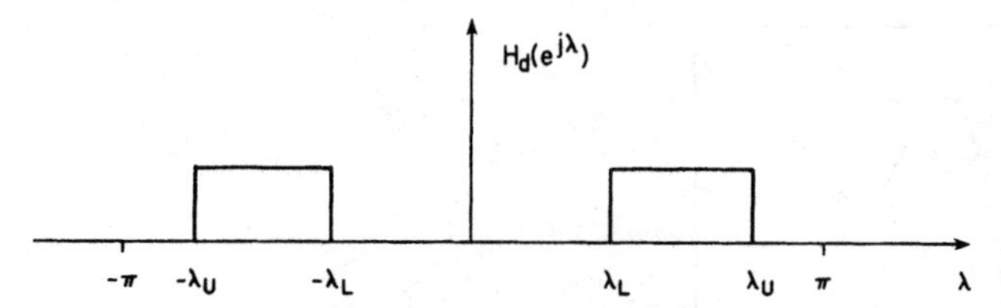

Figure 14.8 Frequency response of ideal bandpass digital filter.

Result 14.4 FIR approximation for ideal bandstop filter. The impulse response coefficients for an FIR approximation to the ideal bandstop amplitude response shown in Fig. 14.10 are given by

$$h[n] = \begin{cases} 1 + \dfrac{\lambda_L - \lambda_U}{\pi} & m = 0 \\ \dfrac{1}{n\pi}\left[\sin(m\lambda_L) - \sin(m\lambda_U)\right] & m \neq 0 \end{cases}$$

where $m = n - (N-1)/2$.

The coefficients given by Result 14.4 can be computed using the method `IdealBandstop` provided in Listing 14.5.

Example 14.4 Use Result 14.4 to design a 31-tap FIR filter that approximates the amplitude response of an ideal bandstop filter with a stop band that extends from $\lambda_L = 2\pi/5$ to $\lambda_U = 3\pi/5$.

solution The coefficients $h[n]$ are listed in Table 14.4, and the resulting frequency response is shown in Figs. 14.11 and 14.12.

14.2 Rectangular Window

As shown in the previous section, filters designed via the Fourier series method will, as a consequence of the Gibbs phenomenon, have frequency responses that contain overshoots and ripple. One way to reduce these effects involves multiplying the filter's impulse response by a *window* that tapers off the

TABLE 14.3 Impulse Response Coefficients for the 21-Tap Bandpass Filter of Example 14.3

$h[0] = h[20] =$	0.000000
$h[1] = h[19] =$	0.000000
$h[2] = h[18] =$	0.046774
$h[3] = h[17] =$	0.000000
$h[4] = h[16] =$	−0.100910
$h[5] = h[15] =$	0.000000
$h[6] = h[14] =$	0.151365
$h[7] = h[13] =$	0.000000
$h[8] = h[12] =$	−0.187098
$h[9] = h[11] =$	0.000000
$h[10] =$	0.200000

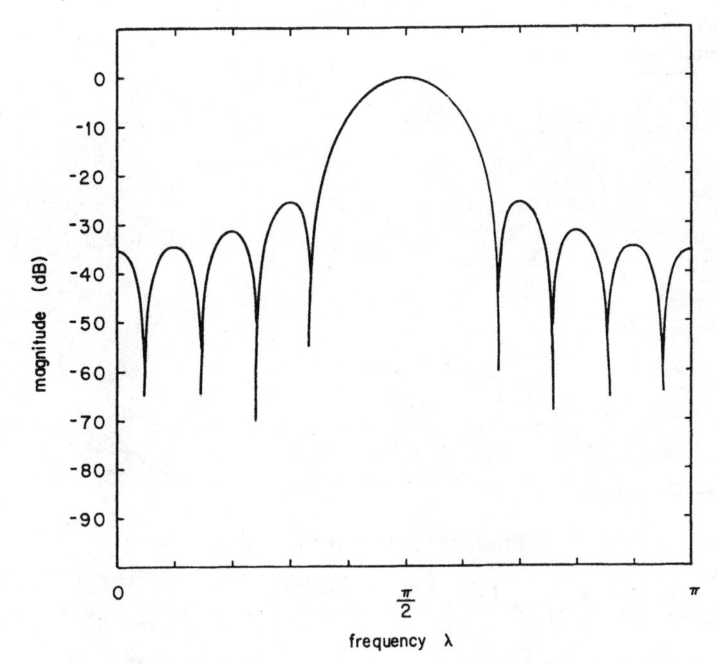

Figure 14.9 Magnitude response (in dB) obtained from the 21-tap bandpass filter of Example 14.3.

impulse response instead of abruptly truncating it to a finite number of terms. The basic idea of windowing is very straightforward, and most of the effort in this area is directed toward finding *good* window functions. A discussion of just what constitutes a good window function will be easier if we first develop a windowing viewpoint of truncation.

Truncating a filter's impulse response can be thought of as multiplying the infinite-length impulse response by a rectangular window such as the one shown in Fig. 14.13. This window has a value of unity for all values of t at which the impulse response is to be preserved, and a value of zero for all values of t at which the impulse response is to be eliminated:

$$w(t) = \begin{cases} 1 & |t| < \dfrac{\tau}{2} \\ 0 & \text{otherwise} \end{cases} \tag{14.3}$$

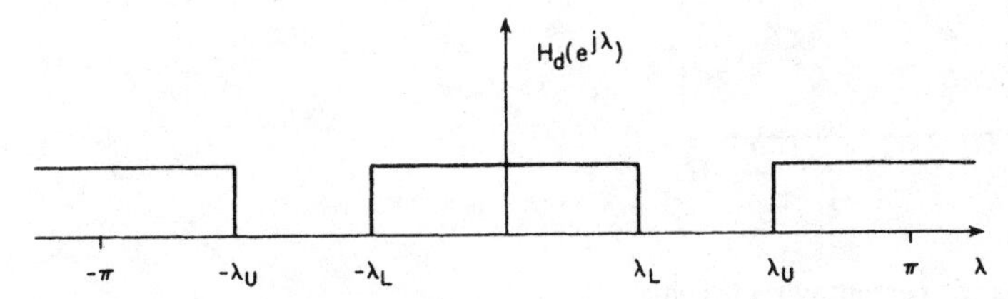

Figure 14.10 Frequency response of ideal bandstop digital filter.

TABLE 14.4 Impulse Response Coefficients for the 31-Tap Bandstop Filter of Example 14.4

$h[0] = h[30] = 0.000000$
$h[1] = h[29] = -0.043247$
$h[2] = h[28] = 0.000000$
$h[3] = h[27] = 0.031183$
$h[4] = h[26] = 0.000000$
$h[5] = h[25] = 0.000000$
$h[6] = h[24] = 0.000000$
$h[7] = h[23] = -0.046774$
$h[8] = h[22] = 0.000000$
$h[9] = h[21] = 0.100910$
$h[10] = h[20] = 0.000000$
$h[11] = h[19] = -0.151365$
$h[12] = h[18] = 0.000000$
$h[13] = h[17] = 0.187098$
$h[14] = h[16] = 0.000000$
$h[15] = 0.800000$

The rectangular window's Fourier transform is given by

$$W(f) = \frac{\tau \sin \pi f \tau}{\pi f \tau} \tag{14.4}$$

The magnitude of Eq. (14.4) is plotted in Fig. 14.14. The peaks of the first through ninth sidelobes are attenuated by 13.3, 17.8, 20.8, 23.0, 24.7, 26.2, 27.4, 28.5, and 29.5 dB, respectively.

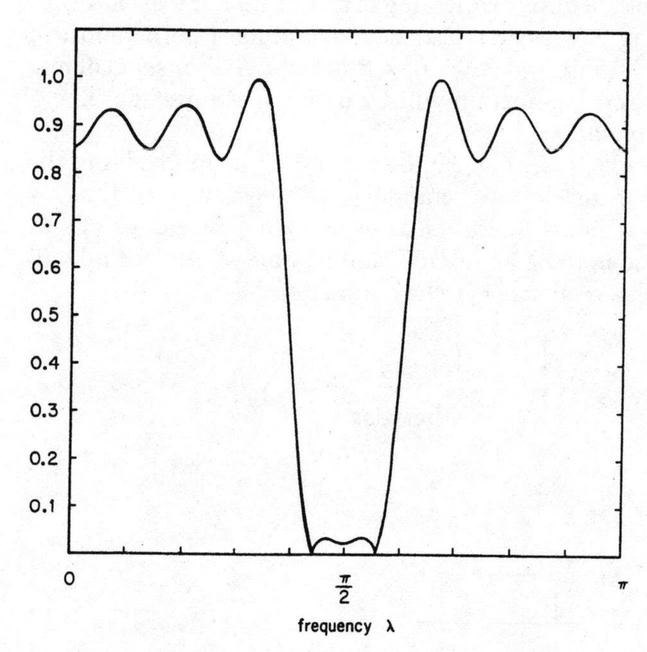

Figure 14.11 Magnitude response (as a percentage of peak) obtained from 31-tap bandstop filter of Example 14.4.

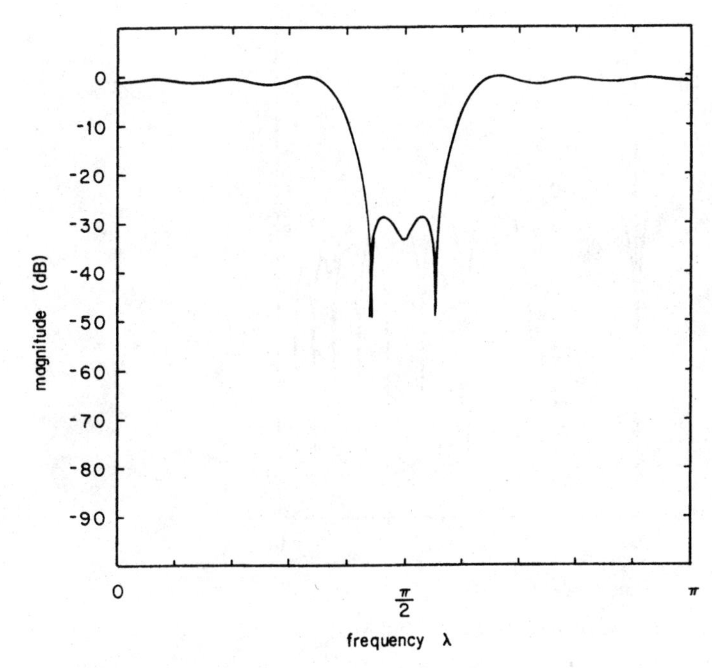

Figure 14.12 Magnitude response (in dB) obtained from 31-tap bandstop filter of Example 14.4.

The rectangular window's response will serve primarily as a benchmark to which the responses of other windows can be compared. [NOTE: By omitting further explanation, some texts such as Stanley (1975) imply that Eq. (14.4) also applies to the discrete-time version of the rectangular window. However, as we will discover in the following, the Fourier transforms of the continuous-time and discrete-time windows differ significantly. A similar situation exists with respect to the triangular window.]

Software notes

The data for Fig. 14.14 was generated using the class `ContRectangularMagResp` which is provided in Listing 14.6. This class by itself is very simple, consisting of

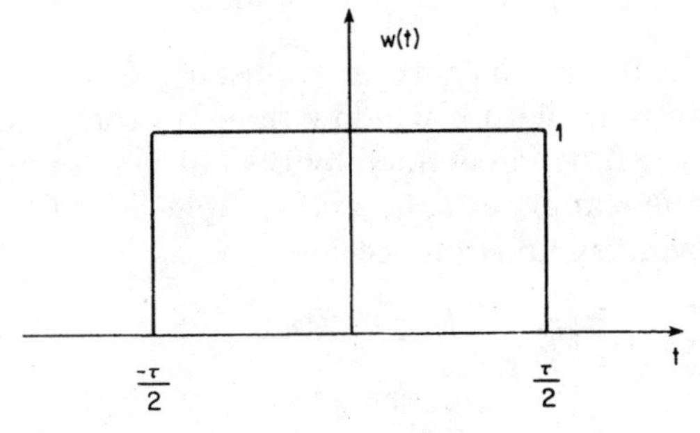

Figure 14.13 Rectangular window.

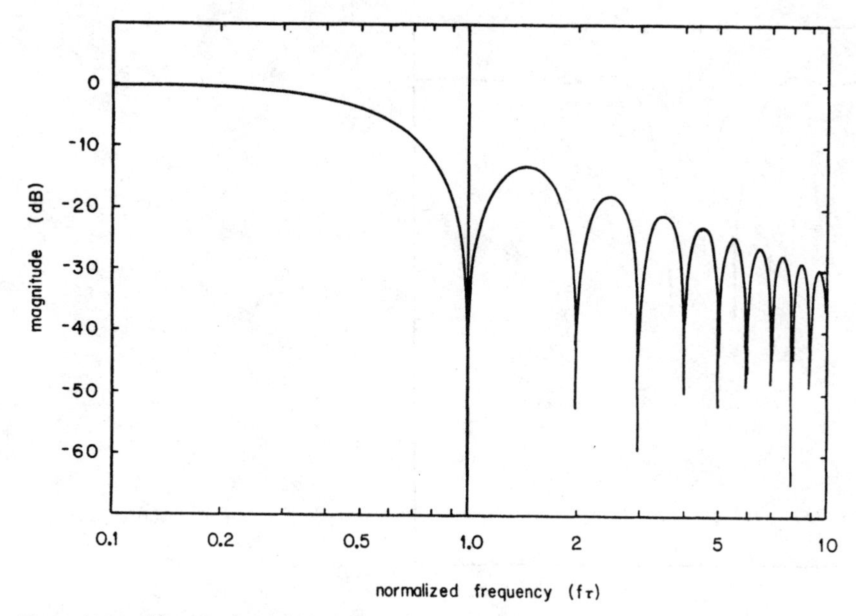

Figure 14.14 Magnitude spectrum for a continuous-time rectangular window.

just one constructor and no data members. All of the necessary data members, as well as the code to support user interactions, are provided by the base class `ContWindowResponse` from which `ContRectangularMagResp` inherits. Because we will be examining several more windows in this chapter, it made sense to separate out those actions which will be common to all window types and perform these actions in a base class from which each specific window response class can be derived. The class definition for `ContWindowResponse` is provided in Listing 14.7, and the constructor (which is the class's only method) is provided in Listing 14.8. Within this class, all user outputs are routed to the stream `uout` and all user inputs are extracted from the stream `uin`. In most applications, the constructor will be called with arguments `&cin` and `&cout`, but the class has been designed to allow references to other appropriate streams to be used as well.

Discrete-time window

Since FIR filter coefficients exist only for integer values of n or discrete values of $t = nT$, it is convenient to work with a window function that is defined in terms of n rather than t. If the function defined by Eq. (14.3) is sampled using $N = 2M + 1$ samples with one sample at $t = 0$ and samples at nT for $n = \pm1$, $\pm2, \ldots, \pm M$, the sampled window function becomes

$$w[n] = \begin{cases} 1 & -M \le n \le M \\ 0 & \text{otherwise} \end{cases} \tag{14.5}$$

For an even number of samples, the rectangular window can be defined as either

$$w[n] = 1 \qquad -(M-1) \le n \le M \tag{14.6}$$

or

$$w[n] = 1 \qquad -M \le n \le (M-1) \tag{14.7}$$

The window specified by Eq. (14.6) will be centered around a point midway between $n = 0$ and $n = 1$, and the window specified by Eq. (14.7) will be centered around a point midway between $n = -1$ and $n = 0$. In many applications (especially in languages like C that use zero-origin indexing), it is convenient to have $w[n]$ defined for $0 \le n \le (N-1)$:

$$w[n] = 1 \qquad 0 \le n \le (N-1) \tag{14.8}$$

In order to emphasize the difference between windows such as Eq. (14.5), which are defined over positive and negative frequencies, and windows such as Eq. (14.8) which are defined over nonnegative frequencies, digital-signal processing borrows terminology from the closely related field of time-series analysis. Using this borrowed terminology, windows such as Eq. (14.5) are called *lag windows,* and windows such as Eq. (14.8) are called *data windows.* Data windows are also referred to as *tapering windows* and occasionally *tapers* or *faders.* To avoid having to deal with windows centered around ½ or −½, many authors state that N must be odd for lag windows. However, even-length *data* windows are widely used for leakage reduction in FFT applications.

Frequency windows and spectral windows

The discrete-time Fourier transform (DTFT) of the lag window Eq. (14.5) is given by

$$W(f) = \frac{\sin\,[\pi f(2M+1)]}{\sin\,(\pi f)} \tag{14.9}$$

The form of Eq. (14.9) is closely related to the so-called Dirichlet kernel $D_n(\cdot)$ which is variously defined as

$$D_n(\theta) \triangleq \frac{1}{2\pi} \sum_{k=-n}^{n} \cos k\theta = \frac{\sin\,\{[n+(1/2)]\theta\}}{\sin\,(\theta/2)} \qquad \text{(Priestley 1981)}$$

$$D_n(x) \triangleq \sum_{k=-n}^{n} \exp\,(2\pi jkx) = \frac{\sin\,[(2n+1)\pi x]}{\sin\,(\pi x)} \qquad \text{(Dym and McKean 1972)}$$

$$D_n(x) \triangleq \frac{1}{2} \sum_{k=-n}^{n} \cos\,(kx) = \frac{\sin\,\{[n+(1/2)]x\}}{2\sin\,(x/2)} \qquad \text{(Weaver 1989)}$$

The magnitude of Eq. (14.9) is plotted in Fig. 14.15 for $N = 11$ and Fig. 14.16 for $N = 21$. As indicated by these two cases, when the number of points in the window increases, the width of the DTFT sidelobes decreases. The sidelobes in Fig. 14.15 are attenuated by 13.0, 17.1, 19.3, 20.5, and 20.8 dB; and the sidelobes in Fig. 14.16 are attenuated by 13.2, 17.6, 20.4, 22.3, 23.7, 24.8, 25.5, 26.1, and 26.3 dB.

The DTFT of the data window Eq. (14.8) is given by

$$W(f) = \exp\,[-j\pi f(N-1)]\,\frac{\sin\,(N\pi f)}{\sin\,(\pi f)} \tag{14.10}$$

A function such as Eq. (14.9), which is the Fourier transform of a lag window, is called a *spectral window.* A function such as Eq. (14.10), which is the Fourier transform of a data window, is called a *frequency window.* The forms of Eqs. (14.9) and (14.10) differ from the form of Eq. (14.4) due to the aliasing that occurs when the continuous-time window function is sampled to obtain a discrete-time window.

Software notes

The magnitude responses for continuous-time windows are generally computed using closed-form expressions such as Eq. (14.4). The base class `Contin-`

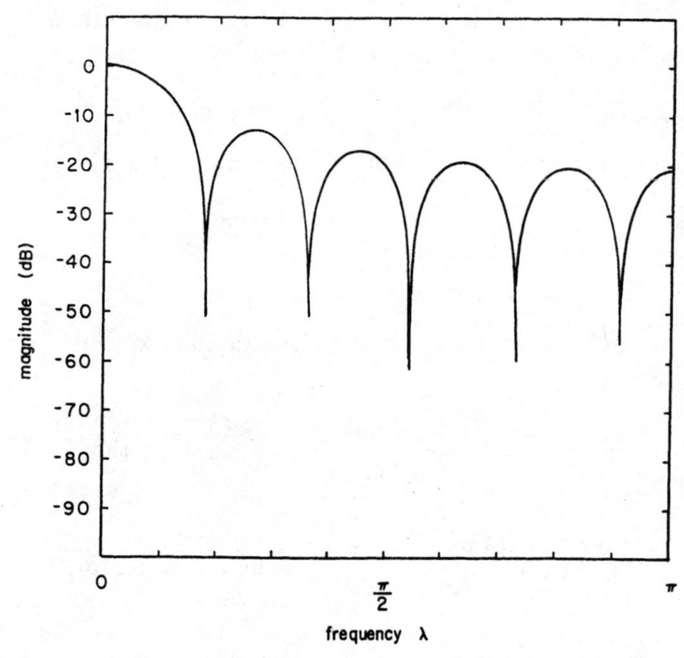

Figure 14.15 Magnitude of the DTFT for an 11-point rectangular window.

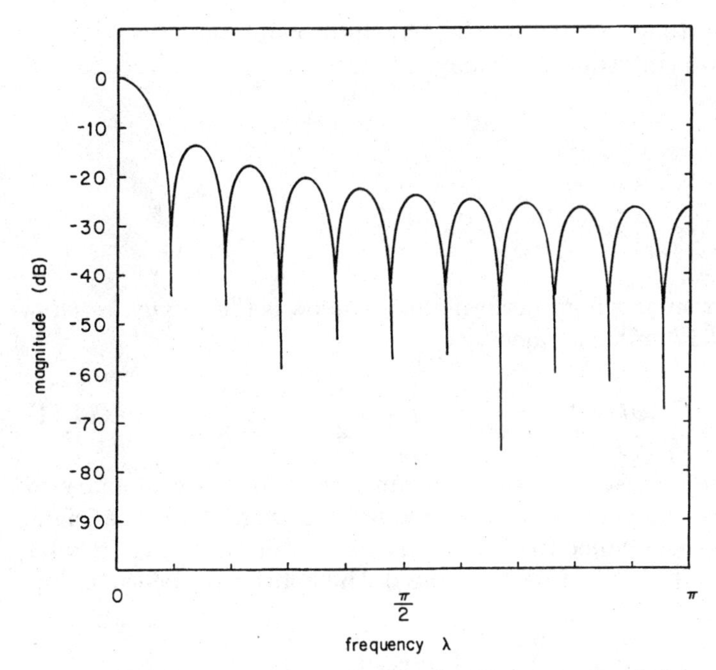

Figure 14.16 Magnitude of the DTFT for a 21-point rectangular window.

`WindowResponse` as well as the derived classes such as `ContRectangularMagResp` were set up with this fact in mind. The approach taken for discrete-time windows and their spectra is very different.

A discrete-time window is also an FIR filter. Therefore, any method that can be used to compute the continuous-frequency response of an FIR filter can also be used to compute the continuous-frequency response of a discrete-time window. The approach used to generate the data for Fig. 14.16 consists of the following steps:

1. Generate the window coefficients. For the moment, let's assume that these coefficients have been placed in an array `window_coeff`. For the case of a rectangular window, this step is almost trivial, because all of the coefficients are 1.00. Some of the issues involved in the design of classes for generating window coefficients are easier to explore using a more complicated window. Therefore, these issues will be explored in Sec. 14.4 after the triangular window is introduced in Sec. 14.3.
2. Construct an FIR filter using these window coefficients. This construction can be accomplished using an alternate constructor for the `FirFilterDesign` class that was introduced in Chap. 13 and which was used as the base class for the derived class `FirIdealFilter` that was discussed in Sec. 14.1:

```
fir_design = new FirFilterDesign(num_taps, window_coeff);
```

3. Compute the magnitude response of this FIR filter using the `FirFilterResponse` class that was introduced in Chap. 13:

```
fir_response = new FirFilterResponse( fir_design, cin, cout );
fir_response->ComputeMagResp( );
fir_response->DumpMagResp( ) ;
```

14.3 Triangular Window

A simple, but not particularly high-performance, window is the *triangular window* shown in Fig. 14.17 and is defined by

$$w(t) = 1 - \frac{2|t|}{\tau} \qquad |t| \leq \frac{\tau}{2} \tag{14.11}$$

Window functions are almost always even symmetric, and it is customary to show only the positive-time portion of the window, as in Fig. 14.18. The triangular window is sometimes called the *Bartlett window* after M. S. Bartlett, who described its use in a 1950 paper (Bartlett 1950). The Fourier transform of Eq. (14.11) is given by

$$W(f) = \frac{\tau}{2}\left[\frac{\sin(\pi f\tau/2)}{(\pi f\tau/2)}\right]^2 \tag{14.12}$$

The magnitude of Eq. (14.12) is plotted in Fig. 14.19. The peaks of the first through fourth sidelobes are attenuated by 26.5, 35.7, 41.6, and 46.0 dB, respectively. The data for Fig. 14.19 was generated using the method `ContTriangularMagResponse` provided in Listing 14.9.

Discrete-time triangular window

If the function defined by Eq. (14.11) is sampled using $N = 2M + 1$ samples with $\tau = 2MT$, one sample at $t = 0$, and samples at nT for $n = \pm 1, \pm 2, \ldots, \pm M$, the sampled window function becomes the lag window defined by

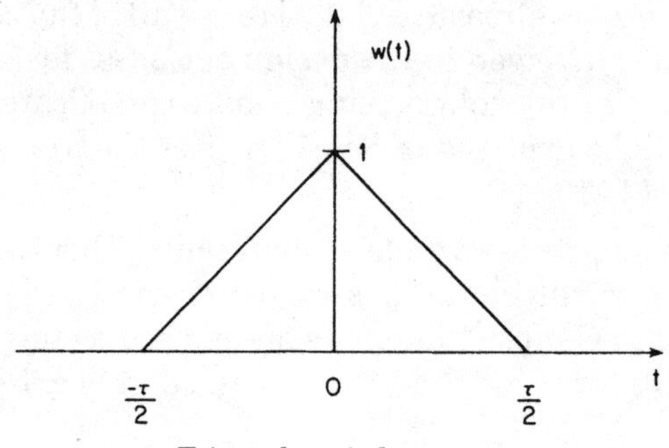

Figure 14.17 Triangular window.

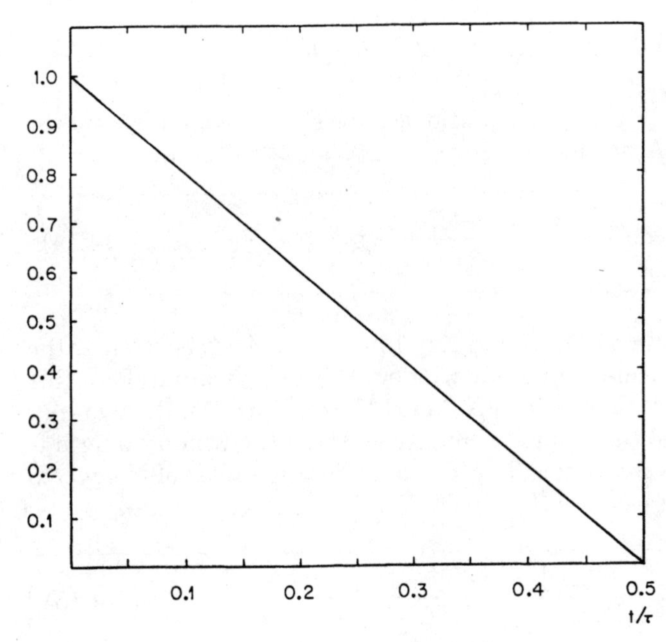

Figure 14.18 One-sided plot of a triangular window.

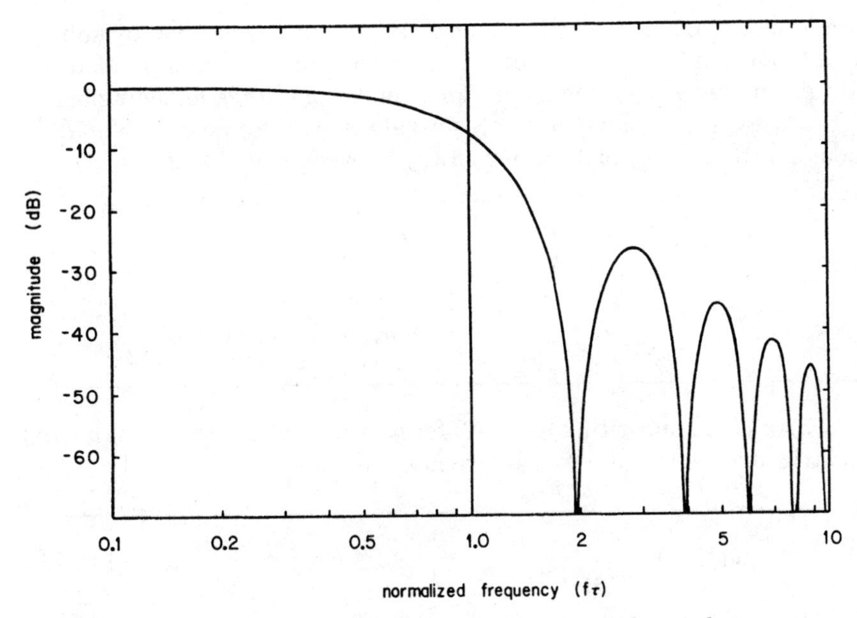

Figure 14.19 Magnitude response of a continuous-time triangular window.

$$w[n] = 1 - \frac{2|n|}{2M} \qquad -M \le n \le M \tag{14.13}$$

for the normalized case of $T = 1$. This equation can be expressed in terms of the total number of samples N by substituting $(N - 1)/2$ for M to obtain

$$w[n] = 1 - \frac{2|n|}{N-1} \qquad \frac{-(N-1)}{2} \le n \le \frac{N-1}{2} \tag{14.14}$$

In some texts (such as Marple 1987 and Kay 1988), Eq. (14.14) is given as the definition of the discrete-time triangular window. However, evaluation of this equation reveals that $w[n] = 0$ for $n = \pm[(N-1)/2]$. This means that the two endpoints do not contribute to the window contents and that the window length is effectively reduced to $N - 2$ samples. In order to maintain a total of N *nonzero* samples, many authors substitute $(N + 2)$ for N in Eq. (14.14) to obtain

$$w[n] = 1 - \frac{|2n|}{N+1} \qquad \frac{-(N-1)}{2} \le n \le \frac{N-1}{2} \qquad N \text{ odd} \tag{14.15}$$

For an even number of samples, the window values can be obtained by substituting $(n + 1/2)$ for n in Eq. (14.15) to obtain a window that is symmetrical about a line midway between $n = -1$ and $n = 0$. (The equals sign in the following box is in quotes because n can assume only integer values; nevertheless, n "=" $-1/2$ is a convenient shorthand way of saying "midway between $n = -1$ and $n = 0$.")

$$w[n] = 1 - \frac{|2n+1|}{N+1} \qquad \frac{-N}{2} \le n \le \frac{N}{2} - 1 \qquad N \text{ even, center at } n \text{ “=” } \frac{-1}{2} \tag{14.16}$$

Alternatively, we could substitute $(n - 1/2)$ for n in Eq. (14.15) to obtain a window symmetric about a line midway between $n = 0$ and $n = 1$:

$$w[n] = 1 - \frac{|2n-1|}{N+1} \qquad \frac{-N}{2} + 1 \le n \le \frac{N}{2} \qquad N \text{ even, center at } n \text{ “=” } \frac{1}{2} \tag{14.17}$$

An expression for the triangular *data* window can be obtained by substituting $[n-(N-1)/2]$ for n in Eq. (14.15) or by substituting $(n-N/2)$ for n in Eq. (14.16) to yield

$$w[n] = 1 - \frac{|2n - N + 1|}{N+1} \qquad 0 \le n \le N-1 \qquad (14.18)$$

Section 14.4 presents class designs for generating various forms of the discrete triangular window. These designs are generalized to support other types of windows to be introduced in subsequent sections.

Frequency and spectral windows

The spectral window obtained from the DTFT of the lag window Eq. (14.14) is given by

$$W(f) = \frac{1}{M}\left[\frac{\sin(M\pi f)}{\sin(\pi f)}\right]^2 \qquad (14.19a)$$

or

$$W(\theta) = \frac{2}{N}\left\{\frac{\sin[(N/4)\theta]}{\sin[(1/2)\theta]}\right\}^2 \qquad (14.19b)$$

where

$$M = \frac{N-1}{2}$$

$$\theta = \frac{2\pi f}{f_s}$$

The form of Eq. (14.19) is closely related to the Fejer kernel $F_n(\cdot)$, which, like the Dirichlet kernel presented in Sec. 14.3, has some variety in its definition:

$$F_n(x) \triangleq \frac{\sin^2(n\pi x)}{n\sin^2(\pi x)} \qquad \text{(Priestley 1981)}$$

$$F_n(\theta) \triangleq \frac{\sin^2(n\theta/2)}{2\pi n\sin^2(\theta/2)} \qquad \text{(Dym and McKean 1972)}$$

The magnitude of Eq. (14.19) for $N = 11$ and $N = 21$ is plotted in Fig. 14.20.

14.4 Window Software

As we saw in the previous section, a window function can come in a number of different varieties—odd-length lag window, even-length lag window centered

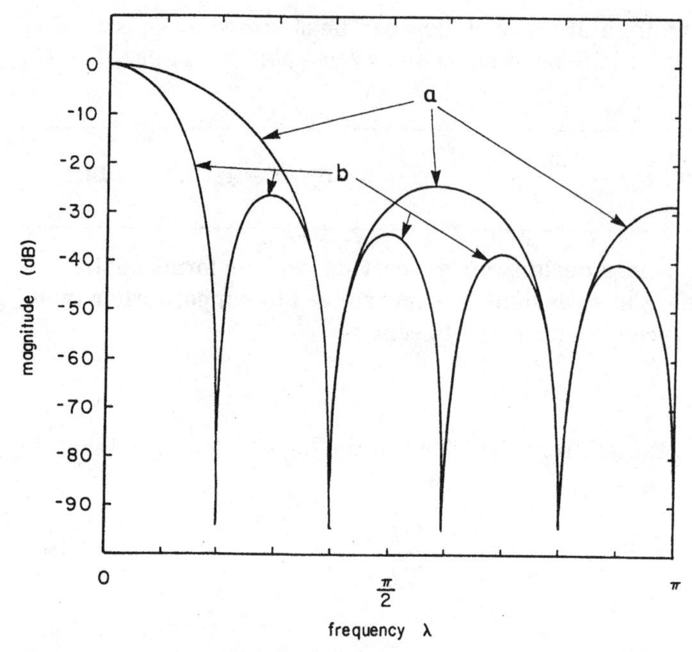

Figure 14.20 Magnitude of the DTFT for (*a*) an 11-point triangular window and (*b*) a 21-point triangular window.

on $n = 1/2$, and so on. As was done for the triangular window, an explicit function for each variety can be derived. However, the task of designing and coding computer programs to generate window coefficients can be simplified somewhat if we view the different varieties from a slightly different perspective. Despite the apparent variety of specific formats, there are really only two basic forms that need to be generated—one form for odd-length windows and one form for even-length windows. All of the specific varieties can be generated as simply horizontal translations of these two forms. Furthermore, since all the windows considered in this book are symmetric, we need to generate the coefficients for only half of each window. An odd-length lag window is probably the most "natural" of the discrete-time windows. Consider the triangular window shown in Fig. 14.21, which has sample values indicated at $t = \pm nT$ for $n = 0, 1, 2, \ldots$ Because of symmetry, we will require our program to generate the $(N+1)/2$ coefficients corresponding to $t = 0, T, 2T, 3T, \ldots, (N-1)T/2$ and place them in locations 0 through $(N-1)/2$ of an array called `Half_Lag_Win`. These coefficients can be obtained using Eq. (14.15). Next, we consider the triangular window shown in Fig. 14.23. This window has been shifted so that its axis of symmetry lies at $t = -T/2$. The sample values indicated in the figure can be obtained from Eq. (14.16). The sample values for either the even-length case of Fig. 14.22 or the odd-length case of Fig. 14.21 can be obtained from the combined formula

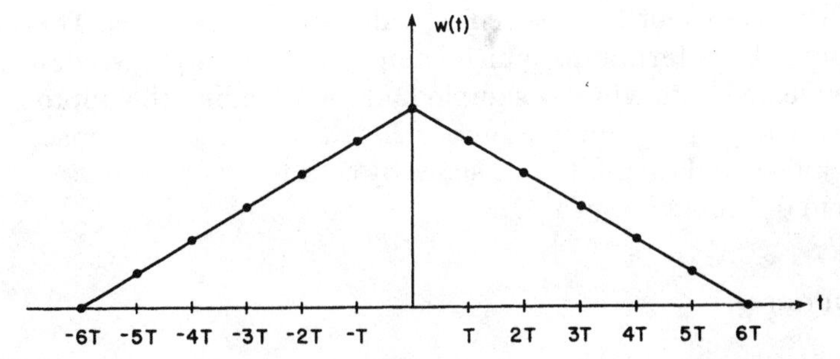

Figure 14.21 Triangular window sampled to produce an odd-length lag window.

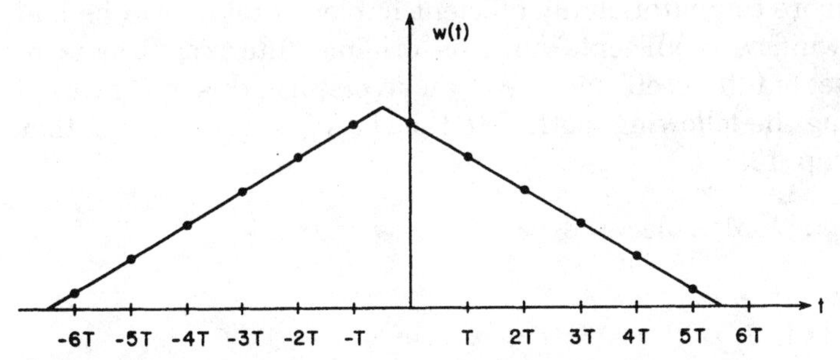

Figure 14.22 Triangular window shifted and sampled to produce an even-length lag window with axis of symmetry midway between $n = -1$ and $n = 0$.

$$w[n] = 1 - \frac{2|x|}{N+1}$$

where

$$x = \begin{cases} n & \text{for } N \text{ odd} \\ n + \dfrac{1}{2} & \text{for } N \text{ even} \end{cases}$$

The class `TriangularWindow`, provided in Listing 14.10, uses this formula to generate coefficients for both odd- and even-length discrete-time triangular windows. For N odd, the value placed in `Half_Lag_Win[0]` lies on the full window's axis of symmetry and is the value of the continuous-time window at $t = 0$. For N even, the value placed in `Half_Lag_Win[0]` lies one-half sample time to the right of the full window's axis of symmetry and is the value of the continuous-time window at $t = T/2$. The class `TriangularWindow` is derived from the base class `GenericWindow`, which is defined in Listing 14.11. This base class contains the attributes and methods which are common to all discrete-time windows. The class method `GetDataWinCoeff` provided in Listing 14.12 can be used to obtain the data window coefficient for a specified value of sample index. This value is actually obtained by determining which sample in the half-lag window corresponds to the requested data window sample and then reading the appropriate location in `Half_Lag_Win[ ]`. The method `GetDataWindow` allocates space for a complete data window and then fills this space by calling `GetDataWinCoeff` for sample indices from 0 through `Length-1`.

14.5 Applying Windows to Fourier Series Filters

Conceptually, a tapering window such as the triangular window is applied to the input of an FIR approximation to an ideal filter. However, since multiplication is associative, a much more computationally efficient implementation can be had by multiplying the window coefficients and the original filter coefficients to arrive at a modified set of filter coefficients. We can accomplish this modification quite simply by adding the following method to the class `FirFilterDesign` that was introduced in Chap. 13:

```
void FirFilterDesign::ApplyWindow( GenericWindow *window)
{
 for(int n=0; n<Num_Taps; n++)
   { Imp_Resp_Coeff[n] *= window->GetDataWinCoeff(n); }
}
```

The following code fragment illustrates how this method can be used in conjunction with a window class and an ideal filter class to produce coefficients for a windowed filter design and then compute the frequency response of the resulting design.

```
disc_window = new TriangularWindow( cin, cout );
num_taps = disc_window->GetNumTaps( );
filter_design = new FirIdealFilter( num_taps, cin, cout );
filter_design->ApplyWindow( disc_window );
filter_design->DumpCoefficients( &CoeffFile );
filter_response = new FirFilterResponse( filter_design, cin, cout );
filter_response->ComputeMagResp( );
filter_response->DumpMagResp( );
```

This fragment uses the generic FIR magnitude response computation implemented by the class `FirFilterResponse`. In order to make use of the more efficient response computations that were derived in Chap. 13 for linear phase FIR filters, the sixth line of the fragment given above must be replaced by the following:

```
filter_response = new LinearPhaseFirResponse(
                                  (LinearPhaseFirDesign*)filter_design,
                                  cin, cout );
```

Example 14.5 Apply a triangular window to the 21-tap low-pass filter of Example 14.1.

solution Table 14.5 lists the original values of the filter coefficients, the corresponding discrete-time window coefficients, and the final values of the filter coefficients after the windowing has been applied. The frequency response of the windowed filter is shown in Figs. 14.23 and 14.24. The response looks pretty good when plotted against a linear axis as in Fig. 14.23, but the poor stopband performance is readily apparent when the response is plotted on a decibel scale as in Fig. 14.24.

14.6 von Hann Window

The continuous-time von Hann window function shown in Fig. 14.25 is defined by

$$w(t) = 0.5 + 0.5 \cos \frac{2\pi t}{\tau} \qquad |t| \leq \frac{\tau}{2} \tag{14.20}$$

The corresponding frequency response, shown in Fig. 14.26, is given by

$$W(f) = 0.54\tau \text{ sinc } (\pi f \tau) + 0.23\tau \text{ sinc } [\pi\tau(f-\tau)] + 0.23\tau \text{ sinc } [\pi\tau(f+\tau)] \tag{14.21}$$

The first sidelobe of this response is 31.4 dB below the main lobe, and the main lobe is twice as wide as the main lobe of the rectangular window. The data for Fig. 14.26 was obtained using the class `ContHannMagResp` provided in Listing 14.13.

References to the von Hann window as the "hanning" window are widespread throughout the signal-processing literature. This is unfortunate for two reasons. First, the window gets its name from Julius von Hann, *not* some nondescript "Mr. Hanning." Second, the term *hanning* is easily (and often) confused with *Hamming.* Oppenheim and Schafer (1975) insinuate that the incorrect use of *hanning* is due to Blackman and Tukey (1958). This window is occasionally called a *raised-cosine window.*

TABLE 14.5 Coefficients for a 21-Tap Low-Pass Filter

n	$h[n]$	$w[n]$	$w[n] \cdot h[n]$
0, 20	0.000000	0.000000	0.000000
1, 19	−0.033673	0.090909	−0.006116
2, 18	−0.023387	0.181818	−0.006378
3, 17	0.026728	0.272727	0.009719
4, 16	0.050455	0.363636	0.022934
5, 15	0.000000	0.454545	0.000000
6, 14	−0.075683	0.545454	−0.048162
7, 13	−0.062366	0.636364	−0.045357
8, 12	0.093549	0.727273	0.076540
9, 11	0.302731	0.909091	0.275210
10	0.400000	1.00	0.400000

NOTE: $h[n]$ are the original coefficients; $w[n]$ are triangular window coefficients.

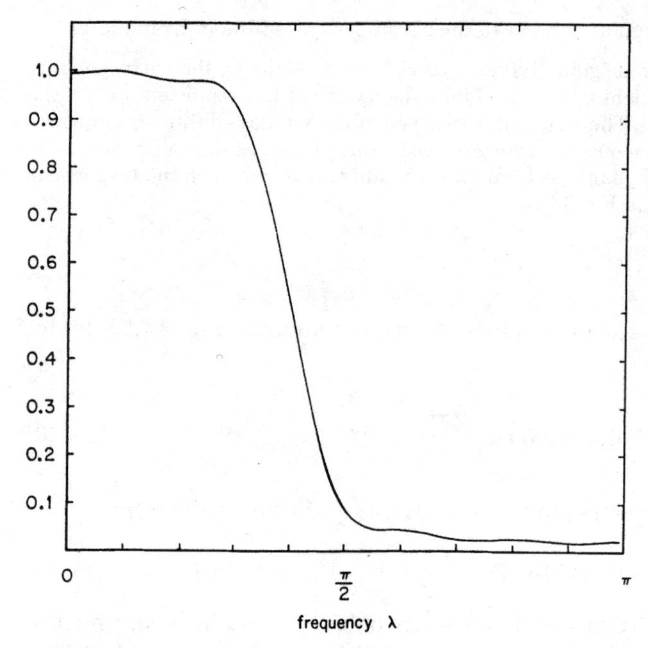

Figure 14.23 Magnitude response (as a percentage of peak) for a triangular-windowed 21-tap low-pass filter.

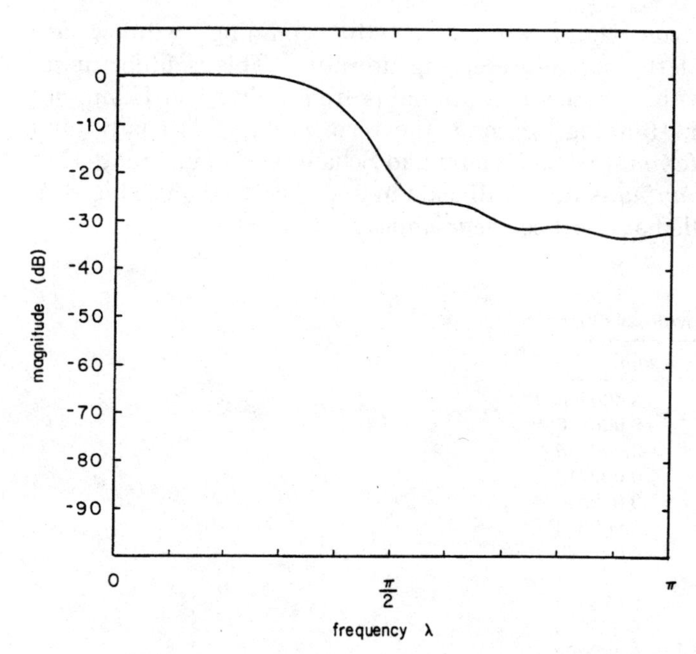

Figure 14.24 Magnitude response (in dB) for a triangular-windowed 21-tap low-pass filter.

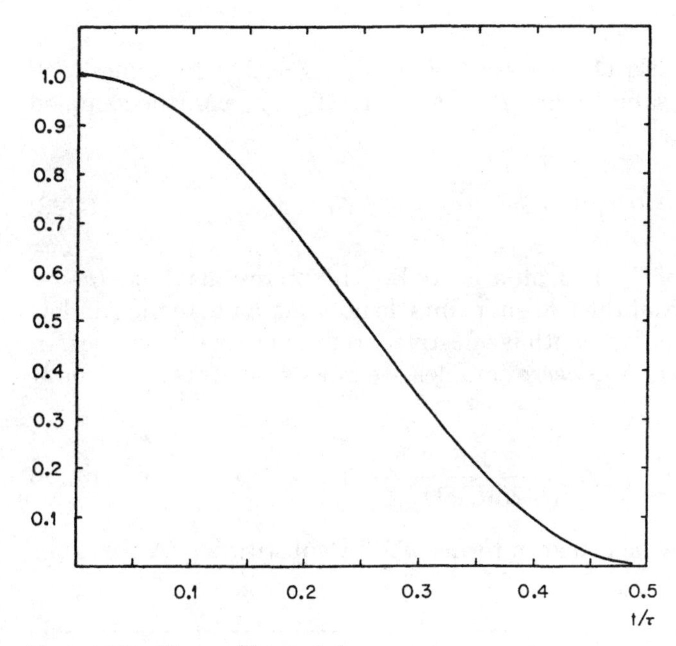

Figure 14.25 The von Hann window.

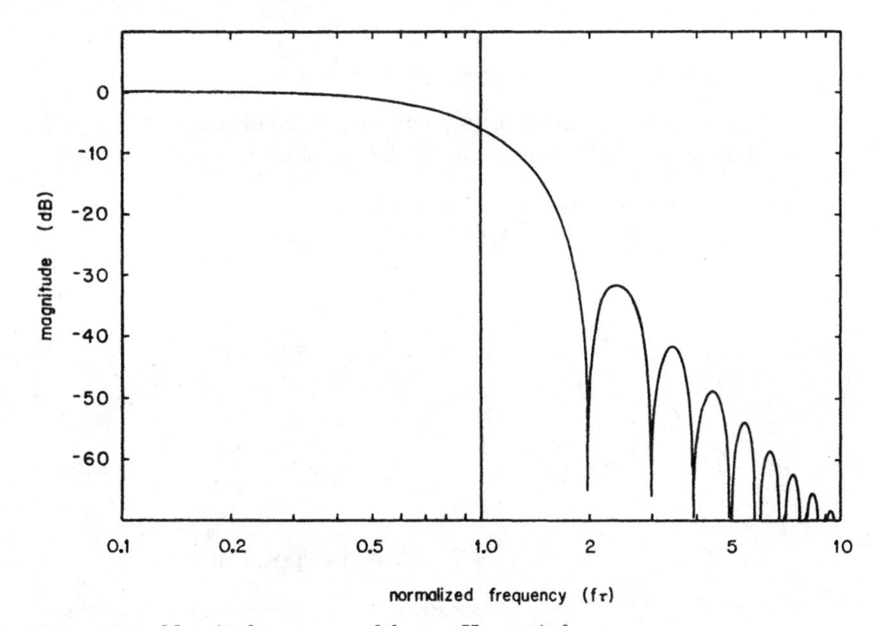

Figure 14.26 Magnitude response of the von Hann window.

Discrete-time von Hann window

If the function defined by Eq. (14.20) is sampled using $N = 2M + 1$ samples with one sample at $t = 0$ and samples at nT for $n = \pm 1, \pm 2, \ldots, \pm M$, the sampled window function becomes

$$w[n] = 0.5 + 0.5 \cos \frac{\pi n}{M} \qquad -M \leq n \leq M \tag{14.22}$$

for the normalized case of $T = 1$. Evaluation of Eq. (14.22) reveals that $w(n) = 0$ for $n = \pm M$. This means that the two endpoints do not contribute to the window contents and that the window length is effectively reduced to $N - 2$ samples. In order to maintain a total of N *nonzero* samples, we must substitute $M + 1$ for M in Eq. (14.22) to yield

$$w[n] = 0.5 + 0.5 \cos \frac{2\pi n}{2(M+1)} \qquad -M \leq n \leq M \tag{14.23}$$

Equation (14.23) can now be recast in terms of N by substituting $(N - 1)/2$ for M to obtain

$$w[n] = 0.5 + 0.5 \cos \frac{2\pi n}{N-1} \qquad \frac{-(N-1)}{2} \leq n \leq \frac{N-1}{2} \qquad n \text{ odd} \tag{14.24}$$

For an even number of samples, the window values can be obtained by substituting either $(n + 1/2)$ or $n(-1/2)$ for n in Eq. (14.24) to obtain

$$w[n] = 0.5 + 0.5 \cos \frac{\pi(2n+1)}{N-1} \qquad \frac{-N}{2} \leq n \leq \frac{N}{2} - 1 \tag{14.25}$$

$$N \text{ even, center at } n \text{ “=” } \frac{-1}{2}$$

$$w[n] = 0.5 + 0.5 \cos \frac{\pi(2n-1)}{N-1} \qquad \frac{-N}{2} + 1 \leq n \leq \frac{N}{2} \tag{14.26}$$

$$N \text{ even, center at } n \text{ “=” } \frac{1}{2}$$

The class `HannWindow`, provided in Listing 14.14, generates coefficients for the von Hann window.

Example 14.6 Apply a von Hann window to the 21-tap low-pass filter of Example 14.1.

solution Table 14.6 lists the original values of the filter coefficients, the corresponding discrete-time window coefficients, and the final values of the filter coefficients after the windowing has been applied. The frequency response of the windowed filter is shown in Fig. 14.27.

14.7 Hamming Window

The continuous-time Hamming window function shown in Fig. 14.28 is defined by

$$w(t) = 0.54 + 0.46 \cos \frac{2\pi t}{\tau} \qquad |t| \leq \frac{\tau}{2} \tag{14.27}$$

The Fourier transform of Eq. (14.27) is given by

$$W(f) = 0.54\tau \text{ sinc } (\pi f \tau) + 0.23\tau \text{ sinc } [\pi\tau(f - \tau)] + 0.23\tau \text{ sinc } [\pi\tau(f + \tau)] \tag{14.28}$$

The magnitude of Eq. (14.28) is plotted in Fig. 14.29. The highest sidelobe of this response is 42.6 dB below the main lobe, and the main lobe is twice as wide as the main lobe of the rectangular window's response. The data for Fig. 14.29 was obtained using the class `ContHammingMagResp`, provided in Listing 14.15. This window gets its name from R. W. Hamming, a pioneer in the areas of numerical analysis and signal processing, who opened his numerical analysis text (Hamming 1962) with the now famous and oft-quoted pearl, "The purpose of computing is insight, not numbers."

Discrete-time Hamming windows

If the function defined by Eq. (14.27) is sampled using $N = 2M + 1$ samples with one sample at $t = 0$ and samples at nT for $n = \pm 1, \pm 2, \ldots, \pm M$, the sampled window function becomes the lag window defined by

TABLE 14.6 Coefficients for a 21-Tap Low-Pass Filter

n	$h[n]$	$w[n]$	$w[n] \cdot h[n]$
0, 20	0.000000	0.000000	0.000000
1, 19	−0.033637	0.024472	−0.000823
2, 18	−0.023387	0.095492	−0.002233
3, 17	0.026728	0.206107	0.005509
4, 16	0.050455	0.345492	0.017432
5, 15	0.000000	0.500000	0.000000
6, 14	−0.075683	0.654508	−0.049535
7, 13	−0.062366	0.793893	−0.049512
8, 12	0.093549	0.904508	0.084616
9, 11	0.302731	0.975527	0.295323
10	0.400000	1.00	0.400000

NOTE: $h[n]$ are the original coefficients; $w[n]$ are von Hann window coefficients.

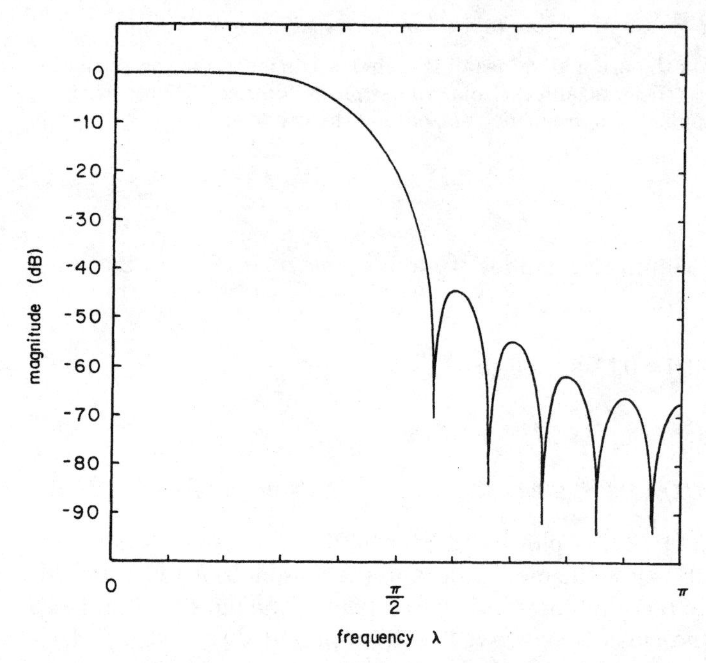

Figure 14.27 Magnitude response for a von Hann–windowed 21-tap low-pass filter.

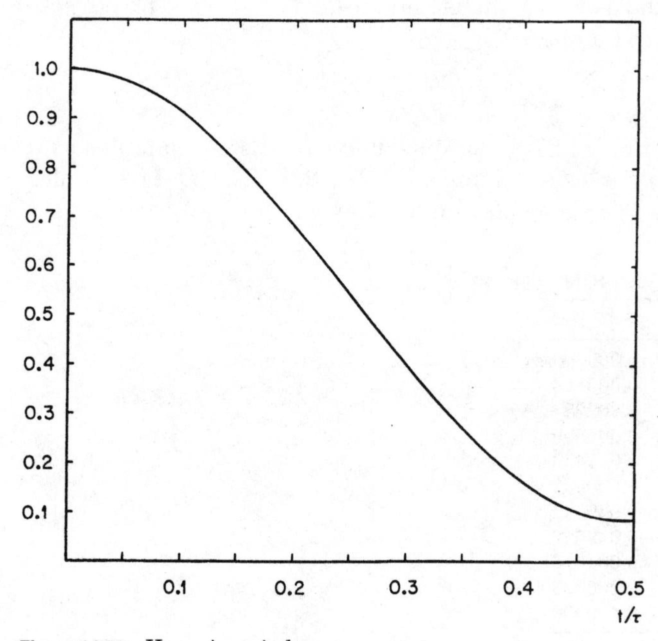

Figure 14.28 Hamming window.

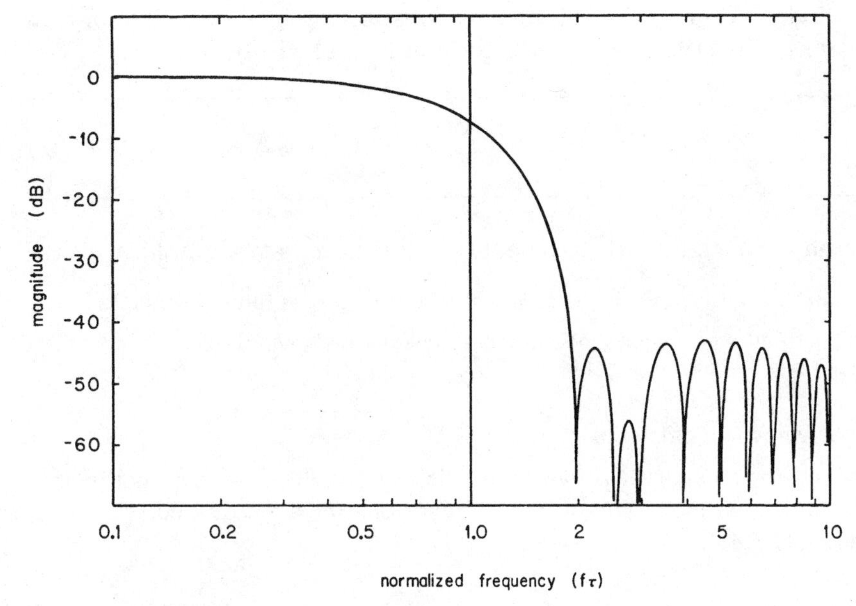

Figure 14.29 Magnitude response of the Hamming window.

$$w[n] = 0.54 + 0.46 \cos \frac{2\pi n}{2M} \qquad -M \le n \le M \tag{14.29}$$

for the normalized case of $T = 1$. Equation (14.29) can be expressed in terms of the total number of samples N by substituting $(N - 1)/2$ for M to obtain

$$w[n] = 0.54 + 0.46 \cos \frac{2\pi n}{N-1} \qquad \frac{-(N-1)}{2} \le n \le \frac{N-1}{2} \tag{14.30}$$

$$n \text{ odd}$$

For an even number of samples, the window values can be obtained by substituting $n + 1/2$ for n in Eq. (14.30) to obtain

$$w[n] = 0.54 + 0.46 \cos \frac{\pi(2n+1)}{N-1} \qquad \frac{-N}{2} \le n \le \frac{N}{2} - 1 \tag{14.31}$$

$$N \text{ even, center at } n \text{ “=” } \frac{-1}{2}$$

The data window form can be obtained by substituting $[n - (N - 1)/2]$ for n in Eq. (14.30) or by substituting $(n - N/2)$ for n in Eq. (14.31) to yield

$$w[n] = 0.54 - 0.46 \cos \frac{2\pi n}{N-1} \qquad 0 \le n \le N-1 \tag{14.32}$$

(Note the change in sign for the cosine term—this is *not* a typographical error.)

Example 14.7 Apply a Hamming window to the 21-tap low-pass filter of Example 14.1.

solution The windowed values of $h[k]$ are listed in Table 14.7, and the corresponding frequency response is shown in Fig. 14.30.

Computer generation of window coefficients

The class `HammingWindow( )`, provided in Listing 14.16, generates coefficients for the Hamming window. The output conventions for even and odd N are as described in Sec. 14.4.

14.8 Dolph-Chebyshev Window

The Dolph-Chebyshev window is somewhat different from the other windows in this chapter in that a closed-form expression for the time domain window is not known. Instead, this window is defined as the inverse Fourier transform of the sampled-frequency response, which is given by

$$W[k] = (-1)^k \frac{\cos \{N \cos^{-1} [\beta \cos (\pi k/N)]\}}{\cosh (N \cosh^{-1} \beta)} \qquad -(N-1) \le k \le N-1 \tag{14.33}$$

A sidelobe level of −80 dB is often claimed for this response, but, in fact, Eq. (14.33) defines a family of windows in which the minimum stopband attenua-

TABLE 14.7 Coefficients for a 21-Tap Hamming-Windowed Low-Pass Filter

k	$h[k]$
0, 20	0.000000
1, 19	−0.003448
2, 18	−0.003926
3, 17	0.007206
4, 16	0.020074
5, 15	0.000000
6, 14	−0.051627
7, 13	−0.050540
8, 12	0.085330
9, 11	0.295915
10	0.400000

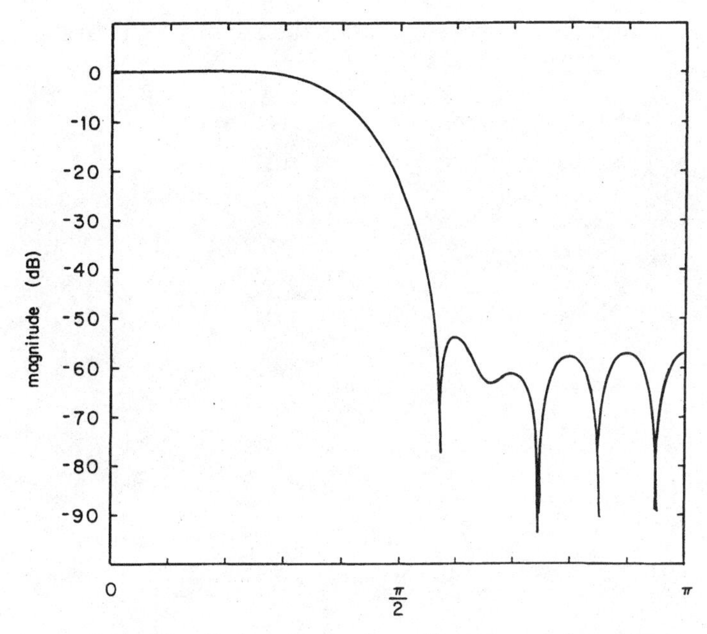

Figure 14.30 Magnitude response for a Hamming-windowed 21-tap low-pass filter.

tion is a factor of β. A stopband attenuation of 20α dB is obtained for a value of β given by

$$\beta = \cosh\left[\frac{1}{N}\cosh^{-1}(10^{\alpha})\right] \tag{14.34}$$

Often, β > 1 and, consequently, evaluation of Eq. (14.32) may entail taking the inverse cosine of values with magnitudes greater than unity. In such cases, the following formula can be used:

$$\cos^{-1} x = \begin{cases} \dfrac{\pi}{2} - \tan^{-1}\left(\dfrac{x}{\sqrt{1-x^2}}\right) & |x| < 1 \\ \ln\left(x + \sqrt{x^2 - 1}\right) & |x| \geq 1 \end{cases} \tag{14.35}$$

The Dolph-Chebyshev window takes its name from C. L. Dolph and Pafnuti Chebyshev. The function $W(k)$ is a normalized form of the function developed by Dolph (1946) for specifying an antenna pattern optimized to achieve a narrow main lobe while simultaneously restricting the sidelobe response. Helms (1968) applied Dolph's result to the analogous problem of optimizing a filter response for a narrow transition band while simultaneously restricting sidelobe response. The name of Chebyshev is associated with this window because for integer values of z, the numerator of Eq. (14.33) is the zth order Chebyshev polynomial:

$$T_z(x) \equiv \cos\,(z \cos^{-1} x)$$

Listing 14.1 Ideal FIR Filter

```
//
//  File = firideal.cpp
//

#include <math.h>
#include <stdlib.h>
#include "misdefs.h"
#include "typedefs.h"
#include "fir_dsgn.h"
#include "firideal.h"

FirIdealFilter::FirIdealFilter( )
{
}
FirIdealFilter::FirIdealFilter( istream& uin,
                                ostream& uout)
               :LinearPhaseFirDesign()
{
  int num_taps;

  num_taps = 0;
  while( !(num_taps%2) )
    {
     uout << "number of taps in ideal FIR filter?\n"
          << "  ( must be odd because\n"
          << "     ideal FIRs are all type 1)"
          << endl;
     uin >> num_taps;
    }

  Initialize( num_taps );
  DefineFilter( num_taps, uin, uout );
  return;
}
//==================================================

FirIdealFilter::FirIdealFilter( int num_taps,
                                istream& uin,
                                ostream& uout )
```

```
                :LinearPhaseFirDesign( num_taps )
{
 if( num_taps%2 )
   {
    DefineFilter(num_taps, uin, uout );
   }
 else
   {
    uout << "Error -- even number of taps requested\n"
         << "  for type 1 'ideal' linear phase FIR"
         << endl;
    exit(-1);
   }
}
//==================================================

void FirIdealFilter::DefineFilter( int num_taps,
                                   istream& uin,
                                   ostream& uout )
{
 int band_config;

 Fir_Type = 1;
 uout << "band configuration?\n"
      << (int)_LOWPASS_RESP_ << " = lowpass\n"
      << (int)_HIGHPASS_RESP_ << " = highpass\n"
      << (int)_BANDPASS_RESP_ << " = bandpass\n"
      << (int)_BANDSTOP_RESP_ << " = bandstop\n"
      << endl;
 uin >> band_config;
 Band_Config = (BAND_CONFIG_TYPE)band_config;

 if ((Band_Config == _LOWPASS_RESP_) ||
     (Band_Config == _HIGHPASS_RESP_) )
   {
   uout << "cutoff frequency in radians per second?"
        << endl;
   uin >> Lambda_1;
   }
 else
   {
   uout << "lower cutoff frequency in radians per second?"
        << endl;
   uin >> Lambda_1;
   uout << "upper cutoff frequency?" << endl;
   uin >> Lambda_2;
   }
```

```
 switch (Band_Config)
   {
   case _LOWPASS_RESP_:
     Ideal_Lowpass();
     break;

   case _BANDPASS_RESP_:
     Ideal_Bandpass();
     break;

   case _HIGHPASS_RESP_:
     Ideal_Highpass();
     break;

   case _BANDSTOP_RESP_:
     Ideal_Bandstop();
     break;
   }  // end of switch on Band_Config
}
```

Listing 14.2 Ideal Low-Pass FIR Filter

```
//=======================================================

void FirIdealFilter::Ideal_Lowpass(void)
{
 int n,n_max;
 double m;

 if(Num_Taps%2)
   {
    n_max = (Num_Taps-1)/2;
    Imp_Resp_Coeff[n_max] = Lambda_1/PI;
   }
 else
   {
    n_max = Num_Taps/2;
   }

 for(n=0; n<n_max; n++)
   {
    m = n - (double)(Num_Taps-1.0)/2.0;
    Imp_Resp_Coeff[n] = sin(m*Lambda_1) / (m*PI);
    Imp_Resp_Coeff[Num_Taps-1-n] = Imp_Resp_Coeff[n];
   }
}
```

Listing 14.3 Ideal High-Pass FIR Filter

```
//=============================================================

void FirIdealFilter::Ideal_Highpass( void )
{
 int n,n_max;
 double m;

 if(Num_Taps%2)
   {
    n_max = (Num_Taps-1)/2;
    Imp_Resp_Coeff[n_max] = 1.0 - Lambda_1/PI;
   }
 else
   {
    n_max = Num_Taps/2;
   }

 for(n=0; n<n_max; n++)
   {
    m = n - (double)(Num_Taps-1.0)/2.0;
    Imp_Resp_Coeff[n] = -sin(m*Lambda_1) / (m*PI);
    Imp_Resp_Coeff[Num_Taps-1-n] = Imp_Resp_Coeff[n];
   }
}
```

Listing 14.4 Ideal Bandpass FIR Filter

```
//=============================================================

void FirIdealFilter::Ideal_Bandpass( void )
{
 int n,n_max;
 double m;

 if(Num_Taps%2)
   {
    n_max = (Num_Taps-1)/2;
    Imp_Resp_Coeff[n_max] = (Lambda_2 - Lambda_1)/PI;
   }
 else
   {
    n_max = Num_Taps/2;
   }

 for(n=0; n<n_max; n++)
   {
```

```
    m = n - (double)(Num_Taps-1.0)/2.0;
    Imp_Resp_Coeff[n] = (sin(m*Lambda_2) - sin(m*Lambda_1)) / (m*PI);
    Imp_Resp_Coeff[Num_Taps-1-n] = Imp_Resp_Coeff[n];
   }
 return;
}
```

Listing 14.5 Ideal Bandstop FIR Filter

```
//=====================================================================

void FirIdealFilter::Ideal_Bandstop( void )
{
 int n,n_max;
 double m;

 if(Num_Taps%2)
   {
    n_max = (Num_Taps-1)/2;
    Imp_Resp_Coeff[n_max] = 1.0 + (Lambda_1 - Lambda_2)/PI;
   }
 else
   {
    n_max = Num_Taps/2;
   }

 for(n=0; n<n_max; n++)
   {
    m = n - (double)(Num_Taps-1.0)/2.0;
    Imp_Resp_Coeff[n] = (sin(m*Lambda_1) - sin(m*Lambda_2)) / (m*PI);
    Imp_Resp_Coeff[Num_Taps-1-n] = Imp_Resp_Coeff[n];
   }
 return;
}
```

Listing 14.6 Magnitude Response for a Continuous-Time Rectangular Window

```
//
//  File = con_rect.cpp
//

#include <math.h>
#include <iostream.h>
#include "misdefs.h"
#include "typedefs.h"
#include "con_rect.h"
#include "mymath.h"
```

```
ContRectangularMagResp::ContRectangularMagResp( istream& uin,
                                                ostream& uout )
                       : ContinWindowResponse( uin, uout )
{
 double tau, freq, freq_exp, value;
 double freq_cyc;

 tau = 1.0;
 freq_cyc = 2.0;

 for(int n=0; n<Num_Resp_Pts; n++)
   {
    freq_exp = 1.0 + freq_cyc*(n-Num_Resp_Pts)/((double)Num_Resp_Pts);
    freq = pow( (double)10.0, freq_exp);
    value = fabs(sinc(PI * freq * tau));
    if(Db_Scale_Enab) value = 20.0*log10(value);
    (*Response_File) << freq << ", " << value << endl;
   }
 return;
}
```

Listing 14.7 Header for the Base Class `ContWindowResponse`

```
//
//  File = con_resp.h
//

#ifndef _CON_RESP_H_
#define _CON_RESP_H_

#include <fstream.h>
#include "typedefs.h"

class ContinWindowResponse
{
 public:

  // constructor

  ContinWindowResponse( istream& uin,
                        ostream& uout );

 protected:

  int Num_Resp_Pts;
  logical Db_Scale_Enab;
  int Window_Shape;
  ofstream *Response_File;
```

```
};
#endif
```

Listing 14.8 Constructor for the Base Class `ContWindowResponse`

```
//
// File = con_resp.cpp
//

#include <stdlib.h>
#include "misdefs.h"
#include "con_resp.h"

ContinWindowResponse::ContinWindowResponse( istream& uin,
                                            ostream& uout)
{
  logical default_file_ok;

  uout << "shape of window?\n "
       << "0 = Quit\n "
       << _RECTANGULAR << " = rectangular\n "
       << _TRIANGULAR << " = triangular\n "
       << _HAMMING << " = Hamming\n "
       << _HANN << " = Hann (hanning, vonHann)\n "
       << _DOLPH_CHEBY << " = Dolph-Chebyshev\n "
       << endl;
  uin >> Window_Shape;

  if( Window_Shape < _RECTANGULAR)
    { exit(0);}

  uout << "number of points in plot?" << endl;
  uin >> Num_Resp_Pts;
  uout << "scaling?\n"
       << " 0 = linear, 1 = dB" << endl;
  uin >> Db_Scale_Enab;

  if( Db_Scale_Enab != 0) Db_Scale_Enab = 1;

  uout << "default name for magnitude response output\n"
       << "file is cwinresp.txt\n\n"
       << "is this okay?"
       << " 0 = NO, 1 = YES"
       << endl;
  uin >> default_file_ok;
```

```
  if( default_file_ok)
    {
     Response_File = new ofstream("cwinresp.txt", ios::out);
    }
  else
    {
     char *file_name;
     file_name = new char[31];

     uout << "enter complete name for output file"
          << endl;
     uin >> file_name;
     Response_File = new ofstream(file_name, ios::out);
     delete []file_name;
    }

}
```

Listing 14.9 Magnitude Response for a Continuous-Time Triangular Window

```
//
//  File = con_tngl.cpp
//

#include <math.h>
#include <iostream.h>
#include "con_tngl.h"
#include "misdefs.h"
#include "typedefs.h"
#include "mymath.h"

ContTriangularMagResp::ContTriangularMagResp( istream& uin,
                                              ostream& uout )
                         :ContinWindowResponse( uin, uout )
{
 double amp0, x, value;
 double tau, freq, freq_exp, freq_cyc;

 tau = 1.0;
 freq_cyc = 2.0;

 for(int n=0; n<Num_Resp_Pts; n++)
   {
    freq_exp = 1.0 + freq_cyc*(n-Num_Resp_Pts)/((double)Num_Resp_Pts);
    freq = pow( (double)10.0, freq_exp);
    amp0 = 0.5 * tau;
```

```
    x = PI * freq * tau /2.0;
    value = 0.5 * tau * sinc_sqrd(x) / amp0;
    if(Db_Scale_Enab) value = 20.0*log10(value);
    (*Response_File) << freq << ", " << value << endl;
   }

}
```

Listing 14.10 Discrete-Time Triangular Window

```
//
//  File = trianglr.cpp
//

#include <math.h>
#include <iostream.h>
#include "trianglr.h"
#include "misdefs.h"
#include "mymath.h"

TriangularWindow::TriangularWindow( istream& uin,
                                    ostream& uout )
{
 int num_taps, zero_ends;

 uout << "number of taps?" << endl;
 uin >> num_taps;

 uout << "include zero end-points in total tap count?\n"
      << "  0 = no, 1 = yes" << endl;
 uin >> zero_ends;

 Initialize(num_taps);
 GenerateWindow( num_taps, zero_ends );
 return;
}
//==========================================================

TriangularWindow::TriangularWindow( int length,
                                    int zero_ends )
                 :GenericWindow(length)
{
  GenerateWindow( length, zero_ends );
}
//==========================================================
```

```
void TriangularWindow::GenerateWindow( int length,
                                       int zero_ends )
{
 if( zero_ends)
   {
    if(length%2)   // odd length window centered at zero
      {
       for(int n=0; n<Half_Length; n++)
         {
          Half_Lag_Win[n] = 1.0 - (2.0*n)/((double)(Length-1));
         }
      }
    else     // even length window centered at -1/2
      {
       for(int n=0; n<Half_Length; n++)
         {
          Half_Lag_Win[n] = 1.0 - (2.0*n + 1.0)/((double)(Length-1));
         }
      }
   }
 else
   {
    if(length%2)   // odd length window centered at zero
      {
       for(int n=0; n<Half_Length; n++)
         {
          Half_Lag_Win[n] = 1.0 - (2.0*n)/((double)(Length+1));
         }
      }
    else     // even length window centered at -1/2
      {
       for(int n=0; n<Half_Length; n++)
         {
          Half_Lag_Win[n] = 1.0 - (2.0*n + 1.0)/((double)(Length+1));
         }
      }
   }
 return;
}
```

Listing 14.11 Header for Generic Discrete-Time Window Base Class

```
//
//  File = gen_win.h
//
```

```
#ifndef _GEN_WIN_H_
#define _GEN_WIN_H_

#include <fstream.h>

class GenericWindow
{
public:

  // constructors

  GenericWindow( void );
  GenericWindow( int length );

  void Initialize( int length );

  double GetDataWinCoeff( int samp_indx);

  void DumpHalfLagWindow( ofstream* output_stream);

  double* GetDataWindow( void );

  double* GetHalfLagWindow( void );

  double* GetLagWindow( void );

  int GetNumTaps( void );

protected:

  int Length;
  int Half_Length;
  double *Half_Lag_Win;
  double *Lag_Win;
  double *Data_Win;
};

#endif
```

Listing 14.12 Method for Obtaining the Data Window Coefficient for a Specified Value of Sample Index

```
//
//  File = gen_win.cpp
//
```

```
#include <math.h>
#include "gen_win.h"
#include "misdefs.h"

GenericWindow::GenericWindow( void )
{
 Length = 0;
 Half_Length = 0;
 Half_Lag_Win = NULL;
 Data_Win = NULL;
}
//---------------------------------------
GenericWindow::GenericWindow( int length )
{
 Initialize(length);
}
//---------------------------------------
void GenericWindow::Initialize( int length )
{
 Length = length;
 if(length%2)
   { Half_Length = (length+1)/2; }
 else
   { Half_Length = length/2; }

 Half_Lag_Win = new double[Half_Length];
 Data_Win = NULL;

 return;
}

//-----------------------------------------------
double GenericWindow::GetDataWinCoeff( int samp_indx)
{
 int middle;

 if(Length%2)
   {
    middle = (Length-1)/2;
    if(samp_indx < middle)
      { return(Half_Lag_Win[middle-samp_indx]); }
    else
      { return( Half_Lag_Win[samp_indx-middle]); }
   }
 else
   {
    middle = Length/2;
```

```
    if(samp_indx < middle)
      { return(Half_Lag_Win[middle-1-samp_indx]); }
    else
      { return(Half_Lag_Win[samp_indx-middle]); }
   }
}

//----------------------------------------------------------------
void GenericWindow::DumpHalfLagWindow( ofstream *output_stream)
{
 for(int n=0; n<Half_Length; n++)
   {
    (*output_stream) << n << ", " << Half_Lag_Win[n] << endl;
   }
 return;
}

//---------------------------------------------
double* GenericWindow::GetDataWindow( void )
{
 if( Data_Win == NULL )
   {
    Data_Win = new double[Length];
    for(int n=0; n<Length; n++)
    {
     Data_Win[n] = GetDataWinCoeff(n);
    }
   }
 return(Data_Win);
}

//----------------------------------------------------
double* GenericWindow::GetHalfLagWindow( void )
{
 return(Half_Lag_Win);
}

//--------------------------------------------------
double* GenericWindow::GetLagWindow( void )
{
 return(Lag_Win);
}

//------------------------------------
int GenericWindow::GetNumTaps( void )
{
  return(Length);
}
```

Listing 14.13 Magnitude Response for a Continuous-Time von Hann Window

```
//
//  File = hann.cpp
//

#include <math.h>
#include <iostream.h>
#include "typedefs.h"
#include "con_hann.h"
#include "misdefs.h"
#include "mymath.h"

ContHannMagResp::ContHannMagResp( istream& uin,
                                  ostream& uout )
                : ContinWindowResponse( uin, uout )
{
 double x, amp0, tau, freq, freq_exp, freq_cyc;

 tau = 1.0;
 freq_cyc = 2.0;
 amp0 = 0.5;

 for(int n=0; n<Num_Resp_Pts; n++)
   {
    freq_exp = 1.0 + freq_cyc*(n-Num_Resp_Pts)/((double)Num_Resp_Pts);
    freq = pow( (double)10.0, freq_exp);
    x = 0.5 * tau * sinc(PI * tau * freq);
    x += (0.25 * tau * sinc(PI * tau * (freq-tau)));
    x += (0.25 * tau * sinc(PI * tau * (freq+tau)));
    if(Db_Scale_Enab) x = 20.0*log10(fabs(x/amp0));
    (*Response_File) << freq << ", " << x << endl;
   }
}
```

Listing 14.14 Discrete-Time von Hann Window

```
//
//  File = hann.cpp
//

#include <math.h>
#include <iostream.h>
#include "hann.h"
#include "misdefs.h"
#include "mymath.h"
```

```
HannWindow::HannWindow( istream& uin,
                        ostream& uout )
{
 int num_taps, zero_ends;

 uout << "number of taps?" << endl;
 uin >> num_taps;

 uout << "include zero end-points in total tap count?\n"
      << "  0 = no, 1 = yes" << endl;
 uin >> zero_ends;

 Initialize(num_taps);
 GenerateWindow( num_taps, zero_ends );
 return;
}
//========================================================

HannWindow::HannWindow( int length,
                        int zero_ends )
          :GenericWindow(length)
{
  GenerateWindow( length, zero_ends );
}
//========================================================

void HannWindow::GenerateWindow( int length, int zero_ends )
{
 for(int n=0; n<Half_Length; n++)
   {
    if(length%2) // odd length
      {
       if(zero_ends)
         {Half_Lag_Win[n] = 0.5 + 0.5 * cos( TWO_PI*n/(length-1));}
       else
         {Half_Lag_Win[n] = 0.5 + 0.5 * cos( TWO_PI*n/(length+1));}
      }
    else
      {
       if(zero_ends)
         {Half_Lag_Win[n] = 0.5 + 0.5 * cos( (2*n+1)*PI/(length-1));}
       else
         {Half_Lag_Win[n] = 0.5 + 0.5 * cos( (2*n+1)*PI/(length+1));}
      }
    cout << n << "  " << Half_Lag_Win[n] << endl;
   }
 return;
}
```

Listing 14.15 Magnitude Response for a Continuous-Time Hamming Window

```
//
//  File = con_hamm.cpp
//

#include <math.h>
#include <iostream.h>
#include "misdefs.h"
#include "typedefs.h"
#include "con_hamm.h"
#include "mymath.h"

ContHammingMagResp::ContHammingMagResp( istream& uin,
                                        ostream& uout )
                  : ContinWindowResponse( uin, uout )
{
 double x, amp0, tau, freq, freq_exp, freq_cyc;

 tau = 1.0;
 freq_cyc = 2.0;
 amp0 = 0.54;

 for(int n=0; n<Num_Resp_Pts; n++)
   {
    freq_exp = 1.0 + freq_cyc*(n-Num_Resp_Pts)/((double)Num_Resp_Pts);
    freq = pow( (double)10.0, freq_exp);
    x = 0.54 * tau * sinc(PI * tau * freq);
    x += (0.23 * tau * sinc(PI * tau * (freq-tau)));
    x += (0.23 * tau * sinc(PI * tau * (freq+tau)));
    if(Db_Scale_Enab) x = 20.0*log10(fabs(x/amp0));
    (*Response_File) << freq << ", " << x << endl;
   }
}
```

Listing 14.16 Discrete-Time Hamming Window

```
//
//  File = hamming.cpp
//

#include <math.h>
#include <iostream.h>
#include "hamming.h"
#include "misdefs.h"
#include "mymath.h"
```

```
HammingWindow::HammingWindow( istream& uin,
                              ostream& uout )
{
 int num_taps;
 uout << "number of taps?" << endl;
 uin >> num_taps;

 Initialize(num_taps);
 GenerateWindow( num_taps );
 return;
}
//==========================================================

HammingWindow::HammingWindow( int length )
              :GenericWindow(length)
{
  GenerateWindow( length );
}
//==========================================================
void HammingWindow::GenerateWindow( int length )
{
 for(int n=0; n<Half_Length; n++)
   {
    if(length%2) // odd length
      { Half_Lag_Win[n] = 0.54 + 0.46 * cos( TWO_PI*n/(length-1));}
    else
      { Half_Lag_Win[n] = 0.54 + 0.46 * cos( (2*n+1)*PI/(length-1));}
    cout << n << "  " << Half_Lag_Win[n] << endl;
   }

 return;
}
```

Chapter

15

FIR Filter Design: Frequency Sampling Method

15.1 Introduction

In Chap. 14, the desired frequency response for an FIR filter is specified in the continuous-frequency domain, and the discrete-time impulse response coefficients are obtained via the Fourier series. We can modify this procedure so that the desired frequency response is specified in the discrete-frequency domain and then use the inverse discrete Fourier transform (DFT) to obtain the corresponding discrete-time impulse response.

Example 15.1 Consider the case of a 21-tap low-pass filter with a normalized cutoff frequency of $\lambda_U = 3\pi/7$. The sampled magnitude response for positive frequencies is shown in Fig. 15.1. The normalized cutoff frequency λ_U falls midway between $n = 4$ and $n = 5$, and the normalized folding frequency of $\lambda = \pi$ falls midway between $n = 10$ and $n = 11$. (Note that $45/10.5 = 3/7$.) We assume that $H_d(-n) = H_d(n)$ and use the inverse DFT to obtain the filter coefficients listed in Table 15.1. The actual continuous-frequency response of an FIR filter having these coefficients is shown in Figs. 15.2 and 15.3. Figure 15.2 is plotted against a linear ordinate, and dots are placed at points corresponding to the discrete frequencies specified in Fig. 15.1. Figure 15.3 is included to provide a convenient baseline for comparison of subsequent plots that will have to be plotted against decibel ordinates in order to show low stopband levels.

The ripple performance in both the passband and stopband responses can be improved by specifying one or more transition-band samples at values somewhere between the passband value of $H_d(m) = 1$ and the stopband value of $H_d(m) = 0$. Consider the case depicted in Fig. 15.4 where we have modified the response of Fig. 15.1 by introducing a one-sample transition band by setting $H_d(5) = 0.5$. The continuous-frequency response of this modified filter is shown in Fig. 15.5, and the coefficients are listed in Table 15.2.

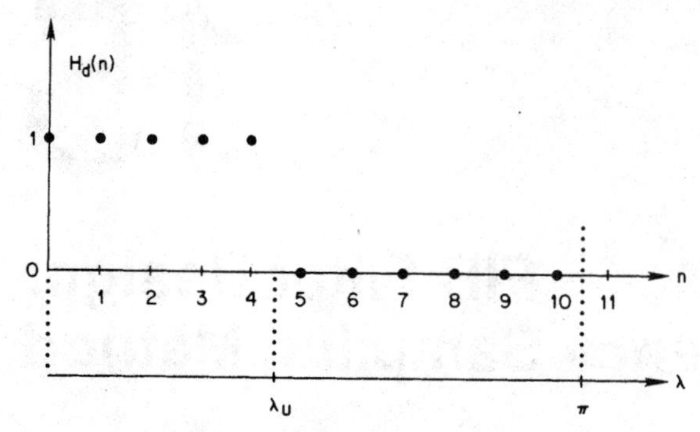

Figure 15.1 Desired discrete-frequency magnitude response for a low-pass filter with $\lambda_U = 3\pi/7$.

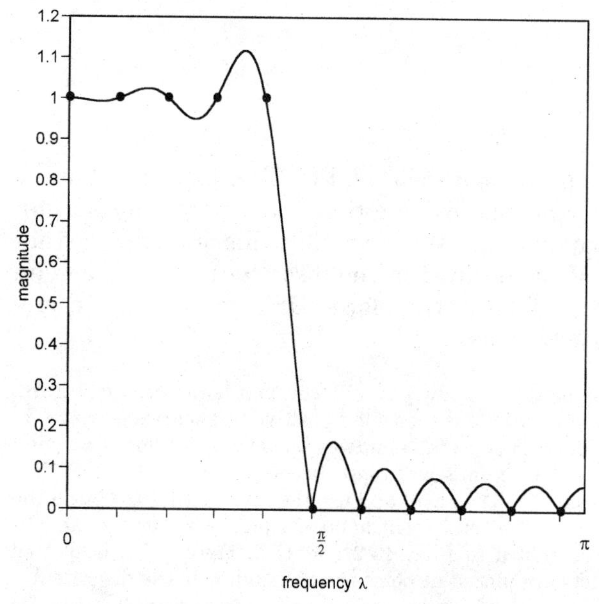

Figure 15.2 Magnitude response for filter of Example 15.1.

The peak stopband ripple has been reduced by 13.3 dB. An even greater reduction can be obtained if the transition-band value is optimized rather than just arbitrarily set halfway between the passband and the stopband levels. It is also possible to have more than one sample in the transition band. The methods for optimizing transition-band values are iterative and involve repeatedly computing sets of impulse response coefficients and the corresponding frequency responses. Therefore, before moving on to specific optimization approaches, we will examine some of the mathematical details and explore some ways for introducing some computational efficiency into the process.

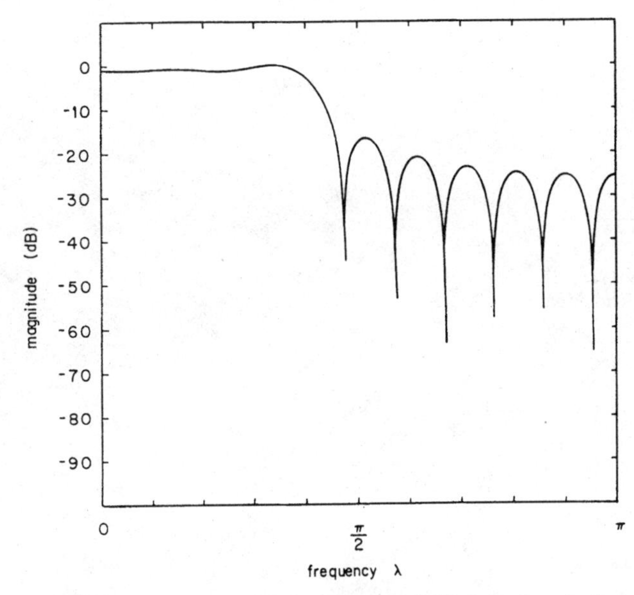

Figure 15.3 Filter response for Example 15.1 plotted on decibel scale.

15.2 Odd *N* versus Even *N*

Consider the desired response shown in Fig. 15.6 for the case of an odd-length filter with no transition band. If we assume that the cutoff lies midway between $n = n_p$ and $n = n_p + 1$ as shown, the cutoff frequency is $2\pi F(n_p + 1/2)$, where F is the interval between frequency domain samples. For the normalized case where $T = 1$, we find $F = 1/N$, so the normalized cutoff is given by

$$\lambda_U = \frac{\pi(2n_p + 1)}{N} \tag{15.1}$$

This equation allows us to compute the cutoff frequency when n_p and N are given. However, in most design situations we will need to start with known

TABLE 15.1 Coefficients for the 21-Tap Filter of Example 15.1

Coefficients
$h[0] = h[20] = 0.037334$
$h[1] = h[19] = -0.021192$
$h[2] = h[18] = -0.049873$
$h[3] = h[17] = 0.000000$
$h[4] = h[16] = 0.059380$
$h[5] = h[15] = 0.030376$
$h[6] = h[14] = -0.066090$
$h[7] = h[13] = -0.085807$
$h[8] = h[12] = 0.070096$
$h[9] = h[11] = 0.311490$
$h[10] = 0.428571$

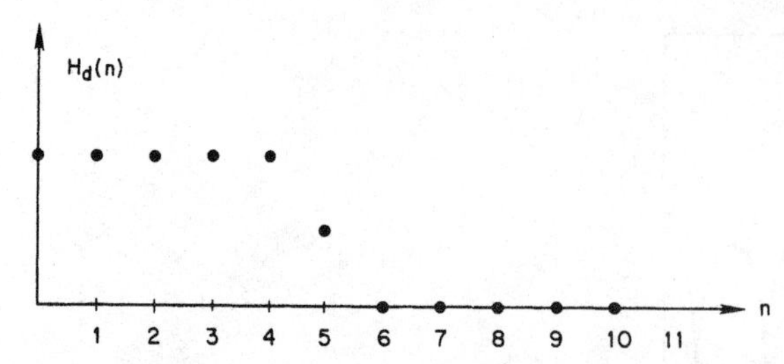

Figure 15.4 Discrete-frequency magnitude response with one transition-band sample midway between the ideal passband and stopband levels.

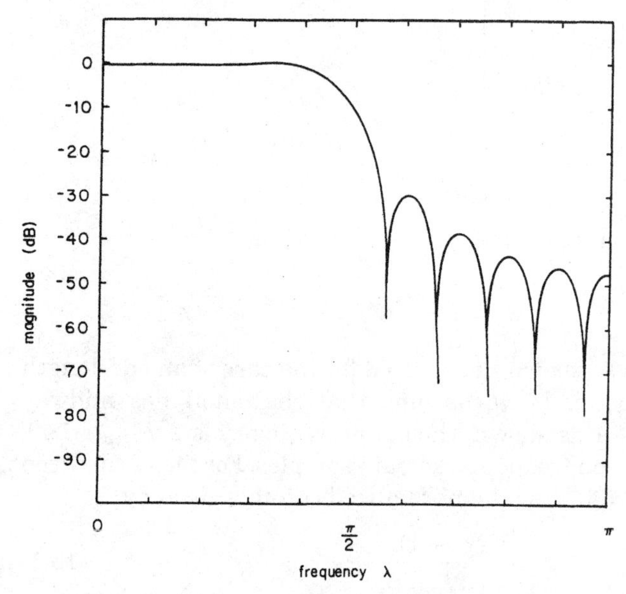

Figure 15.5 Continuous-frequency magnitude response corresponding to the discrete-frequency response of Fig. 15.3.

(desired) values of N and λ_U and then determine n_p. We can solve Eq. (15.1) for n_p, but for an arbitrary value λ_U, the resulting value of n_p might not be an integer. Therefore, we write

$$n_p = \left\lfloor \frac{N\lambda_{UD}}{2\pi} - \frac{1}{2} \right\rfloor \tag{15.2}$$

where λ_{UD} denotes desired λ_U and $\lfloor \cdot \rfloor$ denotes the floor function that truncates the fractional part from its argument. Equation (15.2) yields a value for n_p that guarantees that the cutoff will lie *somewhere* between n_p and $n_p + 1$, but not necessarily at the midpoint. The difference $\Delta\lambda = |\lambda_U - \lambda_{UD}|$ is an indication of how good the choices of n_p and N are—the smaller $\Delta\lambda$ is, the better the choices are.

TABLE 15.2 Coefficients for the 21-Tap Filter with a Single Transition-Band Sample Value of 0.5

$h[0] = h[20] = 0.002427$
$h[1] = h[19] = 0.008498$
$h[2] = h[18] = -0.010528$
$h[3] = h[17] = -0.023810$
$h[4] = h[16] = 0.016477$
$h[5] = h[15] = 0.047773$
$h[6] = h[14] = -0.020587$
$h[7] = h[13] = -0.096403$
$h[8] = h[12] = 0.023009$
$h[9] = h[11] = 0.315048$
$h[10] = 0.476190$

It is a common practice to assume that the cutoff frequency lies midway between $n = n_p$ and $n = n_p + 1$ as in the preceding analysis. If the continuous-frequency amplitude response is a straight line between $A(n) = 1$ at $n = n_p$ and $A(n) = 0$ at $n = n_p + 1$, the value of the response midway between these points will be 0.5. However, since $A(n)$ is the *amplitude* response, the attenuation at the assumed cutoff is 6 dB. For an attenuation of 3 dB, the cutoff should be assigned to lie at a point which is 0.293 to the right of n_p and 0.707 to the left of $n_p + 1$.

If we assume that the cutoff lies at $n_p + 0.293$, the cutoff frequency is $2\pi F(n_p + 0.293)$ and the normalized cutoff is given by

$$\lambda_U = \frac{2\pi(n_p + 0.293)}{N} \tag{15.3}$$

The required number of samples in the two-sided pass band is $2n_p + 1$ where

$$n_p = \left\lfloor \frac{N\lambda_{UD}}{2\pi} - 0.293 \right\rfloor$$

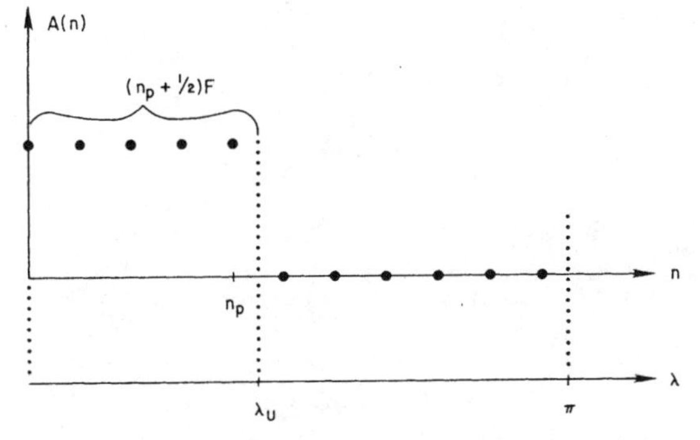

Figure 15.6 Desired frequency-sampled response for an odd-length filter with no transition-band samples.

For convenience we will denote the λ_U given by Eq. (15.1) as λ_6 and the λ_U given by Eq. (15.3) as λ_3.

Even N

Now let's consider the response shown in Fig. 15.7 for the case of an even-length filter with no transition band. If we assume that the cutoff lies midway between $n = n_p$ and $n = n_p + 1$, the cutoff frequency is $2\pi F n_p$ and the normalized cutoff is

$$\lambda_6 = \frac{2\pi n_p}{N}$$

Solving for n_p and using the floor function to ensure integer values, we obtain

$$n_p = \left\lfloor \frac{N\lambda_{6D}}{2\pi} \right\rfloor$$

If we assume that the cutoff lies at $n_p + 0.293$, the cutoff frequency is $2\pi F(n_p - 0.207)$ and the normalized cutoff is

$$\lambda_3 = \frac{2\pi(n_p - 0.207)}{N}$$

The required number of samples in the two-sided pass band $2n_p$ where

$$n_p = \left\lfloor \frac{N\lambda_{3D}}{2\pi} + 0.207 \right\rfloor$$

If processing constraints or other implementation considerations place an upper limit $N_{\max}$ on the total number of taps that can be used in a particular situation, it might be smart to choose between $N = N_{\max}$ and $N = (N_{\max} - 1)$ based upon which value of N yields λ_U that is closer to λ_{UD}.

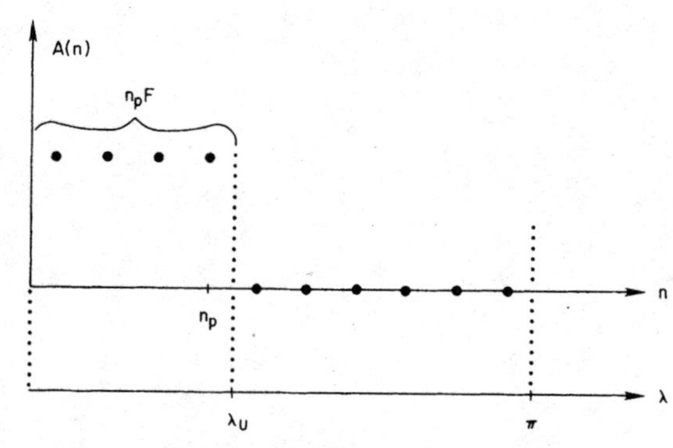

Figure 15.7 Desired frequency-sampled response for an even-length filter with no transition-band samples.

Example 15.2 For $N_{max} = 21$ and $\lambda_{6D} = 3\pi/7$, determine whether $N = 21$ or $N = 20$ would be the better choice based on values of $\Delta\lambda$.

solution For $N = 20$,

$$n_p = \left\lfloor \frac{20[(3\pi/7)]}{2\pi} \right\rfloor = \left\lfloor \frac{30}{7} \right\rfloor = 4$$

$$\lambda_6 = \frac{2\pi(4)}{20} = \frac{2\pi}{5}$$

$$\Delta\lambda = \left| \frac{3\pi}{7} - \frac{2\pi}{5} \right| = \frac{\pi}{35}$$

For $N = 21$,

$$n_p = \left\lfloor \frac{21[(3\pi/7)]}{2\pi} - \frac{1}{2} \right\rfloor = \lfloor 4 \rfloor = 4$$

$$\lambda_6 = \frac{9\pi}{21} = \frac{3\pi}{7}$$

$$\Delta\lambda = \left| \frac{3\pi}{7} - \frac{3\pi}{7} \right| = 0$$

For this contrived case, $N = 21$ is not only the better choice—it is the best choice, yielding $\Delta\lambda = 0$.

Example 15.3 For $N_{max} = 21$ and $\lambda_{3D} = 2\pi/5$, determine whether $N = 21$ or $N = 20$ would be the better choice based on values of $\Delta\lambda$.

solution For $N = 20$,

$$n_p = \left\lfloor \frac{20[(2\pi/5)]}{2\pi} + 0.207 \right\rfloor = \lfloor 4.209 \rfloor = 4$$

$$\lambda_3 = \frac{2\pi(4 - 0.207)}{20} = 1.1916$$

$$\Delta\lambda = \left| \frac{2\pi}{5} - 1.1916 \right| = 0.065$$

For $N = 21$,

$$n_p = \left\lfloor \frac{21[(2\pi/5)]}{2\pi} - 0.293 \right\rfloor = \lfloor 3.907 \rfloor = 3$$

$$\lambda_3 = \frac{2\pi(3.293)}{21} = 0.9853$$

$$\Delta\lambda = \left| \frac{2\pi}{5} - 0.9853 \right| = 0.2714$$

Since $0.065 < 0.2714$, the better choice appears to be $N = 20$.

15.3 Design Formulas

The inverse DFT can be used as it was in Example 15.1 to obtain the impulse response coefficients $h(n)$ from a desired frequency response that has been specified at uniformly spaced discrete frequencies. However, for the special case of FIR filters with constant group delay, the inverse DFT can be modified to take advantage of symmetry conditions. Back in Sec. 13.2, the DTFT was adapted to the four specific types of constant-group-delay FIR filters to obtain the dedicated formulas for $H(\omega)$ and $A(\omega)$ that were summarized in Table 13.2. For the discrete-frequency case, the DFT can be similarly adapted to obtain the explicit formulas for $A(k)$ given in Table 15.3. (The entries in the table are for the normalized case where $T = 1$.) After some trigonometric manipulation, we can arrive at the corresponding inverse relations or *design formulas* listed in Table 15.4. These formulas are implemented by the function `FreqSampFilter-Design( )` provided in Listing 15.1.

15.4 Frequency Sampling Design with Transition-Band Samples

As mentioned in the introduction to this chapter, the inclusion of one or more samples in a transition band can greatly improve the performance of filters designed via the frequency sampling method. In Sec. 15.1, some improvement was obtained by simply placing one transition-band sample halfway between the pass band's unity amplitude and the stop band's zero value. However, even

TABLE 15.3 Discrete-Frequency Amplitude Response of FIR Filters with Constant Group Delay

Type	
1 $h[n]$ symmetric N odd	$h[M] + \sum_{n=0}^{M-1} 2h[n] \cos\left[\frac{2\pi(M-n)k}{N}\right] = h[M] + \sum_{n=1}^{M} 2h[M-n] \cos\left(\frac{2\pi kn}{N}\right)$
2 $h[n]$ symmetric N even	$\sum_{h=0}^{(N/2)-1} 2h[n] \cos\left[\frac{2\pi(M-n)k}{N}\right] = \sum_{n=1}^{N/2} 2h\left[\frac{N}{2}-n\right] \cos\left\{\frac{2\pi k[n-(1/2)]}{N}\right\}$
3 $h[n]$ antisymmetric N odd	$\sum_{n=0}^{M-1} 2h[n] \sin\left[\frac{2\pi(M-n)k}{N}\right] = \sum_{n=1}^{M} 2h[M-n] \sin\left(\frac{2\pi kn}{N}\right)$
4 $h[n]$ antisymmetric N even	$\sum_{n=0}^{(N/2)-1} 2h[n] \sin\left[\frac{2\pi(M-n)k}{N}\right] = \sum_{n=1}^{N/2} 2h\left[\frac{N}{2}-n\right] \sin\left\{\frac{2\pi k[n-(1/2)]}{N}\right\}$

TABLE 15.4 Formulas for Frequency Sampling Design of FIR Filters with Constant Group Delay

Type	$h[n]\ n = 0, 1, 2, \ldots, N-1$
1 $h[n]$ symmetric N odd	$\frac{1}{N}\left\{A(0) + \sum_{k=1}^{M} 2A(k) \cos\left[\frac{2\pi(n-M)k}{N}\right]\right\}$
2 $h[n]$ symmetric N even	$\frac{1}{N}\left\{A(0) + \sum_{k=1}^{(N/2)-1} 2A(k) \cos\left[\frac{2\pi(n-M)k}{N}\right]\right\}$
3 $h[n]$ antisymmetric N odd	$\frac{1}{N}\left\{\sum_{k=1}^{M} 2A(k) \sin\left[\frac{2\pi(M-n)k}{N}\right]\right\}$
4 $h[n]$ antisymmetric N even	$\frac{1}{N}\left\{A\left(\frac{N}{2}\right) \sin\left[\pi(M-n)\right] + \sum_{k=1}^{(N/2)-1} 2A(k) \sin\left[\frac{2\pi(M-n)k}{N}\right]\right\}$

more improvement can be obtained if the value of this single transition-band sample is optimized. Before proceeding, we need to first decide just what constitutes an *optimal* value for this sample—we could seek the sample that minimizes passband ripple, minimizes stopband ripple, or minimizes some function that depends upon both stopband and passband ripple. The most commonly used approach is to optimize the transition-band value so as to minimize the peak stopband ripple.

For any given set of desired amplitude response samples, determination of the peak stopband ripple entails the following steps:

1. From the specified set of desired amplitude response samples H_d, compute the corresponding set of impulse response coefficients h using the function `FreqSampFilterDesign( )` presented in Sec. 15.3.
2. From the impulse response coefficients generated in Step 1, compute a fine-grained discrete-frequency approximation to the continuous-frequency amplitude response using the function `LinearPhaseFirResponse( )` presented in Listing 13.5.
3. Search the amplitude response generated in Step 2 to find the peak value in the stop band. This search can be accomplished using the function `FindStopbandPeak( )` given in Listing 15.2.

In general, we will need five parameters to specify the location of the stop band(s) so that `FindStopbandPeak( )` knows where to search. The first parameter specifies the band configuration—low-pass, high-pass, bandpass, or band-stop. The other parameters are indices of the first and last samples in the filter's pass bands and stop bands. Low-pass and high-pass filters need only two parameters n_1 and n_2, but bandpass and bandstop filters need four: n_1, n_2, n_3, and n_4. The specific meaning of these parameters for each of the basic filter configurations is shown in Fig. 15.8.

To see how this information is used, consider the low-pass case where n_2 is the index of the first stopband sample in the desired response $H_d[n]$. The goal is to find the peak stopband value in the filter's *continuous-frequency* magnitude response. The computer must compute samples of a discrete-frequency approximation to this continuous-frequency response. This approximation should not be confused with the desired response $H_d[n]$, which is also a discrete-frequency magnitude response. The latter contains only N samples, where N is the number of taps in the filter. The approximation to the continuous-frequency response must contain a much larger number of points. For the examples in this chapter, numbers ranging from 120 to 480 have been used. In searching for the peak of a

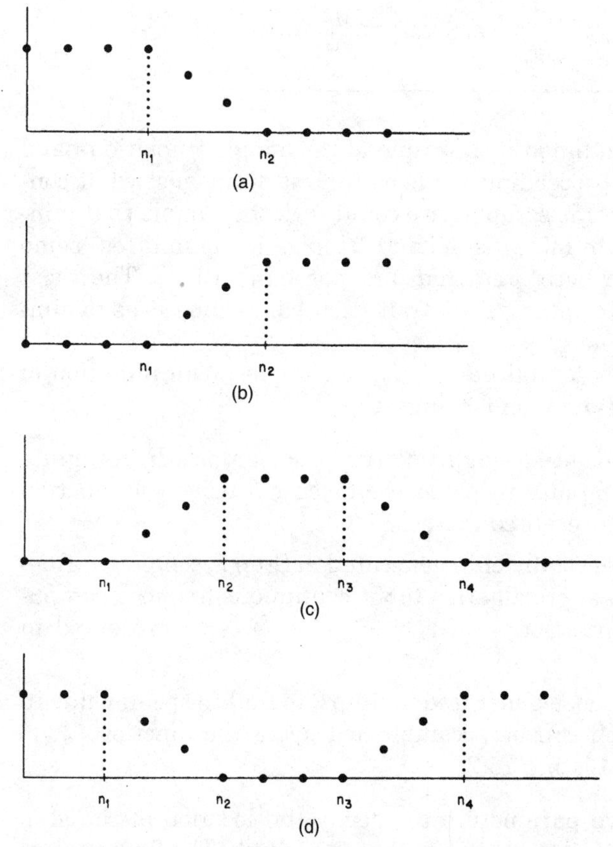

Figure 15.8 Parameters for specifying band configurations: (*a*) low-pass, (*b*) high-pass, (*c*) bandpass, and (*d*) bandstop.

low-pass response, `FindStopbandPeak( )` directs its attention to samples n_s and beyond in the discrete-frequency approximation to the continuous-frequency amplitude response where

$$n_s = \frac{2Ln_2}{N}$$

and

L = number of samples in the one-sided approximation to the continuous response (that is, `numPts`)
N = number of taps in the filter
n_2 = index of first sample in the desired positive-frequency stop band

For high-pass, bandpass, and bandstop filters, the search is limited to the stop band in a similar fashion.

The approach for finding the peak, as previously outlined in Steps 1 through 3, contains some fat that could be eliminated to gain speed at the expense of clarity and modularity. For example, computing the entire amplitude response is not necessary, since only the stopband values are of interest to the optimization procedure. Also, for any given filter, consecutive peaks in the response will be separated by a number of samples that remains more or less constant—this fact could be exploited to compute and examine only those portions of the response falling within areas where stopband ripple peaks can be expected.

Optimization

In subsequent discussions, T_A will be used to denote the value of the single transition-band sample. One simple approach for optimizing the value of T_A is to just start with $T_A = 1$ and keep decreasing by some fixed increment, evaluating the peak stopband ripple after each decrease. At first, the ripple will decrease each time T_A is decreased, but once the optimal value is passed, the ripple will increase as we continue to decrease T_A. Therefore, once the peak ripple starts to increase, we should decrease the size of the increment and begin *increasing* instead of decreasing T_A. Once peak ripple again stops decreasing and starts increasing, we again decrease the increment and reverse the direction. Eventually, T_A should converge to the optimum value. A slightly more sophisticated strategy for finding the optimum value of T_A is provided by the so-called *golden section search* (Press, et al. 1986). This method is based on the fact that the minimum of a function $f(x)$ is known to be bracketed by a triplet of points $a < b < c$ provided that $f(b) < f(a)$ and $f(b) < f(c)$. Once an initial bracket is established, the span of the bracket can be methodically decreased until the three points a, b, and c converge on the abscissa of the minimum. The name *golden section* comes from the fact that the most efficient search results when the middle point of the bracket is a fraction distance 0.61803 from one endpoint and 0.38197 from the other. A C function `GoldenSearch( )`, provided in Listing 15.3, performs a golden section search for our specific application. This function calls `FreqSampFilterDesign::ComputeCoefficients( )`, `FreqSampFilterResponse::ComputeMagResponse( )`, `FreqSampFilterResponse::NormalizeResponse( )`, and `FreqSampFilterSpec::SetTrans( )`. There is also a call to `QuantizeCoefficients( )`, which is a member of class `FreqSampFilterDesign` that is not shown in Listing 15.1. This function will not be presented until it is needed in Chap. 17. If this function is called with the first parameter `quant_factor=0`, the coefficients will be left in their original unquantized forms. The function `FreqSampFilterSpec::SetTrans( )` is provided in Listing 15.4. For the single-sample case this function is extremely simple, but we shall maintain it as a separate function to facilitate anticipated extensions for the case of multiple samples in the transition band that will be treated in Secs. 15.5 and 15.6.

Example 15.4 For a 21-tap low-pass filter, find the value for the transition-band sample $H_d[5]$ such that the peak stopband ripple is minimized.

solution The optimal value for $H_d[5]$ is 0.400147, and the corresponding amplitude response is shown in Fig. 15.9. The filter coefficients are listed in Table 15.5. Compared to the case where $H_d[5] = 0.5$, the peak stopband ripple has been reduced by 11.2 dB.

15.5 Optimization with Two Transition-Band Samples

The optimization problem gets a bit more difficult when there are two or more samples in the transition band. Let's walk through the case of a type 1 low-pass filter with 21 taps having a desired response specified by

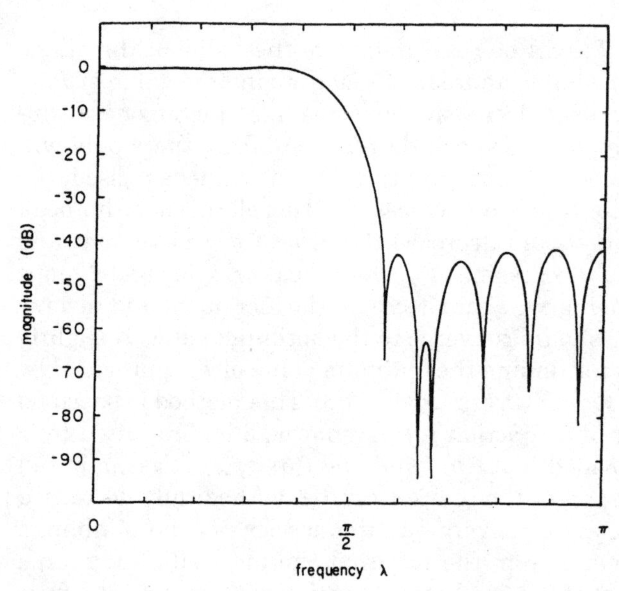

Figure 15.9 Magnitude response of 21-tap filter from Example 15.4.

TABLE 15.5 Coefficients for the Filter of Example 15.4

$h[0] = h[20] = 0.009532$
$h[1] = h[19] = 0.002454$
$h[2] = h[18] = -0.018536$
$h[3] = h[17] = -0.018963$
$h[4] = h[16] = 0.025209$
$h[5] = h[15] = 0.044232$
$h[6] = h[14] = -0.029849$
$h[7] = h[13] = -0.094246$
$h[8] = h[12] = 0.032593$
$h[9] = h[11] = 0.314324$
$h[10] = 0.466498$

$$H_d[n] = \begin{cases} 1.0 & 0 \le |n| \le 4 \\ H_B & |n| = 5 \\ H_A & |n| = 6 \\ 0.0 & 7 \le |n| \le 10 \end{cases}$$

The values of H_A and H_B will be optimized to produce the filter having the smallest peak stopband ripple.

1. Letting $H_B = 1$ and using a stopping tolerance of 0.01 in the single-sample `GoldenSearch( )` function from Sec. 15.4, we find that the peak stopband ripple is minimized for $H_A = 0.398227$. Thus, we have defined one point in the H_A-H_B plane; specifically ($H_{A1} = 0.398227$, $H_{B1} = 1.0$).
2. We define a second point in the plane by setting $H_B = 0.97$ and once again searching for the optimum H_A value that minimizes the peak stopband ripple. This yields a second point at (0.376941, 0.97).
3. The two points (0.398227, 1) and (0.376941, 0.97) can then be used to define a line in the H_A-H_B plane as shown in Fig. 15.10. Our ultimate goal is to determine the ordered pair (H_A, H_B) that minimizes the peak stopband ripple of the filter. In the vicinity of (H_{A1}, 1), the line shown in Fig. 15.10 is the

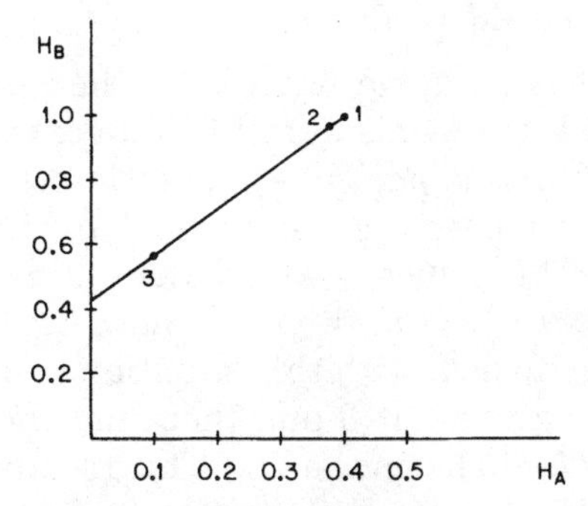

Figure 15.10 Line of steepest descent plotted in the H_A-H_B plane.

best path along which to search and is therefore called the *line of steepest descent.* On the way to achieving our ultimate goal, a useful intermediate goal is to find the point along the line at which the filter's stopband ripple is minimized. In order to use the single-sample search procedure from Sec. 15.4 to search along this line, we can define positions on the line in terms of their projections onto the H_A axis. To evaluate the filter response for a given value of H_A, we need to have H_B expressed as a function of H_A. The slope of the line is easily determined from points 1 and 2 as

$$m = \frac{1 - 0.97}{0.398227 - 0.376941} = 1.4093$$

Thus we can write

$$H_B = 1.4093 H_A + b \tag{15.4}$$

where b is the H_B intercept. We can then solve for b by substituting the values for H_A, H_B at point 1 into Eq. (15.4) to obtain

$$\begin{aligned} b &= H_B - 1.4093 H_A \\ &= 1 - 1.4093(0.398227) = 0.438779 \end{aligned}$$

Thus, the line of steepest descent is defined in the H_A-H_B plane as

$$H_B = 1.4093 H_A + 0.438779 \tag{15.5}$$

The nature of the filter design problem requires that $0 \leq H_A \leq 1$ and $0 \leq H_B \leq 1$. Furthermore, examination of Eq. (15.5) indicates that $H_B < H_A$ for all values of H_A between zero and unity. Thus, the fact that H_B must not exceed unity can be used to further restrict the values of H_A. We find that $H_B = 1$ for $H_A = 0.39823$. Therefore, the search along the line is limited to values of H_A such that $0 \leq H_A \leq 0.39823$. The point along the line of Eq. (15.5) at which the peak stopband ripple is minimized is found to be (0.099248, 0.57863). The peak stopband ripple at this point is –66.47 dB.

4. The ripple performance of –66.47 is respectable, but it is not the best that we can do. The straight line shown in Fig. 15.10 is in fact just an extrapolation from points 1 and 2. Generally, the actual *path* of steepest descent will not be a straight line and will diverge farther from the extrapolated line as the distance from point 1 increases. Thus when we find the optimum point (labeled as point 3) *lying along the straight line,* we really have not found the optimum point *in general.* One way to deal with this situation is to hold H_B constant at the value corresponding to point 3 and then find the optimal value of H_A—without constraining H_A to lie on the line. This results in point 4 as shown in Fig. 15.11. (Figure 15.11 uses a different scale than does Fig. 15.10 so that fine details can be more clearly shown.) The coordinates of point 4 are (0.98301, 0.57863).

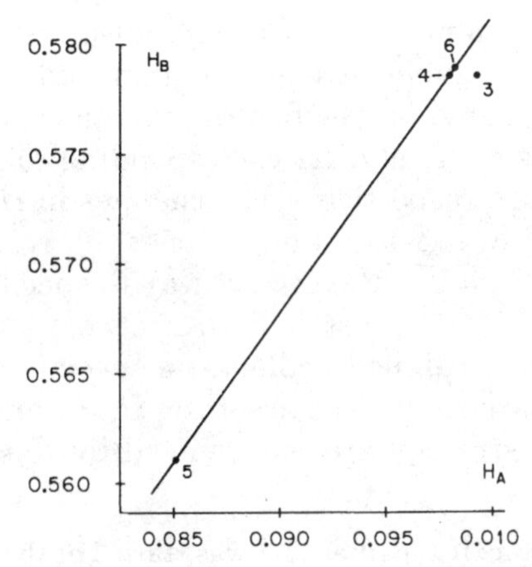

Figure 15.11 Second line of steepest descent.

5. We now perturb H_B by taking 97 percent of the value corresponding to point 4 [that is, $H_B = (0.97)(0.57863) = 0.561271$]. Searching for the value of H_A that minimizes the peak stopband ripple, we obtain point 5 at (0.085145, 0.561271).
6. The two points (0.099248, 0.57863) and (0.085145, 0.561271) can then be used to define the new line of steepest descent shown in Fig. 15.11. Using the approach discussed above in 3, we then find the point along the line at which the peak stopband ripple is minimized. This point is found to be (0.098592, 0.579014), and the corresponding peak ripple is –69.680885 dB.
7. We can continue this process of defining lines of steepest descent and optimizing along the line until the change in peak stopband ripple from one iteration to the next is smaller than some preset limit. Typically, the optimization is terminated when the peak ripple changes by less than 0.1 dB between iterations. Using this criterion, the present design converges after the fourth line of steepest descent is searched to find the point (H_A = 0.098403, H_B = 0.579376) where the peak stopband ripple is –71.08 dB.

Programming considerations

Optimizing the value of H_A, with H_B expressed as a function of H_A, requires some changes to the way in which the function `GoldenSearch( )` interfaces to the function `SetTrans( )`. In the single-sample case, the search was conducted with H_A as the independent variable. For the two-sample-transition case, the software has been designed to conduct the search in terms of the displacement ρ measured along an arbitrary line. (This approach is more general than it needs to be for the two-sample case, but doing things this way makes extension to three or more samples relatively easy—see Sec. 15.6 for details.) The function `GoldenSearch2` given in Listing 15.5 has been modified to include a call to a new overloaded version of `SetTrans` which takes three parameters. This new function, shown in Listing 15.6, accepts ρ as an input and resolves it into the

H_A and H_B components needed for computation of the impulse response and the subsequent estimation of the continuous-frequency amplitude response. The line along which ρ is being measured is specified to `SetTrans` via the `origins` and `slopes` arrays. The values of H_A and H_B corresponding to $\rho = 0$ are passed in `origins[1]` and `origins[2]`, respectively. The changes in H_A and H_B corresponding to $\Delta\rho = 1$ are passed in `slopes[1]` and `slopes[2]`, respectively. Setting `slopes[1]` = 1 and `origins[1]` = 0 is the correct way to specify $H_A = \rho$. (Note that if we set `slopes[1]` = 1, `origins[1]` = 0, `slopes[2]` = 0, and `origins[2]` = 0, the single-sample case can be handled as a special case of the two-sample case, since these values are equivalent to setting $H_A = \rho$ and $H_B = 0$.) The iterations of the optimization strategy are mechanized by the function `optimize2( )` given in Listing 15.7.

Example 15.5 Complete the design of the 21-tap filter that was started at the beginning of this section.

solution As mentioned previously, when `GoldenSearch2( )` is used with a stopping tolerance of 0.01, the example design converges after four lines of steepest descent have been searched. Each line involves 3 points—2 points to define the line plus 1 point at which the ripple is minimized. The coordinates and peak stopband ripple levels for the 12 points of the example design are listed in Table 15.6. Each of these points required 8 iterations of `GoldenSearch2( )`. The impulse response coefficients for the filter corresponding to the transition-band values of $H_A = 0.098403$ and $H_B = 0.579376$ are listed in Table 15.7. The corresponding magnitude response is plotted in Fig. 15.12.

Careful examination of the values in Table 15.6 reveals several anomalies. Points 1, 2, 4, 5, 7, 8, 10, and 11 define lines of steepest descent, and points 3, 6, 9, and 12 are the corresponding optimal points along these lines. The ripple performance of the optimal point 6 is –69.68 while the performance at point 4 is –69.93. These two points lie on the same line, and the performance at point 4 is better than the performance at point 6. A similar situation occurs with points 7 and 9. Such behavior indicates that the stopping criterion for `GoldenSearch2( )` is not stringent enough, thereby allowing the search to stop before the best point on the line is found.

TABLE 15.6 Points Generated in the Optimization Procedure for Example 15.5

Iteration	H_A	H_B	Stopband peak, dB
1	0.398227	1.0	–42.22
2	0.376941	0.97	–42.76
3	0.099248	0.578630	–66.47
4	0.098301	0.578630	–69.93
5	0.085145	0.561271	–65.87
6	0.098592	0.579014	–69.68
7	0.098301	0.579014	–71.05
8	0.085145	0.561643	–65.20
9	0.098473	0.579241	–70.89
10	0.098301	0.579241	–71.02
11	0.085145	0.561864	–64.61
12	0.098403	0.579376	–71.08

TABLE 15.7 Impulse Response Coefficients for the Filter of Example 15.5

$h[0] = h[20] = \ \ 0.002798$
$h[1] = h[19] = \ \ 0.004783$
$h[2] = h[18] = -0.006541$
$h[3] = h[17] = -0.018285$
$h[4] = h[16] = \ \ 0.007862$
$h[5] = h[15] = \ \ 0.042175$
$h[6] = h[14] = -0.007896$
$h[7] = h[13] = -0.092308$
$h[8] = h[12] = \ \ 0.007530$
$h[9] = h[11] = \ \ 0.313553$
$h[10] = 0.492659$

Example 15.6 Redesign the filter of Example 15.5 using `tol` = 0.001 instead of `tol` = 0.01.

solution The number of iterations required for each point increases from 8 to 14, but the design procedure terminates after only two lines of steepest descent. The coordinates and peak stopband ripple levels for the six points of this design are listed in Table 15.8. The impulse response coefficients are listed in Table 15.9.

Comparison of Tables 15.6 and 15.8 reveals that the performance obtained in Example 15.6 is 0.7 dB worse than the performance obtained in Example 15.5. Furthermore, within Example 15.6, the performance at point 3 is slightly better than the performance at point 6. Possible strategies for combatting these numeric effects would be to use a tweaking factor larger than 97 percent, or to have the tweaking factor approach unity with successive iterations.

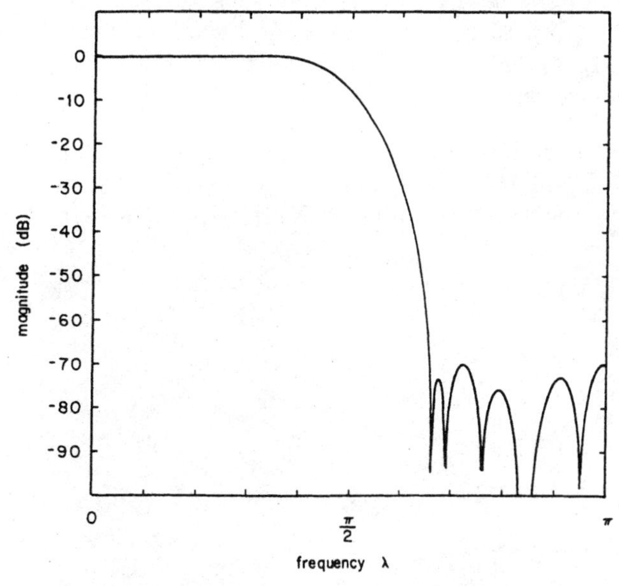

Figure 15.12 Magnitude response for Example 15.5.

TABLE 15.8 Points Generated in the Optimization Procedure for Example 15.6

Iteration	H_A	H_B	Stopband peak, dB
1	0.399133	1.0	−42.24
2	0.377674	0.97	−42.73
3	0.100240	0.582148	−70.46
4	0.100220	0.582148	−70.34
5	0.087517	0.564683	−65.10
6	0.100425	0.582429	−70.39

TABLE 15.9 Impulse Response Coefficients for the Filter of Example 15.6

$h[0] = h[20] = 0.002636$
$h[1] = h[19] = 0.004775$
$h[2] = h[18] = -0.006170$
$h[3] = h[17] = -0.018170$
$h[4] = h[16] = 0.007275$
$h[5] = h[15] = 0.042024$
$h[6] = h[14] = -0.007122$
$h[7] = h[13] = -0.092186$
$h[8] = h[12] = 0.006629$
$h[9] = h[11] = 0.313507$
$h[10] = 0.493605$

15.6 Optimization with Three Transition-Band Samples

Just as the two-transition-sample case was more complicated than the single-sample case, the three-sample case is significantly more complicated than the two-sample case. Let's consider the case of a type 1 low-pass filter having a desired response as shown in Fig. 15.13. (The following discussion assumes that the three variables H_A, H_B, and H_C are each assigned to one of the axes in a three-dimensional rectilinear coordinate system.)

1. Consider points along the line defined by $H_C = 1, H_B = 1$. (NOTE: $H_C = 1$ defines a plane parallel to the H_A-H_B plane, and $H_B = 1$ defines a plane that intersects the $H_C = 1$ plane in a line which is parallel to the H_A axis.) Use a single-

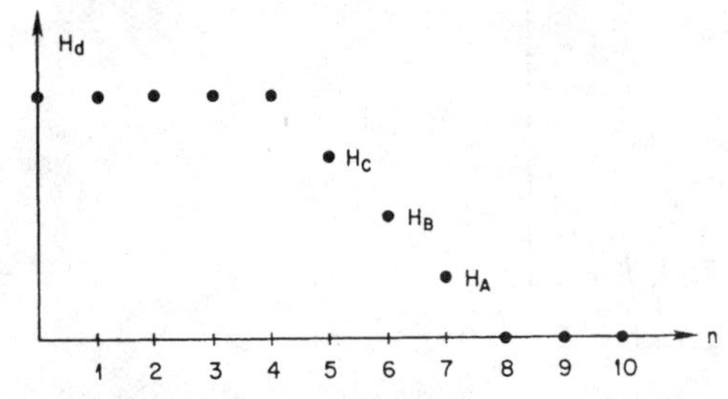

Figure 15.13 Desired response for a 21-tap type 1 filter with three samples in the transition band.

variable search strategy (such as the golden section search) to locate the point along this line for which the peak stopband ripple is minimized. Denote the value of H_A at this point as H_{A1}.

2. Consider points along the line defined by $H_C = 1$, $H_B = 1 - \epsilon$. Use a single-variable search strategy to locate the point along this line for which the peak stopband ripple is minimized. Denote the value of H_A at this point as H_{A2}.

3. The points $(H_{A1}, 1)$ and $(H_{A2}, 1 - \epsilon)$ define a line in the H_A-H_B plane as shown in Fig. 15.10 for the two-sample case. [Actually the points and the line are in the plane defined by $H_C = 1$, and their *projections* onto the H_A-H_B plane are shown by Fig. 15.10. However, since the planes are parallel, everything looks the same regardless of whether we plot the points in the $H_C = 1$ plane or their projections in the H_A-H_B (that is, $H_C = 0$) plane.] In the vicinity of $(H_{A1}, 1)$, this line is the best path along which to search and is therefore called the *line of steepest descent.* Search along the line to find the point at which the peak stopband ripple is minimized. Denote the values of H_A and H_B at this point as H_{A3} and H_{B3}, respectively. As noted previously, the true path of steepest descent is in fact curved, and the straight line just searched is merely an extrapolation based on the two points $(H_{A1}, 1)$ and $(H_{A2}, 1 - \epsilon)$. Thus, the point (H_{A3}, H_{B3}) is not a true minimum. However, this point can be taken as a starting point for a second round of Steps 1, 2, and 3 which will yield a refined estimate of the minimum's location. This refined estimate can in turn be used as a starting point for a third round of Steps 1, 2, and 3. This cycle of Steps 1, 2, and 3 is repeated until the peak ripple at (H_{A3}, H_{B3}) changes by less than some predetermined amount (say, 0.1 dB).

Listing 15.1 Frequency-Sampling Filter Design Program

```
//
//  File = fs_dsgn.cpp
//

#include <math.h>
#include <stdlib.h>
#include "misdefs.h"
#include "fs_dsgn.h"

FreqSampFilterDesign::FreqSampFilterDesign( )
{
}

FreqSampFilterDesign::FreqSampFilterDesign( int band_config,
                                            int fir_type,
                                            int num_taps,
                                            double *imp_resp_coeff)
```

```
{
 Band_Config = band_config;
 Fir_Type = fir_type;
 Num_Taps = num_taps;
 Imp_Resp_Coeff = new double[num_taps];
 Original_Coeff = new double[num_taps];

 for(int n=0; n<num_taps; n++)
   {
    Imp_Resp_Coeff[n] = imp_resp_coeff[n];
    Original_Coeff[n] = imp_resp_coeff[n];
   }
 return;
}

FreqSampFilterDesign::FreqSampFilterDesign( FreqSampFilterSpec &filter_spec)
{
 Filter_Spec = new FreqSampFilterSpec( filter_spec);
 Num_Taps = Filter_Spec->Num_Taps;
 Fir_Type = Filter_Spec->Fir_Type;
 Imp_Resp_Coeff = new double[Num_Taps];
 Original_Coeff = new double[Num_Taps];
 return;
}

void FreqSampFilterDesign::ComputeCoefficients( FreqSampFilterSpec *filter_spec)
{

 int n,k, num_taps, status;
 double x, mid_pt, work;

 num_taps = filter_spec->GetNumTaps();
 status = 0;
 mid_pt = (num_taps-1.0)/2.0;
 switch (filter_spec->GetFirType())
   {
   //---------------------------------------
   case 1:     // even symmetry, odd length
     if(num_taps%2)
       {
       for(n=0; n<num_taps; n++)
         {
         work = filter_spec->GetMagRespSamp(0);
         x = TWO_PI * (n-mid_pt)/num_taps;

         for(k=1; k<=(num_taps-1)/2; k++)
           {
```

```
        work += (2.0*cos(x*k)*(filter_spec->GetMagRespSamp(k)));
        }
      Imp_Resp_Coeff[n] = work/num_taps;
      }
    }
  else
    {
    cout << "FATAL ERROR -- type 1 FIR cannot have even length"
          << endl;
    exit(-1);
    }
  break;
//---------------------------------------
case 2:     // even symmetry, even length
  if(num_taps%2)
    {
    cout << "FATAL ERROR -- type 2 FIR cannot have odd length"
         << endl;
    exit(-1);
    }
  else
    {
    for(n=0; n<num_taps; n++)
      {
      work = filter_spec->GetMagRespSamp(0);
      x = TWO_PI * (n-mid_pt)/num_taps;

      for(k=1; k<=(num_taps/2-1); k++)
        {
        work += (2.0*cos(x*k)*(filter_spec->GetMagRespSamp(k)));
        }
      Imp_Resp_Coeff[n] = work/num_taps;
      }
    }
  break;
//---------------------------------------
case 3:     // odd symmetry, odd length
  if(num_taps%2)
    {
    for(n=0; n<num_taps; n++)
      {
      work = 0;
      x = TWO_PI * (mid_pt-n)/num_taps;
      for(k=1; k<=(num_taps-1)/2; k++)
        {
        work += (2.0*sin(x*k)*(filter_spec->GetMagRespSamp(k)));
        }
      Imp_Resp_Coeff[n] = work/num_taps;
```

```
        }
      }
    else
      {
      cout << "FATAL ERROR -- type 3 FIR cannot have even length"
           << endl;
      exit(-1);
      }
    break;
  //-----------------------------------------
  case 4:     // odd symmetry, even length
    if(num_taps%2)
      {
      cout << "FATAL ERROR -- type 4 FIR cannot have odd length"
           << endl;
      exit(-1);
      }
    else
      {
      for(n=0; n<num_taps; n++)
        {
        work = sin(PI*(mid_pt-n))*
               (filter_spec->GetMagRespSamp(num_taps/2));
        x = TWO_PI * (n-mid_pt)/num_taps;

        for(k=1; k<=(num_taps/2-1); k++)
          {
          work += (2.0*sin(x*k)*(filter_spec->GetMagRespSamp(k)));
          }
        Imp_Resp_Coeff[n] = work/num_taps;
        }
      }
    break;
  }
 for(n=0; n<num_taps; n++)
  {
  Original_Coeff[n] = Imp_Resp_Coeff[n];
  }
 return;
}
```

Listing 15.2 Find Peak in Stopband Response

```
#include "fs_spec.h"
#include <iostream.h>
```

```
double FindStopbandPeak(  FreqSampFilterSpec *filter,
                          int numPts,
                          double H[])
{
double peak;
int n, nBeg, nEnd, indexOfPeak;

cout << "doing case " << filter->GetBandConfig() << endl;
switch (filter->GetBandConfig())
  {
   case 1:       /* lowpass */
     nBeg = 2*numPts*(filter->GetN2())/(filter->GetNumTaps());
     nEnd = numPts-1;
    break;
  case 2:       /* highpass */
  case 3:       /* bandpass */
    nBeg = 0;
    nEnd = 2*numPts*filter->GetN1()/filter->GetNumTaps();
    break;
  case 4:       /* bandstop */
    nBeg = 2*numPts*filter->GetN2()/filter->GetNumTaps();
    nEnd = 2*numPts*filter->GetN3()/filter->GetNumTaps();
    break;
  }
cout << "nBeg = " << nBeg << endl;
cout << "nEnd = " << nEnd << endl;

peak = -9999.0;
for(n=nBeg; n<nEnd; n++) {
  if(H[n]>peak) {
    peak=H[n];
    indexOfPeak = n;
    }
  }
if(filter->GetBandConfig() == 4) {   /* bandpass has second stopband */
  nBeg = 2*numPts*filter->GetN4()/filter->GetNumTaps();
  nEnd = numPts;
  for(n=nBeg; n<nEnd; n++) {
    if(H[n]>peak) {
      peak=H[n];
      indexOfPeak = n;
      }
    }
  }
return(peak);
}
```

Listing 15.3 Golden Search Method for One Transition Sample

```
//
//  File = goldsrch.cpp
//

#include "misdefs.h"
#include "typedefs.h"
#include "goldsrch.h"
#include "fs_util.h"
#include "fs_dsgn.h"
#include "cgd_resp.h"
#include "sb_peak.h"
#include "fs_spec.h"
#include <fstream.h>
#include <math.h>
#include <stdlib.h>

extern ofstream DebugFile;
extern ofstream LogFile;
extern logical PauseEnabled;

double GoldenSearch( double tol,
                     FreqSampFilterSpec *filter_spec,
                     FreqSampFilterDesign *filter_design,
                     FreqSampFilterResponse *filter_resp,
                     long quant_factor,
                     double *fmin)
{
 double x0, x1, x2, x3, xmin, f0, f1, f2, f3, oldXmin;
 double leftOrd, rightOrd, midOrd, x, xb;
 double trans_val;
 double delta;
 int n;
 logical db_scale, rounding_enab;

 cout << "in goldenSearch\n" << endl;
 db_scale = TRUE;
 rounding_enab = FALSE;

 //-----------------------------------------
 filter_spec->SetTrans(0.0);
 filter_design->ComputeCoefficients(filter_spec);
 filter_design->QuantizeCoefficients(quant_factor,rounding_enab);
 filter_resp->ComputeMagResp(filter_design, db_scale);
 filter_resp->NormalizeResponse(db_scale);
 leftOrd = filter_resp->GetStopbandPeak();
```

```
cout << "leftOrd = " << leftOrd << endl;

filter_spec->SetTrans(1.0);
filter_design->ComputeCoefficients(filter_spec);
filter_design->QuantizeCoefficients(quant_factor, rounding_enab);
filter_resp->ComputeMagResp(filter_design, db_scale);
filter_resp->NormalizeResponse(db_scale);
rightOrd = filter_resp->GetStopbandPeak();
cout << "rightOrd = " << rightOrd << endl;
pause(PauseEnabled);

if(leftOrd < rightOrd) {
  trans_val=1.0;
  for(;;) {
    cout << "checkpoint 3" << endl;
    trans_val = GOLD3 * trans_val;
    filter_spec->SetTrans(trans_val);
    filter_design->ComputeCoefficients(filter_spec);
    filter_design->QuantizeCoefficients(quant_factor, rounding_enab);
    filter_resp->ComputeMagResp(filter_design, db_scale);
    filter_resp->NormalizeResponse(db_scale);
    midOrd = filter_resp->GetStopbandPeak();
    cout << "midOrd = " << midOrd << endl;
    if(midOrd < leftOrd) break;
    }
  }
else {
  x = 1.0;
  for(;;) {
    x = GOLD3 * x;
    trans_val = 1.0 - x;
    cout << "checkpoint 4" << endl;
    filter_spec->SetTrans(trans_val);
    filter_design->ComputeCoefficients(filter_spec);
    filter_design->QuantizeCoefficients(quant_factor, rounding_enab);
    filter_resp->ComputeMagResp(filter_design, db_scale);
    filter_resp->NormalizeResponse(db_scale);
    midOrd = filter_resp->GetStopbandPeak();
    cout << "midOrd = " << midOrd << endl;
    if(midOrd < rightOrd) break;
    }
  }

xb = trans_val;
//----------------------------------------
x0 = 0.0;
x3 = 1.0;
x1 = xb;
```

```
x2 = xb + GOLD3 * (1.0 - xb);
cout << "x0= " << x0 << " x1= " << x1
     << " x2= " << x2 << " x3= " << x3 << endl;

filter_spec->SetTrans(x1);
filter_design->ComputeCoefficients(filter_spec);
filter_design->QuantizeCoefficients(quant_factor, rounding_enab);
filter_resp->ComputeMagResp(filter_design, db_scale);
filter_resp->NormalizeResponse(db_scale);
f1 = filter_resp->GetStopbandPeak();

filter_spec->SetTrans(x2);
filter_design->ComputeCoefficients(filter_spec);
filter_design->QuantizeCoefficients(quant_factor, rounding_enab);
filter_resp->ComputeMagResp(filter_design, db_scale);
filter_resp->NormalizeResponse(db_scale);
f2 = filter_resp->GetStopbandPeak();

oldXmin = 0.0;

for(n=1; n<=100; n++) {
  if(f1<=f2) {
    x3 = x2;
    x2 = x1;
    x1 = GOLD6 * x2 + GOLD3 * x0;
    f3 = f2;
    f2 = f1;
    filter_spec->SetTrans(x1);
    filter_design->ComputeCoefficients(filter_spec);
    filter_design->QuantizeCoefficients(quant_factor, rounding_enab);
    filter_resp->ComputeMagResp(filter_design, db_scale);
    filter_resp->NormalizeResponse(db_scale);
    f1 = filter_resp->GetStopbandPeak();
    cout << "x0= " << x0 << " x1= " << x1
         << " x2= " << x2 << " x3= " << x3 << endl;
    }
  else {
    x0 = x1;
    x1 = x2;
    x2 = GOLD6 * x1 + GOLD3 * x3;
    f0 = f1;
    f1 = f2;
    filter_spec->SetTrans(x2);
    filter_design->ComputeCoefficients(filter_spec);
    filter_design->QuantizeCoefficients(quant_factor, rounding_enab);
    filter_resp->ComputeMagResp(filter_design, db_scale);
    filter_resp->NormalizeResponse(db_scale);
    f2 = filter_resp->GetStopbandPeak();
```

```
    cout << "x0= " << x0 << " x1= " << x1
         << " x2= " << x2 << " x3= " << x3 << endl;
    }

  delta = fabs(x3 - x0);
  oldXmin = xmin;
  cout << "at iter " << n << " delta = " << delta << endl;
  cout << "tol = " << tol << endl;
  if(delta <= tol) break;
  }
if(f1<f2)
  {xmin = x1;
  *fmin=f1;}
else
  {xmin = x2;
  *fmin=f2;}
cout << "minimum of " << *fmin << " at x = " << xmin << endl;
LogFile << "minimum of " << *fmin << " at x = " << xmin << endl;
return(xmin);
}
```

Listing 15.4 Set Transition Sample Value

```
//-------------------------------------------------

void FreqSampFilterSpec::SetTrans( double trans_val)
{
 switch (Band_Config)
   {
    case 1:    // lowpass
      Des_Mag_Resp[N2-1] = trans_val;
      break;

    case 2:    // bandpass
      Des_Mag_Resp[N1+1] = trans_val;
      Des_Mag_Resp[N4-1] = trans_val;

    case 3:    // highpass
      Des_Mag_Resp[N1+1] = trans_val;

    case 4:    // bandstop
      Des_Mag_Resp[N2-1] = trans_val;
      Des_Mag_Resp[N3+1] = trans_val;
      break;
   }

 return;
}
```

Listing 15.5 Golden Search Method for Multiple Transition Samples

```
//
// File = goldsrch.cpp
//

#include "misdefs.h"
#include "typedefs.h"
#include "goldsrch.h"
#include "fs_util.h"
#include "fs_dsgn.h"
#include "cgd_resp.h"
#include "sb_peak.h"
#include "fs_spec.h"
#include <fstream.h>
#include <math.h>
#include <stdlib.h>

extern ofstream DebugFile;
extern ofstream LogFile;
extern logical PauseEnabled;

double GoldenSearch2( double tol,
                      FreqSampFilterSpec *filter_spec,
                      FreqSampFilterDesign *filter_design,
                      FreqSampFilterResponse *filter_resp,
                      double rho_min,
                      double rho_max,
                      double *origins,
                      double *slopes,
                      double *fmin)
{
 double x0, x1, x2, x3, xmin, f0, f1, f2, f3, oldXmin;
 double leftOrd, rightOrd, midOrd, x, xb;
 double trans_val;
 double delta;
 int n;
 logical db_scale;

 cout << "in goldenSearch\n" << endl;
 db_scale = TRUE;

 /*------------------------------------------*/
 filter_spec->SetTrans(origins, slopes, 0.0);
 filter_design->ComputeCoefficients(filter_spec);
 filter_resp->ComputeMagResp(filter_design, db_scale);
 filter_resp->NormalizeResponse(db_scale);
```

```
 leftOrd = filter_resp->GetStopbandPeak();
 cout << "leftOrd = " << leftOrd << endl;

 filter_spec->SetTrans(origins, slopes, 1.0);
 filter_design->ComputeCoefficients(filter_spec);
 filter_resp->ComputeMagResp(filter_design, db_scale);
 filter_resp->NormalizeResponse(db_scale);
 rightOrd = filter_resp->GetStopbandPeak();
 cout << "rightOrd = " << rightOrd << endl;
 pause(PauseEnabled);

if(leftOrd < rightOrd) {
  trans_val=1.0;
  for(;;) {
    trans_val = GOLD3 * trans_val;
    filter_spec->SetTrans(origins, slopes, trans_val);
    filter_design->ComputeCoefficients(filter_spec);
    filter_resp->ComputeMagResp(filter_design, db_scale);
    filter_resp->NormalizeResponse(db_scale);
    midOrd = filter_resp->GetStopbandPeak();
    cout << "midOrd = " << midOrd << endl;
    if(midOrd < leftOrd) break;
    }
  }
else {
  x = rho_max;
  for(;;) {
    x = GOLD3 * x;
    trans_val = rho_max - x;
    filter_spec->SetTrans(origins, slopes, trans_val);
    filter_design->ComputeCoefficients(filter_spec);
    filter_resp->ComputeMagResp(filter_design, db_scale);
    filter_resp->NormalizeResponse(db_scale);
    midOrd = filter_resp->GetStopbandPeak();
    cout << "midOrd = " << midOrd << endl;
    if(midOrd < rightOrd) break;
    }
  }

xb = trans_val;
/*-----------------------------------------*/
x0 = rho_min;
x3 = rho_max;
x1 = xb;
x2 = xb + GOLD3 * (rho_max - xb);
cout << "x0= " << x0 << " x1= " << x1
     << " x2= " << x2 << " x3= " << x3 << endl;
```

```
filter_spec->SetTrans(origins, slopes, x1);
filter_design->ComputeCoefficients(filter_spec);
filter_resp->ComputeMagResp(filter_design, db_scale);
filter_resp->NormalizeResponse(db_scale);
f1 = filter_resp->GetStopbandPeak();

filter_spec->SetTrans(origins, slopes, x2);
filter_design->ComputeCoefficients(filter_spec);
filter_resp->ComputeMagResp(filter_design, db_scale);
filter_resp->NormalizeResponse(db_scale);
f2 = filter_resp->GetStopbandPeak();

oldXmin = 0.0;

for(n=1; n<=100; n++) {
  if(f1<=f2) {
    x3 = x2;
    x2 = x1;
    x1 = GOLD6 * x2 + GOLD3 * x0;
    f3 = f2;
    f2 = f1;
    filter_spec->SetTrans(origins, slopes, x1);
    filter_design->ComputeCoefficients(filter_spec);
    filter_resp->ComputeMagResp(filter_design, db_scale);
    filter_resp->NormalizeResponse(db_scale);
    f1 = filter_resp->GetStopbandPeak();
    cout << "x0= " << x0 << " x1= " << x1
         << " x2= " << x2 << " x3= " << x3 << endl;
    }
  else {
    x0 = x1;
    x1 = x2;
    x2 = GOLD6 * x1 + GOLD3 * x3;
    f0 = f1;
    f1 = f2;
    filter_spec->SetTrans(origins, slopes, x2);
    filter_design->ComputeCoefficients(filter_spec);
    filter_resp->ComputeMagResp(filter_design, db_scale);
    filter_resp->NormalizeResponse(db_scale);
    f2 = filter_resp->GetStopbandPeak();
    cout << "x0= " << x0 << " x1= " << x1
         << " x2= " << x2 << " x3= " << x3 << endl;
    }

  delta = fabs(x3 - x0);
  oldXmin = xmin;
  cout << "at iter " << n << " delta = " << delta << endl;
  cout << "tol = " << tol << endl;
```

```
  if(delta <= tol) break;
  }
if(f1<f2)
  {xmin = x1;
  *fmin=f1;}
else
  {xmin = x2;
  *fmin=f2;}
cout << "minimum of " << *fmin << " at x = " << xmin << endl;
LogFile << "minimum of " << *fmin << " at x = " << xmin << endl;
return(xmin);
}
```

Listing 15.6 Method Added to Class `FreqSampFilterSpec` for Setting Transition Values

```
//==================================================================

void FreqSampFilterSpec::SetTrans( double *origins,
                                   double *slopes,
                                   double rho)
{
 int num_trans_samps, n;

 num_trans_samps = N2 - N1 - 1;

 switch (Band_Config)
   {
    case 1:    // lowpass
      for( n=1; n<=num_trans_samps; n++)
        {
         Des_Mag_Resp[N2-n] = origins[n] + rho * slopes[n];
        }
      break;

    case 2:    // highpass
      for( n=1; n<=num_trans_samps; n++)
        {
         Des_Mag_Resp[N1+n] = origins[n] + rho * slopes[n];
        }
      break;

    case 3:    // bandpass
      for( n=1; n<=num_trans_samps; n++)
        {
         Des_Mag_Resp[N1+n] = origins[n] + rho * slopes[n];
```

```
          Des_Mag_Resp[N4-n] = Des_Mag_Resp[N1+n];
        }
      break;

    case 4:     // bandstop
      for( n=1; n<=num_trans_samps; n++)
        {
          Des_Mag_Resp[N2-n] = origins[n] + rho * slopes[n];
          Des_Mag_Resp[N3+n] = Des_Mag_Resp[N2-n];
        }
      break;
   }
 return;
}
```

Listing 15.7 Optimization Procedure

```
//
//  File = optmiz2.cpp
//

#include <math.h>
#include "optmiz2.h"
#include "goldsrh2.h"

void optimize2( FreqSampFilterSpec *filter_spec,
                FreqSampFilterDesign *filter_design,
                FreqSampFilterResponse *filter_resp,
                double y_base_init,
                double tol,
                double tweak_factor,
                double rectComps[])
{
double x1, x2, x3, y3, min_func_val;
double slopes[5], origins[5];
double old_min, x_max;
double y_base;
double rho_min, rho_max;

y_base = y_base_init;
old_min = 9999.0;

for(;;)
  {
  //-----------------------------------------------
  //  do starting point for new steepest descent line
```

```
slopes[1] = 1.0;
slopes[2] = 0.0;
origins[1] = 0.0;
origins[2] = y_base;
rho_min = 0.0;
rho_max = 1.0;

x1 = GoldenSearch2( tol,
                    filter_spec,
                    filter_design,
                    filter_resp,
                    rho_min,
                    rho_max,
                    origins,
                    slopes,
                    &min_func_val);

/*-------------------------------------*/
/*  do perturbed point to get          */
/*    slope for steepest descent line  */

origins[2]=y_base * tweak_factor;

x2 = GoldenSearch2( tol,
                    filter_spec,
                    filter_design,
                    filter_resp,
                    rho_min,
                    rho_max,
                    origins,
                    slopes,
                    &min_func_val);

/*-------------------------------------*/
/* define line of steepest descent     */
/*  and find optimal point along line  */

slopes[2] = y_base*(1-tweak_factor)/(x1-x2);
origins[2] = y_base - slopes[2] * x1;
x_max = (1.0 - origins[2])/slopes[2];

x3 = GoldenSearch2( tol,
                    filter_spec,
                    filter_design,
                    filter_resp,
                    rho_min,
                    x_max,
```

```
                        origins,
                        slopes,
                        &min_func_val);
  y3=origins[2] + x3 * slopes[2];

  /*-------------------------------------------------------------*/
  /*  if ripple at best point on current line is within specified  */
  /*    tolerance of ripple at best point on previous line,        */
  /*    then stop; otherwise stay in loop and define a new line    */
  /*    starting at the best point on line just completed.         */

  if(fabs(old_min-min_func_val) < tol) break;
  old_min = min_func_val;
  y_base = y3;
  }
rectComps[0] = x3;
rectComps[1] = origins[2] + x3 * slopes[2];
return;
}
```

Chapter

16

FIR Filter Design: Remez Exchange Method

In general, an FIR approximation to an ideal low-pass filter will have an amplitude response of the form shown in Fig. 16.1. This response differs from the ideal low-pass response in three quantifiable ways:

1. The pass band has ripples that deviate from unity by $\pm\delta_p$.
2. The stop band has ripples that deviate from zero by $\pm\delta_s$. (Note that Fig. 16.1 shows an *amplitude* response rather than the usual magnitude response, and therefore negative ordinates are possible.)
3. There is a transition band of finite nonzero width ΔF between the pass band and stop band.

The usual design goals are to, in some sense, minimize δ_p, δ_s, and ΔF. As it is generally not possible to simultaneously minimize for three different variables, some compromise is unavoidable. *Chebyshev approximation* is one approach to this design problem.

16.1 Chebyshev Approximation

In the Chebyshev approximation approach, the amplitude response of a type 1 (that is, odd-length, even-symmetric) linear phase low-pass N-tap FIR filter is formulated as a sum of r cosines:

$$A(f) = \sum_{k=0}^{r-1} c_k \cos(2\pi k f) \tag{16.1}$$

where $r = (N + 1)/2$, and the coefficients c_k are chosen so as to yield an $A(f)$ which is optimal in a sense that will be defined shortly.

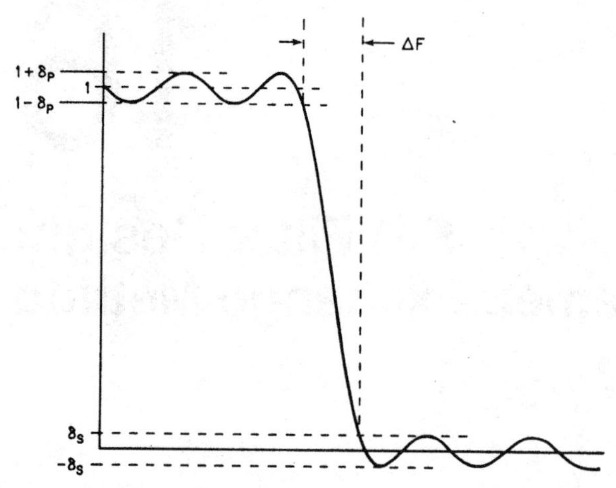

Figure 16.1 Typical amplitude response of an FIR approximation to an ideal low-pass filter.

For a low-pass filter the pass band B_p and stop band B_s are defined as

$$B_p = \{F : 0 \leq F \leq F_p\} \tag{16.2}$$

$$B_s = \{F : F_s \leq F \leq 0.5\} \tag{16.3}$$

where F_p and F_s are, respectively, the edge frequencies for the pass band and stop band. [Equation (16.2) is read as "B_p is the set of all F such that F is greater than or equal to zero and less than or equal to F_p.] We can then define a set $\mathcal{F}$ as the union of B_p and B_s:

$$\mathcal{F} = B_p \cup B_s \tag{16.4}$$

In other words, $\mathcal{F}$ is the set of all frequencies between 0 and 0.5 not including the transition frequencies $F : F_p < F < F_s$. In mathematical terms, $\mathcal{F}$ is described as a *compact subset* of [0, 0.5]. The desired response $D(f)$ is the ideal low-pass response given by

$$D(f) = \begin{cases} 1 & F \in B_p \\ 0 & F \in B_s \end{cases} \tag{16.5}$$

Thus, we could define the optimal approach as the one that minimizes the maximum error given by

$$\max_{F \in \mathcal{F}} |D(f) - A(f)| \tag{16.6}$$

However, the maximum error given by Eq. (16.6) treats passband error and stopband error as equally important. A more general approach is to include a weighting function:

$$W(f) = \begin{cases} \frac{1}{K} & F \in B_p \\ 1 & F \in B_s \end{cases} \tag{16.7}$$

which allows stopband errors to be given more importance than passband errors, or vice versa. Thus, we define the maximum approximation error as

$$\|E(f)\| = \max_{F \in \mathcal{F}} W(f) \cdot |D(f) - A(f)| \tag{16.8}$$

The crux of the Chebyshev approximation design approach is to identify the coefficients c_k for Eq. (16.1) that minimize $\|E(f)\|$.

Several examples of FIR design via Chebyshev approximation appear in the early literature (Martin 1962; Tufts, Rorabacher, and Moses 1970; Tufts and Francis 1970; Helms 1971; Herrman 1970; Hofstetter, Oppenheim, and Siegel 1971). However, the Chebyshev approximation method did not begin to enjoy widespread use until it was shown that the Remez exchange algorithm could be used to design linear phase FIR filters with the Chebyshev error criterion (Parks and McClellan 1972). Use of the Remez exchange algorithm depends upon an important mathematical result known as the *alternation theorem.*

Alternation theorem

The response $A(f)$ given by Eq. (16.1) will be the unique, best-weighted Chebyshev approximation to the desired response $D(f)$ if and only if the error function $E(f) = W(f)[D(f) - A(f)]$ exhibits at least $r + 1$ extrema at frequencies in $\mathcal{F}$. (NOTE: *Extrema* is a generic term that includes both maxima and minima.) The frequencies at which extrema occur are called *extremal frequencies.* Let f_n denote the nth extremal frequency such that

$$f_1 < f_2 < \cdots < f_{n-1} < f_n < f_{n+1} < \cdots < f_r < f_{r+1}$$

Then it can be proven (Cheyney 1966) that

$$E(f_n) = -E(f_{n+1}) \qquad n = 1, 2, \ldots, r \tag{16.9}$$

and

$$|E(f_n)| = \max_{f \in \mathcal{F}} E(f) \tag{16.10}$$

Together, Eqs. (16.9) and (16.10) mean simply that the error is equal at all the extremal frequencies. Equation (16.9) further indicates that maxima and minima alternate (hence, *alternation* theorem).

16.2 Strategy of the Remez Exchange Method

The alternation theorem given in the previous section tells us how to recognize an optimal set of c_k for Eq. (16.1) when we have one, but it does not tell us how to go about obtaining such c_k. The Remez exchange algorithm provides an approach for finding the FIR filter corresponding to the optimal c_k as follows:

1. Make an initial guess of the $r + 1$ extremal frequencies.
2. Compute the error function corresponding to the candidate set of extremal frequencies (see Sec. 16.3).
3. Search to find the extrema (and therefore the extremal frequencies) of the error function (see Sec. 16.4).
4. Adopt the extremal frequencies found in Step 3 as the new set of candidate extremal frequencies and return to Step 2.
5. Repeat Steps 2, 3, and 4 until the extremal frequencies have converged (see Sec. 16.4).
6. Use the final set of extremal frequencies to compute $P(f)$ and the corresponding impulse response coefficients for the filter (see Sec. 16.5).

The error function mentioned in Step 2 is computed as

$$E(f) = W(f)\,[D(f) - A(f)] \tag{16.11}$$

where $D(f)$ is given by Eq. (16.5) and $W(f)$ is given by Eq. (16.7). Although Eq. (16.1) gives the form of $A(f)$, some other means must be used to evaluate $A(f)$ since the coefficients c_k are unknown. We can obtain $A(f)$ from the extremal frequencies F_k using

$$A(f) = \begin{cases} \gamma_k & \text{for } f = F_0, F_1, \ldots, F_{r-1} \\ \dfrac{\displaystyle\sum_{k=0}^{r-1} \frac{\beta_k}{x - x_k}\gamma_k}{\displaystyle\sum_{k=0}^{r-1} \frac{\beta_k}{x - x_k}} & \text{otherwise} \end{cases} \tag{16.12}$$

The parameters needed for evaluation of (16.12) are given by

$$\beta_k = \prod_{\substack{i=0 \\ i \neq k}}^{r-1} \frac{1}{x_k - x_i}$$

$$\gamma_k = D(F_k) - (-1)^k \frac{\delta}{W(F_k)}$$

$$\delta = \frac{\displaystyle\sum_{k=0}^{r} \alpha_k D(F_k)}{\displaystyle\sum_{k=0}^{r} \frac{(-1)^k \alpha_k}{W(F_k)}}$$

$$\alpha_k = \prod_{\substack{i=0 \\ i \neq k}}^{r} \frac{1}{x_k - x_i}$$

$$x = \cos(2\pi f)$$

$$x_k = \cos(2\pi F_k)$$

If estimates of the extremal frequencies rather than their "true" values are used in the evaluation of $A(f)$, the resulting error function $E(f)$ will exhibit extrema at frequencies that are different from the original estimates. If the frequencies of these newly observed extrema are then used in a subsequent evaluation of $A(f)$, the new $E(f)$ will exhibit extrema at frequencies that are closer to the true extremal frequencies. If this process is performed repeatedly, the observed extremal frequencies will eventually converge to the true extremal frequencies, which can then be used to obtain $A(f)$ and the filter's impulse response.

Although $A(f)$ is defined over continuous frequency, computer evaluation of $A(f)$ must necessarily be limited to a finite number of discrete frequencies—therefore, $A(f)$ is evaluated over a closely spaced set or *dense grid* of frequencies. The convergence of the observed extremal frequencies will be limited by the granularity of this dense grid, but it has been empirically determined that an average grid density of 16 to 20 frequencies per extremum will be adequate for most designs. Since the maximization of $E(f)$ is only conducted over $f \in \mathcal{F}$, it is not necessary to evaluate $A(f)$ at all within the transition band (except for possibly at the very end, just to see what sort of transition-band response the final filter design actually provides). The frequency interval between consecutive points should be approximately the same in both the pass band and stop band. Furthermore, the grid should be constructed in such a way that frequency points are provided at $f = 0$, $f = F_p$, $f = F_s$, and $f = 0.5$. An integrated procedure for defining the dense grid and making the initial (equispaced) guesses for the candidate extremal frequencies is provided in Algorithm 16.1.

Algorithm 16.1 Constructing the dense-frequency grid

Step 1. Compute the number of candidate extremal frequencies to be placed in the pass band as

$$m_p = \left\lfloor \frac{rF_p}{0.5 + F_p - F_s} - 0.5 \right\rfloor$$

Step 2. Determine the candidate extremal frequencies within the pass band as

$$F_k = \frac{kF_p}{m_p} \qquad k = 1, 2, \ldots, m_p$$

Step 3. Compute the number of candidate extremal frequencies to be placed in the stop band as

$$m_s = r + 1 - m_p$$

Step 4. Determine the candidate extremal frequencies within the stop band as

$$F_k = F_s + \frac{k(0.5 - F_s)}{m_s - 1} \qquad k = 0, 1, \ldots, m_s - 1$$

Step 5. Determine the passband grid frequencies as

$$f_j = jI_p \qquad j = 0, 1, 2, \ldots, m_pL$$

where $I_p = \dfrac{F_p}{m_pL}$

L = average grid density (in points per extremum)

Step 6. Determine the stopband grid frequencies as

$$f_j = F_s + nI_s \qquad n = 0, 1, \ldots, (m_s - 1)L$$

$$j = m_pL + n + 1$$

where

$$I_s = \frac{(0.5 - F_s)}{(m_s - 1)L}$$

For computer calculations, the dense grid of frequencies can be implemented by the function `SetupGrid( )` shown in Listing 16.1. This function is a member of class `RemezAlgorithm`. A grid of actual frequency values is never really created—instead, most of the frequency bookkeeping is done using integers to represent the frequencies' locations within the grid. A call to `SetupGrid( )` is used to convert an integer location index into the corresponding floating-point frequency value when needed for a calculation. Several parameters used by `SetupGrid( )` are computed once and subsequently held constant.

Generating the desired response and weighting functions

Based upon the requirements of the intended application, the desired response function $D(f)$ is defined in accordance with Eq. (16.5) for each frequency $f = f_j$ in the dense grid. For frequency-selective filters, $D(f)$ will usually take on only one of two values—unity in the pass band and zero in the stop band. The ideal low-pass response is generated by the `DesiredResponse( )` function provided in Listing 16.2.

The passband ripple limit δ_1 and stopband ripple limit δ_2, as shown in Fig. 16.1, are determined by the designer in a manner consistent with the requirements of the intended application. The weight function $W(f)$ is then computed in accordance with Eq. (16.7) for each frequency in the dense grid with $K = \delta_1/\delta_2$. The function `WeightFunction` shown in Listing 16.3 determines whether the frequency value provided as input lies in the stop band or pass band and then returns the appropriate value for $W(f)$.

16.3 Evaluating the Error

Algorithm 16.2 provides a step-by-step procedure for evaluating the error function defined by Eq. (16.11).

Algorithm 16.2 Evaluating the estimation error for the Remez exchange

Step 1. For $k = 0, 1, \ldots, r-1$, use the candidate extremal frequencies F_k to compute β_k as

$$\beta_k = \prod_{\substack{i=0 \\ i \neq k}}^{r-1} \frac{1}{\cos 2\pi F_k - \cos 2\pi F_i}$$

Step 2. For $k = 0, 1, \ldots, r-1$, use the β_k from Step 1 to compute α_k as

$$\alpha_k = \frac{\beta_k}{\cos 2\pi F_k - \cos 2\pi F_r}$$

Step 3. Use the α_k from Step 2 and the extremal frequencies F_k to compute δ as

$$\delta = \frac{\sum_{k=0}^{r} \alpha_k D(F_k)}{\sum_{k=0}^{r} \frac{(-1)^k \alpha_k}{W(F_k)}}$$

where $D(f)$ and $W(f)$ are the desired response and weight functions discussed in Sec. 16.2.

Step 4. For $k = 0, 1, \ldots, r-1$, use δ from Step 3 to compute γ_k as

$$\gamma_k = D(F_k) - (-1)^k \frac{\delta}{W(F_k)}$$

Step 5. Use β_k from Step 1, the γ_k from Step 4, and the candidate extremal frequencies F_k to compute $P(f)$ for each frequency $f = f_j$ in the dense grid as

$$A(f_j) = \begin{cases} \gamma_k & \text{for } f = F_0, F_1, \ldots, F_{r-1} \\ \dfrac{\displaystyle\sum_{k=0}^{r-1} \frac{\beta_k}{x_j - x_k} \gamma_k}{\displaystyle\sum_{k=0}^{r-1} \frac{\beta_k}{x_j - x_k}} & \text{otherwise} \end{cases}$$

where $x_j = \cos(2\pi f_j)$
$x_k = \cos(2\pi F_k)$

Step 6. For each frequency f_j in the dense grid, use $A(f_j)$ from Step 5 to compute $E(f_j)$ as

$$E(f_j) = W(f_j)[D(f_j) - A(f_j)]$$

For computer evaluation, the error function is calculated by `RemezError( )`, which makes use of `ComputeRemezAmplitudeResponse( )`. These two functions are provided in Listings 16.4 and 16.5, respectively. The function `ComputeRemezAmplitudeResponse( )` could have been made an integral part of `RemezError( )` and designed to automatically generate $A(\ )$ and $E(\ )$ for all frequencies within the dense grid. However, a function in this form would not be usable for generating the uniformly spaced samples of the final $A(\ )$ that are needed to conveniently obtain the impulse response of the filter.

16.4 Selecting Candidate Extremal Frequencies

Once Eq. (16.11) has been evaluated, the values of $E(f_j)$ must be checked in order to determine what the values of F_k should be for the next iteration of the optimization algorithm. Based upon the particular frequencies being checked, the testing can be divided into the five different variations that are described in the following paragraphs. A C function, `RemezSearch( )`, that performs this testing is provided in Listing 16.6.

Testing $E(f)$ for $f = 0$

If $E(0) > 0$ and $E(0) > E(f_1)$, then a ripple peak (local maximum) exists at $f = 0$. (Note that f_1 denotes the first frequency within the dense grid after $f = 0$, and due to the way we have defined the frequency spacing with the grid, we know that $f_1 = I_p$.) Even if a peak or valley exists at $f = 0$, it may be a *superfluous* extremum not needed for the next iteration. If a ripple peak does exist at $f = 0$, and $|E(0)| \geq |\rho|$, then the maximum is not superfluous and $f = f_0 = 0$ should be used as the first-candidate extremal frequency—in other words, set $F_0 = f_0 = 0$. Similarly, if $E(0) < 0$ and $E(0) < E(f_1)$, a ripple trough (ripple valley, local minimum) exists at $f = 0$. If $|E(0)| \geq |\rho|$, this minimum is not superfluous and we should set $F_0 = f_0 = 0$.

Testing *E*(*f*) within the pass band and the stop band

The following discussion applies to testing of $E(f)$ for all values of f_j for which $f_0 < f_j < f_p$ or for which $f_s < f_j < 0.5$. A ripple peak exists at f_j if

$$E(f_j) > E(f_{j-1}) \quad \text{and} \quad E(f_j) > E(f_{j+1}) \quad \text{and} \quad E(f_j) > 0 \tag{16.13}$$

Equation (16.13) can be rewritten as Eq. (16.14) for frequencies in the pass band and as Eq. (16.15) for frequencies within the stop band:

$$E(f_j) > E(f_j - I_p) \quad \text{and} \quad E(f_j) > E(f_j + I_p) \quad \text{and} \quad E(f_j) > 0 \tag{16.14}$$

$$E(f_j) > E(f_j - I_s) \quad \text{and} \quad E(f_j) > E(f_j + I_s) \quad \text{and} \quad E(f_j) > 0 \tag{16.15}$$

A ripple trough exists at f_j if

$$E(f_j) < E(f_{j-1}) \quad \text{and} \quad E(f_j) < E(f_{j+1}) \quad \text{and} \quad E(f_j) < 0 \tag{16.16}$$

Equation (16.16) can be rewritten as Eq. (16.17) for frequencies in the pass band and as Eq. (16.18) for frequencies within the stop band:

$$E(f_j) < E(f_j - I_p) \quad \text{and} \quad E(f_j) < E(f_j + I_p) \quad \text{and} \quad E(f_j) < 0 \tag{16.17}$$

$$E(f_j) < E(f_j - I_s) \quad \text{and} \quad E(f_j) < E(f_j + I_s) \quad \text{and} \quad E(f_j) < 0 \tag{16.18}$$

If either Eq. (16.13) or Eq. (16.16) is satisfied, $f = f_j$ should be selected as a candidate extremal frequency—that is, set $F_k = f_j$ where k is the index of the next extremal frequency due to be specified.

Testing of *E*(*f*) at the passband and stopband edges

There is some disagreement within the literature regarding the testing of the passband and stopband edge frequencies f_p and f_s. Some authors (such as Antoniou 1982) indicate the following testing strategy for f_p and f_s:

> If $E(f_p) > 0$ and $E(f_p) > E(f_p - I_p)$, then a ripple peak (local maximum) is deemed to exist at $f = f_p$ regardless of how $E(f)$ behaves in the transition band which lies immediately to the right of $f = f_p$. If a ripple peak does exist at $f = f_p$, and if $|E(f_p)| \geq |\rho|$, then the maximum is not superfluous and $f = f_p$ should be selected as a candidate extremal frequency—i.e., set $F_k = f_p$ where k is the index of the next extremal frequency due to be specified. Similarly, if $E(f_p) < 0$ and $E(f_p) < E(f_p - I_p)$, a ripple trough exists at $f = f_p$. If $|E(f_p)| \geq |\rho|$, this minimum is not superfluous and we should set $F_k = f_p$ where k is the index of the next extremal frequency due to be specified. If $E(f_s)$

> 0 and $E(f_s) > E(f_s + I_s)$, then a ripple peak is deemed to exist at $f = f_s$ regardless of how $E(f)$ behaves in the transition band which lies immediately to the left of $f = f_s$. If a ripple peak does exist at $f = f_s$, and if $|E(f_s)| \geq |\rho|$, then the maximum is not superfluous and $f = f_s$ should be selected as a candidate extremal frequency—i.e., set $F_k = f_s$ where k is the index of the next extremal frequency due to be specified. Similarly, if $E(f_s) < 0$ and $E(f_s) < E(f_s + I_s)$, a ripple trough exists at $f = f_s$. If $|E(f_p)| \geq |\rho|$, this minimum is not superfluous and we should set $F_k = fs_p$ where k is the index of the next extremal frequency due to be specified.

Other authors (such as Parks and Burrus 1987) indicate that f_p and f_s are *always* extremal frequencies. In my experience the testing indicated by Antoniou is always satisfied, so f_p and f_s are always selected as extremal frequencies. I have opted to eliminate this testing both to reduce execution time and to avoid the danger of having small numerical inaccuracies cause one of these points to erroneously fail the test and thereby be rejected.

Testing of $E(f)$ for $f = 0.5$

If $E(0.5) > 0$ and $E(0.5) > E(0.5 - I_s)$, then a ripple peak exists at $f = 0.5$. If a ripple peak does exist at $f = 0.5$, and if $|E(0)| \geq |\rho|$, then the maximum is not superfluous and $f = f_0 = 0.5$ should be used as the final candidate extremal frequency. Similarly, if $E(0.5) < 0$ and $E(0.5) < E(0.5 - I_s)$, a ripple trough (ripple valley, local minimum) exists at $f = 0.5$. If $|E(0)| \geq |\rho|$, this minimum is not superfluous.

Rejecting superfluous candidate frequencies

The Remez algorithm requires that only $r + 1$ extremal frequencies be used in each iteration. However, when the search procedures just described are used, it is possible to wind up with more than $r + 1$ candidate frequencies. This situation can be very easily remedied by retaining only the $r + 1$ frequencies F_k for which $|E(F_k)|$ is the largest. The retained frequencies are renumbered from 0 to r before proceeding. An alternative approach is to reject the frequency corresponding to the smaller of $|E(F_0)|$ and $|E(F_r)|$, regardless of how these two values compare to the absolute errors at the other extrema. Since there is only one solution for a given set of filter specifications, both approaches should lead to the same result. However, one approach may lead to a faster solution or be less prone to numeric difficulties. This would be a good area for a small research effort.

Deciding when to stop

There are two schools of thought on deciding when to stop the exchange algorithm. The original criterion (Parks and McClellan 1972) examines the extremal frequencies and stops the algorithm when they do not change from one iteration to the next. This criterion is implemented in the C function `RemezStop( )` provided in Listing 16.7. This approach has worked well for me, but it does have a potential flaw. Suppose that one of the true extremal frequencies for a particular filter lies at $f = F_T$, and due to the way the dense grid has been defined, F_T lies midway between two grid frequencies such that

$$F_T = \frac{f_n + f_{n+1}}{2}$$

It is conceivable that on successive iterations, the observed extremal frequency could alternate between f_j and f_{n+1} and therefore never allow the stopping criteria to be satisfied.

A different criterion, advocated by Antoniou (1982), uses values of the error function rather then the locations of the extremal frequencies. In theory, when the Remez algorithm is working correctly each successive iteration will produce continually improving estimates of the correct extremal frequencies, and the values of $|E(F_k)|$ will become exactly equal for all values of k. However, due to the finite resolution of the frequency grid, as well as finite-precision arithmetic, the estimates may, in fact, never converge to exact equality. One remedy is to stop when the largest $|E(F_k)|$ and the smallest $|E(F_k)|$ differ by some reasonably small amount. The difference as a fraction of the largest $|E(F_k)|$ is given by

$$Q = \frac{\max\ |E(F_k)| - \min\ |E(F_k)|}{\max\ |E(F_k)|}$$

Typically, the iterations are stopped when $Q \leq 0.01$. This second stopping criterion is implemented in the C function `RemezStop2( )` provided in Listing 16.8.

16.5 Obtaining the Impulse Response

Back in Sec. 16.2, the final step in the Remez exchange design strategy consisted of using the final set of extremal frequencies to obtain the filter's impulse response. This can be accomplished by using Eq. (16.10) to obtain $P(f)$ from the set of extremal frequencies and then performing an inverse DFT on $P(f)$ to obtain the corresponding impulse response. An alternative approach involves deriving a dedicated inversion formula similar to the dedicated formulas presented in Sec. 15.3. For the case of the type 1 filter that has been considered thus far, the required inversion formula is

$$h[n] = h[-n] = \frac{1}{N}\left[A(0) + \sum_{k=1}^{r-1} 2A\left(\frac{2\pi k}{N}\right)\cos\left(\frac{2\pi kn}{N}\right)\right]$$

This formula is implemented via the `FreqSampFilterDesign( )` function (from Chap. 15), which is called by the C function `RemezFinish( )` provided in Listing 16.9. Although the filter's final frequency response could be obtained using calls to `ComputeRemezAmplitudeResponse( )`, I have found it more convenient to use `LinearPhaseFirResponse( )` from Chap. 13, since this function produces output in a form that is directly compatible with my plotting software.

16.6 Using the Remez Exchange Method

All of the constituent functions of the Remez method that have been presented in previous sections are called in the proper sequence by the function `RemezAlgorithm`, which is presented in Listing 16.10. This function accepts the inputs listed in Table 16.1 and produces two outputs—`extremal_freqs` and `filter_coeffs`.

Deciding on the filter length

To use the Remez exchange method, the designer must specify N, f_s, f_p, and the ratio δ_1/δ_2. The algorithm will provide the filter having the smallest values of $|\delta_1|$ and $|\delta_2|$ that can be achieved under these constraints. However, in many applications, the values specified are f_p, f_s, δ_1, and δ_2 with the designer left free to set N as required. Faced with such a situation, the designer can use f_p, f_s, and $K = \delta_1/\delta_2$ as dictated by the application and design filters for increasing values of N until the δ_1 and δ_2 specifications are satisfied. An approximation of the required number of taps can be obtained by one of the formulas given in the following. For filters having pass bands of "moderate" width, the approximate number of taps required is given by

$$\tilde{N} = 1 + \frac{-20 \log \sqrt{\delta_1 \delta_1} - 13}{14.6(f_s - f_p)} \tag{16.19}$$

For filters with very narrow pass bands, Eq. (16.19) can be modified to be

$$\tilde{N} = \frac{0.22 - (20 \log \delta_2)/27}{(f_s - f_p)} \tag{16.20}$$

For filters with very wide pass bands, the required number of taps is approximated by

$$\tilde{N} = \frac{0.22 - (20 \log \delta_1)/27}{(f_s - f_p)} \tag{16.21}$$

Example 16.1 Suppose we wish to design a low-pass filter with a maximum passband ripple of $\delta_1 = 0.025$ and a minimum stopband attenuation of 60 dB or $\delta_2 = 0.001$. The normal-

TABLE 16.1 Input Parameters for `RemezAlgorithm()` Function

Mathematical symbol	C++ variable
N	`filter_length`
L	`grid_density`
K	`ripple_ratio`
f_p	`passband_edge_freq`
f_s	`stopband_edge_freq`

ized cutoff frequencies for the pass band and stop band are, respectively, $f_p = 0.215$ and $f_s = 0.315$. Using Eq. (16.19) to approximate the required filter length N, we obtain

$$\tilde{N} = 1 + \frac{-20 \log \sqrt{(0.001)(0.025)} - 13}{14.6(0.315 - 0.215)}$$

$$= 23.6$$

The next larger odd length would be $N = 25$. If we run `RemezAlgorithm( )` with the following inputs:

`filter_length` = 25 `grid_density` = 16

`ripple_ratio` = 25.0 `passband_edge_freq` = 0.215 `stopband_edge_freq` = 0.315

we obtain the extremal frequencies listed in Table 16.2 and the filter coefficients listed in Table 16.3. The frequency response of the filter is shown in Figs. 16.2 and 16.3. The actual passband and stopband ripple values of 0.0195 and 0.000780 are significantly better than the specified values of 0.025 and 0.001.

Example 16.2 The ripple performance of the 25-tap filter designed in Example 16.1 exhibits a certain amount of overachievement, and the estimate of the minimum number of taps was closer to 23 than 25. Therefore, it would be natural for us to ask if we could in fact achieve the desired performance with a 23-tap filter. If we rerun `RemezAlgorithm( )` with `filter_length` = 23, we obtain the extremal frequencies and filter coefficients listed in Tables 16.4 and 16.5. The frequency response of this filter is shown in Figs. 16.4 and 16.5. The passband ripple is approximately 0.034, and the stopband ripple is approximately 0.00138—therefore, we conclude that a 23-tap filter does not satisfy the specified requirements.

16.7 Extension of the Basic Method

So far we have considered use of the Remez exchange method for odd-length, linear phase FIR filters having even-symmetric impulse responses (that is,

TABLE 16.2 Extremal Frequencies for Example 16.1

k	f_k
0	0.000000
1	0.042232
2	0.084464
3	0.126696
4	0.165089
5	0.199643
6	0.215000
7	0.315000
8	0.322708
9	0.343906
10	0.372813
11	0.407500
12	0.447969
13	0.500000

TABLE 16.3 Coefficients for 25-Tap FIR Filter of Example 16.1

Coefficients
$h[0] = h[24] = -0.004069$
$h[1] = h[23] = -0.010367$
$h[2] = h[22] = -0.001802$
$h[3] = h[21] = 0.015235$
$h[4] = h[20] = 0.003214$
$h[5] = h[19] = -0.027572$
$h[6] = h[18] = -0.005119$
$h[7] = h[17] = 0.049465$
$h[8] = h[16] = 0.007009$
$h[9] = h[15] = -0.096992$
$h[10] = h[14] = -0.008320$
$h[11] = h[13] = 0.315158$
$h[12] = 0.508810$

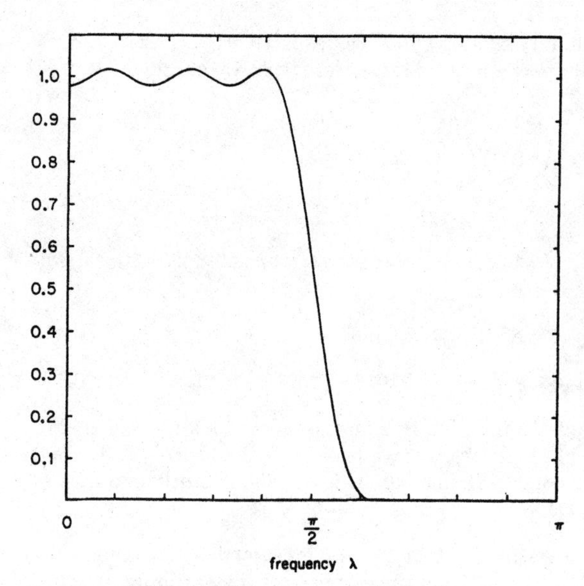

Figure 16.2 Magnitude response (as a fraction of peak) for the filter of Example 16.1.

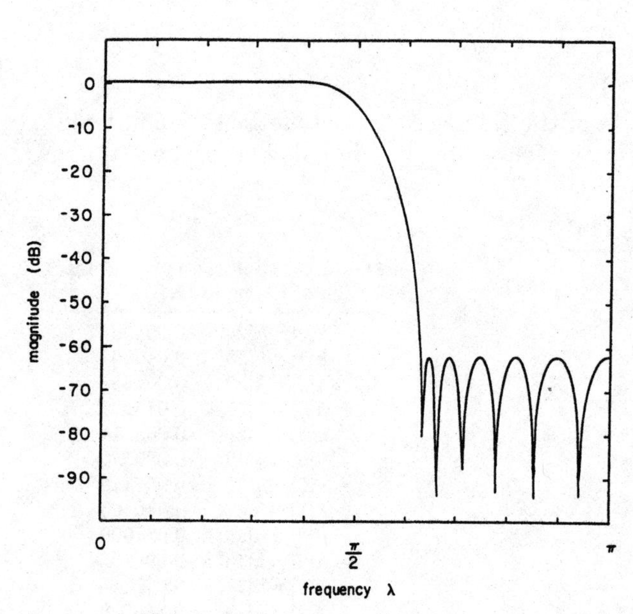

Figure 16.3 Magnitude response (in dB) for the filter of Example 16.1.

TABLE 16.4 Extremal Frequencies for Example 16.2

k	f_k
0	0.000000
1	0.051510
2	0.103021
3	0.152292
4	0.194844
5	0.215000
6	0.315000
7	0.324635
8	0.349688
9	0.382448
10	0.419062
11	0.459531
12	0.500000

TABLE 16.5 Coefficients for 23-Tap FIR Filter of Example 16.2

$h[0] = h[22] = -0.000992$
$h[1] = h[21] = 0.007452$
$h[2] = h[20] = 0.018648$
$h[3] = h[19] = 0.002873$
$h[4] = h[18] = -0.026493$
$h[5] = h[17] = -0.003625$
$h[6] = h[16] = 0.048469$
$h[7] = h[15] = 0.005314$
$h[8] = h[14] = -0.096281$
$h[9] = h[13] = -0.006601$
$h[10] = h[12] = -0.314911$
$h[11] = 0.507077$

type 1 filters). The Remez method was originally adapted specifically for the design of type 1 filters (Parks and McClellan 1972). However, in a subsequent paper, Parks and McClellan (1973) noted that the amplitude response of any constant-group-delay FIR filter can be expressed as

$$A(f) = Q(f)\,P(f)$$

where

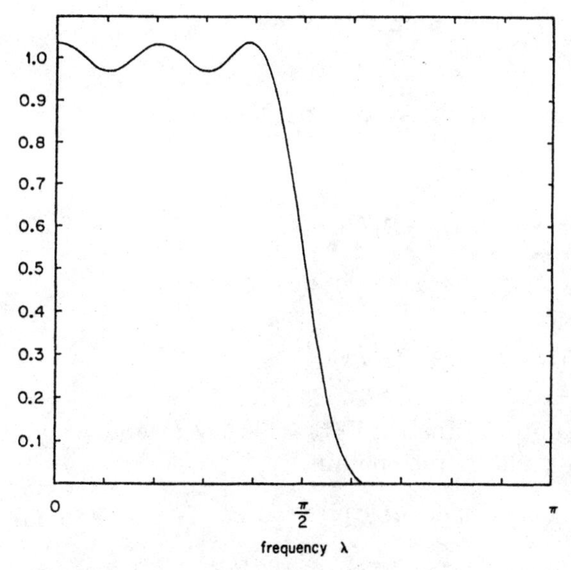

Figure 16.4 Magnitude response (as a fraction of peak) for the filter of Example 16.2.

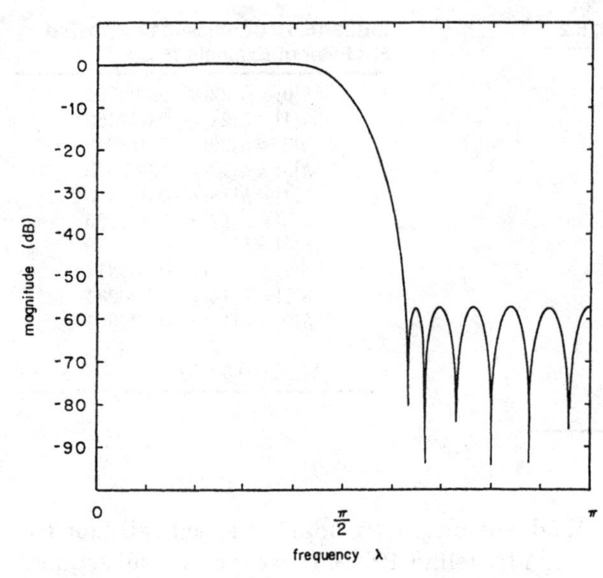

Figure 16.5 Magnitude response (in dB) for the filter of Example 16.2.

$$P(f) = \sum_{k=0}^{r-1} c_k \cos(2\pi k f)$$

$$Q(f) = \begin{cases} 1 & h[n] \text{ symmetric, } N \text{ odd} \\ \cos \pi f & h[n] \text{ symmetric, } N \text{ even} \\ \sin 2\pi f & h[n] \text{ antisymmetric, } N \text{ odd} \\ \sin \pi f & h[n] \text{ antisymmetric, } N \text{ even} \end{cases}$$

Recall that the error $E(f)$ was defined as

$$E(f) = W(f)[D(f) - A(f)] \tag{16.22}$$

If we substitute $Q(f)P(f)$ and factor out $Q(f)$, we obtain

$$E(f) = W(f)Q(f)\left[\frac{D(f)}{Q(f)} - P(f)\right]$$

We can then define a new weighting function $\hat{W}(f) = W(f)Q(f)$ and a new desired response $\hat{D}(f) = D(f)/Q(f)$, and thereby obtain

$$E(f) = \hat{W}(f)[\hat{D}(f) - P(f)] \tag{16.23}$$

Equation (16.23) is of the same form as Eq. (16.22) with $\hat{W}(f)$ substituted for $W(f)$, $\hat{D}(f)$ substituted for $D(f)$, and $P(f)$ substituted for $A(f)$. Therefore, the procedures developed in previous sections can be used to solve for $P(f)$ provided that $\hat{W}(f)$ is used in place of $W(f)$ and $\hat{D}(f)$ is used in place of $D(f)$. Once this $P(f)$ is obtained, we can multiply by the appropriate $Q(f)$ to obtain $A(f)$. The appropriate formula from Table 15.4 can then be used to obtain the impulse response coefficients $h[n]$.

Listing 16.1 Setup Grid for Remez Algorithm

```
//===========================================================

void RemezAlgorithm::SetupGrid( void )
{
 double work;
 work = (0.5 + PB_Edge_Freq - SB_Edge_Freq)/Num_Approx_Funcs;

 Num_PB_Freqs = (int)floor(0.5 + PB_Edge_Freq/work);

 Num_Grid_Pts_PB = Num_PB_Freqs * Grid_Density;

 Num_SB_Freqs = Num_Approx_Funcs + 1 - Num_PB_Freqs;

 PB_Increment = PB_Edge_Freq / Num_Grid_Pts_PB;

 SB_Increment = ( 0.5 - SB_Edge_Freq )/((Num_SB_Freqs-1) * Grid_Density);
 return;
}
```

Listing 16.2 Function to Define Desired Response

```
double RemezAlgorithm::DesiredResponse(double freq)
{
 double result;

 result = 0.0;
 if(freq <= PB_Edge_Freq) result = 1.0;
 return(result);
}
```

Listing 16.3 Function for Weighting of Desired Response

```
//====================================================

double RemezAlgorithm::WeightFunction(double freq)
{
 double result;
```

```
 result = 1.0;
 if(freq <= PB_Edge_Freq) result = 1.0/Ripple_Ratio;
 return(result);
}
```

Listing 16.4 Function for Calculating the Error Relative to the Desired Response

```
//=============================================

void RemezAlgorithm::RemezError( void)
{
 int j;
 double freq;
 double ampl_resp;

 ampl_resp = ComputeRemezAmplitudeResponse( 1, 0.0);

 for( j=0; j<= Max_Grid_Indx; j++)
   {
    freq = GetFrequency(j);

    ampl_resp = ComputeRemezAmplitudeResponse( 0, freq);

    Error[j] = WeightFunction(freq) * (DesiredResponse(freq) - ampl_resp);
   }
 return;
}
```

Listing 16.5 Amplitude Response for Candidate Filter Design

```
//======================================================

double RemezAlgorithm::ComputeRemezAmplitudeResponse(
                                                    int init_flag,
                                                    double contin_freq)
{
 static int i, j, k, sign;
 static double freq, denom, numer, alpha, delta;
 static double absDelta, xCont, term;
 static double x[50], beta[50], gamma[50];
 double aa;

 if(init_flag)
   {
    for(j=0; j<=Num_Approx_Funcs; j++)
```

```
      {
       freq = GetFrequency(Ext_Freq[j]);
       x[j] = cos(TWO_PI * freq);
      }

    //  compute delta
    denom = 0.0;
    numer = 0.0;
    sign = -1;
    for( k=0; k<=Num_Approx_Funcs; k++)
      {
       sign = -sign;
       alpha = 1.0;
       for( i=0; i<=(Num_Approx_Funcs-1); i++)
         {
          if(i==k) continue;
            alpha = alpha / (x[k] - x[i]);
         }
       beta[k] = alpha;
       if( k != Num_Approx_Funcs )
                           alpha = alpha/(x[k] - x[Num_Approx_Funcs]);
       freq = GetFrequency(Ext_Freq[k]);
       numer = numer + alpha * DesiredResponse(freq);

       denom = denom + sign*(alpha/WeightFunction(freq));
      } // end of loop over k

    delta = numer/denom;
    absDelta = fabs(delta);

    sign = -1;
    for( k=0; k<=Num_Approx_Funcs-1; k++)
      {
       sign = -sign;
       freq = GetFrequency(Ext_Freq[k]);
       gamma[k] = DesiredResponse(freq) - sign * delta /
            WeightFunction(freq);
      }
   } // end of if(init_flag)
 else
   {
    xCont = cos(TWO_PI * contin_freq);
    numer = 0.0;
    denom = 0.0;
    for( k=0; k<Num_Approx_Funcs; k++)
      {
       term = xCont - x[k];
       if(fabs(term)<1.0e-7)
```

```
          {
           aa = gamma[k];
           goto done;
          }
        else
          {
           term = beta[k]/(xCont - x[k]);
           denom += term;
           numer += gamma[k]*term;
          }
      }
    aa = numer/denom;
   }
 done:
 return(aa);
}
```

Listing 16.6 Search the Error Function

```
//=============================================

void RemezAlgorithm::RemezSearch(void)
{
 int i,j,k,extras,indexOfSmallest;
 double minVal;

 k=0;

 /* test for extremum at f=0 */
 if( ( (Error[0]>0.0) &&
       (Error[0]>Error[1]) &&
       (fabs(Error[0])>=Abs_Delta) ) ||
     ( (Error[0]<0.0) &&
       (Error[0]<Error[1]) &&
       (fabs(Error[0])>=Abs_Delta) ) )
   {
    Ext_Freq[k]=0;
    k++;
   }

 /* search for extrema in passband */
 for(j=1; j<Num_Grid_Pts_PB; j++)
   {
    if( ( (Error[j]>=Error[j-1]) &&
          (Error[j]>Error[j+1]) &&
          (Error[j]>0.0) ) ||
```

```
        ( (Error[j]<=Error[j-1]) &&
          (Error[j]<Error[j+1]) && (Error[j]<0.0) ))
      {
       Ext_Freq[k] = j;
       k++;
      }
   }

/* pick up an extremal frequency at passband edge */
Ext_Freq[k]=Num_Grid_Pts_PB;
k++;

/* pick up an extremal frequency at stopband edge */
j=Num_Grid_Pts_PB+1;
Ext_Freq[k]=j;
k++;

/* search for extrema in stopband */

for(j=Num_Grid_Pts_PB+2; j<Max_Grid_Indx; j++)
   {
    if( ( (Error[j]>=Error[j-1]) &&
          (Error[j]>Error[j+1]) &&
          (Error[j]>0.0) ) ||
        ( (Error[j]<=Error[j-1]) &&
          (Error[j]<Error[j+1]) &&
          (Error[j]<0.0) ))
      {
       Ext_Freq[k] = j;
       k++;
      }
   }
/* test for extremum at f=0.5 */
j = Max_Grid_Indx;
if( ( (Error[j]>0.0) &&
      (Error[j]>Error[j-1]) &&
      (fabs(Error[j])>=Abs_Delta) ) ||
    ( (Error[j]<0.0) &&
      (Error[j]<Error[j-1]) &&
      (fabs(Error[j])>=Abs_Delta) ) )
   {
    Ext_Freq[k]=Max_Grid_Indx;
    k++;
   }
/*------------------------------------------------*/
/*  find and remove superfluous extremal frequencies  */
```

```
 if( k>Num_Approx_Funcs+1)
   {
    extras = k - (Num_Approx_Funcs+1);
    for(i=1; i<=extras; i++)
      {
       minVal = fabs(Error[Ext_Freq[0]]);
       indexOfSmallest = 0;
       for(j=1; j< k; j++)
         {
          if(fabs(Error[Ext_Freq[j]]) >= minVal) continue;
            minVal = fabs(Error[Ext_Freq[j]]);
            indexOfSmallest = j;
         }
       k--;
       for(j=indexOfSmallest; j<k; j++) Ext_Freq[j] = Ext_Freq[j+1];
      }
   }
 return;
}
```

Listing 16.7 Function to Evaluate Stopping Criteria

```
//==================================================

int RemezAlgorithm::RemezStop( void)
{
 static int Old_Ext_Freq[50];
 int j, result;

 result = 1;

 for(j=0; j<=Num_Approx_Funcs; j++)
   {
    if(Ext_Freq[j] != Old_Ext_Freq[j]) result = 0;
    Old_Ext_Freq[j] = Ext_Freq[j];
   }
 return(result);
}
```

Listing 16.8 Function to Evaluate Improved Stopping Criteria

```
//========================================

int RemezAlgorithm::RemezStop2()
{
```

```
 double maxVal, minVal, qq;
 int j, result;

 result = 0;
 maxVal = fabs(Error[Ext_Freq[0]]);
 minVal = fabs(Error[Ext_Freq[0]]);

 for( j=1; j<= Num_Approx_Funcs; j++)
   {
    if(fabs(Error[Ext_Freq[j]]) < minVal) minVal = fabs(Error[Ext_Freq[j]]);
    if(fabs(Error[Ext_Freq[j]]) > maxVal) maxVal = fabs(Error[Ext_Freq[j]]);
   }
 qq = (maxVal - minVal)/maxVal;
 if(qq<0.01) result = 1;
 return(result);
}
```

Listing 16.9 `RemezFinish()`

```
//=============================================================

void RemezAlgorithm::RemezFinish( double *filter_coeffs )
{
 int k;
 double freq, *aa;
  FreqSampFilterSpec *filter_spec;
  FreqSampFilterDesign *filter_design;
  FreqSampFilterResponse *filter_response;

 aa = new double[Num_Approx_Funcs];

 for( k=0; k<Num_Approx_Funcs; k++)
   {
    freq = (double) k/ (double) Filter_Length;
    aa[k] = ComputeRemezAmplitudeResponse (0, freq);
   }
 filter_spec = new FreqSampFilterSpec( 1, 1, Filter_Length, aa);
 filter_design = new FreqSampFilterDesign( *filter_spec);
 filter_design->ComputeCoefficients( filter_spec);
 filter_design->CopyCoefficients( filter_coeffs);

 for(k=0; k<Filter_Length; k++)
   {
    DebugFile << "Coeff[ " << k << " ] = "
              << filter_coeffs[k] << endl;
   }
}
```

Listing 16.10 `RemezAlgorithm()`

```
//=======================================================

RemezAlgorithm::RemezAlgorithm( int filter_length,
                                int grid_density,
                                double ripple_ratio,
                                double passband_edge_freq,
                                double stopband_edge_freq,
                                double *extremal_freqs,
                                double *filter_coeffs)
{
 int m, j;

 //--------------------------------
 //  set up frequency grid

 Filter_Length = filter_length;
 PB_Edge_Freq = passband_edge_freq;
 SB_Edge_Freq = stopband_edge_freq;
 Num_Approx_Funcs = (filter_length + 1)/2;
 Grid_Density = grid_density;
 Ripple_Ratio = ripple_ratio;

 SetupGrid();

 PB_Edge_Freq = PB_Edge_Freq + (PB_Edge_Freq/(2.0*Num_Grid_Pts_PB));
 Max_Grid_Indx = 1 + Grid_Density*(Num_PB_Freqs+Num_SB_Freqs-1);

 //---------------------------------------------
 //  make initial guess of extremal frequencies

 for(j=0; j<Num_PB_Freqs; j++) Ext_Freq[j] = (j+1)* grid_density;

 for(j=0; j<Num_SB_Freqs; j++) Ext_Freq[j+Num_PB_Freqs] =
                               Num_Grid_Pts_PB + 1 + j * grid_density;

 //---------------------------------------------------
 //  find optimal locations for extremal frequencies

 for(m=1;m<=20;m++)
   {
    RemezError();

    RemezSearch();

    RemezStop2();
```

```
    if(RemezStop()) break;
    DebugFile << "done iteration " << m << endl;
  }

 for(j=0; j<=Num_Approx_Funcs; j++)
   {
    extremal_freqs[j] = GetFrequency(Ext_Freq[j]);
    DebugFile << "extremal_freqs[ " << j << " ] = "
              << extremal_freqs[j] << endl;
   }

 RemezFinish( filter_coeffs);

 return;
};
```

Chapter

17

FIR Filter Design: Practical Case Studies

In the preceding three chapters we have explored three different approaches to the design of FIR filters. In this chapter, we compare these approaches by using them to design practical filters whose performance is evaluated while considering the effects of quantized coefficients and finite-precision arithmetic in the context of the various implementation structures that were introduced in Chap. 13.

17.1 Assessing the Impacts of Quantization and Finite-Precision Arithmetic

Using digital words of finite length to implement FIR filters introduces performance degradations in several different ways. The first source of degradation, namely *coefficient quantization,* is the inability to implement the precise coefficient values that have been determined by the filter design algorithm. In other words, coefficient quantization essentially forces us to implement a filter that is not exactly the filter that we want to implement. However, the resulting filter is still a *linear* system and all of the linear system analysis techniques from previous chapters still apply. As we will discover in subsequent sections, some of the design algorithms can take quantization into account and partially mitigate its impact, while other open-loop algorithms cannot.

A second source of degradation, *signal quantization,* forces our filter to operate upon signal values that may be only approximations of the "true" unquantized signal values. Signal quantization is not a linear process—the quantized sum of two unquantized signals is generally not equal to the sum of the two signals after they have been individually quantized.

A third source of degradation, *finite-precision arithmetic,* appears closely related to signal quantization, but there are subtle differences. FIR filter implementations tend to multiply fractional signal values by fractional coefficient values, producing product terms that are smaller than either of the two constituent factors. Then, a large number of these small terms are added together to produce output values that are in roughly the same size range as the input values. A quantization scheme that preserves adequate precision in the inputs, outputs, and coefficients can still yield terrible performance if the precision of the small intermediate product terms is not preserved.

Direct form realizations

Consider the direct form realization of an FIR filter as depicted in Figs 13.5 and 13.6. Each of the input samples $x[k]$ and each of the coefficients $h[n]$ will be quantized to some finite number of bits. If each $x[k]$ is quantized to B_x bits and each $h[n]$ is quantized to B_h bits, a total of $(B_x + B_h)$ bits will be needed to represent each product term $x[k] \cdot h[n]$ without further loss of precision. Still more bits will be needed to precisely represent the sum of all of these product terms. Most digital filter designs represent a compromise—some performance is sacrificed to allow for easier implementations. How severely will performance be degraded if the filter is implemented with fewer than the required number of bits used to represent each of the arithmetic results? Before we can begin to answer this question, we need to take a closer look at just how the filter's performance should be gauged.

In a truely linear system we can take several different paths to arrive at the same answer. For example, we could compute a linear FIR filter's frequency response in two different ways:

1. In any shift-invariant linear discrete-time system, the frequency response can be obtained as the DTFT of the system's impulse response sequence. In the case of a discrete-time linear FIR filter, this means that the frequency response can be obtained as the DTFT of the filter's coefficients.
2. The response of the filter at any one specific frequency can be measured directly by using a sinusoid of the specific frequency as input to the filter and then comparing the amplitude and phase of the output sinusoid to the amplitude and phase of the input sinusoid. If this process is repeated over many closely spaced frequencies, the result will be a sampled version of the frequency response. This method is the discrete-frequency version of the *swept-tone* technique that is widely used for characterization of analog filter circuits.

For a linear system, the results obtained via these two methods should agree. Unfortunately, signal quantization is not a linear operation. If we use these two methods to compute the response for an FIR filter that uses quantized signal values and finite-precision arithmetic, we have no guarantee that the two different methods will yield the same result. In fact, if just the second method is repeated using several different amplitudes for the input sinusoid, the results will generally be slightly different for each amplitude. Coarser quantization will result in larger differences for different input amplitudes; finer quantization will result in smaller differences. Just how different will these results be for a given filter design? Which is the correct amplitude to use for evaluating the effects of quantization upon a particular design? Some software-based experiments may help us answer these questions.

Software design

Let's assume that an FIR filter is to be implemented in the direct form tapped delay line structure depicted in Fig. 13.6. We need to design some software to emulate the behavior of this structure, including quantization and finite-precision effects. *For ease of implementation we will perform the arithmetic using two's complement arithmetic.* In the analysis of quantization effects, it is customary to assume that both the filter coefficients and the signal values have magnitudes that are *strictly less than* 1. For virtually all practical filter designs, this assumption about the coefficients is satisfied. However, all of the windows presented in Chap. 14 have a peak value that *equals* 1. If we multiply a value of 1 by 2^k, the result in binary form is a single 1 followed by k zeros. Such a result is actually a $(k + 1)$-bit value. So, if we were to actually implement a window using k-bit representations of the coefficients, the coefficients would have to be scaled to reduce the peak to something less than 1. This only becomes an issue if the windows are applied directly to data, as they sometimes are in DFT-based spectral analysis schemes.

A coefficient value can be quantized by multiplying the coefficient h by some quantization factor Q and then truncating the fractional part of the result:

$$h_T = \lfloor hQ \rfloor \tag{17.1}$$

If $Q = 2^k$, the result h_T will be a k-bit integer value. For the quantized coefficient to be a *rounded* approximation to the original coefficient, we need to add 0.5 to hQ before truncating

$$h_R = \left\lfloor hQ + \frac{1}{2} \right\rfloor \tag{17.2}$$

When the coefficient values are signed (i.e., when the coefficients can take on positive or negative values) one bit of the coefficients' binary representation must be reserved for the sign. This means that for k-bit quantization of signed values, a quantization factor of $Q = 2^{k-1}$ should be used instead of $Q = 2^k$. The quantized value of the coefficient will often be more convenient to work with in filter *design* software if it is returned to a floating-point representation by dividing by Q. This is the approach used to quantize coefficients in the software modules described in this chapter.

17.2 Quantized Coefficients in the Window Method of FIR Design

Designing an FIR filter with quantized coefficients using the window method is straightforward, because the quantization step can be tacked onto the end of the usual procedure. Simply obtain the coefficients via the methods of Chap. 14 using double precision floating-point arithmetic and then quantize these coefficients to the desired number of bits. Because window responses were evaluated in Chap. 14 by treating the time domain window as an FIR filter, the methods `ScaleCoefficients` and `QuantizeCoefficients` have been added to class `FirFilterDesign` (see Listing 17.1) to provide a convenient way to scale and quantize window coefficients.

Example 17.1 Obtain the coefficients for a 21-tap triangular window. Compare the DTFT's obtained for the quantized window obtained by *truncating* the window coefficients to 7 bits and the quantized window obtained by *rounding* the window coefficients to 7 bits. Do not include the zero-valued endpoints of the window as part of the total tap count.

solution Since window coefficients are always positive, all of the available bits can be used to represent magnitude. Therefore, a value of $2^7 = 128$ is used for `quant_factor` in the call to `QuantizeCoefficients`. Because the peak window coefficient is 1, all of the window coefficients were scaled by the factor 127/128 prior to quantization so that the peak value will fit into 7 bits. The unquantized coefficients and the corresponding quantized values are listed in Table 17.1, and the DTFT magnitudes for the truncated and rounded coefficients are plotted in Figs. 17.1 and 17.2. The DTFT spectrum for rounded coefficients has deeper nulls than the spectrum for truncated coefficients, but otherwise the two spectra are very similar. Comparison of these figures and trace (*b*) of Fig. 14.21 reveals no significant degradation due to quantization.

Unless explicitly stated to the contrary, all of the quantization performed in the remainder of this chapter will employ rounding rather than simple truncation.

Example 17.2 Obtain the coefficients for a 21-tap von Hann window, quantize each coefficient to 7 bits, and compute the DTFT for the resulting quantized window.

TABLE 17.1 Coefficients for the 21-Tap Triangular Window of Example 17.1

n	Original $h[n]$	Truncated $h[n]$	Quantized $h[n]$
0, 20	0.090909	0.085938	0.093750
1, 19	0.181818	0.179688	0.179688
2, 18	0.272727	0.265625	0.273438
3, 17	0.363636	0.359375	0.359375
4, 16	0.454545	0.445313	0.453125
5, 15	0.545454	0.539063	0.539063
6, 14	0.636364	0.625000	0.632813
7, 13	0.727273	0.718750	0.718750
8, 12	0.818182	0.804688	0.812500
9, 11	0.909091	0.898438	0.898438
10	1.00	0.992188	0.992188

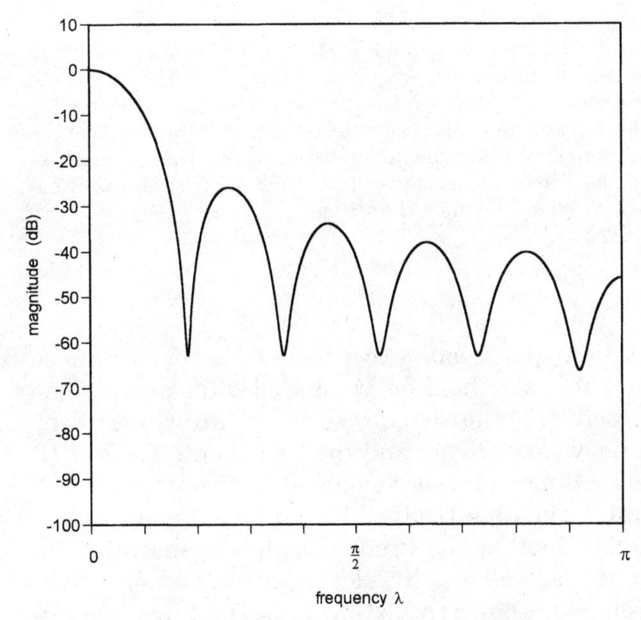

Figure 17.1 Magnitude of the DTFT for a 21-point triangular window with quantized coefficients truncated to 7 bits.

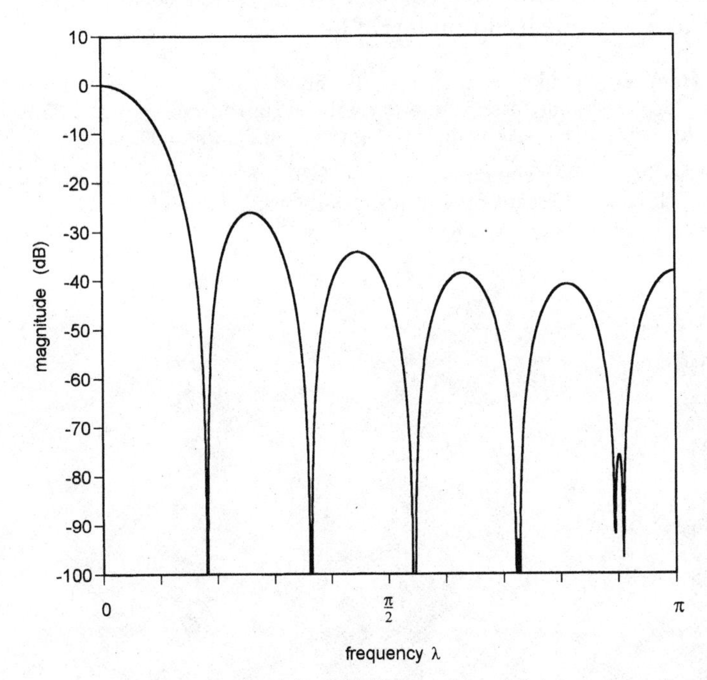

Figure 17.2 Magnitude of the DTFT for a 21-point triangular window with quantized coefficients rounded to 7 bits.

solution The unquantized coefficients and the corresponding quantized values are listed in Table 17.2, and the DTFT magnitudes are plotted in Figs. 17.3 and 17.4. There is no significant difference in the spectra for normalized frequencies below $\pi/4$. The third and fourth lobes of the quantized response are actually a few dB lower than the corresponding lobes of the unquantized response. The null separating the sixth and seventh lobes of the unquantized response does not appear at all in the quantized response. The most noticeable differences occur at normalized frequencies between $3\pi/4$ and π where the attenuation of the quantized response is degraded by more than 10 dB.

Coefficient quantization in windowed filter designs

So far, the impact of quantization upon window responses does not seem to be much cause for concern. Does this also hold for windowed filter designs? As discussed in Sec. 14.5, the coefficients for windowed filters are obtained by multiplying together the window coefficients and the coefficients for an FIR approximation to an ideal filter. Since it is these modified coefficients that will be used to implement the filter, the quantization should be applied to them rather than to the coefficients for either the window or the original filter. In our design software this can be accomplished by adding the method `ApplyWindow` to the `FirFilterDesign` class as shown in Listing 17.2. The filter in question is initialized as the appropriate "ideal" filter and then the `ApplyWindow` method is called to multiply the filter coefficients by the specified window coefficients. Finally, the `QuantizeCoefficients` method is called to quantize the windowed coefficients to the desired number of bits.

Example 17.3 Apply a Hamming window to a 21-tap FIR filter that approximates the amplitude response of an ideal low-pass filter with a normalized cutoff frequency of $2\pi/5$. Assess the performance degradation caused by quantizing the coefficients to 8 bits.

solution Since the filter coefficients are signed values, one of the 8 bits must be reserved for the sign, leaving only 7 bits to represent magnitude. Therefore, a value of $2^7 = 128$ is

TABLE 17.2 Coefficients for the 21-Tap von Hann Window of Example 17.2

n	Original $h[n]$	Quantized $h[n]$
0, 20	0.020254	0.023438
1, 19	0.079373	0.078125
2, 18	0.172570	0.171875
3, 17	0.292292	0.289063
4, 16	0.428843	0.421875
5, 15	0.571157	0.570313
6, 14	0.707708	0.703125
7, 13	0.827430	0.820313
8, 12	0.920627	0.914063
9, 11	0.979746	0.968750
10	1.00	0.992188

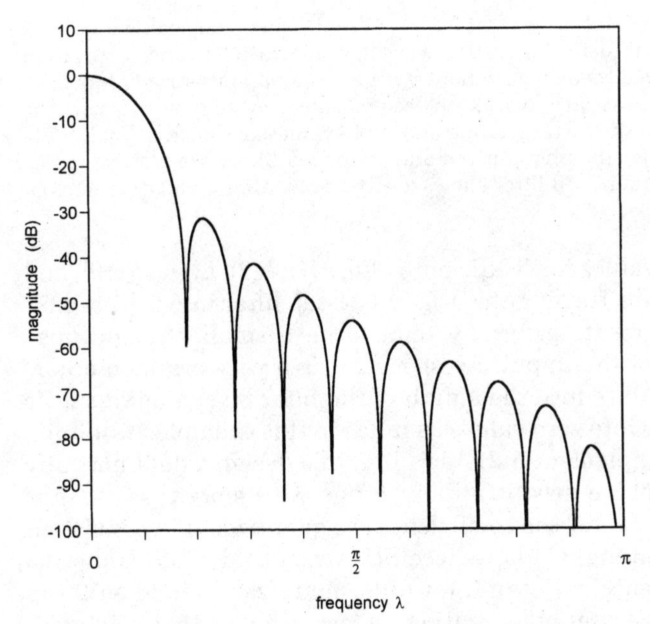

Figure 17.3 Magnitude of the DTFT for a 21-point von Hann window.

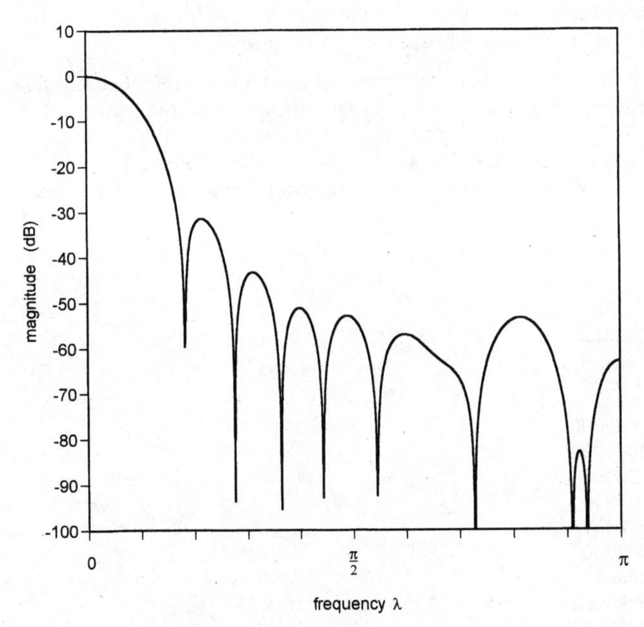

Figure 17.4 Magnitude of the DTFT for a 21-point von Hann window with coefficients quantized to 7 bits.

used for `quant_factor` in the call to `QuantizeCoefficients`. Because the peak window coefficient is 1, and all the ideal coefficients will always have magnitudes strictly less than 1, we know that the windowed coeffcients will always have magnitudes strictly less than 1. Therefore, it will not be necessary to scale the coefficients prior to quantization. The unquantized coefficients and the corresponding quantized values are listed in Table 17.3, and the DTFT magnitudes for the unquantized and quantized filters are plotted in Fig. 17.5. The spectrum for the quantized filter shows a severe (>25 dB) degradation in stopband attenuation.

After quantization, the values for coefficients $h[0], h[1], h[2], h[18], h[19]$, and $h[20]$ have all become 0, thus turning the original 21-tap filter into a 15-tap filter. Since FIR filter coefficients generally tend to have smaller magnitudes close to the ends or *tails* of the impulse response, it is a very common occurrence that quantization will reduce the length of the filter by changing one or more of the tail coefficients into zero values as it has in this example. Assuming we had the capability to implement a 21-tap filter, this design would not fully utilize this capability. What we need is a filter design with more than 21 taps that becomes a 21-tap filter after the coefficients are quantized. If we insist on 8-bit quantization of Hamming-windowed coefficients, such a filter cannot be found. A 27-tap filter becomes a 15-tap filter after quantization, and a 29-tap filter becomes a 23-tap filter after quantization. In fact, filters with 29, 31, or 33 taps all become 23-tap filters after quantization.

Example 17.4 An 8-bit quantized 23-tap Hamming-windowed low-pass filter with a normalized cutoff frequency of $2\pi/5$ can be obtained from the corresponding unquantized filter with 29, 31, or 33 taps. Determine which of the three unquantized filters results in the 23-tap quantized design with the best stopband attenuation performance.

solution The coefficients for a 23-tap unquantized filter and the 23 active coefficients for each of the three quantized filters are listed in Table 17.4, and the DTFT magnitudes for each of the filters are plotted in Figs. 17.6 through 17.9. Each of the three quantized filters has about the same level of peak ripple (≈ −31.5 dB) in the stop band. The 23-tap filter obtained from quantization of a 33-tap filter clearly shows the best transition performance,

TABLE 17.3 Coefficients for the 21-Tap Hamming Windowed Filter of Example 17.3

n	Original $h[n]$	Quantized $h[n]$
0, 20	−0.00000000156	0.0000000
1, 19	−0.00344823783	0.0000000
2, 18	−0.00392559530	0.0000000
3, 17	0.00720644664	0.0078125
4, 16	0.02007367532	0.0234375
5, 15	−0.00000001056	0.0000000
6, 14	−0.05162677423	−0.0468750
7, 13	−0.05054018341	−0.0390625
8, 12	0.08533046527	0.0859375
9, 11	0.29591500600	0.2968750
10	0.399999998044	0.3984375

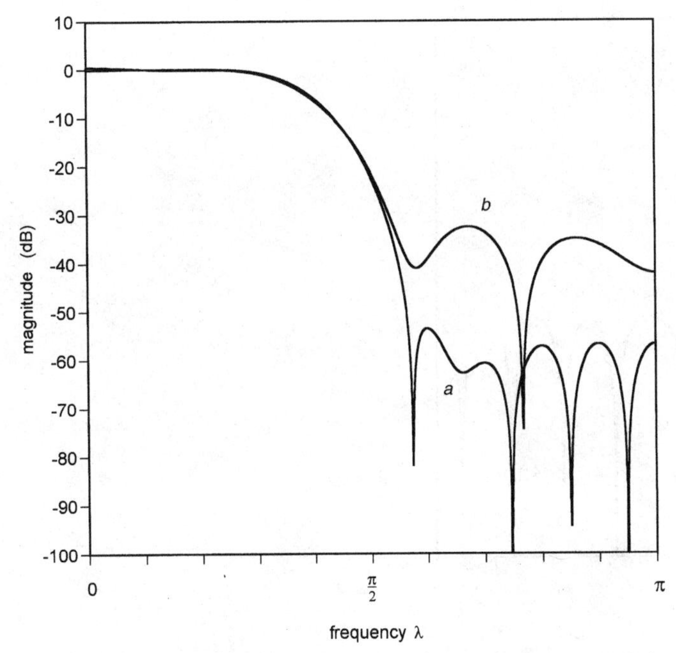

Figure 17.5 Magnitude response for the (*a*) unquantized and (*b*) quantized 21-tap Hamming-windowed low-pass filter of Example

dropping into a deep (≈ −70 dB) null around a normalized frequency of 0.51π. The other two quantized filters have attenuations that are less than 28 dB at this same frequency.

Signal quantization in windowed filter designs

So far we have looked at how quantized coefficient values can degrade the performance of windowed filter designs. Now we will use the swept-tone method

TABLE 17.4 Coefficients for the 23-Tap Hamming Windowed Filters of Example 17.4

n	Unquantized 23-tap	Quantized 29-tap	Quantized 31-tap	Quantized 33-tap
0, 22	0.00220167727	0.0078125	0.0078125	0.0078125
1, 21	−0.00000000193	0.0000000	0.0000000	0.0000000
2, 20	−0.00514720893	0.0000000	−0.0078125	−0.0078125
3, 19	−0.00558402677	0.0000000	0.0000000	−0.0078125
4, 18	0.00932574033	0.0156250	0.0156250	0.0156250
5, 17	0.02394272404	0.0312500	0.0312500	0.0390625
6, 16	−0.00000001184	0.0000000	0.0000000	0.0000000
7, 15	−0.05533091829	−0.0546875	−0.0546875	−0.0546875
8, 14	−0.05246446701	−0.0468750	−0.0468750	−0.0468750
9, 13	0.08671768458	0.0859375	0.0859375	0.0937500
10, 12	0.29708983428	0.2968750	0.2968750	0.2968750
11	0.39999998044	0.3984375	0.3984375	0.3984375

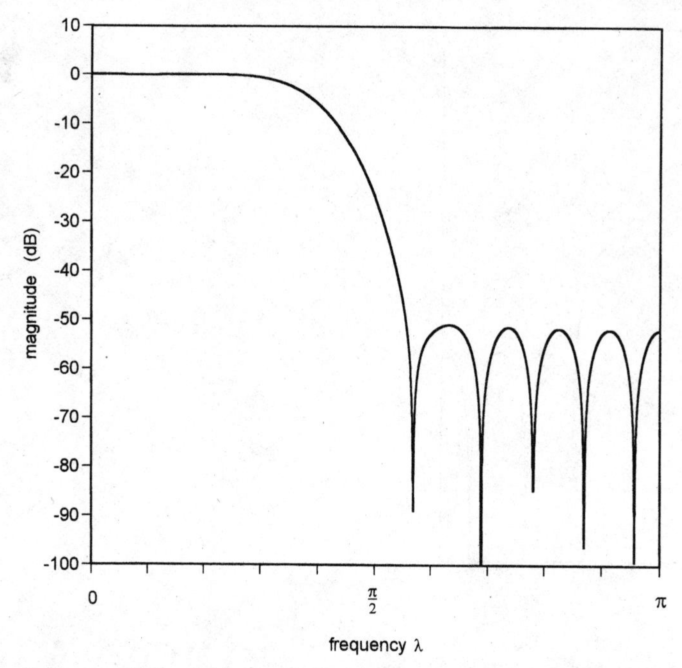

Figure 17.6 Magnitude response for the unquantized 23-tap Hamming-windowed low-pass filter of Example 17.4.

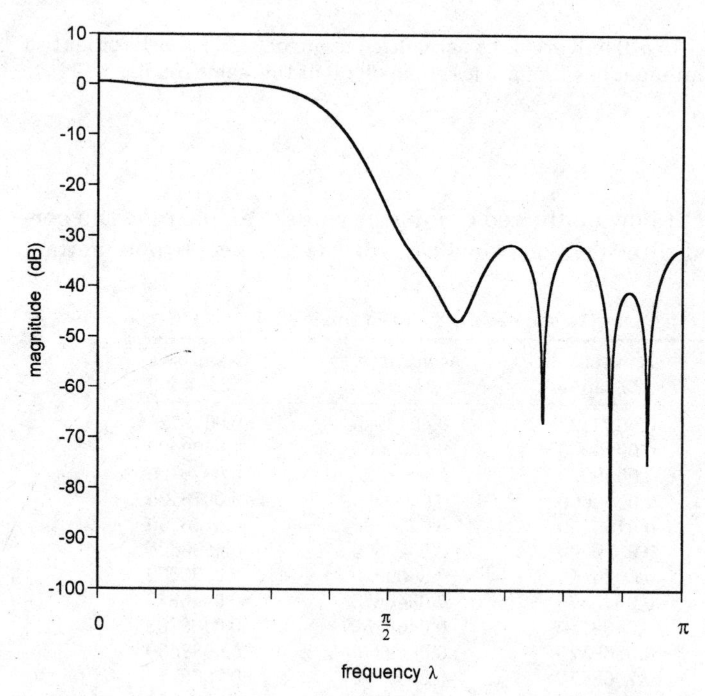

Figure 17.7 Magnitude response for the 23-tap filter that is obtained in Example 17.4 by quantizing a 29-tap Hamming-windowed low-pass filter.

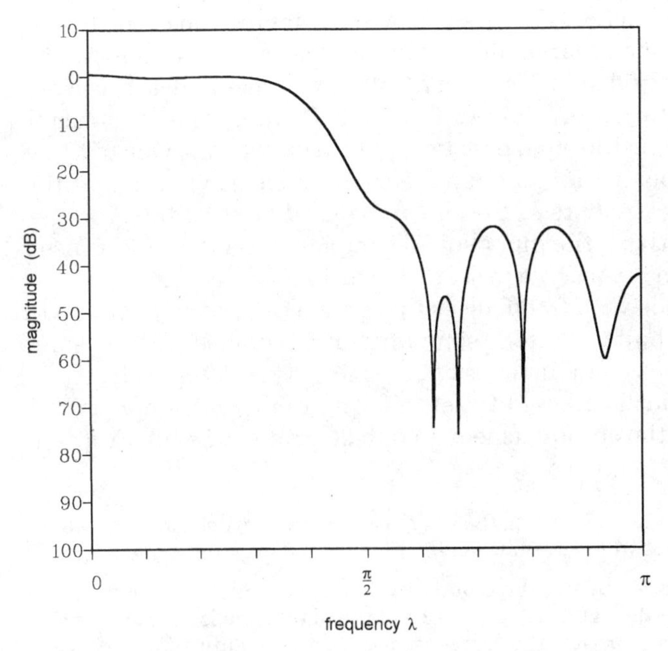

Figure 17.8 Magnitude response for the 23-tap filter that is obtained in Example 17.4 by quantizing a 31-tap Hamming-windowed low-pass filter.

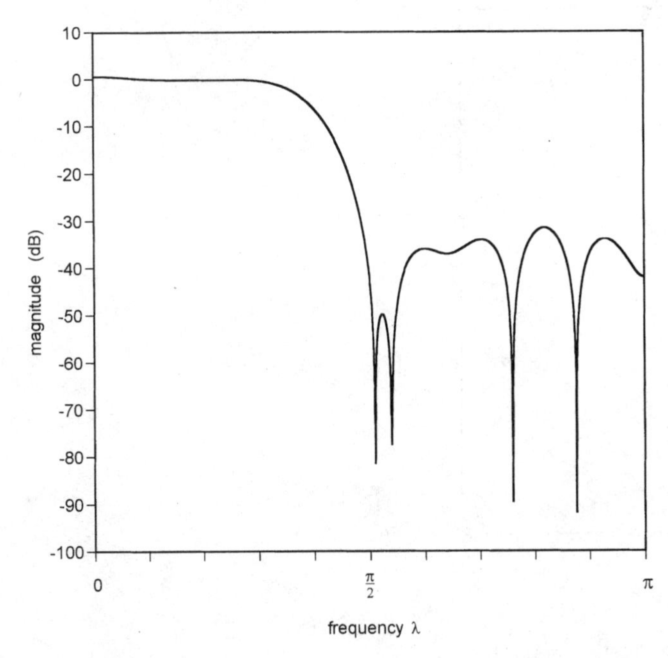

Figure 17.9 Magnitude response for the 23-tap filter that is obtained in Example 17.4 by quantizing a 33-tap Hamming-windowed low-pass filter.

that was briefly described in Sec. 17.1 to see how the combination of coefficient quantization and signal quantization might further degrade performance. The class `DirectFormFir` is provided in Listing 17.3. As its name implies, this class is a software implementation of a direct form 1 FIR filter. The constructor accepts an array of filter coefficients, plus two quantizing factors. One of these factors is used by the constructor to quantize the coefficient values, and the other is stored in a class attribute so that it can be used later by the `ProcessSample` function for quantizing the input signal samples. `DirectFormFir` is used by a second class, `SweptResponse`, which is shown in Listing 17.4. `SweptResponse` generates sinusoids with frequencies that range from nearly zero up to a maximum that equals half the filter's sampling rate. Samples of these sinusoids are provided as input to an instance of `DirectFormFir`. After each step in frequency, the filter output is allowed to settle for a number of sample times, and then the strength of the output is measured to determine the filter's attenuation at that particular frequency.

Example 17.5 Repeat Example 17.4 using the swept-tone method to determine how each of the three quantized filters will perform when the input signal is quantized to 8 bits.

solution The swept responses for the three quantized filters are plotted in Figs. 17.10 through 17.12. As shown in the figures, quantization of the input signals degrades performance by only a small amount beyond the degradation caused by quantization of the coefficients alone.

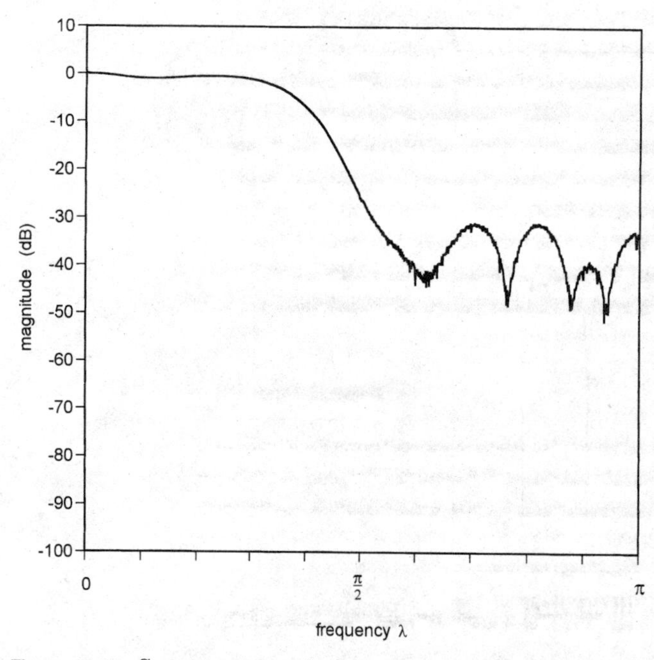

Figure 17.10 Swept-tone magnitude response for the 23-tap filter that is obtained in Example 17.5 by quantizing a 29-tap Hamming-windowed low-pass filter.

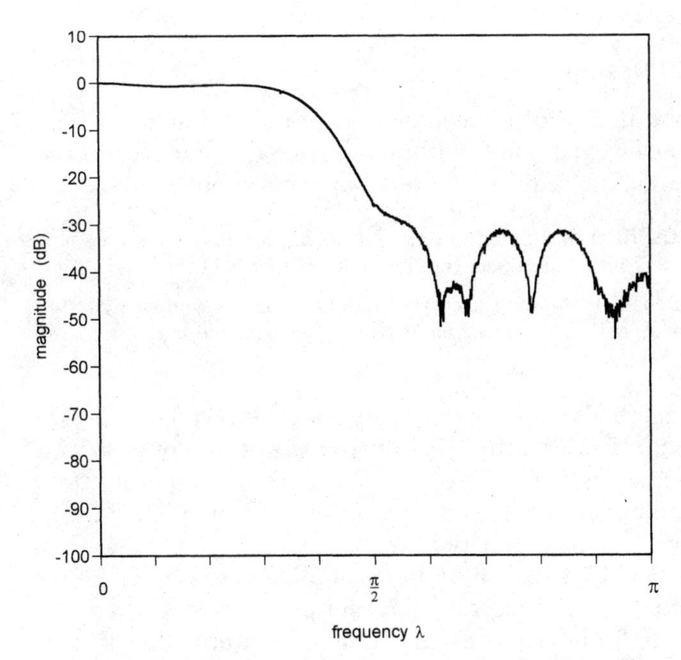

Figure 17.11 Swept-tone magnitude response for the 23-tap filter that is obtained in Example 17.5 by quantizing a 31-tap Hamming-windowed low-pass filter.

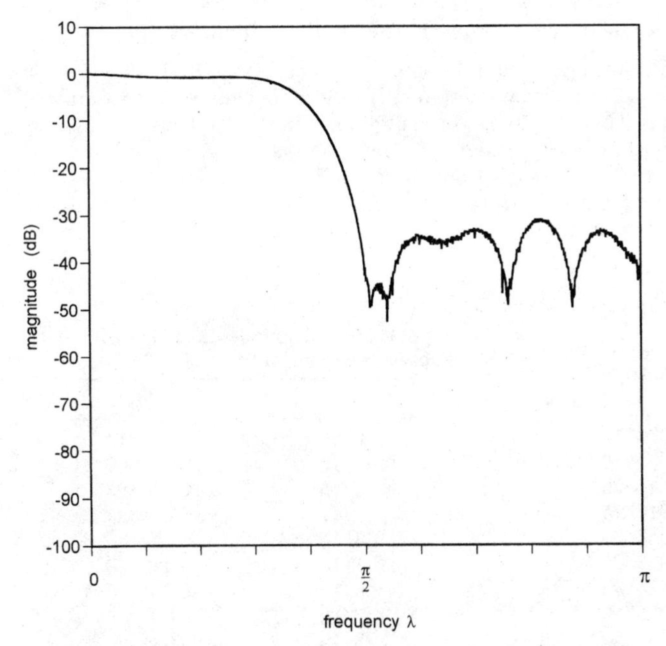

Figure 17.12 Swept-tone magnitude response for the 23-tap filter that is obtained in Example 17.5 by quantizing a 33-tap Hamming-windowed low-pass filter.

17.3 Quantized Coefficients in the Frequency Sampling Method of FIR Design

It is possible to simply obtain FIR filter coefficients via the methods of Chap. 15, using double precision floating-point arithmetic, and then quantize these coefficients to the number of bits required for any particular application.

Example 17.6 Start with the filter design obtained in Example 15.4, and determine how quantizing the coefficients to 7 bits will impact the frequency response of the filter.

solution The original filter coefficients and the corresponding quantized values are listed in Table 17.5. As shown in Fig. 17.13, the stopband ripple performance is degraded by approximately 13 dB.

Unlike the windowing method, the frequency sampling method does provide an opportunity to take quantization into effect during the design process and thereby generate only those coefficient sets whose values can be accurately represented in a given number of bits. This quantization is accomplished using the `FreqSampFilterDesign` member function `QuantizeCoefficients( )` that was briefly mentioned in Sec. 15.4. This function is similar to the `QuantizeCoefficients` member function given in Listing 17.1 for class `FirFilterDesign`. Examination of Listings 15.3 and 15.5 reveals that the quantization is performed just before the coefficients are used to compute the filter's magnitude response inside the optimization loop.

Example 17.7 Repeat Example 15.4, but this time quantize the filter coefficients to 7 bits before computing the magnitude responses that are used in the optimization process.

solution The resulting coefficients are listed in Table 17.6. Comparison of Table 17.6 against the quantized coefficients in Table 17.5 reveals that only difference between the two filters is the value of $h[6]$ and $h[14]$. This seemingly small difference in the coefficients, however, does cause a significant difference in performance. As shown in Fig. 17.14, the stopband ripple performance is degraded by about 5 dB. Comparison of Figs. 17.13 and 17.14, reveals that, for this particular filter, quantizing *during* the design optimization improves performance by about 8 dB relative to quantizing *after* the design optimization is complete.

TABLE 17.5 Coefficients for the 21-Tap Low-Pass Filter of Example 17.6

n	Original $h[n]$	Quantized $h[n]$
0, 20	0.009532	0.007813
1, 19	0.002454	0.000000
2, 18	−0.018536	−0.015625
3, 17	−0.018963	−0.015625
4, 16	0.025209	0.023438
5, 15	0.044232	0.039063
6, 14	−0.029849	−0.023438
7, 13	−0.094246	−0.093750
8, 12	0.032593	0.031250
9, 11	0.314324	0.312500
10	0.466498	0.460938

TABLE 17.6 Coefficients for the 21-Tap Low-Pass Filter of Example 17.7

n	$h[n]$
0, 20	0.007813
1, 19	0.000000
2, 18	−0.015625
3, 17	−0.015625
4, 16	0.023438
5, 15	0.039063
6, 14	−0.031250
7, 13	−0.093750
8, 12	0.031250
9, 11	0.312500
10	0.460938

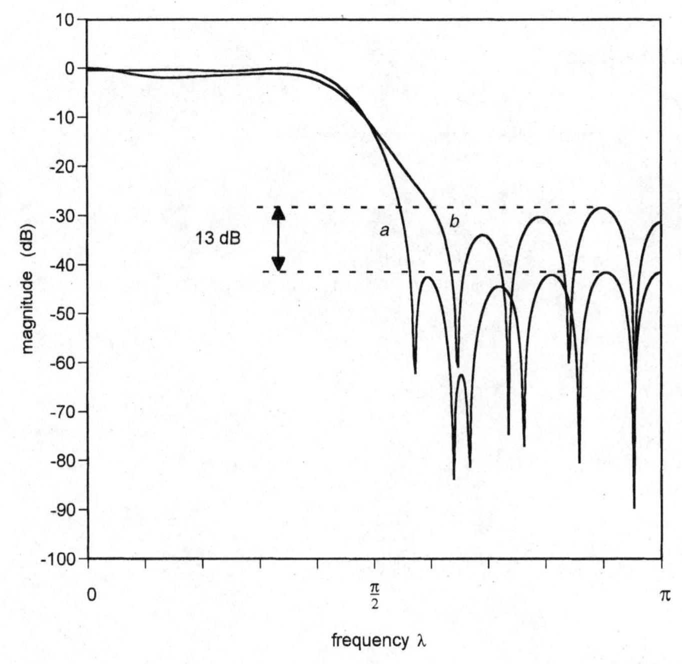

Figure 17.13 Magnitude response of 21-tap filters from (*a*) Example 15.4 and (*b*) Example 17.6.

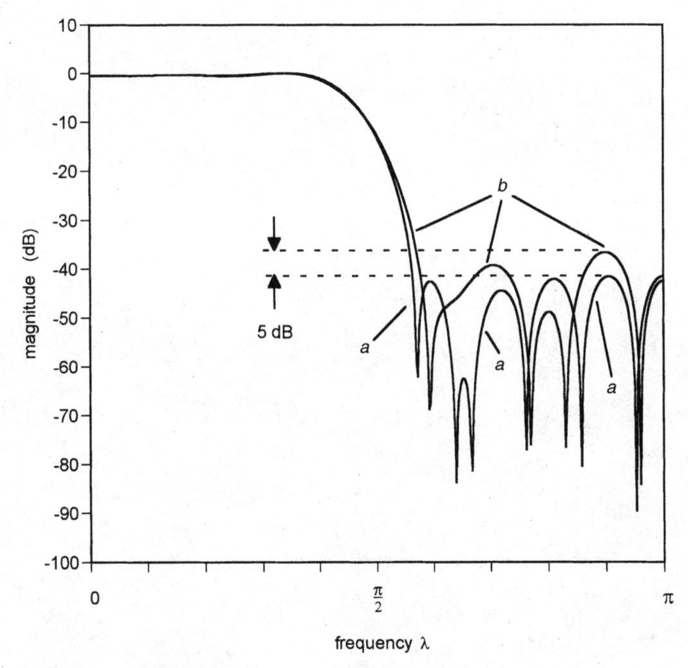

Figure 17.14 Magnitude response of 21-tap filters from (*a*) Example 15.4 and (*b*) Example 17.7.

Listing 17.1 Functions `ScaleCoefficients` and `QuantizeCoefficients` Added to Class `FirFilterDesign`

```
//=============================================================
//  method to quantize coefficients
//-------------------------------------------------------------

void FirFilterDesign::QuantizeCoefficients( long quant_factor,
                                            logical rounding_enabled )
{
 int n;
 long work_long;

 //-----------------------------------
 // if quant_factor == 0, then restore
 // coefficients to their original,
 // unquantized values

 if( quant_factor == 0)
   {
    for( n=0; n<Num_Taps; n++)
      {
       Imp_Resp_Coeff[n] = Original_Coeff[n];
      }
    return;
   }

 //-------------------------------------------
 // quantize the original coefficient values

 for( n=0; n< Num_Taps; n++)
  {
   if(rounding_enabled)
     {work_long = long((quant_factor * Original_Coeff[n])+0.5);}
   else
     {work_long = long(quant_factor * Original_Coeff[n]);}

   Imp_Resp_Coeff[n] = double(work_long)/double(quant_factor);
   }
 return;
}

//=============================================================
//  method to scale coefficients
//-------------------------------------------------------------

void FirFilterDesign::ScaleCoefficients( double scale_factor )
```

```
{
 int n;
 for( n=0; n< Num_Taps; n++)
  {
   Original_Coeff[n] = scale_factor * Original_Coeff[n];
   Imp_Resp_Coeff[n] = Original_Coeff[n];
  }
 return;
}
```

Listing 17.2 Function `ApplyWindow` **Added to Class** `FirFilterDesign`

```
//==========================================================
// apply discrete-time window to filter coefficients
//----------------------------------------------------------

void FirFilterDesign::ApplyWindow( GenericWindow *window)
{
 for(int n=0; n<Num_Taps; n++)
   {
    Imp_Resp_Coeff[n] *= window->GetDataWinCoeff(n);
    Original_Coeff[n] = Imp_Resp_Coeff[n];
   }
}
```

Listing 17.3 Direct Form 1 Realization of an FIR Filter

```
//
//  File = dirform1.cpp
//

#include <stdlib.h>
#include <fstream.h>
#include "dirform1.h"
extern ofstream DebugFile;

DirectFormFir::DirectFormFir( int num_taps,
                              double *coeff,
                              long coeff_quan_factor,
                              long input_quan_factor)
{
 int n;
 Num_Taps = num_taps;
 Input_Buffer = new long[num_taps];
 Quan_Coeff = new long[num_taps];
```

```
 Write_Indx = 0;
 Input_Quan_Factor = input_quan_factor;
 Output_Quan_Factor = double( coeff_quan_factor * input_quan_factor);

 DebugFile << "In DirectFormFir" << endl;

 for(n=0; n<num_taps; n++)
   {
    Quan_Coeff[n] = long((coeff_quan_factor * coeff[n]) + 0.5);
    DebugFile << coeff[n] << " quantized to " << Quan_Coeff[n] << endl;
    Input_Buffer[n] = 0;
   }
 return;
}

double DirectFormFir::ProcessSample( double input_val )
{
 double output_val;
 long term, sum;
 int read_indx, tap_indx;

 Input_Buffer[Write_Indx] = long(Input_Quan_Factor * input_val);

 read_indx = Write_Indx;
 Write_Indx++;
 if(Write_Indx >= Num_Taps) Write_Indx = 0;

 sum = 0;

 for( tap_indx=0; tap_indx<Num_Taps; tap_indx++)
   {
    term = Quan_Coeff[tap_indx] * Input_Buffer[read_indx];
    sum += term;

    read_indx--;
    if(read_indx < 0) read_indx = Num_Taps-1;
   }
 output_val = sum/Output_Quan_Factor;

 return(output_val);
}

int DirectFormFir::GetNumTaps(void)
{
 return(Num_Taps);
}
```

Listing 17.4 Method for Measuring Swept Response of an FIR Filter

```
//
//  File = swept.cpp
//

#include <fstream.h>
#include <math.h>
#include <stdlib.h>
#include "swept.h"
#include "typedefs.h"
#include "misdefs.h"
extern ofstream DebugFile;

SweptResponse::SweptResponse( FilterImplementation *filter_implem,
                              double sampling_interval,
                              istream& uin,
                              ostream& uout )
{
 int resp_indx;
 double lambda, phase_lag;
 double input_val;
 double *output_tone;
 int samp_indx;
 int num_holdoff_samps;
 logical default_file_ok;
 Filter_Implem = filter_implem;

 int phase_indx;
 int max_num_samps;
 int samps_per_corr;
 double cycles_per_corr;
 double max_correl, phase_offset, sum;
 double phase_delta;

 uout << "number of points in plot of frequency response?" << endl;
 uin >> Num_Resp_Pts;

 uout << "maximum swept frequency?" << endl;
 uin >> Max_Sweep_Freq;
 if(Max_Sweep_Freq > (0.5/sampling_interval) )
   {
    uout << "maximum swept frequency will be limited\n"
         << "to folding frequency of "
         << (0.5/sampling_interval) << endl;
    Max_Sweep_Freq = 0.5/sampling_interval;
   }
```

```
uout << "scaling?\n"
     << "  0 = linear, 1 = dB" << endl;
uin >> Db_Scale_Enabled;

uout << "phase resolution?\n"
     << "  (in degrees)" << endl;
uin >> phase_delta;
if(phase_delta > 0.0) phase_delta = -phase_delta;

uout << "numb sinewave cycles per correlation?" << endl;
uin >> cycles_per_corr;

if( Db_Scale_Enabled != 0) Db_Scale_Enabled = 1;

uout << "default name for magnitude response output\n"
     << "file is win_resp.txt\n\n"
     << "is this okay?"
     << "  0 = NO, 1 = YES"
     << endl;
uin >> default_file_ok;

if( default_file_ok)
    {
     Response_File = new ofstream("win_resp.txt", ios::out);
    }
 else
    {
     char *file_name;
     file_name = new char[31];

     uout << "enter complete name for output file (30 chars max)"
          << endl;
     uin >> file_name;
     Response_File = new ofstream(file_name, ios::out);
     delete []file_name;
    }
Mag_Resp = new double[Num_Resp_Pts];
Phase_Resp = new double[Num_Resp_Pts];
max_num_samps = int((cycles_per_corr+1)*Num_Resp_Pts/
                (Max_Sweep_Freq * sampling_interval));
output_tone = new double[max_num_samps+2];
for( resp_indx=1; resp_indx<Num_Resp_Pts; resp_indx++)
  {
   lambda = resp_indx * Max_Sweep_Freq * 2.0 * PI *
             sampling_interval / (double) Num_Resp_Pts;
   samps_per_corr = int(Num_Resp_Pts*cycles_per_corr/
```

```
        (resp_indx * Max_Sweep_Freq * sampling_interval));
  num_holdoff_samps = int(Num_Resp_Pts/
        (resp_indx * Max_Sweep_Freq * sampling_interval));
  for( samp_indx=0;
        samp_indx<(samps_per_corr+num_holdoff_samps);
        samp_indx++)
    {
     input_val = cos(lambda*samp_indx);
     output_tone[samp_indx] =
                 filter_implem->ProcessSample(input_val);
    } .

//===============================================
// Create sinusoids in phase increments of
// phase_delta degrees and correlate them
// with the stored output tone. Phase of sine
// with maximum correlation will be taken as
// phase response at that frquency.

max_correl = 0.0;
for(phase_indx=0; phase_indx < int(-360./phase_delta);
                  phase_indx++)
  {
   phase_offset = (phase_indx * phase_delta * PI )/180.0;
   sum = 0.0;
   for( samp_indx=num_holdoff_samps;
        samp_indx<(samps_per_corr+num_holdoff_samps);
        samp_indx++)
     {
      sum += (output_tone[samp_indx]*
             cos(lambda*samp_indx + phase_offset));
     }
   if(sum > max_correl)
     {
      max_correl = sum;
      phase_lag = double(phase_indx*phase_delta);
     }
  }
//--------------------------------------
// "unwrap" phase to keep it all negative

while(phase_lag >= 180.0)
  { phase_lag -= 360.0; }

DebugFile << "max_correl = " << max_correl
          << "  phase = " << phase_lag << endl;
```

```
    Phase_Resp[resp_indx] = phase_lag;
    if(Db_Scale_Enabled)
      {
      Mag_Resp[resp_indx] =
           20.0 * log10(2.0 * max_correl/samps_per_corr);
      }
    else
      {Mag_Resp[resp_indx] = 2.0 * max_correl/samps_per_corr;}
    }
 if(Normalize_Enabled) NormalizeResponse();
 return;
}
//=========================================================
// destructor
//---------------------------------------------------------

SweptResponse::~SweptResponse()
{
 delete []Mag_Resp;
 delete Response_File;
}
//=========================================================
//  method to normalize magnitude response
//---------------------------------------------------------

void SweptResponse::NormalizeResponse( void )
{
 int n;
 double biggest;

 if(Db_Scale_Enabled)
    {
     biggest = -100.0;

     for( n=1; n < Num_Resp_Pts; n++)
       {if(Mag_Resp[n]>biggest) biggest = Mag_Resp[n];}
     DebugFile << "before normaliz, biggest Mag_Resp was "
               << biggest << endl;
     for( n=1; n < Num_Resp_Pts; n++)
       {Mag_Resp[n] = Mag_Resp[n] - biggest;}
    }
 else
    {
     biggest = 0.0;

     for( n=1; n < Num_Resp_Pts; n++)
       {if(Mag_Resp[n]>biggest) biggest = Mag_Resp[n];}
```

```
    for( n=1; n < Num_Resp_Pts; n++)
      {Mag_Resp[n] = Mag_Resp[n] / biggest;}
   }
 return;
}
//==============================================================
//  method to dump magnitude response to the stream
//  designated by Response_File
//--------------------------------------------------------------

void SweptResponse::DumpMagResp( void )
{
 double freq;

 for(int n=1; n<Num_Resp_Pts; n++)
   {
    freq = n * Max_Sweep_Freq / (double) Num_Resp_Pts;
    (*Response_File) << freq << ", "
                     << Mag_Resp[n] << ", "
                     << Phase_Resp[n] << endl;
   }
 return;
}
```

Chapter

18

IIR Filter Design: Introduction

The general form for an *infinite impulse response* (*IIR*) filter's output $y[k]$ at time k is given by

$$y[n] = \sum_{n=1}^{N} a_n y[k-n] + \sum_{m=0}^{M} b_m x[k-m] \tag{18.1}$$

This equation indicates that the filter's output is a linear combination of the present input, the M previous inputs, and the N previous outputs. The corresponding system function is given by

$$H(z) = \frac{\sum_{m=0}^{M} b_m z^{-m}}{1 - \sum_{n=1}^{N} a_n z^{-n}} \tag{18.2}$$

where at least one of the a_n is nonzero and at least one of the roots of the denominator is not exactly cancelled by one of the roots of the numerator. For a stable filter, all the poles of $H(z)$ must lie inside the unit circle, but the zeros can lie anywhere in the z plane. It is usual for M, the number of zeros, to be less than or equal to N, the number of poles. Whenever the number of zeros exceeds the number of poles, the filter can be separated into an FIR filter with $M - N$ taps in cascade with an IIR filter with N poles and N zeros. Therefore, IIR design techniques are conventionally restricted to cases for which $M \leq N$.

Except for the special case in which all poles lie on the unit circle (in the z plane), it is not possible to design an IIR filter having exactly linear phase. Therefore, unlike FIR design procedures that are concerned almost exclusively with the magnitude response, IIR design procedures are concerned with both the magnitude response and the phase response.

18.1 Frequency Response of IIR Filters

The frequency response of an IIR filter can be computed from the coefficients a_n and b_m as

$$H[k] = \frac{\sum_{m=0}^{L-1} \beta_m \exp(j2\pi mk/L)}{\sum_{n=0}^{L-1} \alpha_n \exp(j2\pi k/L)} \tag{18.3}$$

where

$$\alpha_n = \begin{cases} 1 & n = 0 \\ -a_n & 0 < n \le N \\ 0 & N < n \end{cases}$$

$$\beta_m = \begin{cases} b_m & 0 \le m \le M \\ 0 & M < m \end{cases}$$

A C++ class that uses Eq. (18.3) to compute the response for an IIR filter is provided in Listing 18.1.

18.2 Structures for IIR Realizations

There are a number of different structures that can be used to realize IIR filters. For any given set of filter coefficients, all of these different structures are equivalent, assuming that they are implemented with infinite-precision arithmetic. However, when implemented using finite-precision arithmetic with quantized coefficients and quantized signals, the different structures can exhibit vastly different behavior. Therefore, some care needs to be exercised in the selection of a structure for implementing a particular filter. This section explores several of the most common implementation structures used for IIR filters.

Direct form

A direct realization of Eq. (18.1) is shown in Fig. 18.1 using the signal flow graph notation introduced in Sec. 8.4. The structure shown is known as the *direct form 1 realization or direct form 1 structure* for the IIR filter represented by Eq. (18.1). Examination of the figure reveals that the system can be viewed as two systems in cascade—the first system using input samples $x[k-M]$ through $x[k]$ to generate an intermediate signal that is labeled as $w[k]$ in the figure and the second system using $w[k]$ plus output samples $y[k-N]$ through $y[k-1]$ to generate $y[k]$. Since these two systems are linear time-invariant systems, the order of the cascade can be reversed to yield the equivalent system

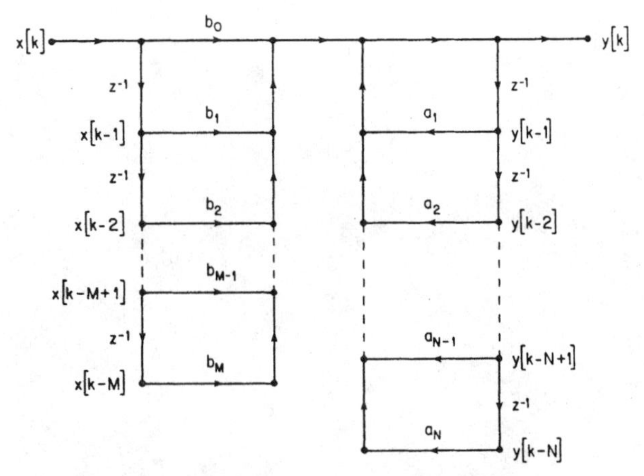

Figure 18.1 Direct form 1 realization for an IIR filter.

shown in Fig. 18.2. Examination of this figure reveals that the unit delays in parallel running down the center of the diagram can be paired such that within each pair the two delays each take the same input signal. This fact can be exploited to merge the two delay chains into a single chain, as shown in Fig. 18.3. The structure shown in this figure is known as the *direct form 2 realization* of the IIR system represented by Eq. (18.1).

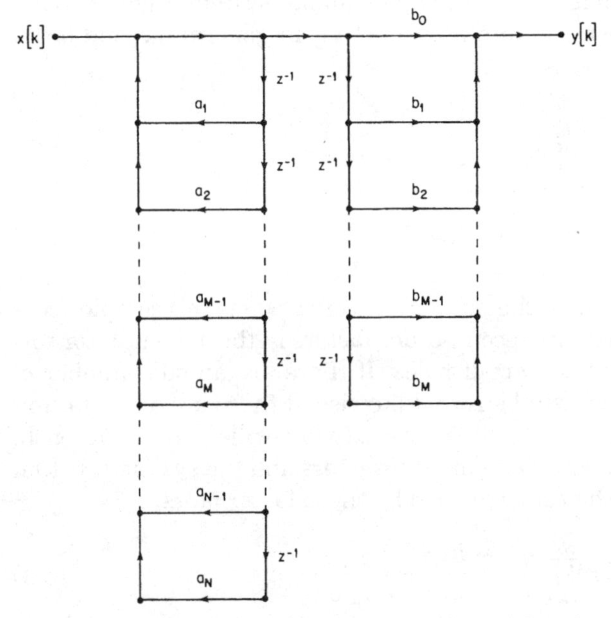

Figure 18.2 Signal flow graph of Fig. 18.1 with cascade order reversed.

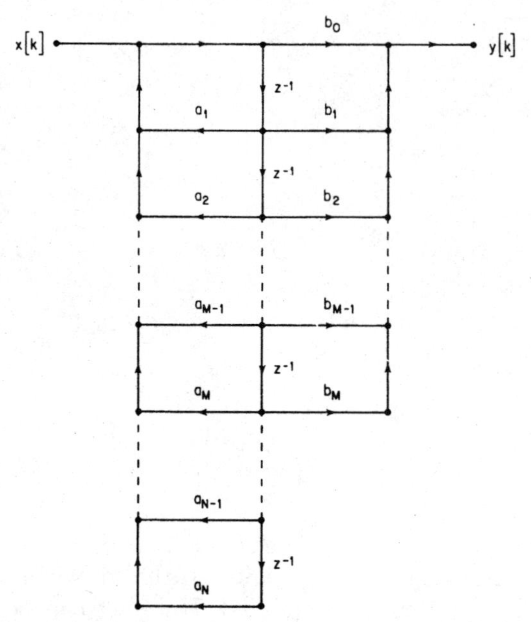

Figure 18.3 Direct form 2 realization for an IIR filter.

Cascade form

Both the numerator and denominator of the polynomial system function given by Eq. (18.2) can each be factored into a product of (in general) second-order polynomials with real coefficients:

$$H(z) = \frac{\prod_{k=1}^{M_S} (d_{0k} + d_{1k} z^{-1} + d_{2k} z^{-2})}{\prod_{k=1}^{N_S} (c_{0k} + c_{1k} z^{-1} + c_{2k} z^{-2})}$$

Each of the second-order factors in the numerator corresponds to a complex conjugate pair of zeros, and each of the second-order factors in the denominator corresponds to a complex conjugate pair of poles. If there are an odd number of poles, one of the coefficients c_{2k} will be zero. Likewise, if there are an odd number of zeros, one of the coefficients d_{2k} will be zero. In one widely used approach, numerator factors are paired with denominator factors and the system function is expressed as a product of the ratios formed by these factor pairs:

$$H(z) = \prod_{k=1}^{N_S} \frac{d_{0k} + d_{1k} z^{-1} + d_{2k} z^{-2}}{c_{0k} + c_{1k} z^{-1} + c_{2k} z^{-2}} \tag{18.4}$$

Each term in the numerator and denominator of Eq. (18.4) can be divided by c_{0k} to yield

$$H(z) = \prod_{k=1}^{N_S} \frac{(d_{0k}/c_{0k}) + (d_{1k}/c_{0k})\, z^{-1} + (d_{2k}/c_{0k})\, z^{-2}}{1 + (c_{1k}/c_{0k})\, z^{-1} + (c_{2k}/c_{0k})\, z^{-2}} \tag{18.5}$$

Making the substitutions

$$a_{1k} = \frac{c_{1k}}{c_{0k}}$$

$$a_{2k} = \frac{c_{2k}}{c_{0k}}$$

$$b_{0k} = \frac{d_{0k}}{c_{0k}}$$

$$b_{1k} = \frac{d_{1k}}{c_{0k}}$$

$$b_{2k} = \frac{d_{2k}}{c_{0k}}$$

puts Eq. (18.5) into the more convenient form given by

$$H(z) = \prod_{k=1}^{N_S} \frac{b_{0k} + b_{1k}\, z^{-1} + b_{2k}\, z^{-2}}{1 + a_{1k}\, z^{-1} + a_{2k}\, z^{-2}} \tag{18.6}$$

Each one of the N_S factors in Eq. (18.6) corresponds to an IIR section of the form shown in Fig. 18.4. The complete filter represented by Eq. (18.6) can be realized by cascading N_S of these sections.

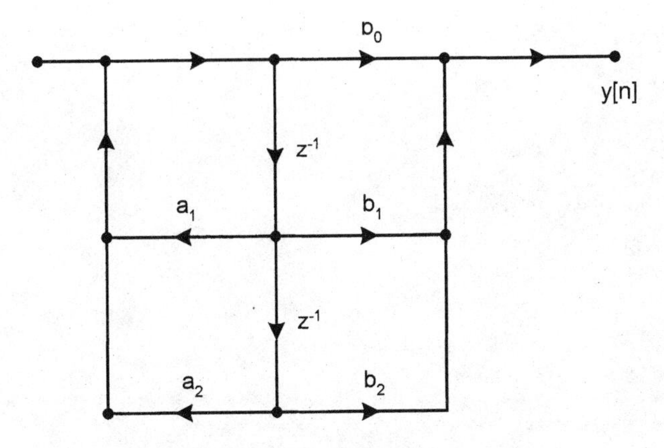

Figure 18.4 Direct form 2 realization for an IIR filter section that implements two poles and two zeros.

Listing 18.1 Frequency Response for IIR Filters

```
//
//  File = iir_resp.cpp
//
//  Member functions for class IirFilterResponse
//

#include <math.h>
#include <stdlib.h>
#include "d_cmplx.h"
#include "iir_resp.h"
#include "typedefs.h"
#include "misdefs.h"
extern ofstream DebugFile;
//==================================================
//  constructor with all configuration parameters
//  passed in as arguments
//--------------------------------------------------

IirFilterResponse::IirFilterResponse( IirFilterDesign *filter_design,
                                      int num_resp_pts,
                                      int db_scale_enabled,
                                      int normalize_enabled,
                                      char* resp_file_name )
{
 Filter_Design = filter_design;
 Num_Resp_Pts = num_resp_pts;
 Db_Scale_Enabled = db_scale_enabled;
 Normalize_Enabled = normalize_enabled;

 if( resp_file_name == NULL)
   { Response_File = new ofstream("iir_resp.txt", ios::out);}
 else
   { Response_File = new ofstream(resp_file_name, ios::out);}

 Num_Numer_Coeffs = Filter_Design->GetNumNumerCoeffs();
 Num_Denom_Coeffs = Filter_Design->GetNumDenomCoeffs();
 Freq_Resp = (double_complex*) new double[2*Num_Resp_Pts];
 Mag_Resp = new double[Num_Resp_Pts];
 Phase_Resp = new double[Num_Resp_Pts];

 return;
}

//=============================================================
// alternate constructor with interactive setting of
```

```
// configuration parameters
//----------------------------------------------------------------------
IirFilterResponse::IirFilterResponse( IirFilterDesign *filter_design,
                                       istream& uin,
                                       ostream& uout )

{
 logical default_file_ok;
 Filter_Design = filter_design;

 uout << "number of points in plot of frequency response?" << endl;
 uin >> Num_Resp_Pts;

 uout << "scaling?\n"
      << "  0 = linear, 1 = dB" << endl;
 uin >> Db_Scale_Enabled;

 if( Db_Scale_Enabled != 0) Db_Scale_Enabled = 1;
 Normalize_Enabled = 1;

 uout << "default name for magnitude response output\n"
      << "file is iir_resp.txt\n\n"
      << "is this okay?"
      << "  0 = NO, 1 = YES"
      << endl;
 uin >> default_file_ok;

 if( default_file_ok)
    {
     Response_File = new ofstream("iir_resp.txt", ios::out);
    }
  else
    {
     char *file_name;
     file_name = new char[31];

     uout << "enter complete name for output file (30 chars max)"
          << endl;
     uin >> file_name;
     Response_File = new ofstream(file_name, ios::out);
     delete []file_name;
    }

 Num_Numer_Coeffs = Filter_Design->GetNumNumerCoeffs();
 Num_Denom_Coeffs = Filter_Design->GetNumDenomCoeffs();
 Freq_Resp = (double_complex*)new double[2*Num_Resp_Pts];
 Mag_Resp = new double[Num_Resp_Pts];
 Phase_Resp = new double[Num_Resp_Pts];
```

```
 return;
}

//=====================================================
//  method to compute frequency response
//-----------------------------------------------------
void IirFilterResponse::ComputeResponse( void )
{
 int resp_indx, tap_indx;
 double delta_time, delta_freq;
 double theta, phi;
 double real_sum, imag_sum;
 double *numer_coeff, *denom_coeff;
 double_complex numerator, denominator;

 cout << " in IirFilterResponse::ComputeResponse" << endl;
 numer_coeff = Filter_Design->GetNumerCoefficients();
 denom_coeff = Filter_Design->GetDenomCoefficients();
 delta_time = Filter_Design->GetSamplingInterval();

 delta_freq = 0.5/( delta_time * Num_Resp_Pts );
 theta = delta_freq * delta_time;

 for( resp_indx=0; resp_indx<Num_Resp_Pts; resp_indx++)
   {
    real_sum = 0.0;
    imag_sum = 0.0;

    for( tap_indx=0; tap_indx<Num_Numer_Coeffs; tap_indx++)
     {
      phi = theta * resp_indx * tap_indx;
      real_sum += (numer_coeff[tap_indx] * cos(phi));
      imag_sum -= numer_coeff[tap_indx] * sin(phi);
     }
    numerator = double_complex(real_sum, imag_sum);

    real_sum = 1.0;
    imag_sum = 0.0;

    for( tap_indx=1; tap_indx<=Num_Denom_Coeffs; tap_indx++)
      {
       phi = theta * tap_indx * resp_indx;
       real_sum -= (denom_coeff[tap_indx] * cos(phi));
       imag_sum += (denom_coeff[tap_indx] * sin(phi));
      }
    denominator = double_complex(real_sum, imag_sum);
    Freq_Resp[resp_indx] = numerator/denominator;
   }
```

```
 //----------------------------------------------
 //  compute magnitude and phase of response

 for( resp_indx=0; resp_indx<Num_Resp_Pts; resp_indx++)
   {
    Phase_Resp[resp_indx] = arg(Freq_Resp[resp_indx]);
   if(Db_Scale_Enabled)
     {Mag_Resp[resp_indx] = 20.0 * log10(norm(Freq_Resp[resp_indx]));}
   else
     {Mag_Resp[resp_indx] = norm(Freq_Resp[resp_indx]);}
   }
 return;
}


//=====================================================
//  method to normalize magnitude response
//-----------------------------------------------------


void IirFilterResponse::NormalizeResponse( void )
{
 int n;
 double biggest;

 if(Db_Scale_Enabled)
   {
    biggest = -100.0;

    for( n=0; n < Num_Resp_Pts; n++)
      {if(Mag_Resp[n]>biggest) biggest = Mag_Resp[n];}
    for( n=0; n < Num_Resp_Pts; n++)
      {Mag_Resp[n] = Mag_Resp[n] - biggest;}
   }
 else
   {
    biggest = 0.0;

    for( n=0; n < Num_Resp_Pts; n++)
      {if(Mag_Resp[n]>biggest) biggest = Mag_Resp[n];}
    for( n=0; n < Num_Resp_Pts; n++)
      {Mag_Resp[n] = Mag_Resp[n] / biggest;}
   }
 return;
}
//==============================================
//  method to return a pointer to the magnitude
//  response that is stored inside this class
//----------------------------------------------
```

```
double* IirFilterResponse::GetMagResp( void)
{
 return(Mag_Resp);
}

//==============================================================
//  method to dump magnitude response to the stream
//  designated by Response_File
//--------------------------------------------------------------

void IirFilterResponse::DumpMagResp( void )
{
 double freq, delta_time, delta_freq, phase;

 delta_time = Filter_Design->GetSamplingInterval();
 delta_freq = 0.5/( delta_time * Num_Resp_Pts );

 for(int n=1; n<Num_Resp_Pts; n++)
   {
    freq = n*delta_freq;
    phase = 180.0 * Phase_Resp[n] /PI;
    while(phase > 0.0)
      {
       phase -= 360.0;
      }
    (*Response_File) << freq << ", "
                     << Mag_Resp[n] << ", "
                     << phase << endl;
   }
 return;
}
//=======================================================
//  searches the magnitude response over the interval
//  from sample intrvl_beg thru the sample intrvl_end
//  and then returns the largest value found in this
//  interval.
//-------------------------------------------------------
double IirFilterResponse::GetIntervalPeak( int nBeg,
                                           int nEnd)
{
 double peak;
 int n, indexOfPeak;

 peak = -9999.0;
 for(n=nBeg; n<nEnd; n++)
   {
    if(Mag_Resp[n]>peak)
```

```
      {
       peak=Mag_Resp[n];
       indexOfPeak = n;
      }
   }
 return(peak);
}
```

Chapter

19

IIR Filter Design: Invariance and Pole-Zero Placement Methods

This chapter presents three different methods for the design of IIR filters. The *impulse invariance* method is based on setting the unit sample response of the digital filter equal to a sequence of uniformly spaced samples from the impulse response of an analog filter. The *step invariance* method is based on setting the unit step response of the digital filter equal to a sequence of uniformly spaced samples from the step response of an analog filter. The *matched z transformation* method is based upon a direct mapping of s-plane pole and zero locations into the corresponding z-plane locations. A fourth method, *bilinear transformation,* is presented in Chap. 20.

19.1 Impulse Invariance

The basic idea behind the impulse-invariance approach is a very simple one—the unit sample response of the digital filter is set equal to a sequence of uniformly spaced samples from the impulse response of an analog filter:

$$h[n] = h_a(nT) \tag{19.1}$$

(An analog filter used in this context is usually refered to as a *prototype* filter.) This approach is conceptually simple, but from a practical viewpoint, evaluation of Eq. (19.1) is not a straightforward matter. By definition, for an *infinite* impulse response filter, the sequence $h[n]$ will be nonzero over an infinite domain of n. Furthermore, based on the s-plane-to-z-plane mapping discussed in Sec. 10.2, we can conclude that the imposition of Eq. (19.1) will not result in a simple relationship between the frequency response corresponding to $h[n]$

and the frequency response corresponding to $h_a(t)$. In fact, this relationship can be shown to be

$$H(e^{j\lambda}) = \frac{1}{T} \sum_{k=-\infty}^{\infty} H_a\left(j\frac{\lambda + 2\pi k}{T}\right) \tag{19.2}$$

where $h[n] \overset{\text{DTFT}}{\longleftrightarrow} H(e^{j\lambda})$
$h_a(t) \overset{\text{FT}}{\longleftrightarrow} H_a(j\omega)$

Put simply, Eq. (19.2) indicates that $H(e^{j\lambda})$ will be an aliased version of $H_a(j\omega)$. The only way the aliasing can be avoided is if $H_a(j\omega)$ is band limited such that

$$H_a(j\omega) = 0 \qquad \text{for} \quad |\omega| \geq \frac{\pi}{T} \tag{19.3}$$

If Eq. (19.3) is satisfied, then

$$H(e^{j\lambda}) = \frac{1}{T} H_a\left(j\frac{\lambda}{T}\right) \qquad |\lambda| \leq \pi \tag{19.4}$$

For a practical analog filter, Eq. (19.3) will never be satisfied exactly, but the impulse-invariance method can be used to advantage with responses that are nonzero but negligible beyond some frequency.

The transfer function of the analog prototype filter can be expressed in the form of a partial-fraction expansion as

$$H_a(s) = \sum_{k=1}^{N} \frac{A_k}{s - s_k} \tag{19.5}$$

where the s_k are the poles of $H_a(s)$ and the A_k are given by

$$A_k = [(s - s_k)\, H_a(s)]\,\big|_{s = s_k}$$

Based on transform pair 8 from Table 3.2, the impulse response can then be written as

$$h_a(t) = \sum_{k=1}^{N} A_k\, e^{s_k t}\, u(t) \tag{19.6}$$

The unit-sample response of the digital filter is then formed by sampling the prototype filter's impulse response to obtain

$$h[n] = \sum_{k=1}^{N} A_k (e^{s_k T})^n\, u(t) \tag{19.7}$$

The corresponding system function for the digital filter $H(z)$ is obtained as the z transform of Eq. (19.7):

$$H(z) = \sum_{k=1}^{N} \frac{A_k}{1 - e^{s_k T} z^{-1}} \tag{19.8}$$

Based on the foregoing, we can state the following algorithm for impulse-invariant design of an IIR filter.

Algorithm 19.1 Impulse-invariant design of IIR filters

Step 1. Obtain the transfer function $H_a(s)$ for the desired analog prototype filter. (The material provided in Chaps. 4 through 7 will prove useful here.)

Step 2. For $k = 1, 2, \ldots, N$, determine the poles s_k of $H_a(s)$ and compute the coefficients A_k using

$$A_k = [(s - s_k)\, H_a(s)]\,\big|_{s = s_k} \tag{19.9}$$

Step 3. Using the coefficients A_k obtained in Step 2, generate the digital filter system function $H(z)$ as

$$H(z) = \sum_{k=1}^{N} \frac{A_k}{1 - \exp\,(s_k T) z^{-1}} \tag{19.10}$$

where T is the sampling interval of the digital filter.

Step 4. The result obtained in Step 3 will be a sum of fractions. Obtain a common denominator, and express $H(z)$ as a ratio of polynomials in z^{-1} in the form

$$H(z) = \frac{\sum_{k=0}^{M} b_k z^{-k}}{1 - \sum_{k=1}^{N} a_k z^{-k}} \tag{19.11}$$

Step 5. Use the a_k and b_k obtained in Step 4 to realize the filter in any of the structures given in Sec. 18.2.

Example 19.1 Use the technique of impulse invariance to derive a low-pass IIR digital filter from a second-order Butterworth analog filter with a 3-dB cutoff frequency of 3 kHz. The sampling rate for the digital filter is 30,000 samples per second.

solution From Sec. 4.1 we obtain the normalized-transfer function for a second-order Butterworth filter as

$$H(s) = \frac{1}{(s - s_1)(s - s_2)}$$

where

$$s_1 = \cos\frac{3\pi}{4} + j\sin\frac{3\pi}{4}$$

$$= \frac{-\sqrt{2}}{2} + j\frac{\sqrt{2}}{2}$$

$$s_2 = \cos\frac{5\pi}{4} + j\sin\frac{5\pi}{4}$$

$$= \cos\frac{3\pi}{4} - j\sin\frac{3\pi}{4}$$

$$= \frac{-\sqrt{2}}{2} - j\frac{\sqrt{2}}{2}$$

The specified cutoff frequency of $f = 3000$ yields $\omega_c = 6000\pi$, and the denormalized response (see Sec. 3.9) is given by

$$H_a(s) = \frac{\omega_c^2}{(s - \omega_c s_1)(s - \omega_c s_2)}$$

$$= \frac{\omega_c^2}{[s + \omega_c(\sqrt{2}/2) - j\omega_c(\sqrt{2}/2)][s + \omega_c(\sqrt{2}/2) + j\omega_c(\sqrt{2}/2)]}$$

The partial-fraction expansion of $H_a(s)$ is given by

$$H_a(s) = \frac{A_1}{s + \omega_c(\sqrt{2}/2) - j\omega_c(\sqrt{2}/2)} + \frac{A_2}{s + \omega_c(\sqrt{2}/2) + j\omega_c(\sqrt{2}/2)}$$

where

$$A_1 = \frac{-j\sqrt{2}}{2\omega_c}$$

$$A_2 = \frac{j\sqrt{2}}{2\omega_c}$$

Using these values for A_1 and A_2 plus the fact that

$$\omega_c T = \frac{6000\pi}{30{,}000} = \frac{\pi}{5}$$

we obtain from Eq. (19.10) the discrete system function $H(z)$ as

$$H(z) = \frac{-j\sqrt{2}/(2\omega_c)}{1 - \exp\left(\dfrac{-\pi\sqrt{2}}{10} + j\dfrac{\pi\sqrt{2}}{10}\right) z^{-1}} + \frac{j\sqrt{2}/(2\omega_c)}{1 - \exp\left(\dfrac{-\pi\sqrt{2}}{10} - j\dfrac{\pi\sqrt{2}}{10}\right) z^{-1}}$$

$$= \frac{2.06797 \times 10^{-5} z^{-1}}{1 - 1.158045z^{-1} + 0.4112407z^{-2}}$$

Programming considerations

Step 1. Butterworth, Chebyshev, and Bessel filters are *all-pole* filters—their transfer functions have no finite zeros. Closed-form expressions are available for the poles of Butterworth [Eq. (4.2)] and Chebyshev [Eq. (5.4)] filters. The poles of Bessel filters can be readily obtained by finding the roots of the denominator polynomial as discussed in Chap. 7. The transfer function for an elliptical filter has both poles and zeros. The poles are readily available by using the quadratic formula to find the denominator roots for each factor in Eq. (6.22). The zeros $\pm j\alpha\sqrt{\alpha_i}$ are obtained by inspection of Eq. (6.22). The software for performing the impulse-invariance transformation is therefore designed to accept $H_a(s)$ specified as an array of poles and an array of zeros.

Step 2. Evaluation of A_k for Step 2 of the algorithm is straightforward. The coefficients A_k can be written as $A_k = N_{Ak}/D_{Ak}$ where the numerator N_{Ak} is obtained as

$$N_{Ak} = \begin{cases} H_0 \prod_{m=1}^{M} (p_k - q_m) & M \neq 0 \\ H_0 & M = 0 \end{cases}$$

and q_m is the mth zero of $H_a(s)$, p_k is the kth pole of $H_a(s)$, and M is the total number of zeros. Equation (19.9) can be evaluated using simple arithmetic—there is no symbolic manipulation needed. The denominator D_{Ak} is obtained as

$$D_{Ak} = \prod_{\substack{n=1 \\ n \neq k}}^{N} (p_k - p_n)$$

Step 3. Evaluation of $H(z)$ is more than plain, straightforward arithmetic. At this point, for each value of k, the coefficient A_k is known and the coefficient $\exp(s_k T)$ can be evaluated. However, z remains a variable and hence will demand some special consideration. To simplify the notation in the subsequent development, let us rewrite $H(z)$ as

$$H(z) = \sum_{k=1}^{N} \frac{A_k}{1 + \beta_k z^{-1}} \qquad (19.12)$$

where $\beta_k = -\exp(s_k T)$

Step 4. For the summation in (19.12), the common denominator will be the product of each summand's denominator:

$$D(z) = \prod_{k=1}^{N} (1 + \beta_k z^{-1}) \qquad (19.13)$$

To see how Eq. (19.13) can be easily evaluated by computer, let's examine the sequence of partial products $\{D_k(z)\}$ encountered in the evaluation:

$$D_1(z) = (1 + \beta_1 z^{-1})$$

$$D_2(z) = (1 + \beta_2 z^{-1})\, D_1(z) = D_1(z) + \beta_2 z^{-1} D_1(z)$$

$$D_3(z) = (1 + \beta_3 z^{-1})\, D_2(z) = D_2(z) + \beta_3 z^{-1} D_2(z)$$

$$D_4(z) = (1 + \beta_4 z^{-1})\, D_3(z) = D_3(z) + \beta_4 z^{-1} D_3(z)$$

$$\vdots$$

$$D(z) = D_N(z) = (1 + \beta_N z^{-1})\, D_{N-1}(z) = D_{N-1}(z) + \beta_N z^{-1} D_{N-1}(z)$$

Examination of this sequence reveals that the partial product $D_k(z)$ at iteration k can be expressed in terms of the partial product $D_{k-1}(z)$ as

$$D_k(z) = D_{k-1}(z) + \beta_k z^{-1} D_{k-1}(z)$$

The partial product $D_{k-1}(z)$ will be a $(k-1)$-degree polynomial in z^{-1}:

$$D_{k-1}(z) = \delta_0 (z^{-1})^0 + \delta_1 (z^{-1})^1 + \delta_2 (z^{-1})^2 + \cdots + \delta_{k-1} (z^{-1})^{k-1}$$

The product $\beta_k z^{-1} D_{k-1}(z)$ is then given by

$$\beta_k z^{-1} D_{k-1}(z) = \delta_0 \beta_k (z^{-1})^1 + \delta_1 \beta_k (z^{-1})^2 + \delta_2 \beta_k (z^{-1})^3 + \cdots + \delta_{k-1} \beta_k (z^{-1})^k$$

and $D_k(z)$ is given by

$$D_k(z) = \delta_0 (z^{-1})^0 + (\delta_1 + \delta_0 \beta_k)(z^{-1})^1 + (\delta_2 + \delta_1 \beta_k)(z^{-1})^2 + \cdots$$
$$+ (\delta_{k-1} + \delta_{k-2} \beta_k)(z^{-1})^{k-1} + \delta_{k-1} \beta_k (z^{-1})^k$$

Therefore, we can conclude that if δ_n is the coefficient for the $(z^{-1})^n$ term in $D_{k-1}(z)$, then the coefficient for the $(z^{-1})^n$ term in $D_k(z)$ is $(\delta_n + \delta_{n-1}\beta_k)$ with the proviso that $\delta_k \triangleq 0$ in $D_{k-1}(z)$. The polynomial $D_{k-1}(z)$ can be represented in the computer as an array of k coefficients, with the array index corresponding to the subscript on δ and the superscript (exponent) on (z^{-1}): `delta[0]` $= \delta_0$, `delta[1]` $= \delta_1$, and so on. The coefficients for the partial product $D_k(z)$ can be obtained from the coefficients for $D_{k-1}(z)$ as indicated by the following code fragment

```
for( j=k; j > = 1; j--)
    {delta[j]=delta[j] + beta * delta[j - 1];}
```

The loop is executed in reverse order so that the coefficients can be updated in place without prematurely overwriting the old values. If this fragment is placed within an outer loop with k ranging from 1 to `numPoles`, the final values in `delta[n]` will be the coefficients a_n for Eq. (19.11).

For the summation in Eq. (19.10), the numerator can be computed as

$$N(z) = \sum_{k=1}^{N} \left[A_k \prod_{\substack{n=1 \\ n \neq k}}^{N} (1 - \beta_n z^{-1}) \right] \tag{19.14}$$

For each value of k, the product in Eq. (19.14) can be evaluated in a manner similar to the way in which the denominator is evaluated. The major difference is that the factor $(1 - \beta_k z^{-1})$ is not included in the product. It is then a simple matter to add the coefficients of each of the N products to obtain the coefficients for the numerator polynomial $N(z)$. A complete function for computing the coefficients a_n and b_n is provided in Listing 19.1.

19.2 Step Invariance

One major drawback to filters designed via the impulse-invariance method is their sensitivity to the specific characteristics of the input signal. The digital filter's unit-sample response is a sampled version of the prototype filter's impulse response. However, the prototype filter's response to an arbitrary input cannot, in general, be sampled to obtain the digital filter's response to a sampled version of the same arbitrary input. In many applications a filter's step response is of more concern than is the filter's impulse response. In such cases, the impulse-invariance technique can be modified to design a digital filter based on the principle of step invariance.

Algorithm 19.2 Step-invariant design of IIR filters

Step 1. Obtain the transfer function $H_a(s)$ for the desired analog prototype filter.

Step 2. Multiply $H_a(s)$ by $1/s$ to obtain $G_a(s)$, the filter's response to the unit step function.

Step 3. For $k = 1, 2, \ldots, N$, determine the poles s_k of $G_a(s)$ and compute the coefficients A_k using

$$A_k = [(s - s_k)\, G_a(s)]\,\big|_{s = s_k}$$

Step 4. Using the coefficients A_k obtained in Step 3, generate the system function $G(z)$ as

$$G(z) = \sum_{k=1}^{N} \frac{A_k}{1 - \exp(s_k T)\, z^{-1}}$$

Step 5. Multiply $G(z)$ by $(1 - z^{-1})$ to remove the z transform of a unit step and thereby obtain $H(z)$ as

$$H(z) = (1 - z^{-1}) \sum_{k=1}^{N} \frac{A_k}{1 - \exp(s_k T)\, z^{-1}}$$

Step 6. Obtain a common denominator for the terms in the summation of Step 5, and express $H(z)$ as a ratio of polynomials in z^{-1} in the form

$$G(z) = \frac{\sum_{k=0}^{M} b_k z^{-k}}{1 - \sum_{k=1}^{N} a_k z^{-k}}$$

Step 7. Use the a_k and b_k obtained in Step 6 to realize the filter in any of the structures given in Sec. 18.2.

Programming considerations

The step-invariance method is similar to the impulse-invariance method, with two important differences. In Step 2 of Algorithm 19.2, the transfer function $H_a(s)$ is multiplied by $1/s$. Assuming that $H_a(s)$ is represented in terms of its poles and zeros, multiplication by $1/s$ is accomplished by simply adding a pole at $s = 0$. (Strictly speaking, if the analog filter has a zero at $s = 0$, multiplication by $1/s$ creates a pole at $s = 0$, which cancels the zero. However, since none of the analog prototype filters within the scope of this book have zeros at $s = 0$, we shall construct the software without provisions for handling a zero at $s = 0$.)

In Step 5 of Algorithm 19.2, the system function $G(z)$ is multiplied by $(1 - z^{-1})$ to remove the z transform of a unit step and thereby obtain the system function $H(z)$. Conceptually, this multiplication is appropriately located in Step 5. However, for ease of implementation, it makes sense to defer the multiplication until after the coefficients a_n and b_n are generated in Step 6. A function modified to perform the step-invariance technique is provided in Listing 19.2.

19.3 Matched *z* Transformation

Starting with an analog prototype filter having both poles and zeros, it is possible to derive an IIR digital filter by direct mapping of the s-plane poles and zeros into the z-plane using the replacement relations

$$s + a \rightarrow 1 - z^{-1} e^{-aT} \tag{19.15}$$

$$(s + a - jb)(s + a + jb) = s^2 + 2as + a^2 + b^2 \rightarrow$$
$$1 - 2z^{-1} e^{-aT} \cos(bT) + z^{-2} e^{-2aT} \tag{19.16}$$

where T is the sampling interval. Equation (19.15) is used for mapping real poles or zeros located at $s = -a$. Equation (19.16) is used for mapping complex conjugate pairs of poles or zeros located at $s = -a \pm jb$. This mapping is sometimes called the matched z transformation and is useful only for analog systems having *both* poles and zeros and for which the zeros lie at frequencies less than half the sampling frequency.

Example 19.2 Apply the matched z transformation to the ninth order elliptical filter having a normalized transfer function given by

$$H(s) = \frac{H_0}{s + p_0} \prod_{i=1}^{4} \frac{s^2 + A_i}{s^2 + B_i s + C_i} \tag{19.17}$$

where A_i, B_i, and C_i are as given in Table 19.1, $H_0 = 0.015317$, and $p_0 = 0.470218$. Denormalize the filter to have a cutoff frequency of 3 kHz, and assume a sampling rate of 30,000 samples per second.

solution The values in Table 19.1 are denormalized using the rules given in Sec. 6.3 to obtain the values for A'_i, B'_i, and C'_i as given in Table 19.2. The zeros of Eq. (19.17) occur in complex conjugate pairs, so we set the numerator of each factor in the product of Eq. (19.17) equal to the left-hand side of Eq. (19.16) and solve for a_i and b_i in terms of A'_i.

$$s^2 + A'_i = s^2 + 2as + a^2 + b^2$$

$$b_i = \sqrt{A'_i}$$

$$a_i = 0$$

Therefore, the numerator of $H[z]$ can be written as

$$N[z] = \prod_{n=1}^{4} \left[1 - 2z^{-1} \cos\,(T\sqrt{A_n}) + z^{-2}\right]$$

$$= \prod_{n=1}^{4} [1 - \alpha_n z^{-1} + z^{-2}]$$

TABLE 19.1 Normalized Analog Filter Coefficients for Example 19.2

i	a_i	b_i	c_i
1	4.174973	0.6786235	0.4374598
2	1.606396	0.3091997	0.7415493
3	1.182293	0.1127396	0.8988261
4	1.076828	0.0272625	0.9538953

TABLE 19.2 Denormalized Analog Filter Coefficients for Example 19.2

i	a_i	b_i	c_i
1	37574757	2035.8705	3937138
2	14457564	927.5991	6673943
3	10640637	338.2188	8089434
4	9691452	81.7875	8585057

TABLE 19.3 Digital Filter Coefficients for Example 19.2

i	α_n	β_n	γ_n
0	—	0.954067	—
1	0.204328	1.930162	0.934389
2	0.126744	1.962256	0.969553
3	0.108733	1.979858	0.988789
4	0.103770	1.987759	0.997278

where the α_n are as given in Table 19.2. The single real pole of Eq. (19.17) lies at $s = -p_0$. The remaining poles of Eq. (19.17) occur in complex conjugate pairs, so we set the denominator of each factor in the product of Eq. (19.17) equal to the left-hand side of Eq. (19.16) and solve for a_i and b_i in terms of B'_i and C'_i.

$$s^2 + B'_i s + C'_i = s^2 + 2a_i s + a_i^2 + b_i^2$$

$$a_i = \frac{B'_i}{2}$$

$$b_i = \sqrt{C'_i - \frac{(B'_i)^2}{4}}$$

Therefore the denominator of $H[z]$ can be written as

$$D[z] = [1 - z^{-1} \exp(-p_0 T)] \prod_{n=1}^{4} \left[1 - 2z^{-1} \exp\left(\frac{-B'_n T}{2}\right) \cos\left(T\sqrt{C'_i - \frac{(B'_i)^2}{4}}\right) + z^{-2} \exp(-B_n T)\right]$$

$$= (1 - \beta_0 z^{-1}) \prod_{n=1}^{4} [1 - \beta_n z^{-1} + \gamma_n z^{-2}]$$

where the β_n and γ_n are as given in Table 19.3.

Listing 19.1 Impulse Invariance Technique for Generating IIR Filters

```
//
//  file = impinvar.cpp
//

#include "impinvar.h"

void ImpulseInvar( double_complex *pole,
                   int num_poles,
                   double_complex *zero,
                   int num_zeros,
                   double h_sub_zero,
                   double big_t,
                   double_complex *a,
                   double_complex *b)
```

```
{
int k, n, j, maxCoef;
double_complex *delta, *big_a;
double_complex beta, denom, numer, work2;

delta = new double_complex[num_poles+1];
big_a = new double_complex[num_poles+1];

for(j=0; j<num_poles+1; j++)
  {
  delta[j] = double_complex(0.0,0.0);
  a[j] = double_complex(0.0,0.0);
  b[j] = double_complex(0.0,0.0);
  }
//-----------------------------------------------
//  compute partial fraction expansion coefficients

for( k=1; k<=num_poles; k++) {
  numer = double_complex(h_sub_zero,0.0);
  for(n=1; n<=num_zeros; n++)
    {
    numer = numer * (pole[n] - zero[n]);
    }
  denom = double_complex(1.0,0.0);
  for( n=1; n<=num_poles; n++)
    {
    if(n==k) continue;
    denom = denom * (pole[k] - pole[n]);
    }
  big_a[k] = numer/denom;
  }

//------------------------------------
//  compute numerator coefficients

for( k=1; k<=num_poles; k++)
  {
  delta[0] = double_complex(1.0, 0.0);
  for(n=1; n<=num_poles; n++)
    {
    delta[n] = double_complex(0.0,0.0);
    }
  maxCoef = 0;
  for( n=1; n<=num_poles; n++)
    {
    if(n==k) continue;
      maxCoef++;
```

```
        beta = -cexp(big_t * pole[n]);
        for(j=maxCoef; j>=1; j--)
          {
          delta[j] += (beta * delta[j-1]);
          }
      }
    for( j=0; j<num_poles; j++)
      {
      b[j] += (big_a[k] * delta[j]);
      }
    }

//-------------------------------------
//  compute denominator coefficients
a[0] = double_complex(1.0,0.0);
for( n=1; n<=num_poles; n++)
  {
  beta = -cexp(big_t * pole[n]);

  for( j=n; j>=1; j--)
    {
    a[j] += (beta * a[j-1]);
    }
  }
for( j=1; j<=num_poles; j++)
  {
  a[j] = -a[j];
  }
return;
}
```

Listing 19.2 Step Invariance Technique for Generating IIR Filters

```
//
//  File = stpinvar.cpp
//

#include "stpinvar.h"

void StepInvar( double_complex *pole,
                int num_poles,
                double_complex *zero,
                int num_zeros,
                double h_sub_zero,
                double big_t,
                double_complex *a,
```

```
                double_complex *b)
{
int k, n, j, max_coef;
double_complex *delta, *big_a;
double_complex beta, denom, numer, work2;

delta = new double_complex[num_poles+1];
big_a = new double_complex[num_poles+1];

for(j=0; j<=num_poles; j++) {
  delta[j] = double_complex(0.0,0.0);
  a[j] = double_complex(0.0,0.0);
  b[j] = double_complex(0.0,0.0);
  }
pole[0] = double_complex(0.0,0.0);

//-----------------------------------------------------
//  compute partial fraction expansion coefficients

for( k=0; k<=num_poles; k++)
  {
  numer = double_complex(h_sub_zero,0.0);
  for(n=1; n<=num_zeros; n++)
    {
    numer *= (pole[n] - zero[n]);
    }
  denom = double_complex(1.0,0.0);
  for( n=0; n<=num_poles; n++)
    {
    if(n==k) continue;
      denom *= (pole[k] - pole[n]);
    }
  big_a[k] = numer/denom;
  }

//-------------------------------------
//  compute numerator coefficients

for( k=1; k<=num_poles; k++)
  {
  delta[0] = double_complex(1.0, 0.0);
  for(n=1; n<=num_poles; n++)
    {delta[n] = double_complex(0.0,0.0);}
  max_coef = 0;
  for( n=0; n<=num_poles; n++) {
    if(n==k) continue;
    max_coef++;
```

```
    beta = -cexp(big_t * pole[n]);

    for(j=max_coef; j>=1; j--)
      {
      delta[j] += (beta * delta[j-1]);
      }
    }
  for( j=0; j<num_poles; j++)
    {
    b[j] += (big_a[k] * delta[j]);
    }

// multiply by 1-z**(-1)
  beta = double_complex(-1.0,0.0);
  for(j=num_poles+1; j>=1; j--)
    {
    b[j] += (beta * b[j-1]);
    }
  }

//-----------------------------------
//  compute denominator coefficients

a[0] = double_complex(1.0,0.0);
for( n=1; n<=num_poles; n++)
  {
  beta = -cexp(big_t * pole[n]);
  for( j=n; j>=1; j--)
    {
    a[j] += (beta * a[j-1]);
    }
  }
for( j=1; j<=num_poles; j++)
  {
  a[j] = -a[j];
  }
return;
}
```

Chapter

20

IIR Filter Design: Bilinear Transformation

A popular technique for the design of IIR digital filters is the *bilinear transformation method,* which offers several advantages over the techniques presented in the previous chapter.

20.1 Bilinear Transformation

The bilinear transformation converts the transfer function for an analog filter into the system function for a digital filter by making the substitution

$$s \rightarrow \frac{2}{T} \frac{1-z^{-1}}{1+z^{-1}}$$

If the analog prototype filter is stable, the bilinear transformation will result in a stable digital filter.

Algorithm 20.1 Bilinear transformation

Step 1. Obtain the transfer function $H_a(s)$ for the desired analog prototype filter.

Step 2. In the transfer function obtained in Step 1, make the substitution

$$s = \frac{2}{T} \frac{1-z^{-1}}{1+z^{-1}}$$

where T is the sampling interval of the digital filter. Call the resulting digital system function $H(z)$.

Step 3. The analog prototype filter's transfer function $H_a(s)$ will, in general, be a ratio of polynomials in s. Therefore, the system function $H(z)$ obtained in Step 2 will, in general, contain various powers of the ratio $(1 - z^{-1})/(1 + z^{-1})$ in both the numerator and the denominator. Multiply both the numerator and denominator by the highest power of $1 + z^{-1}$, and collect terms to obtain $H(z)$ as a ratio of polynomials in z^{-1} of the form

$$H(z) = \frac{\sum_{k=0}^{M} b_k z^{-k}}{1 - \sum_{k=1}^{N} a_k z^{-k}} \tag{20.1}$$

Step 4. Use the a_k and b_k obtained in Step 3 to realize the filter in any of the structures given in Sec. 18.2.

Example 20.1 Use the bilinear transform to obtain an IIR filter from a second-order Butterworth analog filter with a 3-dB cutoff frequency of 3 kHz. The sampling rate for the digital filter is 30,000 samples per second.

solution The analog prototype filter's transfer function is given by

$$H_a(s) = \frac{\omega_c^2}{s^2 + \sqrt{2}\omega_c s + \omega_c^2}$$

where $\omega_c = 6000\pi$. Making the substitution $s = 2(1 - z^{-1})/(T(1 + z^{-1}))$ yields

$$H(z) = \frac{\omega_c^2}{\left(\frac{2}{T}\right)^2 \left(\frac{1 - z^{-1}}{1 + z^{-1}}\right)^2 + \sqrt{2}\omega_c \left(\frac{2}{T}\right)\left(\frac{1 - z^{-1}}{1 + z^{-1}}\right) + \omega_c^2}$$

where $T = 1/30{,}000$. After the appropriate algebraic simplifications and making use of the fact that

$$\omega_c T = \frac{6000\pi}{30{,}000} = \frac{\pi}{5}$$

we obtain the desired form of $H(z)$ as

$$H(z) = \frac{0.063964 + 0.127929z^{-1} + 0.063964z^{-2}}{1 - 1.168261z^{-1} + 0.424118z^{-2}} \tag{20.2}$$

Comparison of Eqs. (15.1) and (15.2) reveals that

$$a_1 = -1.168261 \qquad a_2 = 0.424118$$

$$b_0 = 0.063964 \qquad b_1 = 0.127929 \qquad b_2 = 0.063964$$

20.2 Factored Form of the Bilinear Transformation

Often, an analog prototype filter will be specified in terms of its poles and zeros—that is, the numerator and denominator of the filter's transfer function will be in factored form. The bilinear transformation can be applied directly to this factored form. An additional benefit of this approach is that the process of finding the *digital* filter's poles and zeros is greatly simplified. Each factor in the numerator of the analog filter's transfer function will be of the form $(s - q_n)$, and each factor of the denominator will be of the form $(s - p_n)$, where q_n and p_n are, respectively, the nth zero and nth pole of the filter. When the bilinear transform is applied, the corresponding factors become

$$\left(\frac{2}{T}\frac{1-z^{-1}}{1+z^{-1}} - q_n\right) \quad \text{and} \quad \left(\frac{2}{T}\frac{1-z^{-1}}{1+z^{-1}} - p_n\right)$$

The zeros of the digital filter are obtained by finding the values of z for which

$$\frac{2}{T}\frac{1-z^{-1}}{1+z^{-1}} - q_n = 0$$

The desired values of z are given by

$$z_z = \frac{2 + q_n T}{2 - q_n T} \tag{20.3}$$

In a similar fashion, the poles of the digital filter are obtained from the poles of the analog filter using

$$z_p = \frac{2 + p_n T}{2 - p_n T} \tag{20.4}$$

The use of Eqs. (20.3) and (20.4) is straightforward for the analog filter's *finite* poles or zeros. Usually, only the finite poles and zeros of a filter are considered, but in the present context, *all* poles and zeros of the analog filter must be considered. The analog filter's infinite zeros will map into zeros of $z = -1$ for the digital filter.

Algorithm 20.2 Bilinear transformation for transfer functions in factored form

Step 1. For the desired analog prototype filter, obtain the transfer function $H_a(s)$ in the factored form given by

$$H_a(s) = H_0 \frac{\prod_{m=1}^{M} (s - q_m)}{\prod_{n=1}^{N} (s - p_n)}$$

Step 2. Obtain the poles z_{pn} of the analog filter from the poles p_n of the analog filter using

$$z_{pn} = \frac{2 + p_n T}{2 - p_n T} \qquad n = 1, 2, \ldots, N$$

Step 3. Obtain the zeros z_{zm} of the digital filter from the zeros q_m of the analog filter using

$$z_{zm} = \frac{2 + q_m T}{2 - q_m T} \qquad m = 1, 2, \ldots, M$$

Step 4. Using the values of z_{pn} obtained in Step 2 and the values of z_{zm} obtained in Step 3, form $H(z)$ as

$$H(z) = H_0 \frac{T^N}{\prod_{n=1}^{N} (2 - p_n T)} \cdot \frac{(z+1)^{N-M} \prod_{m=1}^{M} (z - z_{zm})}{\prod_{n=1}^{N} (z - z_{pn})} \tag{20.5}$$

The factor $(z + 1)^{N-M}$ supplies the zeros at $z = -1$, which correspond to the zeros at $s = \infty$ for analog filters having $M < N$. The first rational factor in Eq. (20.5) is a constant gain factor that is needed to obtain results which exactly match the results obtained via Algorithm 20.1. However, in practice, this factor is often omitted to yield

$$H(z) = H_0 \frac{(z+1)^{N-M} \prod_{m=1}^{M} (z - z_{zm})}{\prod_{n=1}^{N} (z - z_{pn})}$$

Example 20.2 The Butterworth filter of Example 20.1 has a transfer function given in factored form as

$$H_a(s) = \frac{\omega_c^{\,2}}{\left[s + \omega_c\left(\frac{\sqrt{2}}{2}\right) - j\omega_c\left(\frac{\sqrt{2}}{2}\right)\right]\left[s + \omega_c\left(\frac{\sqrt{2}}{2}\right) + j\omega_c\left(\frac{\sqrt{2}}{2}\right)\right]}$$

Apply the bilinear transform to this factored form to obtain the IIR filter's system function $H(z)$.

solution The analog filter has poles at

$$s = \omega_c \frac{-\sqrt{2}}{2} \pm j\omega_c \frac{\sqrt{2}}{2}$$

Using (20.4), we then obtain the poles of the digital filter as

$$z_{P_1} = \frac{2 + \left(\frac{-\sqrt{2}}{2} + j\frac{\sqrt{2}}{2}\right)\omega_c T}{2 - \left(\frac{-\sqrt{2}}{2} + j\frac{\sqrt{2}}{2}\right)\omega_c T}$$

$$= 0.584131 + 0.28794j$$

$$z_{P_2} = \frac{2 + \left(\frac{-\sqrt{2}}{2} - j\frac{\sqrt{2}}{2}\right)\omega_c T}{2 - \left(\frac{-\sqrt{2}}{2} - j\frac{\sqrt{2}}{2}\right)\omega_c T}$$

$$= 0.584131 - 0.287941j$$

The two zeros at $s = \infty$ map into two zeros at $z = -1$. Thus, the system function is given by

$$H(z) = H_c \frac{(z+1)^2}{(z - 0.584131 + 0.287941j)(z - 0.584131 - 0.287941j)}$$

where

$$H_c = \frac{H_0 T^2}{(2 - p_1 T)(2 - p_2 T)}$$

$$= \frac{(6000\pi)^2}{(30{,}000)^2\left(2 + \frac{\pi\sqrt{2}}{10} - j\frac{\pi\sqrt{2}}{10}\right)\left(2 + \frac{\pi\sqrt{2}}{10} + j\frac{\pi\sqrt{2}}{10}\right)}$$

$$= 0.063964$$

If the numerator and denominator factors are multiplied out and all terms are divided by z^2, we obtain

$$H(z) = \frac{0.063964(1 + 2z^{-1} + z^{-2})}{1 - 1.168261z^{-1} + 0.424118z^{-2}} \tag{20.6}$$

which matches the result of Example 20.1

20.3 Properties of the Bilinear Transformation

Assume that the analog prototype filter has a pole at $s_P = \sigma + j\omega$. The corresponding IIR filter designed via the bilinear transformation will have a pole at

$$z_P = \frac{2 + sT}{2 - sT}$$

$$= \frac{2 + (\sigma + j\omega)T}{2 - (\sigma + j\omega)T}$$

$$= \frac{2 + \sigma T + j\omega T}{2 - \sigma T - j\omega T}$$

The magnitude and angle of this pole are given by

$$|z_P| = \sqrt{\frac{(2 + \sigma T)^2 + (\omega T)^2}{(2 - \sigma T)^2 + (\omega T)^2}} \tag{20.7}$$

$$\arg(z_P) = \tan^{-1}\left(\frac{\omega T}{2 + \sigma T}\right) - \tan^{-1}\left(\frac{-\omega T}{2 - \sigma T}\right)$$

The poles of a stable analog filter must lie in the left half of the s plane—that is, $\sigma < 0$. When $\sigma < 0$, the numerator of Eq. (20.7) will be smaller than the denominator, and thus $|z_P| < 1$. This means that analog poles in the left half of the s plane map into digital poles inside the unit circle of the z plane—stable analog poles map into stable digital poles. Poles that lie on the $j\omega$ axis of the s plane have $\sigma = 0$ and, consequently, map into z-plane poles which have unity magnitude and, hence, lie on the unit circle. Analog poles at $s = 0$ map into digital poles at $z = 1$, and analog poles at $s = \pm j\infty$ map into digital poles at $z = -1$.

Frequency warping

The mapping of the s plane's $j\omega$ axis into the z plane's unit circle is a highly nonlinear mapping. The analog frequency ω_0 can range from $-\infty$ to $+\infty$, but the digital frequency ω_d is limited to the range $\pm\pi$. The relationship between ω_a and ω_d is given by

$$\omega_d = 2 \tan^{-1} \frac{\omega_a T}{2} \tag{20.8}$$

If an analog prototype filter with a cutoff frequency of ω_a is used to design a filter via the bilinear transformation, the resulting digital filter will have a cutoff frequency of ω_d, where ω_d is related to ω_a via Eq. (20.8).

Example 20.3 A low-pass filter with a 3-dB frequency of 3 kHz is used as the prototype for an IIR filter with a sampling rate of 30,000 samples per second. What will be the 3-dB frequency of the digital filter designed via the bilinear transformation?

solution Equation (20.8) yields

$$\omega_d = 2 \tan^{-1} \frac{(6000\pi)(1/30{,}000)}{2}$$

$$= 0.6088$$

Since $\omega_d = \pi$ corresponds to a frequency of 30,000/2 = 15,000 Hz, the cutoff frequency of the filter is given by

$$\omega_c = \frac{0.6088}{\pi}(15{,}000) = 2906.8 \text{ Hz}$$

The frequency-warping effects become more severe as the frequency of interest increases relative to the digital filter's sampling rate.

Example 20.4 Consider the case of an analog filter with a 3-dB frequency of 3 kHz used as the prototype for an IIR filter designed via the bilinear transformation. Determine the impact on the 3-dB frequency if the sampling rate is changed from 10,000 samples per second to 30,000 samples per second in steps of 1000 samples per second.

solution The various sampling rates and the corresponding warped 3-dB frequencies are listed in Table 20.1.

Fortunately, it is a simple matter to counteract the effects of frequency warping by prewarping the critical frequencies of the analog prototype filter in such a way that the warping caused by the bilinear transformation restores the critical frequencies to their original intended values. Equation (20.8) can be inverted to yield the equation needed for this prewarping:

$$\omega_a = \frac{2}{T} \tan \frac{\omega_d}{2} \tag{20.9}$$

Example 20.5 We wish to design an IIR filter with a 3-dB frequency of 3 kHz and a sampling rate of 30,000 samples per second. Determine the prewarped 3-dB frequency required for the analog prototype filter.

TABLE 20.1 Warped Cutoff Frequencies for Example 20.4

Sampling rate	Cutoff frequency, Hz	% error
10,000	2405.8	−19.81
11,000	2480.5	−17.32
12,000	2543.1	−15.23
13,000	2595.8	−13.47
14,000	2640.4	−11.99
15,000	2678.5	−10.72
16,000	2711.1	−9.63
17,000	2739.3	−8.69
18,000	2763.6	−7.88
19,000	2784.9	−7.17
20,000	2803.5	−6.55
21,000	2819.9	−6.00
22,000	2834.4	−5.52
23,000	2847.2	−5.09
24,000	2858.7	−4.71
25,000	2868.9	−4.37
26,000	2878.1	−4.06
27,000	2886.4	−3.79
28,000	2893.8	−3.54
29,000	2900.6	−3.31
30,000	2906.8	−3.11

solution Since $\omega_d = \pi$ corresponds to a frequency of 30,000/2 = 15,000 Hz, a frequency of 3 kHz corresponds to a ω_d of

$$\omega_d = \frac{3000\pi}{15{,}000} = \frac{\pi}{5}$$

The prototype analog frequency ω_a is obtained by using this value of ω_d in Eq. (20.9):

$$\omega_a = \frac{2}{(1/30{,}000)} \tan \frac{\pi}{10} = 19{,}495.18$$

The analog prototype filter must have a 3-dB frequency of $19{,}495.18/(2\pi) = 3102.75$ Hz in order for the IIR filter to have a 3-dB frequency of 3 kHz after warping.

20.4 Programming the Bilinear Transformation

Assume that the transfer function of the analog prototype filter is in the form given by

$$H_a(s) = H_0 \frac{\prod_{m=1}^{M} (s - q_m)}{\prod_{n=1}^{N} (s - p_n)}$$

where p_n and q_n denote, respectively, the filter's poles and zeros. To generate a digital filter via the bilinear transformation, we make the substitution

$$s = \frac{2}{T}\left(\frac{1 - z^{-1}}{1 + z^{-1}}\right)$$

and obtain

$$H(z) = H_0 \frac{\prod_{m=1}^{M} \left[\frac{2}{T}\left(\frac{1 - z^{-1}}{1 + z^{-1}}\right) - q_m\right]}{\prod_{n=1}^{N} \left[\frac{2}{T}\left(\frac{1 - z^{-1}}{1 + z^{-1}}\right) - p_n\right]}$$

which, after some algebraic manipulation, can be put into the form

$$H(z) = H_0 \frac{(1 + z^{-1})^{N-M} \prod_{m=1}^{N} \left[\left(\frac{2}{T} - q_m\right) - \left(\frac{2}{T} + q_m\right)z^{-1}\right]}{\prod_{n=1}^{N} \left[\left(\frac{2}{T} - p_n\right) - \left(\frac{2}{T} + p_n\right)z^{-1}\right]}$$

Thus, the denominator of $H(z)$ is given by

$$D(z) = \prod_{n=1}^{N} (\gamma_n + \delta_n z^{-1}) \tag{20.10}$$

where

$$\gamma_n = \frac{2}{T} - p_n$$

$$\delta_n = \frac{-2}{T} - p_n$$

To see how Eq. (20.10) can be easily evaluated by computer, let's examine the sequence of partial products $\{D_k(z)\}$ encountered in the evaluation:

$$D_1(z) = (\gamma_1 + \delta_1 z^{-1})$$

$$D_2(z) = (\gamma_2 + \delta_2 z^{-1})\, D_1(z) = \gamma_2 D_1(z) + \delta_2 z^{-1} D_1(z)$$

$$D_3(z) = (\gamma_3 + \delta_3 z^{-1})\, D_2(z) = \gamma_3 D_2(z) + \delta_3 z^{-1} D_2(z)$$

$$D_4(z) = (\gamma_4 + \delta_4 z^{-1})\, D_3(z) = \gamma_4 D_3(z) + \delta_4 z^{-1} D_3(z)$$

$$\vdots$$

$$D(z) = D_N(z) = (\gamma_N + \delta_N z^{-1}) D_{N-1}(z) = \gamma_N D_{N-1}(z) + \delta_N z^{-1} D_{N-1}(z)$$

Examination of this sequence reveals that the partial product $D_k(z)$ at iteration k can be expanded in terms of the partial product $D_{k-1}(z)$ as

$$D_k(z) = \gamma_k D_{k-1}(z) + \delta_k z^{-1} D_{k-1}(z)$$

The partial product $D_{k-1}(z)$ will be a $(k-1)$-degree polynomial in z^{-1}:

$$D_{k-1}(z) = \mu_0 (z^{-1})^0 + \mu_1 (z^{-1})^1 + \mu_2 (z^{-1})^2 + \cdots + \mu_{k-1} (z^{-1})^{k-1}$$

The products $\gamma_k D_{k-1}(z)$ and $\delta_k z^{-1} D_{k-1}(z)$ are then given by

$$\gamma_k D_{k-1}(z) = \gamma_k \mu_0 (z^{-1})^0 + \gamma_k \mu_1 (z^{-1})^1 + \gamma_k \mu_2 (z^{-1})^2 + \cdots + \gamma_k \mu_{k-1} (z^{-1})^{k-1}$$

$$\delta_k z^{-1} D_{k-1}(z) = \delta_k \mu_0 (z^{-1})^1 + \delta_k \mu_1 (z^{-1})^2 + \delta_k \mu_2 (z^{-1})^3 + \cdots + \delta_k \mu_{k-1} (z^{-1})^k$$

and $D_k(z)$ is given by

$$D_k(z) = \gamma_k \mu^0 (z^{-1})^0 + (\gamma_k \mu_1 - \delta_k \mu_0)(z^{-1})^1 + (\gamma_k \mu_2 - \delta_k \mu_1)(z^{-1})^2 + \cdots$$
$$+ (\gamma_k \mu_{k-1} - \delta_k \mu_{k-2})(z^{-1})^k - 1 - \delta_k \mu_{k-1} (z^{-1})^k$$

Therefore, we can conclude that if μ_n is the coefficient for the $(z^{-1})^n$ term in $D_{k-1}(z)$, then the coefficient for the $(z^{-1})^n$ term in $D(z)$ is $(\gamma_k\mu_n + \delta_k\mu_{n-1})$ with the proviso that $\mu \triangleq 0$ in $D_{k-1}(z)$. The polynomial $D_{k-1}(z)$ is represented in the computer as an array of k coefficients, with the array index corresponding to the subscript on μ and the superscript (exponent) on (z^{-1}). Thus, array element `mu[0]` contains μ_0, array element `mu[1]` contains μ_1, and so forth. The coefficients for the partial product $D_k(z)$ can be obtained from the coefficients for $D_{k-1}(z)$, as indicated by the following fragment:

```
for( j=k; j >= 1; j--)
    {mu[j] = gamma * mu[j] + beta * mu[j - 1];}
```

The loop is executed in reverse order so that the coefficients can be updated in place without prematurely overwriting the old values. If this fragment is placed within an outer loop with k ranging from 1 to `numPoles`, the final values in `mu[n]` will be the coefficients a_n for Eq. (20.1).

A similar loop can be developed for the numerator product $N(z)$ given by

$$N(z) = \prod_{m=1}^{M} (\alpha_m - \beta_m z^{-1}) \tag{20.11}$$

where

$$\alpha_m = \frac{-2}{T} + q_m$$

$$\beta_m = \frac{-2}{T} - q_m$$

A program for computation of the bilinear transformation is provided in Listing 20.1.

20.5 Computer Examples

In this section we will apply the computer methods from the previous section to a number of different examples.

Example 20.6 Use the bilinear transform design software to obtain an IIR filter from a second-order Butterworth analog filter with a 3-dB cutoff frequency of 3 kHz. The sampling rate for the digital filter is 30,000 samples per second. Compare the frequency responses of the IIR filter and the corresponding ideal Butterworth filter.

solution The magnitude response of the IIR filter is shown in Fig. 20.1, and the phase response is shown in Fig. 20.2. The solid trace shows the response of the IIR filter, which is virtually identical to the response of the analog filter. These plots have been normalized so that the 3-dB cutoff frequency is 1.0 Hz. Because the actual sampling rate is 10 times the unnormalized cutoff frequency, the normalized sampling rate becomes 10 samples per

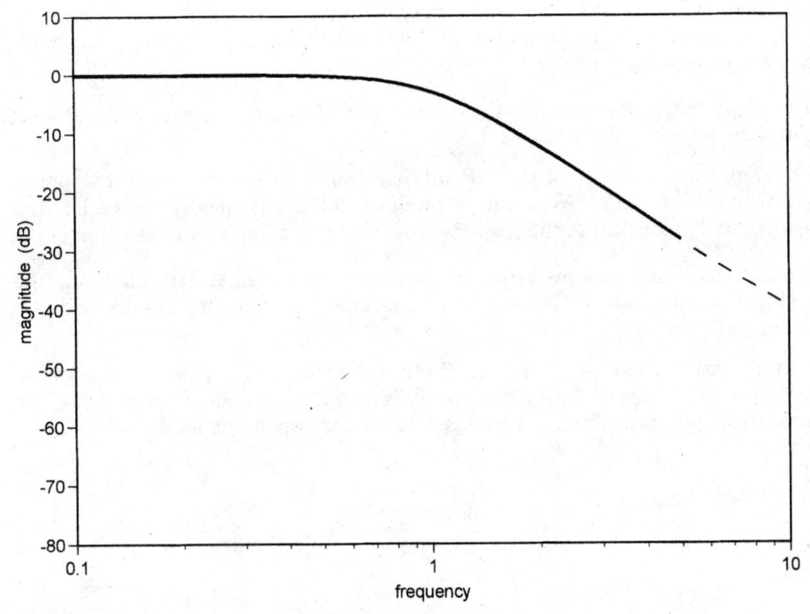

Figure 20.1 Magnitude responses for Example 20.6.

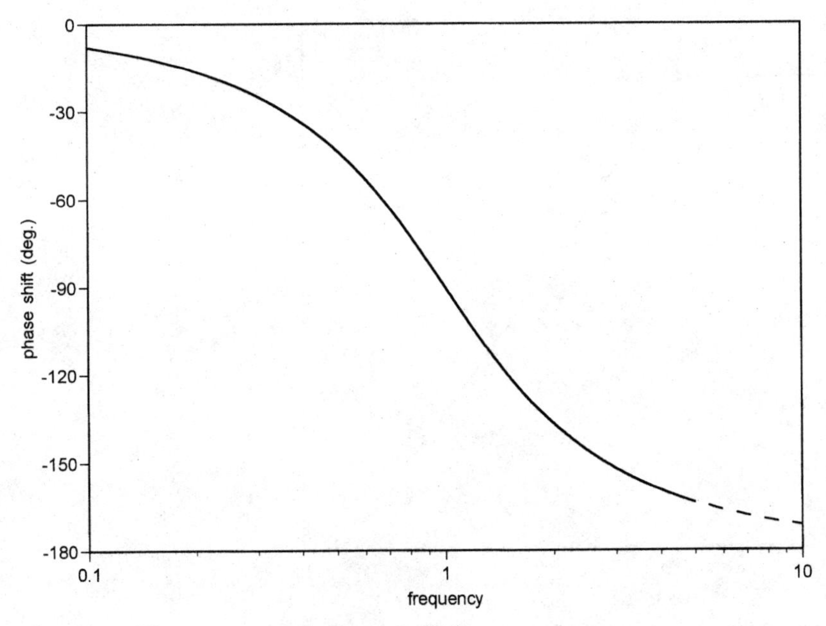

Figure 20.2 Phase responses for Example 20.6.

second. The response of the digital filter is shown only for frequencies up to the folding frequency of 5 Hz. The analog filter's normalized response characteristic continues as shown by the dashed traces in the figures.

Example 20.7 Repeat Example 20.6 for the case of a fourth-order Chebyshev filter with 0.1-dB ripple in the pass band.

solution The magnitude response of the IIR filter is shown in Fig. 20.3, and the phase response is shown in Fig. 20.4. Up to the normalized folding frequency of 5.0 Hz, the responses are virtually identical to the responses of the corresponding analog filter.

Example 20.8 Use the bilinear transform design software to obtain an IIR filter from the ninth-order elliptical filter that was designed in Example 6.2. Compare the responses of the IIR and analog filters.

solution The magnitude response of the IIR filter is shown in Fig. 20.5, and the phase response is shown in Fig. 20.6. Up to the normalized folding frequency of 5.0 Hz, the responses are virtually identical to the responses of the corresponding analog filter.

Listing 20.1 Bilinear Transformation

```
//
//  File = bilinear.cpp
//

#include <stdlib.h>
#include <iostream.h>
```

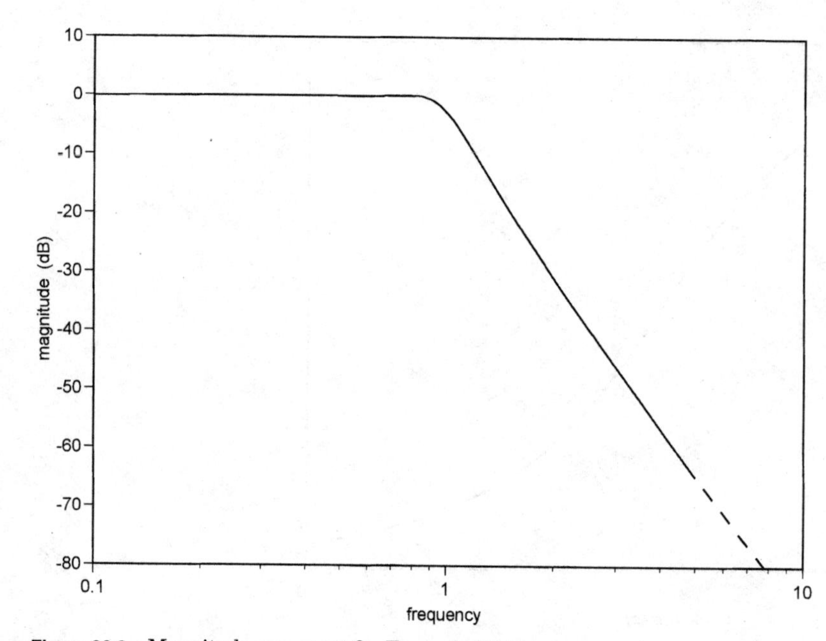

Figure 20.3 Magnitude responses for Example 20.7.

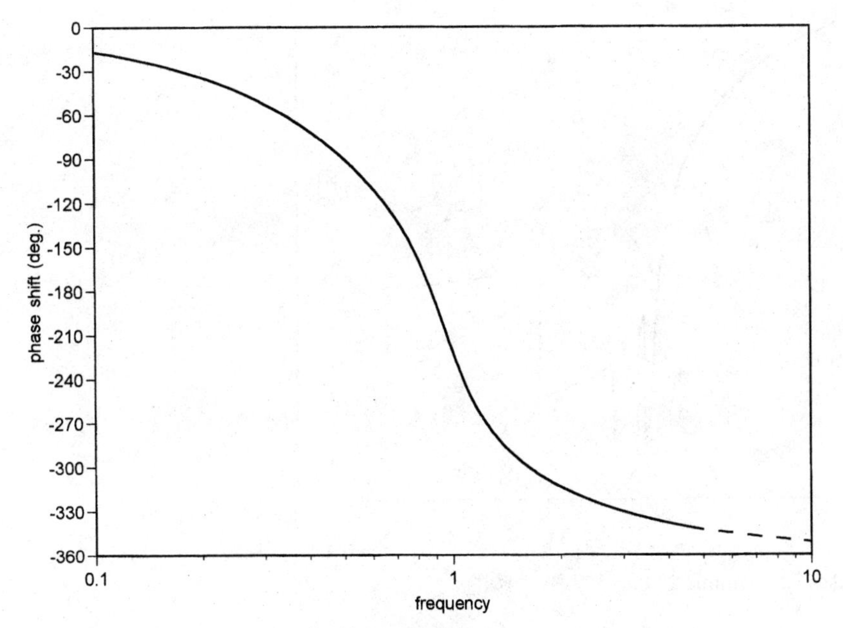

Figure 20.4 Phase responses for Example 20.7.

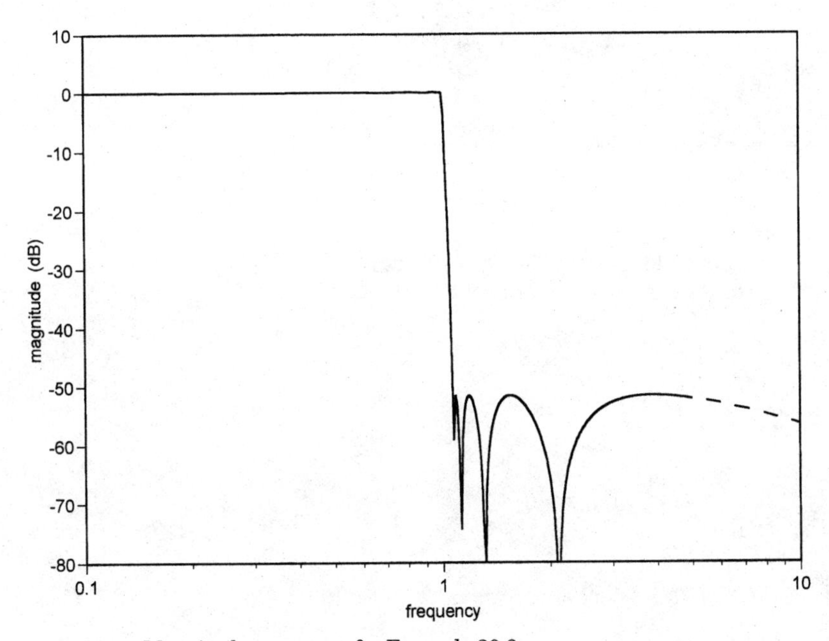

Figure 20.5 Magnitude responses for Example 20.8.

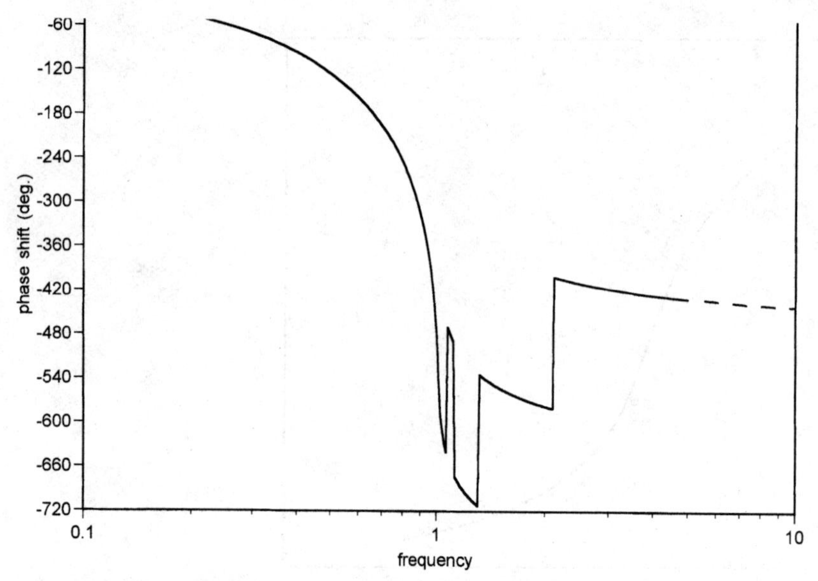

Figure 20.6 Phase responses for Example 20.8.

```
#include <fstream.h>
#include "misdefs.h"
#include "typedefs.h"
#include "d_cmplx.h"
#include "bilinear.h"
extern ofstream DebugFile;

//==================================================
//
//--------------------------------------------------
IirFilterDesign* BilinearTransf(
                          FilterResponse* analog_filter,
                          double sampling_interval)

{
 int max_poles;
 int num_poles, num_zeros;
 int j, m, n;
 int max_coeff, num_numer_coeff;
 double h_const, h_sub_zero, denom_mu_zero;
 double_complex *pole, *zero;
 double_complex *mu;
 double_complex alpha;
 double_complex beta;
 double_complex gamma;
```

```
double_complex delta;
double_complex eta;
double_complex work;
double_complex c_two;
double *a, *b;
IirFilterDesign* iir_filter;

pole = analog_filter->GetPoles(&num_poles);
zero = analog_filter->GetZeros(&num_zeros);
h_sub_zero = analog_filter->GetHSubZero();

if(num_poles > num_zeros)
  { max_poles = num_poles; }
else
  { max_poles = num_zeros; }

//--------------------------------------------
// allocate and initialize working storage

mu = new double_complex[max_poles+1];
a = new double[max_poles+1];
b = new double[max_poles+1];

for(j=0; j<=max_poles; j++)
  {
   mu[j] = double_complex(0.0, 0.0);
   a[j] = 0.0;
   b[j] = 0.0;
  }

//--------------------------------------------
// compute constant gain factor

h_const = 1.0;
work = double_complex(1.0, 0.0);
c_two = double_complex(2.0, 0.0);

for(n=1; n<=num_poles; n++)
  {
   work = work * (c_two - (sampling_interval * pole[n]));
   h_const = h_const * sampling_interval;
  }
h_const = h_sub_zero * h_const / real(work);
//--------------------------------------------------
// compute denominator coefficients

mu[0] = double_complex(1.0, 0.0);
```

```
for(n=1; n<=num_poles; n++)
  {
   gamma = double_complex( (2.0/sampling_interval), 0.0) - pole[n];
   delta = double_complex( (-2.0/sampling_interval), 0.0) - pole[n];

   for(j=n; j>=1; j--)
     {
      mu[j] = gamma * mu[j] + (delta * mu[j-1]);
     }
   mu[0] = gamma * mu[0];
  }
denom_mu_zero = real(mu[0]);
for( j=1; j<=num_poles; j++)
  {
   a[j] = -1.0 * real(mu[j])/denom_mu_zero;
  }
//-----------------------------------------------------
// compute numerator coefficients

mu[0] = double_complex(1.0, 0.0);
for(n=1; n<=max_poles; n++)
  {
   mu[n] = double_complex(0.0, 0.0);
  }

max_coeff = 0;

//- - - - - - - - - - - - - - - - - - - - - - - - -
//  compute (1+z**(-1)) ** (N-M)

for(m=1; m<=(num_poles-num_zeros); m++)
  {
   max_coeff++;
   for(j=max_coeff; j>=1; j--)
     {
      mu[j] = mu[j] + mu[j-1];
     }
  }
for(m=1; m<=num_zeros; m++)
  {
   max_coeff++;
   alpha = double_complex( (2.0/sampling_interval), 0.0) - zero[m];
   beta = double_complex( (-2.0/sampling_interval), 0.0) - zero[m];

   for(j=max_coeff; j>=1; j--)
     {
      mu[j] = alpha * mu[j] + (beta * mu[j-1]);
     }
```

```
    mu[0] = alpha * mu[0];
   }
 num_numer_coeff = max_coeff+1;
 for(j=0; j<num_numer_coeff; j++)
   {
    b[j] = h_sub_zero * real(mu[j])/denom_mu_zero;
   }

 delete []mu;
 iir_filter = new IirFilterDesign( num_numer_coeff,
                                   num_poles,
                                   b, a);
 iir_filter->SetSamplingInterval(sampling_interval);
 return(iir_filter);
}
```

Chapter

21

IIR Filter Design: Practical Case Studies

In the preceding two chapters we explored four different approaches to the design of IIR filters. In this chapter we evaluate the performance of various filter designs, including the effects of quantized coefficients and finite-precision arithmetic in the context of the implementation structures that were introduced in Chap. 18.

21.1 Assessing the Impacts of Quantization and Finite-Precision Arithmetic

When it comes to the effects of quantization and finite precision arithmetic, IIR filters share all of the potential problems that FIR filters have, plus a few that are unique to the recursive structures that are used for IIR implementations. As discussed in Chaps. 13 and 17, the three manifestations of finite digital word length are *coefficient quantization, signal quantization,* and *finite-precision arithmetic.* The first two of these operate in the IIR context similarly to the way they operate in the FIR context. However, due to the feedback that is inherent in recursive implementations of IIR filters, the effects of finite-precision arithmetic can cause problems which are peculiar to the IIR case. These problems include small oscillatory outputs for zero input and limit-cycle oscillations that are caused by arithmetic overflows.

Direct form realizations

Consider the direct form 1 realization of an IIR filter as depicted in Fig. 21.1. Each of the input samples $x[k]$ and each of the coefficients $a[n]$ and $b[m]$ will be quantized to some finite number of bits. If each $x[k]$ is quantized to B_x bits and each $b[m]$ is quantized to B_b bits, a total of $(B_x + B_b)$ bits will be needed to rep-

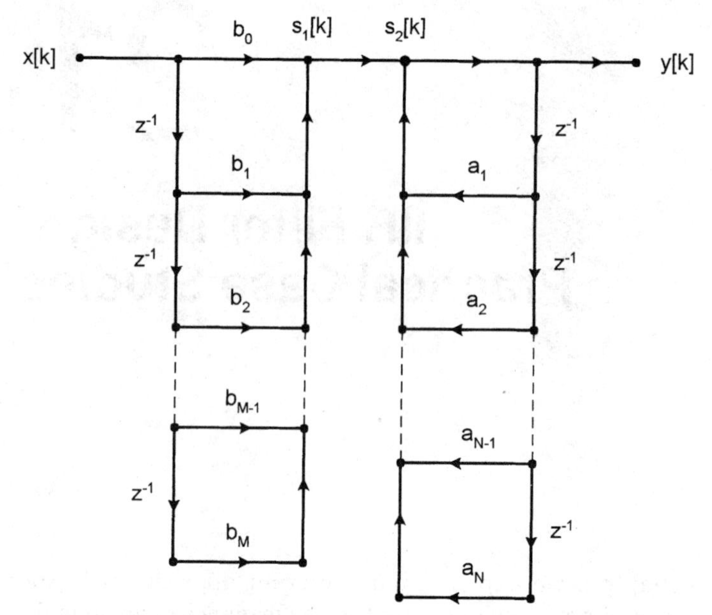

Figure 21.1 Signal flow graph of direct form 1 realization for an IIR filter.

resent each product term $x[k-m] \cdot b[m]$ without further loss of precision. Still more bits will be needed to precisely represent the sum $s_1[k]$ of these product terms. The sum $s_2[k]$ is formed by adding $s_1[k]$ and all of the product terms $a[n] \cdot s_2[k-n]$. Typically, $s_2[k]$ will need to be accumulated with relatively high precision, and this leads to a relatively expensive implementation for the second delay chain. In some schemes, the sum $s_2[k]$ will be accumulated with relatively high precision and then truncated or rounded to a much smaller number of bits before being input to the second delay chain.

Now consider the direct form 2 realization depicted in Fig. 21.2. When implemented with infinite precision, the structures in Figs. 21.1 and 21.2 are equivalent. However, their finite-precision implementations can exhibit significantly different behavior. In the direct form 2 structure it is the sum $s_1[k]$ that must be delayed rather than $s_2[k]$, and the truncation strategy for reducing the cost of the single delay chain will be different.

Software design

The `DirectFormFir` class developed in Chap. 17 has been adapted for evaluation of the IIR case and is presented as `DirectFormIir` in Listing 21.1. The `SweptResponse` class from Chap. 17 can be used as is for evaluating IIR designs. The particular instance of `FilterImplementation` used by `SweptResponse` is constructed externally and passed in as a parameter. `FilterImplementation` is a base class which can be externally instantiated as either `DirectFormFir` or `DirectFormIir`.

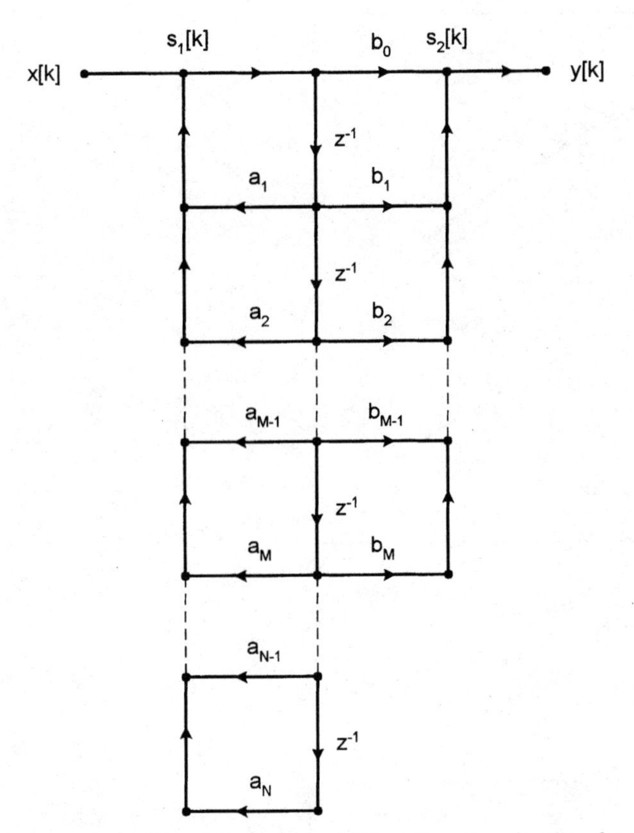

Figure 21.2 Signal flow graph of direct form 2 realization for an IIR filter.

21.2 Quantization in IIR Filters Obtained via Bilinear Transformation

This section explores the impacts of quantization upon the various IIR filters that were designed in Sec. 20.5.

Example 21.1 Assume that the IIR filter obtained from a second-order Butterworth response in Example 20.6 is to be implemented using 8-bit, 10-bit, or 12-bit coefficients. Assume that arithmetic results are not truncated or rounded. Compare the frequency response of the three quantized filters with the response of the unquantized filter.

solution The magnitude responses of the filters are compared in Fig. 21.3, and their phase responses are compared in Fig. 21.4. The response of the filter with 12-bit quantization is very close to the response of the unquantized filter.

For the next example we will use the swept-tone method that was described in Sec. 17.1 to see how the combination of coefficient quantization and signal quantization might further degrade performance. The `SweptResponse` class

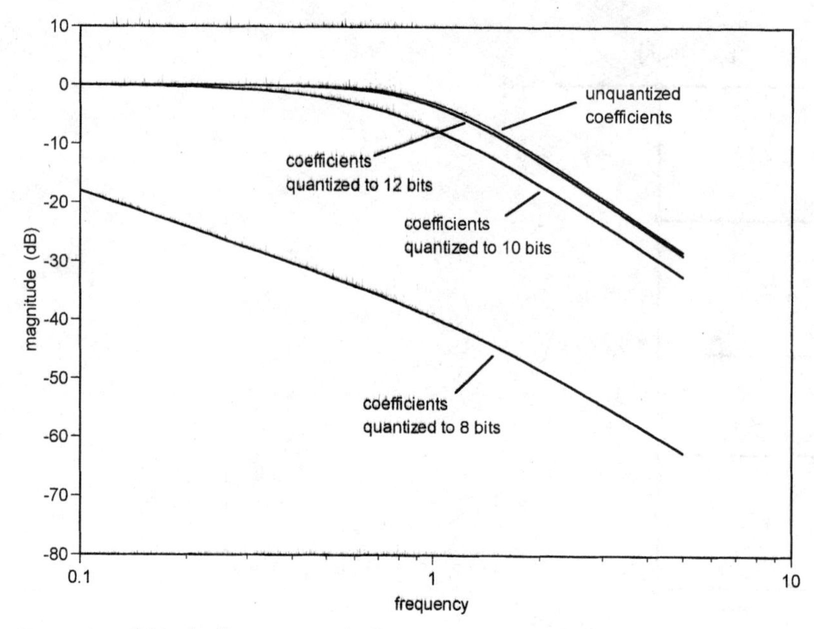

Figure 21.3 Magnitude responses for Example 21.1.

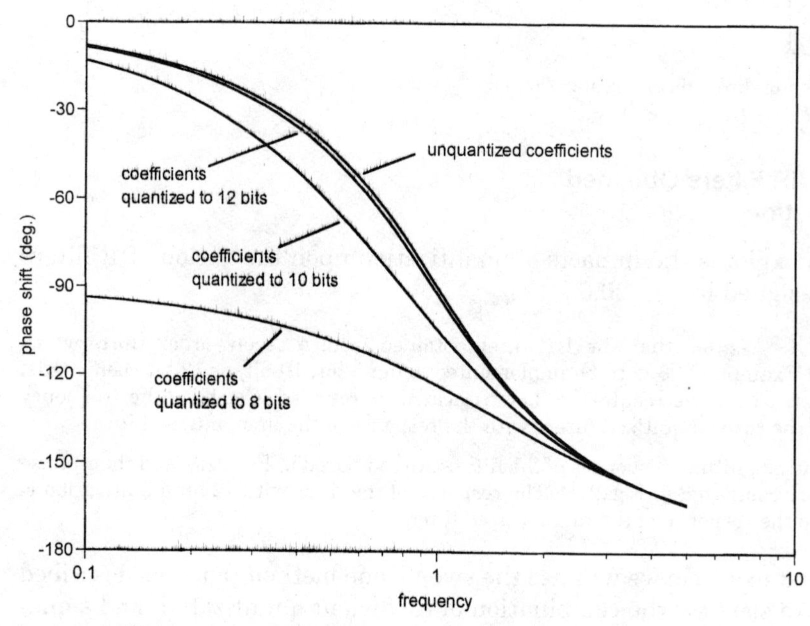

Figure 21.4 Phase responses for Example 21.1.

from Listing 17.4 has been adapted for use with IIR filters, as shown in Listing 21.2.

Example 21.2 Repeat Example 21.1 using the swept-tone method to determine how the filter will perform when the coefficients are quantized to 12 bits and the input signal is quantized to 12 bits.

solution The magnitude responses of the filter with unquantized and quantized inputs are virtually indistinguishable and match the 12-bit trace shown in Fig. 21.3. The two phase responses are compared in Fig. 21.5.

Example 21.3 Assume that the IIR filter obtained from a ninth-order Elliptical response in Example 20.8 is to be implemented using 24-bit coefficients. Assume that arithmetic results are not truncated or rounded. Compare the frequency response of the resulting filter with the response of the unquantized filter.

solution The relative errors introduced by 24-bit quantization of the coefficient values are relatively small, as evidenced by the values listed in Table 21.1. Nevertheless, the performance impact of these seemingly small errors is quite large, as shown by the magnitude responses of the quantized and unquantized filters which are compared in Fig. 21.6. The extremely poor performance of the quantized filter demonstrates the high coefficient sensitivity of high-order elliptical designs.

Example 21.4 Design a fifth-order elliptical low-pass filter having a passband ripple of 0.2 dB, a minimum stopband attenuation of 51 dB, a passband edge frequency of 1.0, and a stopband edge frequency of 1.2. Use the bilinear transformation to obtain an IIR implementation of this filter. Compare performance of this filter for the case of unquantized coefficients and the case of 24-bit coefficients.

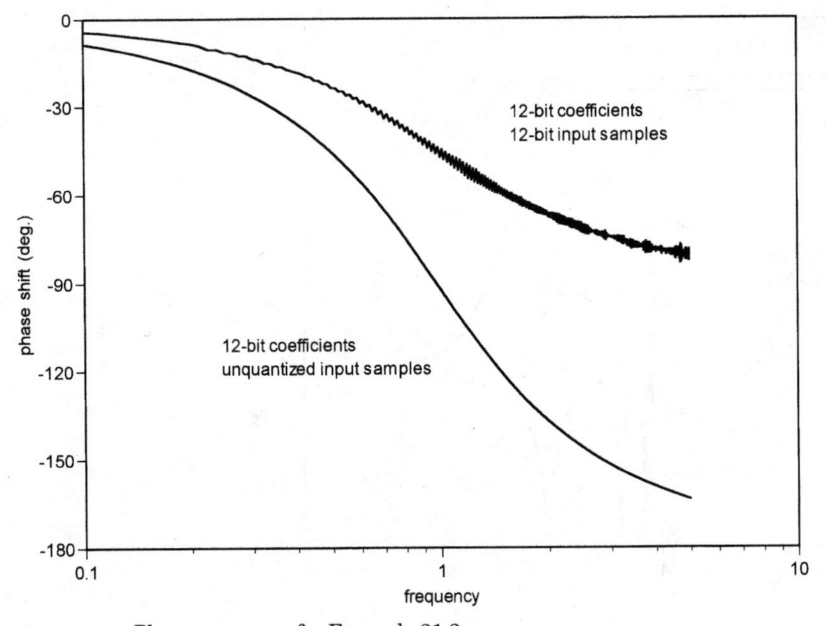

Figure 21.5 Phase responses for Example 21.2.

TABLE 21.1 Coefficient Quantization Errors for the IIR Elliptical Filter of Example 21.3

Coefficient	Fractional error
$b[0],b[9]$	-7.27×10^{-5}
$b[1],b[8]$	-3.05×10^{-5}
$b[2],b[7]$	-4.05×10^{-6}
$b[3],b[6]$	-5.67×10^{-6}
$b[4],b[5]$	-3.87×10^{-6}
$a[1]$	-2.62×10^{-9}
$a[2]$	-2.07×10^{-9}
$a[3]$	5.37×10^{-10}
$a[4]$	-1.38×10^{-9}
$a[5]$	-3.69×10^{-11}
$a[6]$	-2.23×10^{-9}
$a[7]$	-8.93×10^{-10}
$a[8]$	-1.52×10^{-8}
$a[9]$	-3.08×10^{-8}

solution The magnitude responses of the two filters are compared in Fig. 21.7. The performance of the quantized filter is not nearly as degraded as it was for Example 21.3. In fact, at the cost of a slightly wider transition band, the quantized filter response exhibits an initial stopband lobe which is about 8 dB lower than the corresponding lobe in the unquantized filter's response.

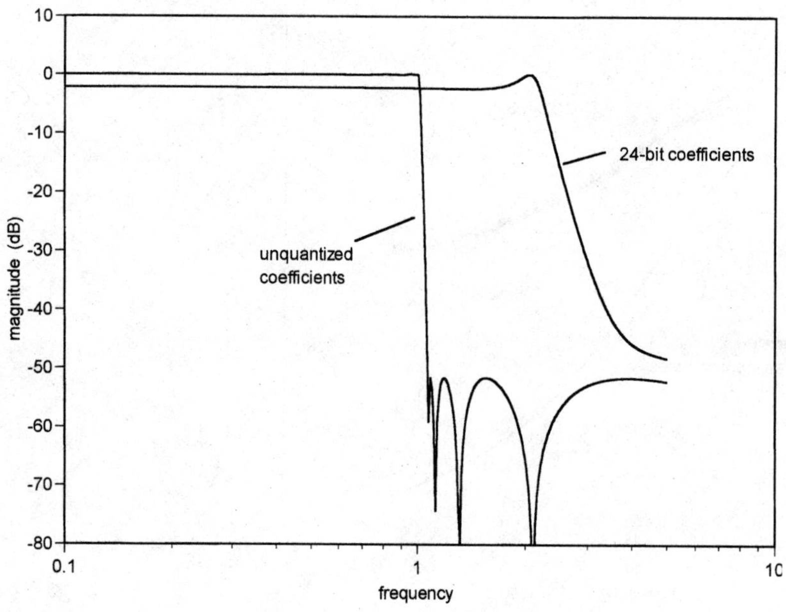

Figure 21.6 Magnitude responses for Example 21.3.

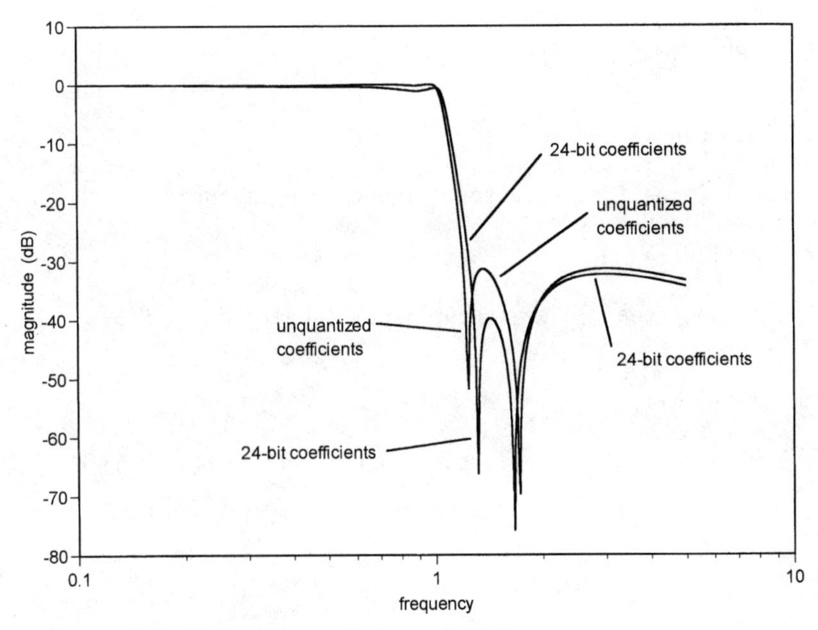

Figure 21.7 Magnitude responses for Example 21.4.

Listing 21.1 Direct Form Realization of an IIR Filter

```
//
//  File = dir1_iir.cpp
//

#include <stdlib.h>
#include <fstream.h>
#include "dir1_iir.h"
extern ofstream DebugFile;

DirectFormIir::DirectFormIir( int num_numer_coeff,
                              int num_denom_coeff,
                              double *numer_coeff,
                              double *denom_coeff,
                              long coeff_quan_factor,
                              long input_quan_factor)
{
 int n;
 Num_Numer_Coeff = num_numer_coeff;
 Num_Denom_Coeff = num_denom_coeff;
 Input_Buffer = new long[num_numer_coeff];
 Output_Buffer = new long[num_denom_coeff+1];
```

```
 Quan_Numer_Coeff = new long[num_numer_coeff];
 Quan_Denom_Coeff = new long[num_denom_coeff+1];
 Input_Write_Indx = 0;
 Output_Write_Indx = 1;
 Input_Quan_Factor = input_quan_factor;
 Coeff_Quan_Factor = coeff_quan_factor;
 Output_Quan_Factor = double( coeff_quan_factor * input_quan_factor);

 for(n=0; n<num_numer_coeff; n++)
   {
    Quan_Numer_Coeff[n] = long((coeff_quan_factor * numer_coeff[n]) + 0.5);
    Input_Buffer[n] = 0;
   }
 for(n=1; n<=num_denom_coeff; n++)
   {
    Quan_Denom_Coeff[n] = long((coeff_quan_factor * denom_coeff[n]) + 0.5);
    Output_Buffer[n] = 0;
   }
 return;
}

double DirectFormIir::ProcessSample( double input_val )
{
 double output_val;
 long term, sum;
 int input_read_indx, output_read_indx, tap_indx;

 Input_Buffer[Input_Write_Indx] =
                   long(Input_Quan_Factor * input_val);
 input_read_indx = Input_Write_Indx;
 Input_Write_Indx++;
 if(Input_Write_Indx >= Num_Numer_Coeff)
                                  Input_Write_Indx = 0;

 sum = 0;

 for( tap_indx=0; tap_indx<Num_Numer_Coeff; tap_indx++)
   {
    term = Quan_Numer_Coeff[tap_indx] *
                   Input_Buffer[input_read_indx];
    sum += term;
    input_read_indx--;
    if(input_read_indx < 0) input_read_indx = Num_Numer_Coeff-1;
   }

 output_read_indx = Output_Write_Indx;
 for( tap_indx=1; tap_indx<=Num_Denom_Coeff; tap_indx++)
```

```
   {
    term = Quan_Denom_Coeff[tap_indx] *
                             Output_Buffer[output_read_indx];
    sum += term;
    output_read_indx--;
    if(output_read_indx < 1)
                         output_read_indx = Num_Denom_Coeff;
   }

 Output_Write_Indx++;
 if(Output_Write_Indx > Num_Denom_Coeff)
                                   Output_Write_Indx = 1;
 Output_Buffer[Output_Write_Indx] = sum/Coeff_Quan_Factor;

 output_val = double(sum)/Output_Quan_Factor;
 return(output_val);
}

int DirectFormIir::GetNumNumerCoeff(void)
{
 return(Num_Numer_Coeff);
}

int DirectFormIir::GetNumTaps(void)
{
 return(Num_Numer_Coeff);
}

int DirectFormIir::GetNumDenomCoeff(void)
{
 return(Num_Denom_Coeff);
}
```

Listing 21.2 Method for Measuring Swept Response of an IIR Filter

```
//
//  File = swept.cpp
//

#include <fstream.h>
#include <math.h>
#include <stdlib.h>
#include "swept.h"
#include "typedefs.h"
#include "misdefs.h"
extern ofstream DebugFile;
```

```
SweptResponse::SweptResponse( FilterImplementation *filter_implem,
                              double sampling_interval,
                              istream& uin,
                              ostream& uout )
{
 int resp_indx;
 double lambda, phase_lag;
 double input_val;
 double *output_tone;
 int samp_indx;
 int num_holdoff_samps;
 logical default_file_ok;
 Filter_Implem = filter_implem;

 int phase_indx;
 int max_num_samps;
 int samps_per_corr;
 double cycles_per_corr;
 double max_correl, phase_offset, sum;
 double phase_delta;

 uout << "number of points in plot of frequency response?" << endl;
 uin >> Num_Resp_Pts;

 uout << "maximum swept frequency?" << endl;
 uin >> Max_Sweep_Freq;
 if(Max_Sweep_Freq > (0.5/sampling_interval) )
   {
    uout << "maximum swept frequency will be limited\n"
         << "to folding frequency of "
         << (0.5/sampling_interval) << endl;
    Max_Sweep_Freq = 0.5/sampling_interval;
   }

 uout << "scaling?\n"
      << "  0 = linear, 1 = dB" << endl;
 uin >> Db_Scale_Enabled;

 uout << "phase resolution?\n"
      << "  (in degrees)" << endl;
 uin >> phase_delta;
 if(phase_delta > 0.0) phase_delta = -phase_delta;

 uout << "numb sinewave cycles per correlation?" << endl;
 uin >> cycles_per_corr;

 if( Db_Scale_Enabled != 0) Db_Scale_Enabled = 1;
```

```
uout << "default name for magnitude response output\n"
     << "file is win_resp.txt\n\n"
     << "is this okay?"
     << "  0 = NO, 1 = YES"
     << endl;
uin >> default_file_ok;

if( default_file_ok)
   {
    Response_File = new ofstream("win_resp.txt", ios::out);
   }
 else
   {
    char *file_name;
    file_name = new char[31];
    uout << "enter complete name for output file (30 chars max)"
         << endl;
    uin >> file_name;
    Response_File = new ofstream(file_name, ios::out);
    delete []file_name;
   }
Mag_Resp = new double[Num_Resp_Pts];
Phase_Resp = new double[Num_Resp_Pts];
max_num_samps = int((cycles_per_corr+1)*Num_Resp_Pts/
                (Max_Sweep_Freq * sampling_interval));
output_tone = new double[max_num_samps+2];
for( resp_indx=1; resp_indx<Num_Resp_Pts; resp_indx++)
  {
   lambda = resp_indx * Max_Sweep_Freq * 2.0 * PI *
            sampling_interval / (double) Num_Resp_Pts;
   samps_per_corr = int(Num_Resp_Pts*cycles_per_corr/
        (resp_indx * Max_Sweep_Freq * sampling_interval));
   num_holdoff_samps = int(Num_Resp_Pts/
        (resp_indx * Max_Sweep_Freq * sampling_interval));
   for( samp_indx=0;
        samp_indx<(samps_per_corr+num_holdoff_samps);
        samp_indx++)
     {
      input_val = cos(lambda*samp_indx);
      output_tone[samp_indx] =
               filter_implem->ProcessSample(input_val);
     }
  //==================================================
  // Create sinusoids in phase increments of
  // phase_delta degrees and correlate them
  // with the stored output tone. Phase of sine
  // with maximum correlation will be taken as
```

```
    // phase response at that frequency.

    max_correl = 0.0;
    for(phase_indx=0; phase_indx < int(-360./phase_delta);
                      phase_indx++)
      {
       phase_offset = (phase_indx * phase_delta * PI )/180.0;
       sum = 0.0;
       for( samp_indx=num_holdoff_samps;
            samp_indx<(samps_per_corr+num_holdoff_samps);
            samp_indx++)
         {
          sum += (output_tone[samp_indx]*
                  cos(lambda*samp_indx + phase_offset));
         }
       if(sum > max_correl)
         {
          max_correl = sum;
          phase_lag = double(phase_indx*phase_delta);
         }
      }
    //-----------------------------------------
    // "unwrap" phase to keep it all negative

    while(phase_lag >= 180.0)
      { phase_lag -= 360.0; }

    DebugFile << "max_correl = " << max_correl
              << " phase = " << phase_lag << endl;

    Phase_Resp[resp_indx] = phase_lag;
    if(Db_Scale_Enabled)
      {
      Mag_Resp[resp_indx] =
           20.0 * log10(2.0 * max_correl/samps_per_corr);
      }
    else
      {Mag_Resp[resp_indx] = 2.0 * max_correl/samps_per_corr;}
    }
 if(Normalize_Enabled) NormalizeResponse();
 return;
}
//=========================================================
// destructor
//---------------------------------------------------------

SweptResponse::~SweptResponse()
{
 delete []Mag_Resp;
 delete Response_File;
```

```
}
//=========================================================
//  method to normalize magnitude response
//---------------------------------------------------------

void SweptResponse::NormalizeResponse( void )
{
 int n;
 double biggest;

 if(Db_Scale_Enabled)
   {
    biggest = -100.0;

    for( n=1; n < Num_Resp_Pts; n++)
      {if(Mag_Resp[n]>biggest) biggest = Mag_Resp[n];}
    DebugFile << "before normaliz, biggest Mag_Resp was "
              << biggest << endl;
    for( n=1; n < Num_Resp_Pts; n++)
      {Mag_Resp[n] = Mag_Resp[n] - biggest;}
   }
 else
   {
    biggest = 0.0;

    for( n=1; n < Num_Resp_Pts; n++)
      {if(Mag_Resp[n]>biggest) biggest = Mag_Resp[n];}
    for( n=1; n < Num_Resp_Pts; n++)
      {Mag_Resp[n] = Mag_Resp[n] / biggest;}
   }
 return;
}
//============================================================
//  method to dump magnitude response to the stream
//  designated by Response_File
//------------------------------------------------------------

void SweptResponse::DumpMagResp( void )
{
 double freq;

 for(int n=1; n<Num_Resp_Pts; n++)
   {
    freq = n * Max_Sweep_Freq / (double) Num_Resp_Pts;
    (*Response_File) << freq << ", "
                     << Mag_Resp[n] << ", "
                     << Phase_Resp[n] << endl;
   }
 return;
}
```

Chapter

22

Filters for Multirate Signal Processing

22.1 Multirate Signal Processing: Basic Concepts

Interpolation and *decimation* are the fundamental operations of interest in multirate signal processing. Interpolation is the process of increasing the sampling rate of a discrete-time signal, and decimation is the process of decreasing the sampling rate.

Decimation

We could conceivably reduce a signal's sampling rate by a factor of M by simply discarding $M - 1$ samples out of every M samples, retaining only every Mth sample from the original sequence. However, the sampling theorem is still in force, and before we can safely reduce the sampling rate, we must first ensure that the signal has no significant spectral content at frequencies greater than half the *new* sampling rate. This is usually accomplished by passing the signal through a digital low-pass antialiasing filter prior to downsampling, as shown in Fig. 22.1. If the original sampling rate was F_s, the filter must effectively bandlimit the signal to less than $F_s/(2M)$.

Interpolation

The idea of using interpolation to produce new sample values between existing samples is straightforward. However, the way in which this interpolation is usually accomplished is not particularly intuitive. Furthermore, several published mathematical explanations of the usual approach to interpolation are confusing, misleading, and in at least one case, incorrect.

Consider the sampled signal and its spectrum shown in Fig. 22.2. Suppose we wish to triple the sampling rate. Following the usual approach, we proceed by inserting two zero-valued samples between each pair of original samples and

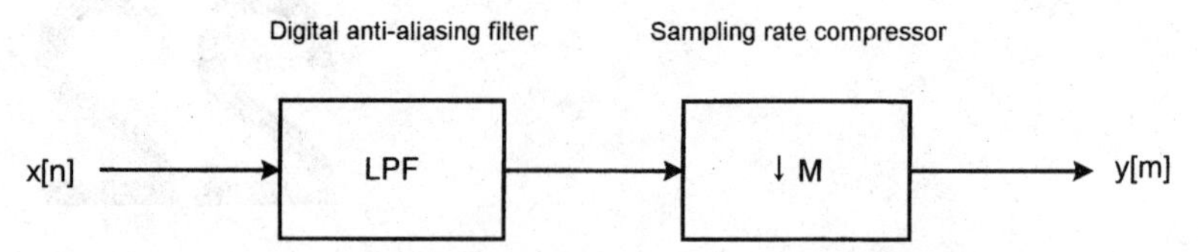

Figure 22.1 Block diagram of system for decimation by a factor of M.

obtain the sample sequence shown in Fig. 22.3. We then use a low-pass filter to limit the signal to a bandwidth equal to half the original sampling rate. The resulting signal and its spectrum is depicted in Fig. 22.4. This works. The problem is with the explanations of why it works or, equivalently, the explanation of why the filtering is needed. Several references either state or imply that the insertion of $L - 1$ zero-valued samples causes the signal's spectrum to be compressed by a factor of L—in other words, if the original signal had a bandwidth of $F_s/2$, insertion of the zeros would compress that bandwidth down to $F_s/(2L)$. If this were true, it would not be possible to recover the original signal by low-pass filtering. A low-pass filter only attenuates signal components outside of the pass band; it would not be able to decompress the compressed spectrum.

As discussed in Sec. 8.1, the spectrum of any discrete-time signal contains images of the original spectrum that are periodically repeated along the frequency axis, as shown in Fig. 22.5. The center-to-center spacing of the images is equal to the sampling rate F_s. In order to avoid aliasing, the original spectrum must fit within the frequency interval from $f = -F_s/2$ to $f = F_s/2$. Therefore, we could take the viewpoint that the discrete-time system in question has a

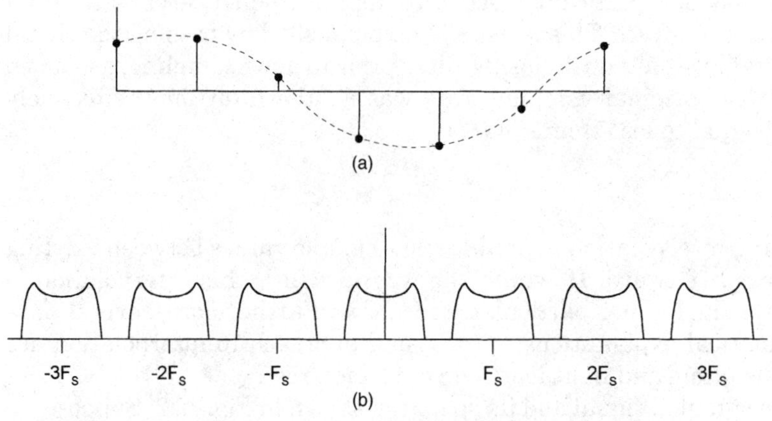

Figure 22.2 (a) Discrete-time signal and (b) its spectrum.

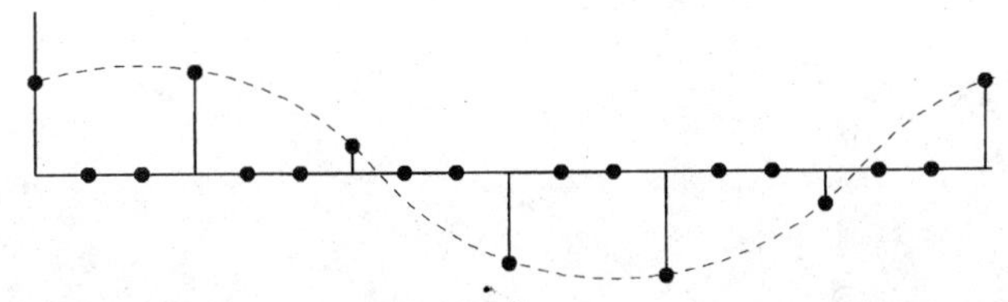

Figure 22.3 Discrete-time signal after zero-valued samples have been inserted.

bandwidth of either $F_s/2$ (one-sided) or F_s (two-sided). As shown in Fig. 22.5*b*, all of the images fall outside of the system bandwidth. What really happens when two zero-valued samples are inserted between each pair of original samples is that the system bandwidth becomes three times wider, as shown in Fig. 22.6. This wider bandwidth will include two images along with the original spectrum. The low-pass filtering operation is needed to remove these images from the system pass band. If the unshaded intervals in Figs. 22.5*b* and 22.6 were redrawn to be the same size, it would appear as though the insertion of zero-valued samples caused the signal's spectrum to be compressed.

22.2 Structures for Decimators and Interpolators

The filter in the M-to-1 decimator of Fig. 22.1 can be realized in a direct form structure to yield the decimator structure shown in Fig. 22.7. To produce each output sample, this structure must process M input samples, performing N

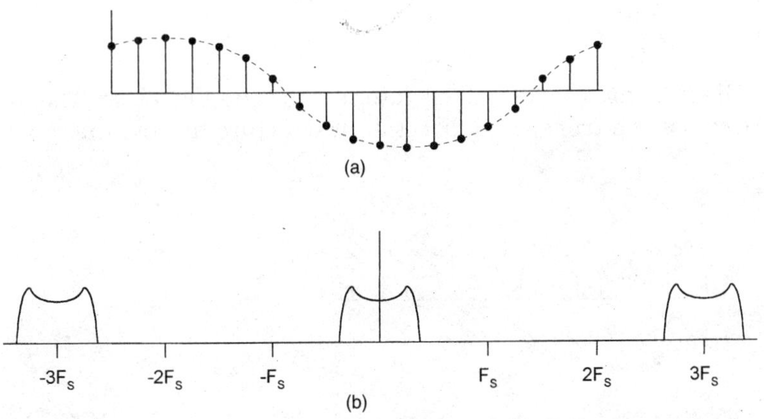

Figure 22.4 (*a*) Discrete-time signal from Fig. 22.3 and (*b*) its spectrum after low-pass filtering.

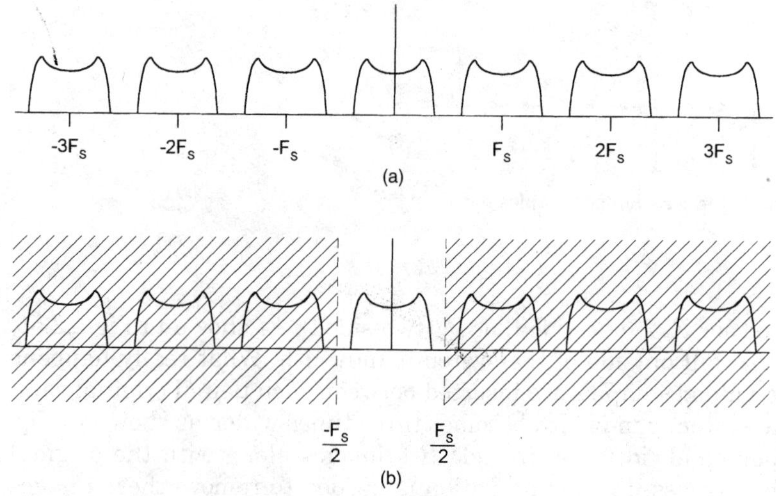

Figure 22.5 Spectrum of a discrete-time signal showing (*a*) spacing of images along the frequency axis, and (*b*) relationship between images and system bandwidth.

multiply-accumulate operations for each one. This is a total of MN multiply-accumulate operations for each output sample. It is possible to commute the order of the multiplications and sampling rate compression to obtain the structure shown in Fig. 22.8. This structure is much more efficient than Fig. 22.7, requiring only N multiply-accumulate operations per output sample. The equation implemented by Fig. 22.8 is given by

$$y[m] = \sum_{n=0}^{N-1} h[n]\, x[Mm - n]$$

Interpolators

The basic block diagram for a 1-to-L interpolator is shown in Fig. 22.9*a*. The filter can be realized using a transposed direct form structure to yield the inter-

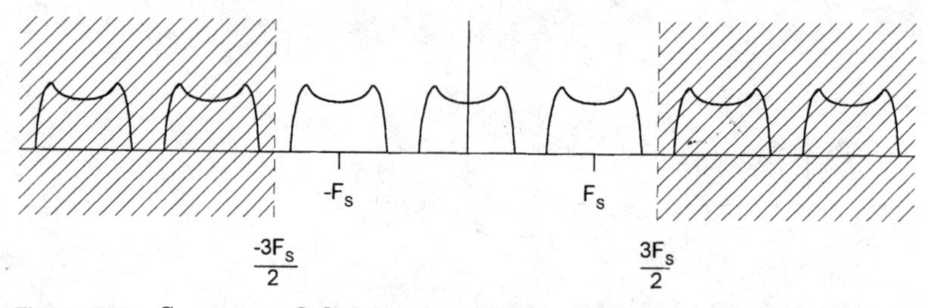

Figure 22.6 Spectrum of discrete-time signal showing relationship between images and system bandwidth after two zero-valued samples have been inserted between each pair of original time samples.

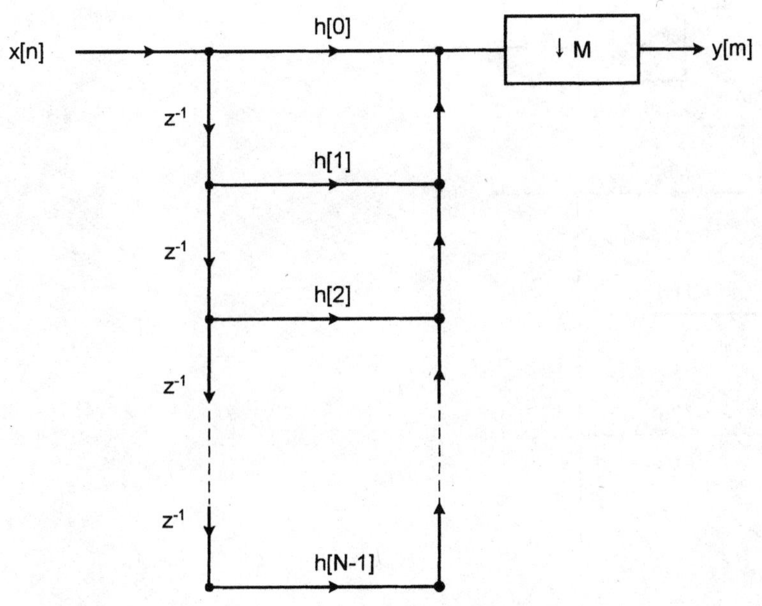

Figure 22.7 Direct form decimator structure obtained by direct expansion of the FIR filter in Fig. 22.1.

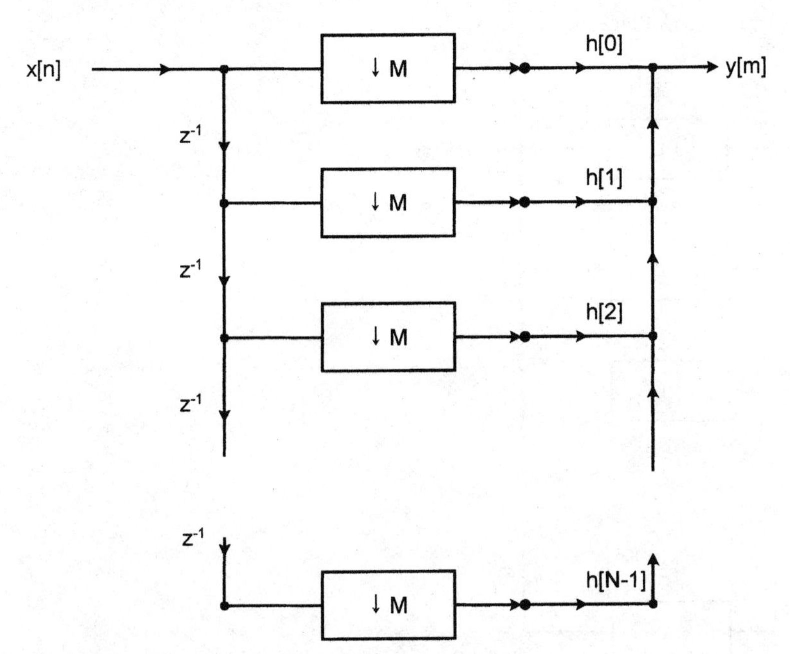

Figure 22.8 Efficient direct form FIR decimator structure.

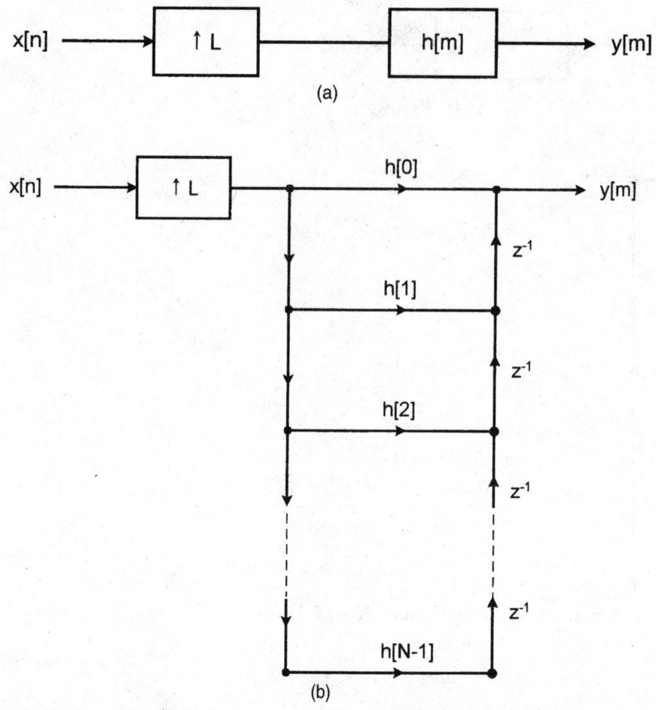

Figure 22.9 FIR interpolator: (*a*) basic block diagram, and (*b*) with filter realized in transposed direct form.

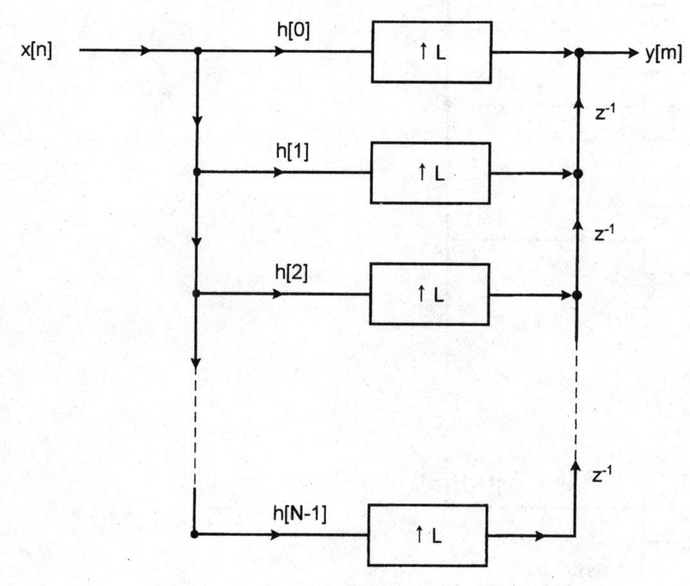

Figure 22.10 Efficient direct form FIR interpolator structure.

polator structure shown in Fig. 22.9*b*. This structure produces L output samples for each input sample and performs LN multiply-accumulate operations per input sample or N multiply-accumulate operations per output sample. It is possible to commute the order of the multiplications and sampling rate expansion to obtain the structure shown in Fig. 22.10. This structure requires only N multiply-accumulate operations per input sample or N/L multiply-accumulate operations per output sample.

Appendix

Mathematical Review

A.1 Exponentials and Logarithms

Exponentials

There is an irrational number, usually denoted as *e*, that is of great importance in virtually all fields of science and engineering. This number is defined by

$$e \triangleq \lim_{x \to +\infty} \left(1 + \frac{1}{x}\right)^x \simeq 2.71828 \cdots \tag{A.1}$$

Unfortunately, this constant remains unnamed, and writers are forced to settle for calling it "the number *e*" or perhaps "the base of natural logarithms." The letter *e* was first used to denote the irrational in Eq. (A.1) by Leonhard Euler (1707–1783), so it would seem reasonable to refer to the number under discussion as "Euler's constant." Such is not the case, however, as the term *Euler's constant* is attached to the constant γ defined by

$$\gamma = \lim_{N \to \infty} \left(\sum_{n=1}^{N} \frac{1}{n} - \log_e N \right) \simeq 0.577215664 \cdots \tag{A.2}$$

The number *e* is most often encountered in situations where it is raised to some real or complex power. The notation $\exp(x)$ is often used in place of e^x, since the former can be written more clearly and typeset more easily than the latter—especially in cases where the exponent is a complicated expression rather just a single variable. The value for *e* raised to a complex power z can be expanded in an infinite series as

$$\exp(z) = \sum_{n=0}^{\infty} \frac{z^n}{n!} \tag{A.3}$$

The series in Eq. (A.3) converges for all complex z having finite magnitude.

Logarithms

The *common logarithm,* or *base-10 logarithm,* of a number x is equal to the power to which 10 must be raised in order to equal x:

$$y = \log_{10} x \Leftrightarrow x = 10^y \tag{A.4}$$

The *natural logarithm,* or *base-e logarithm,* of a number x is equal to the power to which e must be raised in order to equal x:

$$y = \log_e x \Leftrightarrow x = \exp(y) \equiv e^y \tag{A.5}$$

Natural logarithms are also called *Napierian logarithms* in honor of John Napier (1550–1617), a Scottish amateur mathematician who in 1614 published the first account of logarithms in *Mirifici logarithmorum canonis descripto* ("A Description of the Marvelous Rule of Logarithms") (see Boyer 1968). The concept of logarithms can be extended to any positive base b, with the base-b logarithm of a number x equaling the power to which the base must be raised in order to equal x:

$$y = \log_b x \Leftrightarrow x = b^y \tag{A.6}$$

The notation log without a base explicitly indicated usually denotes a common logarithm, although sometimes this notation is used to denote natural logarithms (especially in some of the older literature). More often, the notation ln is used to denote a natural logarithm. Logarithms exhibit a number of properties that are listed in Table A.1. Entry 1 is sometimes offered as the definition of natural logarithms. The multiplication property in entry 3 is the theoretical basis upon which the design of the slide rule is based.

TABLE A.1 Properties of Logarithms

1. $\ln x = \int_1^x \frac{1}{y}\,dy \qquad x > 0$
2. $\frac{d}{dx}(\ln x) = \frac{1}{x} \qquad x > 0$
3. $\log_b (xy) = \log_b x + \log_b y$
4. $\log_b \left(\frac{1}{x}\right) = -\log_b x$
5. $\log_b (y^x) = x \log_b y$
6. $\log_c x = (\log_b x)(\log_c b) = \frac{\log_b x}{\log_b c}$
7. $\ln (1 + z) = \sum_{n=1}^{\infty} (-1)^{n-1} \frac{z^n}{n} \qquad |z| < 1$

Decibels

Consider a system that has an output power of P_{out} and an output voltage of V_{out} given an input power of P_{in} and an input voltage of V_{in}. The gain G, in decibels (dB), of the system is given by

$$G_{dB} = 10 \log_{10}\left(\frac{P_{out}}{P_{in}}\right) = 10 \log_{10}\left(\frac{V_{out}^2/Z_{out}}{V_{in}^2/Z_{in}}\right) \tag{A.7}$$

If the input and output impedances are equal, Eq. (A.7) reduces to

$$G_{dB} = 10 \log_{10}\left(\frac{V_{out}^2}{V_{in}^2}\right) = 20 \log_{10}\left(\frac{V_{out}}{V_{in}}\right) \tag{A.8}$$

Example A.1 An amplifier has a gain of 17.0 dB. For a 3-mW input, what will the output power be? Substituting the given data into Eq. (A.7) yields

$$17.0 \text{ dB} = 10 \log_{10}\left(\frac{P_{out}}{3 \times 10^{-3}}\right)$$

Solving for P_{out} then produces

$$P_{out} = (3 \times 10^{-3})10^{(17/10)} = 1.5 \times 10^{-1} = 150 \text{ mW}$$

Example A.2 What is the range in decibels of the values that can be represented by an 8-bit unsigned integer?

solution The smallest value is 1, and the largest value is $2^8 - 1 = 255$. Thus

$$20 \log_{10}\left(\frac{255}{1}\right) = 48.13 \text{ dB}$$

The abbreviation dBm is used to designate power levels relative to 1 milliwatt (mW). For example:

$$30 \text{ dBm} = 10 \log_{10}\left(\frac{P}{10^{-3}}\right)$$

$$P = (10^{-3})(10^3) = 10^0 = 1.0 \text{ W}$$

A.2 Complex Numbers

A complex number z has the form $a + bj$, where a and b are real and $j = \sqrt{-1}$. The *real part* of z is a, and the *imaginary part* of z is b. Mathematicians use i to denote $\sqrt{-1}$, but electrical engineers use j to avoid confusion with the traditional use of i for denoting current. For convenience, $a + bj$ is sometimes represented by the ordered pair (a, b). The *modulus*, or *absolute value*, of z is denoted as $|z|$ and is defined by

$$|z| = |a + bj| = \sqrt{a^2 + b^2} \tag{A.9}$$

The *complex conjugate* of z is denoted as z^* and is defined by

$$(z = a + bj) \Leftrightarrow (z^* = a - bj) \tag{A.10}$$

Conjugation distributes over addition, multiplication, and division:

$$(z_1 + z_2)^* = z_1^* + z_2^* \tag{A.11}$$

$$(z_1 z_2)^* = z_1^* z_2^* \tag{A.12}$$

$$\left(\frac{z_1}{z_2}\right)^* = \frac{z_1^*}{z_2^*} \tag{A.13}$$

Operations on complex numbers in rectangular form

Consider two complex numbers:

$$z_1 = a + bj \qquad z_2 = c + dj$$

The four basic arithmetic operations are then defined as

$$z_1 + z_2 = (a + c) + j(b + d) \tag{A.14}$$

$$z_1 - z_2 = (a - c) + j(b - d) \tag{A.15}$$

$$z_1 z_2 = (ac - bd) + j(ad + bc) \tag{A.16}$$

$$\frac{z_1}{z_2} = \frac{ac + bd}{c^2 + d^2} + j\frac{bc - ad}{c^2 + d^2} \tag{A.17}$$

Polar form of complex numbers

A complex number of the form $a + bj$ can be represented by a point in a coordinate plane as shown in Fig. A.1. Such a representation is called an *Argand diagram* (Spiegel 1965) in honor of Jean Robert Argand (1768–1822), who published a description of this graphical representation of complex numbers in 1806 (Boyer 1968). The point representing $a + bj$ can also be located using an angle θ and radius r as shown. From the definitions of sine and cosine given in Eqs. (A.25) and (A.26) of Sec. A.3, it follows that

$$a = r \cos \theta \qquad b = r \sin \theta$$

Therefore,

$$z = r \cos \theta + jr \sin \theta = r(\cos \theta + j \sin \theta) \tag{A.18}$$

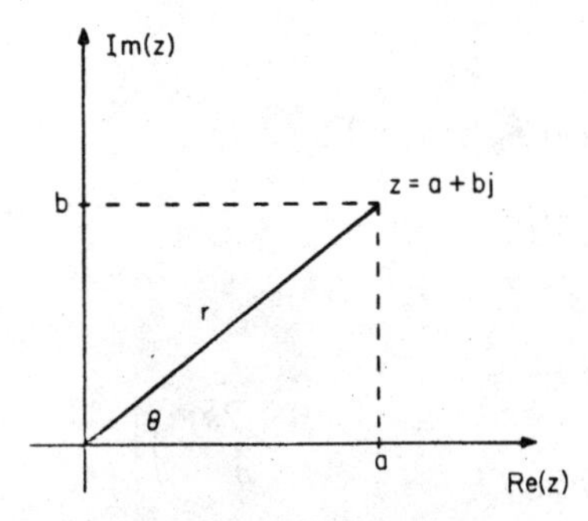

Figure A.1 Argand diagram representation of a complex number.

The quantity $(\cos\theta + j\sin\theta)$ is sometimes denoted as cis θ. Making use of Eq. (A.58) from Sec. A.3, we can rewrite Eq. (A.18) as

$$z = r \text{ cis } \theta = r \exp(j\theta) \tag{A.19}$$

The form in Eq. (A.19) is called the *polar form* of the complex number z.

Operations on complex numbers in polar form

Consider three complex numbers:

$$z = r(\cos\theta + j\sin\theta) = r\exp(j\theta)$$

$$z_1 = r_1(\cos\theta_1 + j\sin\theta_1) = r_1\exp(j\theta_1)$$

$$z_2 = r_2(\cos\theta_2 + j\sin\theta_2) = r_2\exp(j\theta_2)$$

Several operations can be conveniently performed directly upon complex numbers that are in polar form, as follows.

Multiplication

$$z_1 z_2 = r_1 r_2[\cos(\theta_1+\theta_2) + j\sin(\theta_1+\theta_2)]$$

$$= r_1 r_2 \exp[j(\theta_1+\theta_2)] \tag{A.20}$$

Division

$$\frac{z_1}{z_2} = \frac{r_1}{r_2}[\cos(\theta_1-\theta_2) + j\sin(\theta_1-\theta_2)]$$

$$= \frac{r_1}{r_2}\exp[j(\theta_1-\theta_2)] \tag{A.21}$$

Powers

$$z^n = r^n[\cos(n\theta) + j\sin(n\theta)]$$
$$= r^n \exp(jn\theta) \qquad \text{(A.22)}$$

Roots

$$\sqrt[n]{z} = z^{1/n} = r^{1/n}\left[\cos\left(\frac{\theta + 2k\pi}{n}\right) + j\sin\left(\frac{\theta + 2k\pi}{n}\right)\right]$$
$$= r^{1/n}\exp\left[\frac{j(\theta + 2k\pi)}{n}\right] \qquad k = 0, 1, 2, \ldots \qquad \text{(A.23)}$$

Equation (A.22) is known as *De Moivre's theorem.* In 1730, an equation similar to Eq. (A.23) was published by Abraham De Moivre (1667–1754) in his *Miscellanea analytica* (Boyer 1968). In Eq. (A.23), for a fixed n as k increases, the sinusoidal functions will take on only n distinct values. Thus, there are n different nth roots of any complex number.

Logarithms of complex numbers

For the complex number $z = r\exp(j\theta)$, the natural logarithm of z is given by

$$\ln z = \ln[r\exp(j\theta)]$$
$$= \ln\{r\exp[j(\theta + 2k\pi)]\}$$
$$= (\ln r) + j(\theta + 2k\pi) \qquad k = 0, 1, 2, \ldots \qquad \text{(A.24)}$$

The *principal value* is obtained when $k = 0$.

A.3 Trigonometry

For x, y, r, and θ as shown in Fig. A.2, the six trigonometric functions of the angle θ are defined as

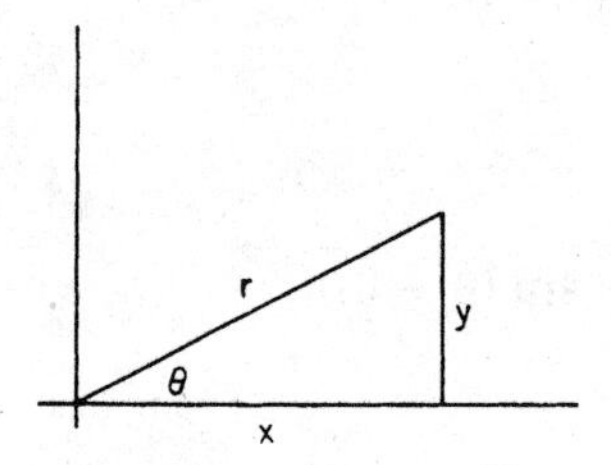

Figure A.2 An angle in the cartesian plane.

$$\text{Sine:} \qquad \sin\theta = \frac{y}{r} \tag{A.25}$$

$$\text{Cosine:} \qquad \cos\theta = \frac{x}{r} \tag{A.26}$$

$$\text{Tangent:} \qquad \tan\theta = \frac{y}{x} \tag{A.27}$$

$$\text{Cosecant:} \qquad \csc\theta = \frac{r}{y} \tag{A.28}$$

$$\text{Secant:} \qquad \sec\theta = \frac{r}{x} \tag{A.29}$$

$$\text{Cotangent:} \qquad \cot\theta = \frac{x}{y} \tag{A.30}$$

Phase shifting of sinusoids

A number of useful equivalences can be obtained by adding particular phase angles to the arguments of sine and cosine functions:

$$\cos(\omega t) = \sin\left(\omega t + \frac{\pi}{2}\right) \tag{A.31}$$

$$\cos(\omega t) = \cos(\omega t + 2n\pi) \qquad n = \text{any integer} \tag{A.32}$$

$$\sin(\omega t) = \sin(\omega t + 2n\pi) \qquad n = \text{any integer} \tag{A.33}$$

$$\sin(\omega t) = \cos\left(\omega t - \frac{\pi}{2}\right) \tag{A.34}$$

$$\cos(\omega t) = \cos[\omega t + (2n+1)\pi] \qquad n = \text{any integer} \tag{A.35}$$

$$\sin(\omega t) = -\sin[\omega t + (2n+1)\pi] \qquad n = \text{any integer} \tag{A.36}$$

Trigonometric identities

The following trigonometric identities often prove useful in the design and analysis of signal processing systems.

$$\tan x = \frac{\sin x}{\cos x} \tag{A.37}$$

$$\sin(-x) = -\sin x \tag{A.38}$$

$$\cos(-x) = \cos x \tag{A.39}$$

$$\tan(-x) = -\tan x \tag{A.40}$$

$$\cos^2 x + \sin^2 x = 1 \tag{A.41}$$

$$\cos^2 x = \frac{1}{2}[1 + \cos(2x)] \tag{A.42}$$

$$\sin(x \pm y) = (\sin x)(\cos y) \pm (\cos y)(\sin y) \tag{A.43}$$

$$\cos(x \pm y) = (\cos x)(\cos y) \mp (\sin x)(\sin y) \tag{A.44}$$

$$\tan(x + y) = \frac{(\tan x) + (\tan y)}{1 - (\tan x)(\tan y)} \tag{A.45}$$

$$\sin(2x) = 2(\sin x)(\cos x) \tag{A.46}$$

$$\cos(2x) = \cos^2 x - \sin^2 x \tag{A.47}$$

$$\tan(2x) = \frac{2(\tan x)}{1 - \tan^2 x} \tag{A.48}$$

$$(\sin x)(\sin y) = \frac{1}{2}[-\cos(x + y) + \cos(x - y)] \tag{A.49}$$

$$(\cos x)(\cos y) = \frac{1}{2}[\cos(x + y) + \cos(x - y)] \tag{A.50}$$

$$(\sin x)(\cos y) = \frac{1}{2}[\sin(x + y) + \sin(x - y)] \tag{A.51}$$

$$(\sin x) + (\sin y) = 2 \sin \frac{x + y}{2} \cos \frac{x - y}{2} \tag{A.52}$$

$$(\sin x) - (\sin y) = 2 \sin \frac{x - y}{2} \cos \frac{x + y}{2} \tag{A.53}$$

$$(\cos x) + (\cos y) = 2 \cos \frac{x + y}{2} \cos \frac{x - y}{2} \tag{A.54}$$

$$(\cos x) - (\cos y) = -2 \sin \frac{x + y}{2} \sin \frac{x - y}{2} \tag{A.55}$$

$$A \cos(\omega t + \psi) + B \cos(\omega t + \phi) = C \cos(\omega t + \theta) \tag{A.56}$$

where

$$C = [A^2 + B^2 - 2AB \cos(\phi - \psi)]^{1/2}$$

$$\theta = \tan^{-1}\left(\frac{A \sin \psi + B \sin \phi}{A \cos \psi + B \cos \phi}\right)$$

$$A \cos(\omega t + \psi) + B \sin(\omega t + \phi) = C \cos(\omega t + \theta) \tag{A.57}$$

where

$$C = [A^2 + B^2 - 2AB \sin(\phi - \psi)]^{1/2}$$

$$\theta = \tan^{-1}\left(\frac{A \sin \psi - B \cos \phi}{A \cos \psi + B \sin \phi}\right)$$

Euler's identities

The following four equations, called *Euler's identities,* relate sinusoids and complex exponentials.

$$e^{jx} = \cos x + j \sin x \tag{A.58}$$

$$e^{-jx} = \cos x - j \sin x \tag{A.59}$$

$$\cos x = \frac{e^{jx} + e^{-jx}}{2} \tag{A.60}$$

$$\sin x = \frac{e^{jx} - e^{-jx}}{2j} \tag{A.61}$$

Series and product expansions

Listed following are infinite series expansions for the various trigonometric functions (Abramowitz and Stegun 1966).

$$\sin x = \sum_{n=0}^{\infty} \frac{(-1)^n x^{2n+1}}{(2n+1)!} \tag{A.62}$$

$$\cos x = \sum_{n=0}^{\infty} \frac{(-1)^n x^{2n}}{(2n)!} \tag{A.63}$$

$$\tan x = \sum_{n=1}^{\infty} \frac{(-1)^{n-1} 2^{2n}(2^{2n} - 1) B_{2n} x^{2n-1}}{(2n)!} \qquad |x| < \frac{\pi}{2} \tag{A.64}$$

$$\cot x = \sum_{n=0}^{\infty} \frac{(-1)^n 2^{2n} B_{2n} x^{2n} - 1}{(2n)!} \qquad |x| < \pi \tag{A.65}$$

$$\sec x = \sum_{n=0}^{\infty} \frac{(-1)^n E_{2n} x^{2n}}{(2n)!} \qquad |x| < \frac{\pi}{2} \tag{A.66}$$

$$\csc x = \sum_{n=0}^{\infty} \frac{(-1)^{n-1} 2(2^{2n-1} - 1) B_{2n} x^{2n-1}}{(2n)!} \qquad |x| < \pi \tag{A.67}$$

Values for the Bernoulli number B_n and Euler number E_n are listed in Tables A.2 and A.3, respectively. In some instances, the infinite product expansions for sine and cosine may be more convenient than the series expansions.

$$\sin x = x \prod_{n=1}^{\infty} \left(1 - \frac{x^2}{n^2\pi^2}\right) \tag{A.68}$$

$$\cos x = \prod_{n=1}^{\infty} \left[1 - \frac{4x^2}{(2n-1)^2\pi^2}\right] \tag{A.69}$$

Orthonormality of sine and cosine

Two functions $\phi_1(t)$ and $\phi_2(t)$ are said to form an *orthogonal* set over the interval $[0, T]$ if

$$\int_0^T \phi_1(t)\phi_2(t)\, dt = 0 \tag{A.70}$$

The functions $\phi_1(t)$ and $\phi_2(t)$ are said to form an *orthonormal* set over the interval $[0, T]$ if in addition to satisfying Eq. (A.70) each function has unit energy over the interval

$$\int_0^T [\phi_1(t)]^2\, dt = \int_0^T [\phi_2(t)]^2\, dt = 1 \tag{A.71}$$

TABLE A.2 Bernoulli Numbers

$B_n = N/D \qquad B_n = 0 \quad \text{for} \quad n = 3, 5, 7, \ldots$

n	N	D
0	1	1
1	−1	2
2	1	6
4	−1	30
6	1	42
8	−1	30
10	5	66
12	−691	2730
14	7	6
16	−3617	510
18	43867	798
20	−174611	330

TABLE A.3 Euler Numbers

$E_n = 0 \quad \text{for} \quad n = 1, 3, 5, 7, \ldots$

n	E_n
0	1
2	−1
4	5
6	−61
8	1385
10	−50521
12	2,702,765
14	−199,360,981
16	19,391,512,145
18	−2,404,879,675,441
20	370,371,188,237,525

Consider the two signals given by

$$\phi_1(t) = A \sin(\omega_0 t) \tag{A.72}$$

$$\phi_2(t) = A \cos(\omega_0 t) \tag{A.73}$$

The signals ϕ_1 and ϕ_2 will form an orthogonal set over the interval $[0, T]$ if $\omega_0 T$ is an integer multiple of π. The set will be orthonormal as well as orthogonal if $A^2 = 2/T$. The signals ϕ_1 and ϕ_2 will form an approximately orthonormal set over the interval $[0, T]$ if $\omega_0 T \gg 1$ and $A^2 = 2/T$. The orthonormality of sine and cosine can be derived as follows.

Substitution of Eqs. (A.72) and (A.73) into Eq. (A.70) yields

$$\int_0^T \phi_1(t)\phi_2(t)\,dt = A^2 \int_0^T \sin \omega_0 t \cos \omega_0 t\,dt$$

$$= \frac{A^2}{2} \int_0^T [\sin(\omega_0 t + \omega_0 t) + \sin(\omega_0 t - \omega_0 t)]\,dt$$

$$= \frac{A^2}{2} \int_0^T \sin 2\omega_0 t\,dt = \frac{A^2}{2}\left(\frac{\cos 2\omega_0 t}{2\omega_0}\right)\Bigg|_{t=0}^{T}$$

$$= \frac{A^2}{4\omega_0 T}(1 - \cos 2\omega_0 T) \tag{A.74}$$

Thus, if $\omega_0 T$ is an integer multiple of π, then $\cos(2\omega_0 T) = 1$ and ϕ_1 and ϕ_2 will be orthogonal. If $\omega_0 T \gg 1$, then Eq. (A.74) will be very small and reasonably approximated by zero; thus ϕ_1 and ϕ_2 can be considered as approximately orthogonal. The energy of $\phi_1(t)$ on the interval $[0, T]$ is given by

$$E_1 = \int_0^T [\phi_1(t)]^2\,dt = A^2 \int_0^T \sin^2 \omega_0 t\,dt$$

$$= A^2\left(\frac{t}{2} - \frac{\sin 2\omega_0 t}{4\omega_0}\right)\Bigg|_{t=0}^{T}$$

$$= A^2\left(\frac{T}{2} - \frac{\sin 2\omega_0 T}{4\omega_0}\right) \tag{A.75}$$

For ϕ_1 to have unit energy, A^2 must satisfy

$$A^2 = \left(\frac{T}{2} - \frac{\sin 2\omega_0 T}{4\omega_0}\right)^{-1} \tag{A.76}$$

When $\omega_0 T = n\pi$, then $\sin 2\omega_0 T = 0$. Thus, Eq. (A.76) reduces to

$$A = \sqrt{\frac{2}{T}} \tag{A.77}$$

Substituting (A.77) into (A.75) yields

$$E_1 = 1 - \frac{\sin 2\omega_0 T}{2\omega_0 T} \tag{A.78}$$

When $\omega_0 T \gg 1$, the second term of Eq. (A.78) will be very small and reasonably approximated by zero, thus indicating that ϕ_1 and ϕ_2 are approximately orthonormal. In a similar manner, the energy of $\phi_2(t)$ can be found to be

$$E_2 = A^2 \int_0^T \cos^2 \omega_0 t \, dt$$

$$= A^2 \left(\frac{T}{2} + \frac{\sin 2\omega_0 T}{4\omega_0} \right) \tag{A.79}$$

Thus

$$E_2 = 1 \quad \text{if} \quad A = \sqrt{\frac{2}{T}} \quad \text{and} \quad \omega_0 T = n\pi$$

$$E_2 \doteq 1 \quad \text{if} \quad A = \sqrt{\frac{2}{T}} \quad \text{and} \quad \omega_0 T \gg 1$$

A.4 Derivatives

Listed following are some derivative forms that often prove useful in theoretical analysis of communication systems.

$$\frac{d}{dx} \sin u = \cos u \frac{du}{dx} \tag{A.80}$$

$$\frac{d}{dx} \cos u = -\sin u \frac{du}{dx} \tag{A.81}$$

$$\frac{d}{dx} \tan u = \sec^2 u \frac{du}{dx} = \frac{1}{\cos^2 u} \frac{du}{dx} \tag{A.82}$$

$$\frac{d}{dx} \cot u = \csc^2 u \frac{du}{dx} = \frac{1}{\sin^2 u} \frac{du}{dx} \tag{A.83}$$

$$\frac{d}{dx} \sec u = \sec u \tan u \frac{du}{dx} = \frac{\sin u}{\cos^2 u} \frac{du}{dx} \tag{A.84}$$

$$\frac{d}{dx}\csc u = -\csc u \cot u \frac{du}{dx} = \frac{-\cos u}{\sin^2 u}\frac{du}{dx} \tag{A.85}$$

$$\frac{d}{dx}e^u = e^u\frac{du}{dx} \tag{A.86}$$

$$\frac{d}{dx}\ln u = \frac{1}{u}\frac{du}{dx} \tag{A.87}$$

$$\frac{d}{dx}\log u = \frac{\log e}{u}\frac{du}{dx} \tag{A.88}$$

$$\frac{d}{dx}\left(\frac{u}{v}\right) = \frac{1}{v^2}\left(v\frac{du}{dx} - u\frac{dv}{dx}\right) \tag{A.89}$$

Derivatives of polynomial ratios

Consider a ratio of polynomials given by

$$C(s) = \frac{A(s)}{B(s)} \qquad B(s) \neq 0 \tag{A.90}$$

The derivative of $C(s)$ can be obtained using Eq. (A.89) to obtain

$$\frac{d}{ds}C(s) = [B(s)]^{-1}\frac{d}{ds}A(s) - A(s)[B(s)]^{-2}\frac{d}{ds}B(s) \tag{A.91}$$

Equation (A.91) will be very useful in the application of the Heaviside expansion.

A.5 Integration

Large integral tables fill entire volumes and contain thousands of entries. However, a relatively small number of integral forms appear over and over again in the study of communications, and these are listed following.

$$\int \frac{1}{x}\,dx = \ln x \tag{A.92}$$

$$\int e^{ax}\,dx = \frac{1}{a}e^{ax} \tag{A.93}$$

$$\int xe^{ax}\,dx = \frac{ax-1}{a^2}e^{ax} \tag{A.94}$$

$$\int \sin(ax)\,dx = -\frac{1}{a}\cos(ax) \tag{A.95}$$

$$\int \cos (ax)\, dx = \frac{1}{a} \sin (ax) \tag{A.96}$$

$$\int \sin (ax + b)\, dx = -\frac{1}{a} \cos (ax + b) \tag{A.97}$$

$$\int \cos (ax + b)\, dx = \frac{1}{a} \sin (ax + b) \tag{A.98}$$

$$\int x \sin (ax)\, dx = -\frac{x}{a} \cos (ax) + \frac{1}{a^2} \sin (ax) \tag{A.99}$$

$$\int x \cos (ax)\, dx = \frac{x}{a} \sin (ax) + \frac{1}{a^2} \cos (ax) \tag{A.100}$$

$$\int \sin^2 ax\, dx = \frac{x}{2} - \frac{\sin 2ax}{4a} \tag{A.101}$$

$$\int \cos^2 ax\, dx = \frac{x}{2} + \frac{\sin 2ax}{4a} \tag{A.102}$$

$$\int x^2 \sin ax\, dx = \frac{1}{a^3}(2ax \sin ax + 2 \cos ax - a^2x^2 \cos ax) \tag{A.103}$$

$$\int x^2 \cos ax\, dx = \frac{1}{a^3}(2ax \cos ax - 2 \sin ax + a^2x^2 \sin ax) \tag{A.104}$$

$$\int \sin^3 x\, dx = -\frac{1}{3} \cos x(\sin^2 x + 2) \tag{A.105}$$

$$\int \cos^3 x\, dx = \frac{1}{3} \sin x(\cos^2 x + 2) \tag{A.106}$$

$$\int \sin x \cos x\, dx = \frac{1}{2} \sin^2 x \tag{A.107}$$

$$\int \sin (mx) \cos (nx)\, dx = \frac{-\cos(m - n)x}{2(m - n)} - \frac{\cos (m + n)x}{2(m + n)} \qquad (m^2 \neq n^2) \tag{A.108}$$

$$\int \sin^2 x \cos^2 x\, dx = \frac{1}{8}\left[x - \frac{1}{4} \sin (4x)\right] \tag{A.109}$$

$$\int \sin x \cos^m x\, dx = \frac{-\cos^{m+1} x}{m + 1} \tag{A.110}$$

$$\int \sin^m x \cos x \, dx = \frac{\sin^{m+1} x}{m+1} \tag{A.111}$$

$$\int \cos^m x \sin^n x \, dx = \frac{\cos^{m-1} x \sin^{n+1} x}{m+n} + \frac{m-1}{m+n} \int \cos^{m-2} x \sin^n x \, dx \qquad (m \neq -n) \tag{A.112}$$

$$\int \cos^m x \sin^n x \, dx = \frac{-\cos^{m+1} x \sin^{n-1} x}{m+n} + \frac{n-1}{m+n} \int \cos^m x \sin^{n-2} x \, dx \qquad (m \neq -n) \tag{A.113}$$

$$\int u \, dv = uv - \int v \, du \tag{A.114}$$

A.6 Dirac Delta Function

In all of electrical engineering, there is perhaps nothing that is responsible for more hand-waving than the so-called *delta function,* or *impulse function,* which is denoted $\delta(t)$ and which is usually depicted as a vertical arrow at the origin as shown in Fig. A.3. This function is often called the *Dirac delta function* in honor of Paul Dirac (1902–1984), an English physicist who used delta functions extensively in his work on quantum mechanics. A number of nonrigorous approaches for defining the impulse function can be found throughout the literature. A *unit impulse* is often loosely described as having a zero width and an infinite amplitude at the origin such that the total area under the impulse is equal to unity. How is it possible to claim that 0 times infinity equals 1? The trick involves defining a sequence of functions $f_n(t)$ such that

$$\int_{-\infty}^{\infty} f_n(t) \, dt = 1 \tag{A.115}$$

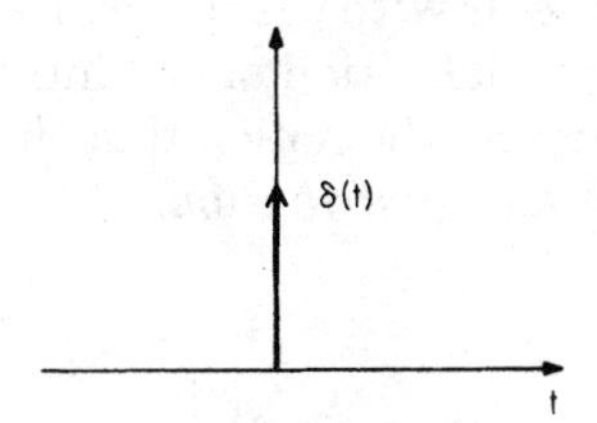

Figure A.3 Graphical representation of the Dirac delta function.

and

$$\lim_{n \to \infty} f_n(t) = 0 \qquad \text{for} \quad t \neq 0 \tag{A.116}$$

The delta function is then defined as

$$\delta(t) = \lim_{n \to \infty} f_n(t) \tag{A.117}$$

Example A.3 Let a sequence of pulse functions $f_n(t)$ be defined as

$$f_n(t) = \begin{cases} \dfrac{n}{2} & |t| \leqslant \dfrac{1}{n} \\ 0 & \text{otherwise} \end{cases} \tag{A.118}$$

Equation (A.115) is satisfied since the area of pulse is equal to $(2n) \cdot (n/2) = 1$ for all n. The pulse width decreases and the pulse amplitude increases as n approaches infinity. Therefore, we intuitively sense that this sequence must also satisfy Eq. (A.116). Thus the impulse function can be defined as the limit of Eq. (A.118) as n approaches infinity. Using similar arguments, it can be shown that the impulse can also be defined as the limit of a sequence of sinc functions or gaussian pulse functions.

A second approach entails simply defining $\delta(t)$ to be that function which satisfies

$$\int_{-\infty}^{\infty} \delta(t)\, dt = 1 \qquad \text{and} \qquad \delta(t) = 0 \qquad \text{for} \quad t \neq 0 \tag{A.119}$$

In a third approach, $\delta(t)$ is defined as that function which exhibits the property

$$\int_{-\infty}^{\infty} \delta(t) f(t)\, dt = f(0) \tag{A.120}$$

While any of these three approaches is adequate to introduce the delta function into an engineer's repertoire of analytical tools, none of the three is sufficiently rigorous to satisfy mathematicians or discerning theoreticians. In particular, notice that none of the approaches presented deals with the thorny issue of just what the value of $\delta(t)$ is for $t = 0$. The rigorous definition of $\delta(t)$ introduced in 1950 by Laurent Schwartz (Schwartz 1950) rejects the notion that the impulse is an ordinary function and instead defines it as a *distribution.*

Distributions

Let S be the set of functions $f(x)$ for which the nth derivative $f^{[n]}(x)$ exists for any n and all x. Furthermore, each $f(x)$ decreases sufficiently fast at infinity such that

$$\lim_{x \to \infty} x^n f(x) = 0 \qquad \text{for all } n \tag{A.121}$$

A *distribution,* often denoted $\phi(x)$, is defined as a continuous linear mapping from the set S to the set of complex numbers. Notationally, this mapping is represented as an inner product

$$\int_{-\infty}^{\infty} \phi(x) f(x)\, dx = z \tag{A.122}$$

or alternatively

$$\langle \phi(x), f(x) \rangle = z \tag{A.123}$$

Notice that no claim is made that ϕ is a function capable of mapping values of x into corresponding values $\phi(x)$. In some texts (such as Papoulis 1962), $\phi(x)$ is referred to as a *functional* or as a *generalized function.* The distribution ϕ is defined only through the impact that it has upon other functions. The impulse function is a distribution defined by the following:

$$\int_{-\infty}^{\infty} \delta(t) f(t)\, dt = f(0) \tag{A.124}$$

Equation (A.124) looks exactly like Eq. (A.120), but defining $\delta(t)$ as a distribution eliminates the need to tap dance around the issue of assigning a value to $\delta(0)$. Furthermore, the impulse function is elevated to a more substantial foundation from which several useful properties may be rigorously derived. For a more in-depth discussion of distributions other than $\delta(t)$, the interested reader is referred to Chap. 4 of Weaver (1989).

Properties of the delta distribution

It has been shown (Weaver 1989; Brigham 1974; Papoulis 1962; Schwartz and Friedland 1965) that the delta distribution exhibits the following properties:

$$\int_{-\infty}^{\infty} \delta(t)\, dt = 1 \tag{A.125}$$

$$\frac{d}{dt}\delta(t) = \lim_{\tau \to 0} \frac{\delta(t) - \delta(t-\tau)}{\tau} \tag{A.126}$$

$$\int_{-\infty}^{\infty} \delta(t - t_0)\, f(t)\, dt = f(t_0) \tag{A.127}$$

$$\delta(at) = \frac{1}{|a|}\delta(t) \tag{A.128}$$

$$\delta(t_0)f(t) = f(t_0)\delta(t_0) \tag{A.129}$$

$$\delta_1(t - t_1) * \delta_2(t - t_2) = \delta[t - (t_1 + t_2)] \tag{A.130}$$

In Eq. (A.129), $f(t)$ is an ordinary function that is continuous at $t = t_0$, and in Eq. (A.130), the asterisk denotes convolution.

Appendix

B

Probability and Random Variables

B.1 Randomness and Probability

Consider the space $\mathbb{S}$ comprising a (possibly infinite) number of events. An example of such a space would be the set of all possible outcomes from rolling a single die. In this space there would be six events—one corresponding to each face of the die. The space $\mathbb{S}$ in its entirety can be called the *certain event* since it is certain that one of the included events must occur. (Let us assume that a die must land on one of its faces—we shall neglect the pathological cases that require the die to remain stably balanced on an edge or on a vertex.) Each event can also be called an *experimental outcome.* Actually, any subset of $\mathbb{S}$ is an event, with those subsets containing a single element being further distinguished as *elementary events.* Some texts (such as Proakis 1983) refer to elementary events as *sample points* of the experiment. In our example, a nonelementary event might be the rolling of a 5. The subset of $\mathbb{S}$, which is the empty set (denoted as $\varnothing$), is called the *impossible event.* A numeric value $P(A)$ can be assigned to every event A in the space $\mathbb{S}$. In probability theory, this value is called the *probability of event* A and is assigned such that

1. The probability of the certain event is unity:

$$P(\mathbb{S}) = 1$$

2. All probabilities of events within $\mathbb{S}$ are nonnegative:

$$P(A) \geq 0$$

3. If events A and B share no common outcomes (i.e., if A and B are *mutually exclusive*), then the probability of either A or B occurring is equal to the probability of event A occurring plus the probability of event B occurring:

$$[A \cap B = \varnothing] \Rightarrow P(A + B) = P(A) + P(B)$$

A single execution of an experiment that selects an event from $\mathbb{S}$ is called a *trial.* A collection of events is called a *field* if it contains the certain event and is closed under finite union and complementation. A collection of events is called a *sigma field* (or σ field) if it contains the certain event and is closed under countable union and complementation. A σ field is also called a *Borel field* in honor of Emile Borel (1871–1956), a French mathematician.

B.2 Bernoulli Trials

In many applications a single experiment can have only two possible outcomes. An electronic component can be tested and found to be either defective or not defective. A coin can be tossed and will land either heads or tails. If n experiments are performed—if n coins are tossed or if a single coin is tossed n times—the probability that a particular outcome will be observed exactly k times is given by

$$\binom{n}{k} p^k (1-p)^{n-k} = \frac{n!}{k!(n-k)!} p^k (1-p)^{n-k} \tag{B.1}$$

where p is the probability of the desired outcome in a single experiment.

Example B.1 Suppose that 10 percent of the resistors produced by a particular machine are defective. If we examine a sample of 20 resistors, what is the probability that less than 3 will be defective?

solution To obtain the probability of finding at most 2 defective units, we must sum together the probability of finding no defects, the probability of finding exactly 1 defective unit, and the probability of finding exactly 2 defective units.

$$P(0 \text{ defects}) = \binom{20}{0} (0.10)^0 (0.90)^{20} = 0.12158$$

$$P(1 \text{ defect}) = \binom{20}{1} (0.10)^1 (0.90)^{19} = 0.27017$$

$$P(2 \text{ defects}) = \binom{20}{2} (0.10)^2 (0.90)^{18} = 0.28518$$

$$P(\text{less than 3 defects}) = 0.6769$$

B.3 Random Variables

If we conduct an experiment (such as rolling a die), we can assign a numeric value to each possible outcome of the experiment. The rule for assigning values to outcomes is called a *random variable.* Although it is called a random *variable,* it is not really a variable in the commonly understood sense. It is more like a function which maps each experimental outcome in the domain into the corresponding numeric value in the range. The outcomes of rolling a single die can be denoted $f_1, f_2, \ldots, f_6$. We can define a random variable $X(f_i)$, which assigns a value to each outcome. The obvious choice would be for $f_1 = 1, f_2 = 2$, and so on. However, we are not limited to just this option—we can define the mapping in many different ways, such as:

$$X(f_i) = 5i \qquad X(f_i) = i^2 \qquad X(f_i) = i - 1$$

Remember: f_i represents the possible outcomes of the experiment, while $X(f_i)$ is the random variable which assigns numeric values to each of these outcomes. (This numeric value should not be confused with the numeric probability value that is assigned to each outcome. In the case of a fair die, the probability of each face landing up is 1/6 regardless of the numeric score that may be printed on or assigned to the face.)

Cumulative distribution functions

The *cumulative distribution function* $F_x(x)$ associated with a random variable x yields the probability that X does not exceed x:

$$F_x(x) \equiv P\{X \leq x\}$$

Since $F_x(x)$ is a probability, we know that $0 \leq F_x(x) \leq 1$. Even though F_x is a function of x and not X, it is often referred to as the *distribution function of the random variable X.* In some of the literature, it is also called the *probability distribution function,* but this is best avoided because the abbreviation *pdf* could also be interpreted as *probability density function.* Although some authors use the lowercase pdf to denote *probability density function* and the uppercase PDF to denote *probability distribution function,* most authors avoid confusion by using cdf and pdf.

In cases where the independent variable and the subscript on F differ, the subscript indicates the random variable (RV) of interest. Thus, $F_x(y)$ represents the distribution function (evaluated at y) of the RV X. This is equal to the probability that the value of the RV X is less than or equal to y. In cases where the independent variable and the subscript are the same, the subscript is often omitted.

Properties of distribution functions

If $F(x)$ is the distribution function of the RV X, then it will exhibit the following properties:

$$F(-\infty) = 0 \tag{B.2}$$

$$F(+\infty) = 1 \tag{B.3}$$

$$\text{If } x_1 < x_2, \text{ then } F(x_1) \leq F(x_2) \tag{B.4}$$

$$\text{If } F(x_1) = 0, \text{ then } F(x) = 0 \text{ for all } x \le x_1 \tag{B.5}$$

$$P\{X > x\} = 1 - F(x) \tag{B.6}$$

$$P\{x_1 < X < x_2\} = F(x_2) - F(x_1) \tag{B.7}$$

$$P\{X = x\} = F(x) - \lim_{0<\epsilon\to 0} F(x - \epsilon) \tag{B.8}$$

$$P\{x_1 \le X \le x_2\} = F(x_2) - \lim_{0<\epsilon\to 0} F(x - \epsilon) \tag{B.9}$$

Probability density function

The derivative of the distribution function is called the *probability density function (pdf)*, *density function,* or *frequency function* of the random variable X.

B.4 Moments of a Random Variable

Mean

The *mean* $E(X)$ of a *discrete* random variable X is defined as

$$E(X) = \sum_{i=-\infty}^{\infty} x_i p_i \tag{B.10}$$

where p_i is the probability of the event $X = x_i$. The mean of a *continuous* random variable is defined as

$$E(X) = \int_{-\infty}^{\infty} x f(x)\, dx \tag{B.11}$$

where $f(x)$ is the probability density function of the RV X.

- The mean is also called the *expected value, expectation, ensemble average,* or *statistical average* and is typically denoted by an overbar or by η_x, η, or μ.

$$\overline{X} = \eta_x = \eta = \mu = E(X)$$

- The mean of the sum of two random variables is equal to the sum of their means.

$$E(Y + Y) = E(X) + E(Y) \tag{B.12}$$

- In general, the mean of a product of two RVs is not equal to the product of their individual means. However, the mean of the product will equal the product of the means if X and Y are uncorrelated.
- The mean of a constant times a random variable is equal to the constant times the mean.

$$E(aX) = aE(X) \tag{B.13}$$

- Taken together, Eqs. (B.12) and (B.13) indicate that expectation is a linear operation.

Mean of a function of a random variable

The mean $E\{g(X)\}$ of a function g of a discrete random variable X is defined as

$$E\{g(X)\} = \sum_{i=1}^{n} p_i g(x_i) \tag{B.14}$$

where p_i is the probability of the event $X = x_i$. If $g(X)$ is a function of a *continuous* random variable X, the mean is defined as

$$E\{g(X)\} = \int_{-\infty}^{\infty} g(x) f(x)\, dx \tag{B.15}$$

where $f(x)$ is the pdf of the random variable X. This result is known as the *fundamental theorem of expectation.*

Moments

The nth *moment* of the *discrete* random variable X is defined as

$$m_n = E(X^n) = \sum_{i=-\infty}^{\infty} x_i^n p_i \tag{B.16}$$

where p_i is the probability of the event $X = x_i$. The nth *moment* of the *continuous* random variable X is defined as

$$m_n = E\{X^n\} = \int_{-\infty}^{\infty} x^n f(x)\, dx \tag{B.17}$$

where $f(x)$ is the pdf of X. Note that the moment m_1 is the same as the mean.

Central moments

The kth *central moment* μ_k of a discrete random variable X is defined by

$$\mu_k = \sum_{i=-\infty}^{\infty} (x_i - \overline{X})^k\, p_i \tag{B.18}$$

where p_i is the probability of the event $X = x_i$. The kth central moment of a continuous random variable X is defined by

$$\mu_k = E\{(X - \overline{X})^k\} = \int_{-\infty}^{\infty} (x - \overline{X})^k f(x)\, dx \tag{B.19}$$

where $f(x)$ is the pdf of X.

- The second central moment is often called the *variance* and denoted by σ^2 rather than μ_n.
- The positive square root of variance is called the *standard deviation.*
- The third central moment is called *skew.*
- The fourth central moment is called the *kurtosis.*

Properties of variance

$$\text{var}\{cX\} = c^2\,\text{var}\{X\}$$

We can relate the mean and variance of a random variable by expanding the definition of variance

$$\begin{aligned}\sigma^2 &= E\{(X - \mu)^2\} \\ &= E\{(X^2 + 2X\mu + \mu^2)\} \\ &= E\{X^2\} - 2\mu E\{X\} + \mu^2 \\ &= E\{X^2\} - 2\mu^2 + \mu^2 \\ &= E\{X^2\} - [E\{X\}]^2\end{aligned}$$

If X and Y are independent, then

$$\text{var}\{X + Y\} = \text{var}\{X\} + \text{var}\{Y\}$$

B.5 Relationships between Random Variables

If X and Y are continuous random variables, their *joint distribution* $F_{xy}(x, y)$ yields the probability that X does not exceed x and Y does not exceed y.

$$F_{xy}(x, y) = P\{X \leq x, Y \leq y\}$$

The *joint density function,* $p_{xy}(x, y)$, of two continuous random variables x and y is defined as the mixed partial derivative of F_{xy}.

$$p_{xy}(x, y) = \frac{\partial^2}{\partial x\,\partial y} F_{xy}(x, y)$$

The individual density functions for X and Y can be obtained from $p_{xy}(x, y)$ by integration:

$$p_x(x) = \int_{-\infty}^{\infty} p_{xy}(x, y)\,dy$$

$$p_y(y) = \int_{-\infty}^{\infty} p_{xy}(x, y)\,dx$$

In this context, $p_x(x)$ and $p_y(y)$ are referred to as *marginal* probability density functions to emphasize the distinction between them and the joint density function.

If X and Y are discrete random variables, their joint probability function p_{ij} is the probability that $X = x_i$ and $Y = y_j$.

$$p_{ij} = P\{X = x_i, Y = y_j\}$$

The marginal probability functions for X and Y can be obtained by summing the joint probability function over all y_j or all x_i

$$P(X = x_i) = \sum_{j=-\infty}^{\infty} P(X = x_i, Y = y_j)$$

$$P(Y = y_j) = \sum_{i=-\infty}^{\infty} P(X = x_i, Y = y_j)$$

Statistical independence

Two random variables are called *statistically independent* if

$$P\{X \in A, Y \in B\} = P\{X \in A\}P\{Y \in B\}$$

where A and B are arbitrary subsets of the ranges of X and Y, respectively. This is equivalent to saying that $\{X \in A\}$ and $\{Y \in B\}$ are independent events. If the random variables X and Y are statistically independent, then the joint density $p_{xy}(x, y)$ equals the product of the marginal densities:

$$p_{xy}(x, y) = p_x(x)p_y(y)$$

If the random variables X and Y are not independent, then the joint density cannot be synthesized from just the marginal densities—either the conditional densities or sufficient other a priori information that characterizes the dependencies will be needed.

B.6 Correlation and Covariance

The *correlation* R_{xy} of two random variables X and Y is defined as

$$R_{xy} = E[XY] = \int_{-\infty}^{\infty}\int_{-\infty}^{\infty} xyp_{xy}(x, y)\, dx\, dy \tag{B.20}$$

The *covariance* C_{xy} of two random variables X and Y is defined as

$$C_{xy} = E\{(X - \mu_x)(Y - \mu_y)\} \tag{B.21}$$

It can be shown that $|C_{xy}| \le \sigma_x\sigma_y$. In some applications, it is more convenient to use a normalized measure called the *correlation coefficient,* which is defined as

$$r_{xy} = \frac{C_{xy}}{\sigma_x\sigma_y} \tag{B.22}$$

where

$$C_{xy} = \text{covariance of } X \text{ and } Y$$
$$\sigma_x = \text{standard deviation of } X$$
$$\sigma_y = \text{standard deviation of } Y$$

It can be shown that $|r_{xy}| \leq 1$.

Two random variables are called *uncorrelated* if their covariance and correlation coefficients are both zero. (Either one being zero is a sufficient condition for uncorrelatedness and implies that the other is also zero.) If X and Y are uncorrelated, then

$$E\{XY\} = E\{X\}E\{Y\} \tag{B.23}$$

and

$$\sigma_{x+y}^2 = \sigma_x^2 + \sigma_y^2 \tag{B.24}$$

If two random variables X and Y are statistically independent, then they are also uncorrelated. However, two RVs may be uncorrelated but not independent. In the case of normal random variables, uncorrelatedness *is* sufficient to establish statistical independence.

Two random variables X and Y are *orthogonal* if and only if $E\{XY\} = 0$. The orthogonality between X and Y can be denoted as $X \perp Y$. If X and Y are *uncorrelated,* then

$$(X - \overline{X}) \perp (Y - \overline{Y}) \tag{B.25}$$

If X and Y are uncorrelated and either or both has zero mean, then X is orthogonal to Y.

B.7 Probability Densities for Functions of a Random Variable

Given:

X is a continuous RV with pdf $p_x(X)$.

Y is a monotonically increasing or monotonically decreasing function of X that is differentiable for all values of X.

Then the pdf of Y is given by

$$p_y(Y) = p_x(Y[X]) \cdot \left|\frac{dY}{dX}\right| \tag{B.26}$$

where $Y[X] \triangleq f^{-1}(y)$ given that $y = f(x)$.

Example B.2 Let X be a random variable uniformly distributed between 0 and 1:

$$p_x(X) = \begin{cases} 1 & 0 \le X \le 1 \\ 0 & \text{otherwise} \end{cases}$$

Find the pdf for $y = -\ln x$.

solution It follows directly that

$$Y[X] = \exp(-Y) \tag{B.27}$$

$$\left|\frac{dY}{dX}\right| = -\exp(-Y) \tag{B.28}$$

Substituting Eqs. (B.27) and (B.28) into Eq. (B.26) yields

$$p_y(Y) = p_x[\exp(-Y)] \cdot |-\exp(-Y)| \tag{B.29}$$

We note that $0 \le \exp(-Y) \le 1$ for all $Y \le 0$; thus

$$p_x[\exp(-Y)] = \begin{cases} 1 & Y \ge 0 \\ 0 & Y < 0 \end{cases}$$

Therefore, Eq. (B.29) simplifies to

$$p_y(Y) = \begin{cases} \exp(-Y) & Y \ge 0 \\ 0 & Y < 0 \end{cases}$$

Bibliography

Abramowitz, M., and I. A. Stegun: *Handbook of Mathematical Functions,* National Bureau of Standards, Appl. Math Series 55, 1966.

Antoniou, A.: *Digital Filters: Analysis and Design,* McGraw-Hill, New York, 1979.

Antoniou, A.: "Accelerated Procedure for the Design of Equiripple Non-recursive Digital Filters," *Proceedings IEE, PART G,* vol. 129, pp. 1–10, 1982.

Bartlett, M. S.: "Periodogram Analysis and Continuous Spectra," *Biometrika,* vol. 37, pp. 1–16, 1950.

Blachman, M. M.: *Noise and Its Effect on Communication,* McGraw-Hill, New York, 1966.

Blackman, R. B., and J. W. Tukey: *The Measurement of Power Spectra,* Dover, New York, 1958.

Boyer, C. B.: *A History of Mathematics,* Wiley, New York, 1968.

Brigham, E. O.: *The Fast Fourier Transform,* Prentice-Hall, Englewood Cliffs, N.J., 1974.

Burrus, C. S., and T. W. Parks: *DFT/FFT and Convolution Algorithms,* Wiley-Interscience, New York, 1984.

Cadzow, J. A.: *Discrete-Time Systems,* Prentice-Hall, Englewood Cliffs, N.J., 1973.

Carlson, A. B.: *Communication Systems: An Introduction to Signals and Noise in Electrical Communication,* McGraw-Hill, New York, 1968.

Chen, C-T.: *Linear System Theory and Design,* Holt, Rinehart and Winston, New York, 1984.

Cheyney, E. W.: *Introduction to Approximation Theory,* McGraw-Hill, New York, 1966.

Cooper, G. R., and C. D. McGillem: *Modern Communication and Spread Spectrum,* McGraw-Hill, New York, 1986.

Dolph, C. L.: "A Current Distribution for Broadside Arrays Which Optimizes the Relationship Between Beam Width and Side-Lobe Level," *Proc. IRE,* vol. 35, pp. 335–348, June 1946.

Dym, H., and H. P. McKean: *Fourier Series and Integrals,* Academic, New York, 1972.

Hamming, R. W.: *Numerical Methods for Engineers and Scientists,* McGraw-Hill, New York, 1962.

Hamming, R. W.: *Digital Filters,* 2d ed., Prentice-Hall, Englewood Cliffs, N.J., 1983.

Harris, F. J.: "On the Use of Windows for Harmonic Analysis with the Discrete Fourier Transform," *Proc. IEEE,* vol. 66, pp. 51–83, January 1978.

Haykin, S.: *Communication Systems,* 2d ed., Wiley, New York, 1983.

Helms, H. D.: "Nonrecursive Digital Filters: Design Methods for Achieving Specifications on Frequency Response," *IEEE Trans. Audio and Electroacoust.,* vol. AU-16, pp. 336–342, September 1968.

Helms, H. D.: "Digital Filters with Equiripple or Minimax Responses," *IEEE Trans Audio Electroacoust.,* vol. AU-19, pp. 87–94, March 1971.

Herrmann, O.: "Design of Nonrecursive Digital Filters with Linear Phase," *Electronics Letters,* vol. 6, pp. 328–329, 1970.

Hofstetter, E. M., A. V. Oppenheim, and J. Siegel: "A New Technique for the Design of Non-Recursive Digital Filters," *Proc. Fifth Annual Princeton Conf. on Inform. Sci. and Syst.,* pp. 64–72, 1971.

Kanefsky, M.: *Communication Techniques for Digital and Analog Signals,* Harper & Row, New York, 1985.

Kay, S. M.: *Modern Spectral Estimators: Theory & Application,* Prentice-Hall, Englewood Cliffs, N.J., 1988.

Knuth, D. K.: *The Art of Computer Programming, Vol. 2: Seminumerical Algorithms,* Addison-Wesley, Reading, Mass., 1981.

Marple, S. L.: *Digital Spectral Analysis with Applications,* Prentice-Hall, Englewood Cliffs, N.J., 1987.

Martin, M. A.: "Digital Filters for Data Processing," Tech. Report no. 62-SD484, Missile and Space Division, General Electric Co., 1962.

Nussbaumer, H. J.: *Fast Fourier Transform and Convolution Algorithms,* Springer-Verlag, New York, 1981.

Oppenheim, A. V., and R. W. Schafer: *Digital Signal Processing,* Prentice-Hall, Englewood Cliffs, N.J., 1975.

Oppenheim, A. V., and R. W. Schafer: *Discrete-Time Signal Processing,* Prentice-Hall, Englewood Cliffs, N.J., 1989.

Papoulis, A.: *The Fourier Integral and Its Applications,* McGraw-Hill, New York, 1962.

Parks, T. W., and C. S. Burrus: *Digital Filter Design,* Wiley-Interscience, New York, 1987.

Parks, T. W., and J. H. McClellan: "Chebyshev Approximation for Nonrecursive Digital Filters with Linear Phase," *IEEE Trans. Circuit Theory,* vol. CT-19, pp. 189–194, March 1972.

Parks, T. W., and J. H. McClellan: "A Computer Program for Designing Optimum FIR Linear Phase Digital Filters," *IEEE Trans. Audio Electroacoust.,* vol. AU-21, pp. 506–526, December 1973.

Peled, A., and B. Liu: *Digital Signal Processing,* Wiley, New York, 1976.

Press, W. H., et al.: *Numerical Recipes,* Cambridge University Press, Cambridge, 1986.

Press, W. H., et al.: *Numerical Recipes in C,* 2d ed., Cambridge University Press, Cambridge, 1992.

Priestley, M. B.: *Spectral Analysis and Time Series,* vol. 1: *Univariate Series,* Academic, London, 1981.

Proakis, J. G.: *Digital Communications,* McGraw-Hill, New York, 1983.

Rabiner, L. R., and B. Gold: *Theory and Application of Digital Signal Processing,* Prentice-Hall, Englewood Cliffs, N.J., 1975.

Roberts, A. A., and C. T. Mullis: *Digital Signal Processing,* Addison-Wesley, Reading, Mass., 1987.

Rorabaugh, B.: *Signal Processing Design Techniques,* TAB Professional and Reference Books, Blue Ridge Summit, Pa., 1986.

Schwartz, L.: *Théorie des distributions,* Herman & Cie, Paris, 1950.

Schwartz, R. J., and B. Friedland: *Linear Systems,* McGraw-Hill, New York, 1965.

Simpson, R. S., and R. C. Houts: *Fundamentals of Analog and Digital Communication Systems,* Allyn and Bacon, Boston, 1971.

Spiegel, M. R.: *Laplace Transforms,* Schaum's Outline Series, McGraw-Hill, New York, 1965.

Stanley, W. D.: *Digital Signal Processing,* Reston, Reston, Va., 1975.

Stein, S., and J. J. Jones: *Modern Communication Principles,* McGraw-Hill, New York, 1967.

Taub, H., and D. L. Schilling: *Principles of Communication Systems,* 2d ed., McGraw-Hill, New York, 1986.

Tufts, D. W., and J. T. Francis: "Designing Digital Low-pass Filters—Comparison of Some Methods and Criteria," *IEEE Trans. Audio Electroacoust.,* vol. AU-18, pp. 487–494, December 1970.

Tufts, D. W., D. W. Rorabacher, and M. E. Mosier: "Designing Simple, Effective Digital Filters," *IEEE Trans. Audio Electroacoust.,* vol. AU-18, pp. 142–158, 1970.

Urkowitz, H.: *Signal Theory and Random Processes,* Artech House, Dedham, Mass., 1983.

Van Valkenburg, M. E.: *Network Analysis,* Prentice-Hall, Englewood Cliffs, N.J., 1974.

Weaver, H. J.: *Theory of Discrete and Continuous Fourier Analysis,* Wiley, New York, 1989.

Whalen, A. D.: *Detection of Signals in Noise,* Academic Press, New York, 1971.

Williams, C. S.: *Designing Digital Filters,* Prentice-Hall, Englewood Cliffs, N.J., 1986.

Index

SOFTWARE AND INFORMATION LICENSE

The software and information on this diskette (collectively referred to as the "Product") are the property of The McGraw-Hill Companies, Inc. ("McGraw-Hill") and are protected by both United States copyright law and international copyright treaty provision. You must treat this Product just like a book, except that you may copy it into a computer to be used and you may make archival copies of the Products for the sole purpose of backing up our software and protecting your investment from loss.

By saying, "just like a book," McGraw-Hill means, for example, that the Product may be used by any number of people and may be freely moved from one computer location to another, so long as there is no possibility of the Product (or any part of the Product) being used at one location or on one computer while it is being used at another. Just as a book cannot be read by two different people in two different places at the same time, neither can the Product be used by two different people in two different places at the same time (unless, of course, McGraw-Hill's rights are being violated).

McGraw-Hill reserves the right to alter or modify the contents of the Product at any time.

This agreement is effective until terminated. The Agreement will terminate automatically without notice if you fail to comply with any provisions of this Agreement. In the event of termination by reason of your breach, you will destroy or erase all copies of the Product installed on any computer system or made for backup purposes and shall expunge the Product from your data storage facilities.

LIMITED WARRANTY

McGraw-Hill warrants the physical diskette(s) enclosed herein to be free of defects in materials and workmanship for a period of sixty days from the purchase date. If McGraw-Hill receives written notification within the warranty period of defects in materials or workmanship, and such notification is determined by McGraw-Hill to be correct, McGraw-Hill will replace the defective diskette(s). Send request to:

Customer Service
McGraw-Hill
Gahanna Industrial Park
860 Taylor Station Road
Blacklick, OH 43004-9615

The entire and exclusive liability and remedy for breach of this Limited Warranty shall be limited to replacement of defective diskette(s) and shall not include or extend to any claim for or right to cover any other damages, including but not limited to, loss of profit, data, or use of the software, or special, incidental, or consequential damages or other similar claims, even if McGraw-Hill has been specifically advised as to the possibility of such damages. In no event will McGraw-Hill's liability for any damages to you or any other person ever exceed the lower of suggested list price or actual price paid for the license to use the Product, regardless of any form of the claim.

THE McGRAW-HILL COMPANIES, INC. SPECIFICALLY DISCLAIMS ALL OTHER WARRANTIES, EXPRESS OR IMPLIED, INCLUDING BUT NOT LIMITED TO, ANY IMPLIED WARRANTY OF MERCHANTABILITY OR FITNESS FOR A PARTICULAR PURPOSE. Specifically, McGraw-Hill makes no representation or warranty that the Product is fit for any particular purpose and any implied warranty of merchantability is limited to the sixty day duration of the Limited Warranty covering the physical diskette(s) only (and not the software or information) and is otherwise expressly and specifically disclaimed.

This Limited Warranty gives you specific legal rights; you may have others which may vary from state to state. Some states do not allow the exclusion of incidental or consequential damages, or the limitation on how long an implied warranty lasts, so some of the above may not apply to you.

This Agreement constitutes the entire agreement between the parties relating to use of the Product. The terms of any purchase order shall have no effect on the terms of this Agreement. Failure of McGraw-Hill to insist at any time on strict compliance with this Agreement shall not constitute a waiver of any rights under this Agreement. This Agreement shall be construed and governed in accordance with the laws of New York. If any provision of this Agreement is held to be contrary to law, that provision will be enforced to the maximum extent permissible and the remaining provisions will remain in force and effect.